INTRODUCTION
TO STATISTICS...

Introduction to
STATISTICS

Frederick C. Mills

Columbia University

HENRY HOLT AND COMPANY · New York

25739—0316
Printed in the United States of America

Preface

This volume, an abridgment of the Third Edition of my *Statistical Methods*, is designed as a general introduction to the subject. Over a wide range of professional and administrative occupations, acquaintance with statistical concepts and competence in handling measurements expressed in physical or monetary units are necessary in day-to-day activities. For the techniques of modern statistics are extensively employed today in private and public administration, as well as in research in the natural and social sciences. The simple methods of dealing with "classified facts respecting the condition . . . of the people of a state," which constituted "statistics" for our grandfathers, have grown into a comprehensive system of concepts and of related procedures for the advancement of knowledge and for dealing with the uncertainties that face men in the ordinary affairs of life.

In the present arrangement of topics these concepts and procedures are presented in an order that I believe to be appropriate to a short beginning course. The opening chapters (with Appendices A and B) are given to some elementary mathematical ideas, and to procedures employed in organizing and describing bodies of quantitative data. Thereafter, at an early stage of the general argument, I have thought it well to develop the basic concepts of statistical inference. A foundation for this is laid in Chapter 6; the two following chapters deal at greater length with procedures for generalizing from sample statistics and for testing hypotheses. The emphasis thus given to inference is, I think, not only logically but pedagogically desirable. Processes of inference are the essence of modern statistics. The concepts that underlie these processes give coherence to an exposition of statistical procedures. Moreover, this aspect of statistics is the most stimulating to the student. Consideration of the doctrines of inference can lift statistics from the humdrum to the (sometimes even) glamorous, as a subject of instruction. An effective presentation of statistical inference can offer the student discipline in scientific method, and can provide an illuminating experience in the uses of applied logic. This subject should be introduced early and should, I venture, be the continuing thread that ties together the topics making up a course in statistics.

Topics of special interest to students of the social sciences and of business administration—index numbers and time series—are given a fairly comprehensive treatment. The chapters on index numbers now include a section on the measurement of productivity changes, a matter of special concern in an era of rapid technological advance. In handling time series, discussion of the more traditional methods of analysis is supplemented by an account of the fruitful techniques used by the National Bureau of Economic Research in the study of business cycles. For the purposes of a brief course, teachers may wish to select areas of emphasis from these two broad fields.

In the organization and presentation of subject matter I have had two objectives. I have sought to make the exposition intelligible to the non-mathematical reader—that is, to the reader whose formal mathematical training does not go beyond the elements of algebra and analytic geometry. While I have tried to set forth the nature of the theory that underlies specific procedures and to establish the logical bases of these procedures, I have not, in general, essayed to give mathematical proofs of the various theorems discussed. As Sir Ronald Fisher has said, this is "an age of technical cooperation." There must be division of labor between the tool-makers in statistics and the great body of students and practitioners who employ statistics in subject-matter fields and in administration. This book is directed to the needs of users. It is of course essential that users understand the assumptions on which particular procedures rest, and the limitations attaching to particular instruments. I have attempted to make these assumptions and limitations clear.

My second objective in presentation has been to give a coherent discussion of statistical methods. The statistical approach embodies a fundamentally unified attitude toward the world of men, things, and events; it entails the application to diverse problems of a central body of principles. A vital element is lost if statistics be regarded as a bundle of unrelated procedures. I hope that I have succeeded in making this book an integrated introduction to the methods of modern statistics.

The list of references at the end of each chapter is designed to serve the needs of readers at different levels of statistical competence, and of varying interests. Most of the lists include elementary texts, intermediate texts, and treatises developing the mathematical foundations of statistics. Certain of the lists include, also, references to original memoirs of special importance and to research studies exemplifying applications of particular methods.

The obligations, both general and specific, that I have incurred in the preparation of this volume are numerous. The writer of any such book as this draws upon a body of knowledge built up through the efforts of many workers over many years. My indebtedness to these workers will be clear; it is acknowledged with pleasure. I am grateful, too, to representatives of public and private agencies who have been uniformly courteous and obliging in complying with requests for data and for information on procedures. Specifically, I would mention the Chief Statistician's Division of the American Telephone and Telegraph Company, the National Bureau of Economic Research, the Bureau of Labor Statistics, and the Bureau of the Census. The tables appended to this volume are drawn from various sources. My chief obligations here are to Sir Ronald Fisher of Cambridge University and his publishers, Messrs. Oliver and Boyd of Edinburgh and London; to Professor George W. Snedecor and the Iowa State College Press; to Professor Truman L. Kelley and the Harvard University Press; and to Dr. W. H. S. Stevens and the Bureau of Transport Economics and Statistics of the Interstate Commerce Commission. Generous help has been given me by members of my family—by William H. Mills and Robert L. Mills on specific points, by Dorothy C. Mills on the many tasks entailed in the making of a book. To them, and to others who have aided me with counsel and suggestion, I am deeply grateful. Finally, I must reaffirm my thanks to those who assisted me in various ways in the preparation of earlier editions.

Although I should like to believe that the text of this book is free of mistakes, typographical and other, I may not do so. I shall be obliged to readers who will inform me of errors they may detect.

F. C. M.

New York, N.Y.
March, 1956

Contents

CONTENTS

CONTENTS

CHAPTER **1**

• • •

On Statistics and Statistical Methods

This book deals with a mode of inquiry — a method of investigating social and natural processes and of providing bases for decisions in research and administration. Seen in detail, statistical techniques are numerous and varied, but in sum they constitute a unified, systematic, and logical approach to the study of the affairs of man and the order of nature. In their workaday applications they furnish investigators and administrators with succinct descriptive summaries of masses of observations. But we should miss the essence of this mode of inquiry if we saw it merely as a collection of techniques for summarizing experience, in the form of averages, standard deviations, coefficients of correlation, index numbers, trend lines, and seasonal and cyclical patterns. For its use does not end with the perhaps prosaic tasks of simple description. In broad as well as in narrow spheres it can provide a foundation for rational action when a choice must be made among alternative procedures. And, perhaps most important of all, in the statistical approach we have a means for the advancement of knowledge that seems to accord in fundamental ways with the nature of things in the world we are seeking to understand.

In their most significant aspect modern statistical techniques are procedures for the making of what Dewey has termed warranted assertions. Such assertions, when statistically based, may be estimates or generalizations that go beyond the sample of observations immediately studied; they may be decisions that accept or reject hypotheses. Inference, in these forms, is the heart of modern statistics. In the detailed development of methods of statistical inference we shall examine the nature and role of random samples; we shall be concerned with populations of persons, things, events, and measurements, and with means of estimating the attributes of such populations on the basis of samples drawn from them. We shall discuss techniques adapted to the testing of hypotheses.

These various methods, we have said, seem to accord with reality — with the ways of men and of nature in the world about us. To explore this subject in detail would take us beyond the direct concerns of the working statistician. And yet this working statistician may properly ask whether his techniques are adapted to the raw materials with which he deals. There is much evidence to indicate that they are, whether the statistician be dealing with the mass attributes of human beings or of other organic forms, or with the behavior of assemblages of physical entities. More than eighty years ago Clerk Maxwell wrote, ". . . our actual knowledge of concrete things is of an essentially statistical nature. . . . .Those uniformities which we observe in our experiments with quantities of matter containing millions of molecules are uniformities . . . arising from the slumping together of multitudes of cases each of which is by no means uniform with the others." The emphasis Maxwell here placed upon *aggregates*, as opposed to individuals, and upon uniformities in group behavior, is the emphasis that characterizes all statistical inquiry. For although omnipresent chance may shape the behavior of individuals, making it unpredictable, valid statements may still be made about aggregates.

Maxwell was concerned with molecular theory. The statistical view of nature that he first made explicit now shapes the approach of physical scientists in studies that go far beyond the field of molecular phenomena. Indeed, such a view is mandatory wherever an element of probability enters into our knowledge of the physical world — and there are few areas into which it does not enter. In the realms of organic nature and of human relations our present funds of useful knowledge rest largely upon conceptions of the same statistical character. Such knowledge deals with things that are individually indeterminate; the behavior of John Jones, the precise yield of corn in a given plot, the transmission of the quality represented by a particular gene, the price of wheat on a given day in a competitive market — these are individually unforeseeable and unpredictable. But when each of the entities of which we are speaking is combined with similar entities we have aggregates in which clear uniformities are discernible. It is with such uniformities in the behavior of aggregates, whether they be aggregates of molecules, of neutrons and protons, of genes, or of human beings, that statistical generalizations deal. Because these uniformities are nearly always imperfect, although definable and in some degree predictable, statistical generalizations are always couched in terms of probabilities. Statistical knowledge is thus imperfect, and always marked by uncertainty. But it is knowledge that is usable in the world of natural and human events.

Procedures by which such knowledge is established and extended are discussed in the pages that follow. They rest, at bottom, upon the rational and informed use of data of observation. Since accurate and relevant observations are the building blocks of statistical inquiry, a word is in order, in this introductory note, about the character of the data available to workers in the fields of human affairs with which this book deals. These data are numerous. They often fall short of specific needs, it is true, but they are more accurate and vastly more comprehensive than those that were available a short quarter century ago. For immediate purposes these data may be regarded as of two types — those acquired by random sampling, and those not so acquired.

In deriving the statistical generalizations we have spoken of the investigator seeks to employ randomly acquired data. What this means, in detail, we shall discuss later. Here we shall say, only, that sample data drawn from a stated population are randomly acquired when the sampling process gives each individual element of that population a definable probability of inclusion in the sample. Some of the data available to statisticians today have been obtained by procedures that yield truly random samples. Indeed, one of the most encouraging of recent developments in the improvement of social, economic, and business "intelligence" (using that word in its military sense) is the growing use of closely controlled survey techniques for obtaining random samples. This is true of a number of current compilations made by federal agencies. Private investigators, too, in increasing degree, design field studies to yield random samples adapted to specific purposes. When randomness is thus realized, the methods of generalization and of testing that will be described in the discussion of statistical inference are applicable.

But vast collections of data available for use in social, economic, and business research have not been randomly obtained. They may be nonrandom because of the way they were compiled. Statistical agencies, both governmental and private, sometimes gather statistics that are readily available rather than those that are desirable for the purpose in hand. (In fact, the truly desirable may be quite unavailable.) Or a given set of data may be nonrandom because of inevitable interdependence among successive observations, a condition usually true of statistics making up time series. In dealing with such nonrandom samples probability concepts, and modes of inquiry and generalization involving such concepts, do not apply, or apply only with important reservations. When these methods are misapplied, serious error may result. This is not to say that nonrandom observations are of no value. There is much information to be gleaned from such data, perhaps all the information needed for particular purposes. In some tasks purely descriptive statistics may play a pre-eminent role in providing brief and effective summaries of varied experience, and may serve as an indispensable aid to rational judgment. But the careful investigator will be scrupulous in limiting the uses to which nonrandom data are put, and cautious in generalizing from them.

These brief introductory remarks anticipate ideas and concepts that will be developed in the pages that follow, but they may serve a purpose in suggesting to the student of statistics something of the nature of the tools we shall be talking about, and of the method of inquiry these tools implement. It is a powerful method, widely applicable today in administration and research. Yet, as goes without saying, it is not all-powerful or all-sufficient. As cautionary aids in the application of the methods discussed in this book, two general points may be left in the mind of the reader.

We have spoken of statistical techniques as tools, or instruments, and the terms are appropriate. But it is obvious that tools must be used with judgment. In statistical work the investigator must have the benefit of guiding principles and rational concepts. For the statistician, as statistician, faces two occupational hazards — the danger that he will overemphasize the accumulation of data, and the danger that he will be overconcerned with techniques of manipulating data. The piling up of evidence, quantitative or otherwise, is not the object of investigation, nor does indiscriminate accumulation necessarily provide a basis for wise decisions. The warranted assertions that are sought in all inquiry are achieved through the rational use of evidence — the use of empirical data in making generalizations that go beyond the limits of observation, in testing hypotheses, in modifying hypotheses when they fail to accord with relevant observations. The play of reason in formulating theories is checked by reference to the data of observation; the accumulation and manipulation of such data are controlled and guided by reason.

The second general warning may sound equally obvious, but it is no less pertinent to the work of the statistician. Techniques can never be given priority over substantive knowledge of the field of inquiry, over what J. L. Henderson has spoken of as ". . . intimate, habitual, intuitive familiarity with things." Sharp tools may be grievously misused without this deep familiarity with reality in the area of investigation — and this statement applies with special force to the use of statistical techniques. If such techniques are to be well and wisely employed they must be adapted, with understanding, to the materials under study.

REFERENCES

Cohen, Morris R., "The Statistical View of Nature," *Journal of the American Statistical Association*, June 1936.
Kelley, Truman L., *Fundamentals of Statistics*, Chap. 1.
Kendall, M. G., "The Statistical Approach," *Economica*, May 1950.
Merz, J. T., *A History of European Thought in the Nineteenth Century*, Vol. II, Chap. 12, "The Statistical View of Nature."
Mills, F. C., "On Measurement in Economics," in *The Trend of Economics*, R. G. Tugwell, ed.
Royce, Josiah, "The Mechanical, the Historical and the Statistical," *Science*, April 17, 1914.
Wirth, L., ed., *Eleven Twenty Six: A Decade of Social Science Research*, section on "Quantification: the Quest for Precision."

The publishers and the dates of publication of the books named in chapter reference lists are given in the bibliography at the end of this volume.

•

•

•

Aspects of Graphic Presentation

Some Relevant Principles and Basic Procedures

The explanation of methods of condensing, analyzing, and interpreting quantitative observations must start with the discussion of some fundamental considerations that are mathematical rather than statistical in character. In doing so it is deemed advisable, even at the risk of treading quite familiar ground, to discuss certain simple mathematical conceptions to which constant reference will be made in later chapters.

Statistical analysis is concerned primarily with data based upon measurement, expressed either in pecuniary or physical units. The methods of coordinate geometry, developed first by the philosopher Descartes, greatly facilitate the manipulation and interpretation of such data. We briefly summarize some relevant principles of coordinate geometry.

Rectangular Coordinates. If two straight lines intersecting each other at right angles are drawn in a plane, it is possible to describe the location of any point in that plane with reference to the point of intersection of the two lines. We will call one of the lines (a vertical line) $Y'Y$, the other line (horizontal) $X'X$, and the point of intersection (or *origin*) O (see Fig. 2.1). If P be any point in the plane, we may draw the line PM, parallel to $Y'Y$ and intersecting $X'X$ at M, and the line PN, parallel to $X'X$ and intersecting $Y'Y$ at N. If we set OM equal to g units and ON equal to h units, g and h constitute the *coordinates* of P, describing its location with reference to the origin O. Thus, in Fig. 2.1, g equals 6 and h equals 5. The distance g along the x-axis is termed the *abscissa* of the point P, while the distance h along the y-axis is termed the *or-*

dinate of the point *P*. (It is a rule of notation always to give the abscissa first, followed by the ordinate.) The coordinates of any other point in the same plane may be determined in the same way. Conversely, any two real numbers determine a point in the plane, if one be taken as the abscissa and the other as the ordinate.

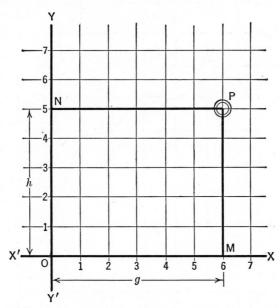

FIG. 2.1. Location of a Point with Reference to Rectangular Coordinates.

A point may lie either to the right or left or above or below the origin, *O*. It is conventional to designate as positive abscissas laid off to the right of the origin, and as negative abscissas laid off to the left of the origin, while ordinates are positive when laid off above the origin and negative when laid off below the origin. In general, the values to be dealt with in economic and social statistics lie in the upper right-hand quadrant, where both abscissa and ordinate are positive.

This conception of coordinates is fundamental in mathematics and of basic importance in statistical work. A very simple example will illustrate the utility of this device in representing economic observations. The figures presented in Table 2–1 may be employed.

These data may be represented graphically on the coordinate system, months being laid off along the *x*-axis and number of automobiles along the y-axis, as in the accompanying diagram (Fig. 2.2). In plotting the abscissas, December, 1953, is considered as located at the point of origin. The x-value of the entry for January,

FIG. 2.2. Factory Sales of Passenger Automobiles, by Months, during the Year 1954.*

* Source: Automobile Manufacturers Association.

1954, is thus 1, of the February figure 2, etc. The coordinates of the point representing the number of cars sold in January, 1954, are 1 and 454,562; for February the values are 2 and 446,676. The coordinates for December are 12 and 669,778. The movement of automobile sales during the year may be more easily followed if the points are connected by a series of straight lines, as is done in the figure.

TABLE 2-1

Factory Sales of Passenger Automobiles in the United States, by Months, during the Year 1954 *

Month	Number of passenger cars sold
January	454,562
February	446,676
March	531,529
April	534,667
May	497,062
June	507,055
July	451,663
August	445,306
September	300,998
October	221,195
November	498,248
December	669,778

* Source: Automobile Manufacturers Association.

Functional Relationship. In the location of any point by means of coordinates, it has been pointed out, two values are involved; every point ties together and expresses a relation between two factors. In the above case these are months and number of passenger automobiles sold at factories. With the passage of time the volume of automobile sales changes, and the broken line shows the direction and magnitude of these changes. Both time and number of cars sold are *variables*, that is, they are quantities not of constant value but characterized by variations in value in the given discussion. Thus in Fig. 2.1 the abscissa has a fixed value of 6, while the ordinate has a fixed value of 5, but in Fig. 2.2 both abscissa and ordinate have varying values, the one varying from 1 to 12, the other from 221,195 to 669,778. The symbols x and y are, by convention, used to designate such variable quantities as these, the former in all cases representing the variable plotted along the horizontal axis, the latter representing the variable plotted along the vertical axis.[1]

Independent and dependent variables. In Fig. 2.2, which depicts

[1] It should be noted that letters at the end of the alphabet are used as symbols for *variables*, while letters at the beginning of the alphabet are used as symbols for *constants*, i.e., quantities the values of which do not change in the given discussion.

the changes taking place in automobile sales with the passage of time, it will be noted that the latter variable changes by an arbitrary unit, one month. Having made an independent change in the time factor we then determine the change in output taking place during the period thus arbitrarily chopped out. The variable which increases or decreases by increments arbitrarily determined is called the *independent variable*, and is generally plotted on the x-axis. The other variable is termed the *dependent variable*, and is plotted on the y-axis. This dependence may be real, in the sense that the values of the second variable are definitely determined by the values of the independent variable, or it may be purely a conventional dependence of the type described. Time, it should be noted, is always plotted as independent, when it constitutes one of the variables.

When two variables y and x are so related that the value of y is determined by a given value of x, y is said to be a function of x. The general expression for such a relationship is $y = f(x)$. Thus the speed at a given moment of a body falling in a vacuum is a function of the time it has been falling, the pressure of a given volume of gas is a function of its temperature, the increase of a given principal sum of money at a fixed rate of interest is a function of time. If the values of the independent variable be laid off on the x-axis of a rectilinear chart and the corresponding values of the function (i.e., the dependent variable) be laid off on the y-axis, a graphic representation of the function will be secured, in the form of a curve.[2] This concept of functional relationship is a very important one in statistical work. Some of the simpler functions may be briefly discussed.

The straight line. The simplest case of relationship between variables is that in which $y = x$. As an example, the relation between the age of a tree and the number of rings in its trunk may be cited. A tree 6 years old will have 6 rings, one 20 years old will have 20 rings, and so on. This relationship may be represented on a coordinate chart, several sample values of x and y being taken. When these points are plotted and a line drawn through them, we secure a straight line passing through the origin (see Fig. 2.3).

Similarly, any equation of the first degree (i.e., not involving xy, or powers of x or y other than the first) may be represented by a

---

[2] The general term "curve" is used to designate any line, straight or curved, when located with reference to a coordinate system.

straight line. The generalized equation can be reduced to the form $y = a + bx$, where a is a constant representing the distance from the origin to the point of intersection of the given line and the y-axis, and b is a constant representing the slope of the given line (that is, the tangent of the angle which the line makes with the horizontal). The constant term a is called the *y-intercept*. It is clear from the generalized equation of the straight line that when x has a value of zero, y will be equal to this constant term. In the example represented by Fig. 2.3 a is equal to 0, and b to 1. The location of a given line depends upon the signs of a and b as well as upon their magni-

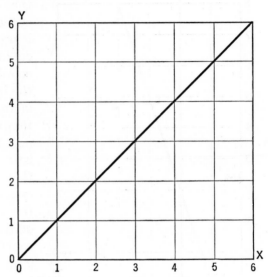

FIG. 2.3. Graph of the Equation $y = x$.

tudes. The practical problem involved in the determination of any straight line is that of finding the values of a and b from the data, a problem that will appear in various forms in the discussion of statistical methods.

These points may be illustrated by the plotting of a simple equation of the first degree. Thus, to construct the graph of the function, $y = 2 + 3x$, various values of x are assumed, and corresponding values of y are determined. These may be arranged in the form of a table:

x	y $(2 + 3x)$
-4	-10
-2	-4
0	2
2	8
4	14

Plotting these values and connecting the plotted points, the graph illustrated in Fig. 2.4 is secured. It will be noted that since this function is linear (that is, the graph takes the form of a straight line) any two of the points would have been sufficient to locate the line. The y-intercept is equal to the constant term 2, and the tangent of the angle that the given line makes with the horizontal (the slope of the line) is equal to 3, the coefficient of x. That this curve represents the equation is proved by the fact that the equation is satisfied by the coordinates of every point on the curve, and that every pair of values satisfying the equation is represented by a point on the curve. It is characteristic of a linear relationship that if one variable be increased by a constant amount, the corresponding increment of the other variable will be constant. In the above case as x grows by constant increments of 2, for example, the constant increment of the y-variable is 6. Series that increase in this way by constant increments are termed *arithmetic series*.

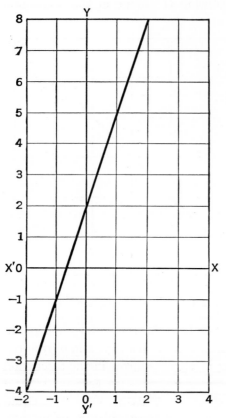

FIG. 2.4. Graph of the Equation $y = 2 + 3x$.

Many examples of linear relationship between variables are found in the physical sciences. An example from the economic world is found in the growth of money at simple interest, that is, interest which is not compounded. If we let r represent the rate of simple interest, x the number of years, and y the sum to which one dollar will amount at the end of x years, the equation of relationship is of the form

$$y = 1 + rx$$

Since in a given case r will be constant, this is of the simple linear type. In statistical work precise relationships of this type rarely if ever occur, but approximations to the straight line relationship are found constantly.

Nonlinear relationship. Nonlinear functions are of many types, of which only a few of the more common will be discussed here. The student should be familiar with the general characteristics of the chief nonperiodic curves, of which the parabolic and hyperbolic types, on the one hand, and the exponential type on the other, are the most important. Polynomials are mentioned as a more general form of rather wide utility. Of periodic functions the sine curve is briefly described, as a fundamental form.

Functional relationships of the parabolic or hyperbolic form are quite common in the physical sciences, and such curves are found to fit certain classes of social and economic data. The general

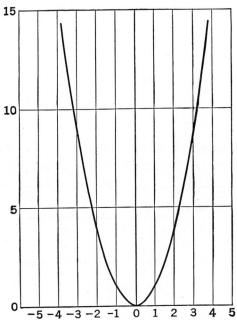

FIG. 2.5. Parabola: Graph of the Equation $y = x^2$.

equation, when there is no constant term, is of the form $y = ax^b$. The curve is *parabolic* when the exponent b is positive, and *hyperbolic* when b is negative. The two following examples will serve to illustrate these types:

Problem: To construct the graph of the function $y = x^2$.

x	y (x^2)
-5	25
-4	16
-3	9
-2	4
-1	1
0	0
1	1
2	4
3	9
4	16
5	25

The graph is shown in Fig. 2.5.

Problem: To construct the graph of the function $y = x^{-1}$, for positive values of x.

x	y (x^{-1})
$\frac{1}{3}$	3
$\frac{1}{2}$	2
1	1
2	$\frac{1}{2}$
3	$\frac{1}{3}$
4	$\frac{1}{4}$
5	$\frac{1}{5}$

The graph of the function, an equilateral hyperbola, is shown in Fig. 2.6. It should be noted that this equation may also be written $y = \frac{1}{x}$ or $xy = 1$.

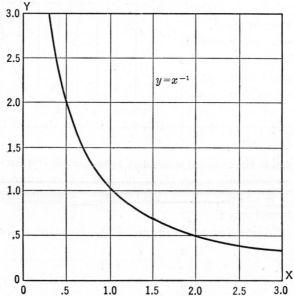

FIG. 2.6. Equilateral Hyperbola: Graph of the Equation $y = x^{-1}$ (for positive values of x).

It is characteristic of relationships of this type that as x changes in geometric progression, y also changes in geometric progression. Thus, in the example of the parabola given above ($y = x^2$), if we select the x values which form a geometric series,[3] the corresponding y values form a similar series:

[3] A geometric series is one each term of which is derived from the preceding term by the application of a constant multiplier.

FIG. 2.9. Graph of the Equation $\log y = 2 \log x$ (logarithmic form of the equation $y = x^2$).

logarithms form arithmetic series. It will be noted that equal distances on the chart, vertical or horizontal, represent equal absolute increments on the scale of logarithms and equal percentage increments on the scale of natural numbers.

The equation $y = 5x^3$ can be reduced in the same way to $\log y = \log 5 + 3 \log x$, a linear form. Similarly, all equations of the type $y = ax^b$, that is to say, all simple parabolas and hyperbolas, can be reduced to the straight line form $\log y = \log a + b \log x$. Graphically this means plotting the logarithms of the y's against the logarithms of the x's.

A different problem is presented by an equation of the type $y = ab^x$, the graph of which is termed an exponential curve. Expressed in logarithmic form, we have $\log y = \log a + x \log b$. This also is of the linear type, the two constants being $\log a$ and $\log b$, while the variables are x and $\log y$. If we plot the natural x's and the logs of the y's with such an equation, a straight line will be secured. A curve of this type is discussed and illustrated below.

Logarithmic and semilogarithmic charts. There are certain disadvantages to the plotting of logarithms, however. If a considerable number of points are being plotted the task of looking up the logarithms may be tedious, and, in addition, the original values, in which chief interest lies, will not appear on the chart. These difficulties may be avoided by constructing charts with the scales laid off logarithmically, but with the natural numbers instead of the logarithms appearing on the scales. This is an arrangement identical with that employed in the construction of slide rules. Thus, although the natural numbers are given on the scales, distances are proportional to the logarithms of the numbers thereon plotted. In Fig. 2.10 such a chart is presented, showing the graph of the equation $y = x^2$.

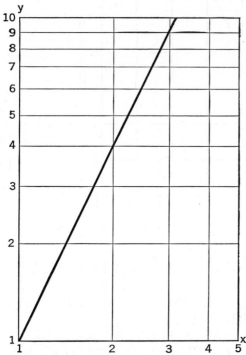

FIG. 2.10. Graph of the Equation $y = x^2$ (plotted on paper with logarithmic scales).

A variation of this type of chart which is of great importance in statistical work is one that is scaled arithmetically on the horizontal axis and logarithmically on the vertical axis. This is equivalent, of course, to plotting the x's on the natural scale and plotting the logarithms of the y's. As was pointed out above, such a combination of scales reduces a curve of the exponential type to a straight line. Plotting paper of this semilogarithmic or "ratio" type may be constructed with the aid of a slide rule or of logarithms, or may be purchased ready-made. It is of particular value in charting social and economic statistics when time is one of the variables, time being plotted on the arithmetic scale.

As an example of this type of curve the compound interest law may be used. If r be taken to represent the rate of interest, x the number of years, p the principal, and y the sum to which the principal amounts at the end of x years (interest being compounded annually), an equation is secured of the form

$$y = p(1 + r)^x$$

Expressed logarithmically this becomes

$$\log y = \log p + x \log (1 + r)$$

the equation to a straight line.

In Fig. 2.11 a curve representing the growth of $10 at compound interest at 6 percent is plotted on the natural scale. This is the graph of the exponential equation

$$y = 10(1 + .06)^x$$

y representing the total amount of principal and interest at the end of x years. Figure 2.12 shows the same data plotted on semilogarithmic paper, the exponential curve being reduced to a straight line.

The use of semilogarithmic paper is not confined to cases in which an exponential curve is straightened out, for the significance of many types of data is most effectively brought out

FIG. 2.11. The Compound Interest Law: Growth of $10.00 at Compound Interest at 6 Percent for 100 Years (plotted on arithmetic scale).

when charts of this type are used. These advantages are more fully explained below.

Types of Graphic Presentation

When the results of observations or statistical investigations have been secured in quantitative form, one of the first steps toward analysis and interpretation of the data is that of presenting these results graphically. Not only is such procedure of scientific value in paving the way for further investigation of relationships,

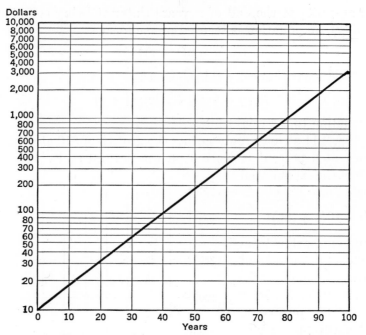

FIG. 2.12. The Compound Interest Law: Growth of $10.00 at Compound Interest at 6 Percent for 100 Years (plotted on semilogarithmic or ratio scale).

but it serves an immediate practical purpose in visualizing the results. The interpretation of a column of raw figures may be a difficult task; the same data in graphic form may tell a simple and easily understood story.

It is beyond the scope of this book to present any detailed account of the multiplicity of graphs employed by engineers and statisticians today. Certain of the more important principles of graphic presentation may be briefly explained, however, and some of the chief types of graphs in daily use may be illustrated. Other examples appear in later chapters of this book.

The selection of the type of chart to be employed in a given case will depend upon the character of the material to be plotted and the purpose to be served. While the data of a given problem may frequently be presented graphically in several different forms, there is generally one type of chart best adapted to that material. It may be true, also, that certain types would be quite inappropriate to the data in question. The selection of a type of chart to employ, therefore, must be made with the characteristics of the data clearly in mind. Perhaps more important is the *purpose* the given chart is designed to serve. Each of the many types of charts in common use is appropriate to certain specific purposes. It will bring out certain characteristics of the data or will emphasize certain relationships. There is no chart that is sovereign for all purposes. Until the purpose is clearly defined the best chart form cannot be selected. The following descriptions of a few standard types will facilitate the selection of an appropriate form.

The Plotting of Time Series. In the graphic presentation of a time series, primary interest attaches to the chronological varia-

FIG. 2.13. Annual Expenditures for Producers' Durable Equipment, United States, 1929–1953.*

* Source: Office of Business Economics, U.S. Department of Commerce.

tions in the values of the data — to the general trend and to fluctuations about the trend. If the purpose is to emphasize the *absolute* variations, the differences in absolute units between the values of the series at different times, a simple chart of the type illustrated in Fig. 2.13 will serve the purpose. This chart depicts total annual expenditures for producers' durable equipment in the United States during the period 1929–1953. Expenditures for such equipment are, of course, one of the major components of gross private domestic investment. Both scales are arithmetic. Points representing the various annual values are shown and, to facilitate interpretation, these points are connected by a series of straight lines. The chart traces clearly the drop in equipment purchases that came with the

1929 recession, the fluctuations of the following decade, and the rise to unprecedentedly high levels in the years following the war. With respect to general make-up, the following points should be noted:

1. The title constitutes a clear description of the material plotted and indicates the period covered.
2. The vertical scale begins at the zero line, enabling a true impression to be gained of the magnitude of the fluctuations.
3. The zero line and the line joining the plotted points are ruled more heavily than the coordinate lines.
4. Figures for the scales are placed at the left and at the bottom of the chart. The vertical scale may be repeated at the right to facilitate reading. All figures are so placed that they may be read from the base as bottom or from the right hand edge of the chart as bottom.

Figure 2.14 is a line chart serving a different purpose. Here are shown patterns of seasonal variation in five basic economic series. The plotted indexes fluctuate about a base line of 100, which represents, for each series, an average annual value.[4] The sharp contrasts among seasonal rhythms in these five major fields are clearly revealed by the paralleling of graphs in this arrangement.

FIG. 2.14. Seasonal Movements of Five Economic Indicators.*

* Chart reproduced by courtesy of the Federal Reserve Bank of Philadelphia from the May 1954 issue of the *Business Review* of that Bank.

Advantages of the ratio chart. If *relative* rather than *absolute* variations are of chief concern, the chart employed should be of the semilogarithmic type, scaled logarithmically on the *y*-axis and

[4] The construction of index numbers of seasonal variation is discussed in Chapter 11.

arithmetically on the x-axis. In such a chart, as we have noted, equal percentage variations are represented by equal vertical distances, as opposed to the ordinary arithmetic type in which equal absolute variations are represented by equal vertical distances. The argument for the use of the semilogarithmic or ratio chart for the representation of time series is that, in general, the significance of a given change depends upon the magnitude of the base from which the change is measured. That is, an increase of 100 on a base of 100 is as significant as an increase of 10,000 on a base of 10,000.

FIG. 2.15. Average Weekly Production of Steel Ingots and Castings in the United States, 1929–1954 * (plotted on semilogarithmic scale).

* Source: American Iron and Steel Institute.

In each case there is an increase of 100 percent. The absolute increase in the second case is 100 times that in the first case, and the two changes would show in this proportion on the arithmetic chart. They would show as of equal importance on the semilogarithmic chart.

Such a chart is presented in Fig. 2.15, which shows the course of steel production in the United States from 1929 to 1954. The absolute magnitudes are plotted, but the vertical scale is so constructed as to represent variations from year to year in proportion to their relative magnitude.

Certain distinctive advantages of the ratio or logarithmic ruling are brought out by a comparison of Fig. 2.16 and Fig. 2.17. Here are shown exports of the United States, from 1939 to 1953, to four broad continental divisions. If the six series are to be presented on a single chart, scaled arithmetically, a scale must be selected that will include the largest item recorded, which is for $9,344,000,000

FIG. 2.16. Exports of the United States to Selected Continental Divisions, 1929–1953.*

* Source: Bureau of the Census, U.S. Department of Commerce (summarized in the *Statistical Abstract of the U.S.*, 1953 and the *Economic Almanac* of the National Industrial Conference Board, 1953–1954).

worth of exports to Europe, in 1944. Such a scale reduces the relative importance of all the smaller magnitudes. Fluctuations in exports to Europe during this period were much greater, in absolute terms, than the fluctuations in trade with other divisions. Variations in trade with Oceania, at the other extreme, seem insignificant. If one is interested in relative variations such a picture is quite misleading. When the data are plotted on the ratio scale, in Fig. 2.17, the picture is placed in truer perspective. Movements at the lower end of the scale are discernible, and the relative amplitudes of changes in the volume of exports to different divisions may

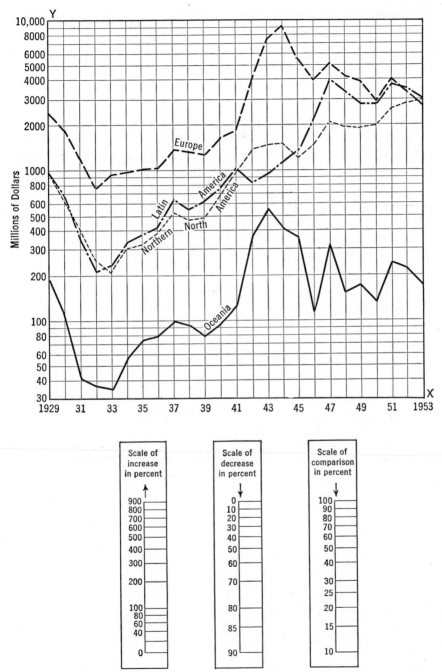

FIG. 2.17. Exports of the United States to Selected Continental Divisions, 1929–1953. Semilogarithmic Plotting, with Scales of Increase, Decrease, and Comparison.

be determined. For the comparison of series that differ materially in magnitude, the ratio ruling has distinct merits.

The scales printed below Fig. 2.17 emphasize certain very useful features of the logarithmic ruling. The *scale of increase* may be used to measure with a fair degree of accuracy the increase in a given series between any two dates. A given vertical distance on the chart, it will be recalled, represents a constant percentage increase at all points on the chart. Thus the distance from 1 to 10, along the vertical scale, is the same as the distance from 100 to 1,000. Any vertical distance may be measured, and the percentage of increase

FIG. 2.18. New Nonfarm Housing Starts in the United States, 1944–54, with Lines Defining Uniform Rates of Growth.*

* Source: U.S. Bureau of Labor Statistics

which it represents may be determined by laying off the given distance along the scale of increase, which is always read from the bottom up. For example, to determine, for exports to Europe, the degree of increase from 1939 to 1941, we measure the vertical distance between the points plotted for these two years. Laying off this distance along the scale, it is found to represent an increase slightly in excess of 40 percent.

The *scale of decrease* is used in a similar fashion. The vertical distance between any two points is measured, and the percentage decrease which it represents is determined by laying off the given distance on the scale from the top downward. The arrows indicate the direction in which the various scales are to be read.

By means of the *scale of comparison* the percentage relation of one series to another at any time may be determined. For example, we may wish to know the percentage relation between exports to Northern North America and exports to Latin America in 1951. The vertical distance between the two plotted points is measured, and laid off on the scale of comparison, reading from the top downward. We find that exports to Northern North America in that year amounted to about 70 percent of exports to Latin America.

Scales of the type illustrated above may be readily constructed on a given chart by using the ratio ruling for the scale intervals. When a series of charts is prepared on semilogarithmic paper of a standard type it is convenient to construct such scales in a more permanent form, in the shape of special rulers.

A ratio chart is particularly useful when interest attaches to rates of growth (or decline) over a considerable period of time. In such a case, the reading of the chart is facilitated by the plotting of straight diagonal lines indicating uniform rates of change. These should radiate from a single point of origin. The procedure is illustrated in Fig. 2.18. Each of the several diagonal lines there shown indicates changes at a uniform annual rate. By reference to these lines the user of the chart may readily determine the approximate rate of growth of the plotted series between any two years.

The chief advantages of the semilogarithmic ruling in chart construction may be briefly summarized:

1. A curve of the exponential type becomes a straight line when plotted on a semilogarithmic chart. For example, a curve representing the growth of any sum of money at compound interest takes the form of a straight line when so plotted.
2. The graph will be a straight line so long as the *rate* of increase or decrease remains constant.
3. Equal relative changes are represented by lines having equal slopes. Thus two series increasing or decreasing at equal rates will be represented by parallel lines.
4. Comparison of the rates of change in two or more series is effected by comparison of the slopes of the plotted lines.
5. The semilogarithmic ruling permits the plotting of absolute magnitudes and the comparison of relative changes.
6. Comparison of series differing materially in the magnitude of individual items is possible with the semilogarithmic chart.
7. Percentages of change may be read and percentage relations between magnitudes determined directly from the chart.

The Use of Bar Charts for the Comparison of Magnitudes and of Relative Values. A simple column diagram may be useful in the comparison of aggregates, when attention is to be drawn to absolute differences. The eye readily distinguishes such differences as those represented in Fig. 2.19, showing total income payments to individuals in six New England states in 1952. The bars may be drawn vertically, as in the example just cited, or horizontally, as in Fig. 2.20. The latter diagram gives the ranking of ten leading

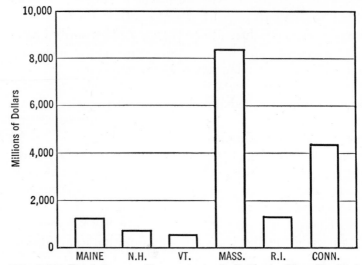

FIG. 2.19. Total Income Payments to Individuals, New England States, 1952.*

* Source: U.S. Department of Commerce.

cities of the United States, by population in 1950. The horizontal representation is particularly advantageous when the chart-maker wishes to present the data with the corresponding bars.

Columns may be employed effectively in setting forth, for comparison, the relative values of several time series for a stated period or date. Fig. 2.21 shows the standing of six elements of the price system in October, 1954, with reference to 1939 as base. The wide range of variation is well brought out by this presentation.

Further examples of column diagrams, as employed in the representation of frequency distributions, are contained in the next chapter. It is there shown how a frequency polygon or frequency curve may grow out of the simple bar diagram, when data of certain kinds are being handled. Such frequency curves constitute very important graphic types, but it will be appropriate to treat them in full at a later point.

Representation of Component Parts. Bar diagrams are well adapted to the showing of the component parts of a given aggregate. These parts may be given in absolute terms, as in Fig. 2.22. This particular illustration shows the same aggregate, the total investment funds of state and local governments in the United States

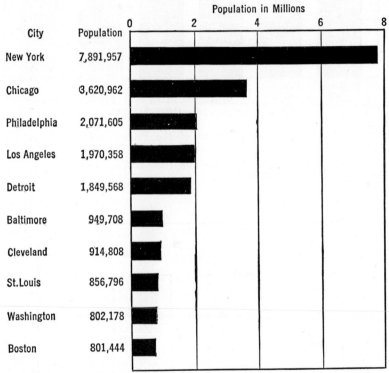

FIG. 2.20. Ranking of Ten Leading Cities of the United States according to Population as of April 1, 1950.*

* Source of data: Bureau of the Census, U.S. Department of Commerce (as presented in the *Economic Almanac*, National Industrial Conference Board, 1953–1954).

during the six-year period 1948–1953, broken up in two ways, to show the *sources* of these funds and the *uses* to which they have been put. In another form, exemplified by Fig. 2.23, the diagrams may show the percentage distribution of an aggregate among its parts at a given date, or at different times. This figure defines the changing industrial composition of the work force of the United States over the period 1870–1950.

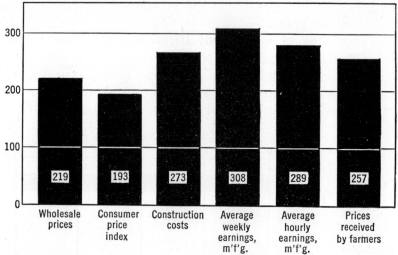

FIG. 2.21. Relations among Elements of the Price Structure, November, 1954 * (1939 = 100).

* Source: U.S. Bureau of Labor Statistics, U.S. Department of Commerce, U.S. Department of Agriculture, *Engineering News Record.*

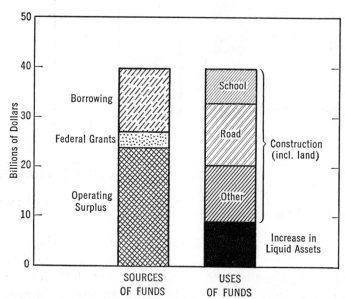

FIG. 2.22. Sources and Uses of the Investment Funds of State and Local Governments Aggregated for the Period 1948–1953.*

* Source of data: Office of Business Economics, U.S. Department of Commerce. Definitions of terms are given in "Private and Public Debt in 1953," by H. D. Osborne and J. A. Gorman, *Survey of Current Business,* October 1954, from which the chart is reproduced.

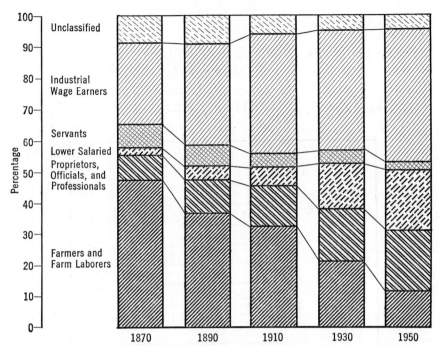

FIG. 2.23. The Changing Industrial Composition of the Work Force of the United States, 1870–1950.* Percentage Distribution in Each of Five Census Years.

* Source: "Industrial Classes in the United States, 1870 to 1950," by Tillman M. Sogge, *Journal of the American Statistical Association*, June, 1954. For the period 1870–1930, the aggregate to which the plotted percentages relate is the total of gainful workers; for 1950 the aggregate is the labor force of the country.

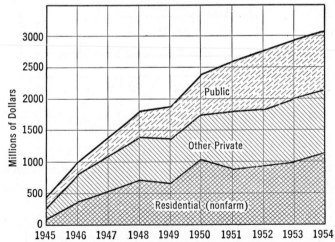

FIG. 2.24. Expenditures for New Construction in the United States, and Three Components Thereof. Monthly Averages, 1945–1954.*

* Source of data: Compiled by various federal agencies; published in *Economic Indicators* by the Joint Committee on the Economic Report.

Shifts, over time, in the absolute magnitude of a given aggregate and in its composition may also be shown by a modification of the ordinary line chart. New construction in the United States increased materially during the nine years following the end of World War II; the elements of the total advanced at varying rates. The record is graphically depicted in Fig. 2.24.

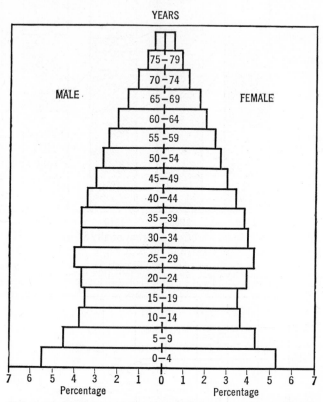

FIG. 2.25. Structure of the Population of the United States, 1950, Showing Percentage Composition by Age and Sex.*

* Source: Bureau of the Census, U.S. Department of Commerce.

Representation of Population Structure. A distinctive type of chart has been used to define the age structure of the population, by sexes. The characteristics of the population of the United States, in 1950, in these respects, are shown by Fig. 2.25. (Those 85 years old or over are not included.) These diagrams change their shape over time, of course, as age structure varies, but ordinarily these changes occur slowly. A picture of a violent alteration in both sex and age structure is given by Fig. 2.26. The ravages of

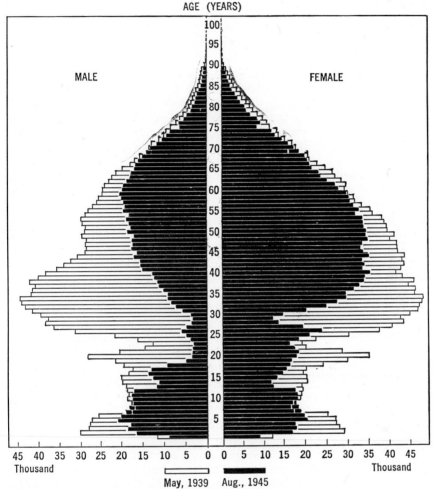

FIG. 2.26. Structure of the Population of Berlin, 1939 and 1945, Showing Composition by Age and Sex.*

* Source: *Statistische Praxis*, Monatszeitschrift des Statistischen Zentralamts, Berlin, October 1946.

war on the population of Berlin during the brief period of six years from 1939 to 1945 are here dramatically depicted.

Note on Procedures in Graphic Presentation. The various illustrations given above will serve as examples of the methods employed in the graphic representation of observations. Much, of course, has been left uncovered concerning the art of graphic portrayal. Principles of effective, pleasing, and honest design have been developed in recent decades, and progress has been made in the standardization of practices in chart making. Although we cannot here set forth these principles in detail, the interests of the beginner may be served by a summary statement of certain recommended procedures in the plotting of time series.

1. Grids should be so proportioned as not to distort the facts. (*Grid* is the term used to define the area or field composed of coordinate rulings.) It is perhaps obvious, but worthy of emphasis, that the relation between the *x*-scale (time) and the *y*-scale (amount) used in portraying a given series of observations has a determining influence on the appearance of a plotted curve, and on the impression given to the chart reader.
2. The amount scale should normally include the zero value or other principle point of reference. In plotting relatives on a stated base, taken to be 100, the point of reference is of course the 100 value.
3. When the zero value or other principle point of reference is omitted, the fact should be clearly indicated in a manner that will attract notice. This omission may be indicated by a wavy line across the bottom of the grid, or by means of a straight line waved at one end.
4. The horizontal axis, zero line, or other line of reference should be accentuated so as to indicate that it is the base of comparison of values.
5. It is advisable not to show any more coordinate lines than are necessary to guide the eye in reading the diagram.
6. The curve lines of a diagram should be sharply distinguished from the ruling. Curves should be sufficiently heavy to attract immediate attention and to impress a visual image on the mind of the reader.
7. Numerals defining the amount scale (the *y*-scale) should be so written and placed that they will clearly indicate the value of the horizontal rulings.
8. A caption should always accompany the scale numerals unless the scale units are otherwise indicated.
9. Time scale designations should be so arranged as to facilitate the reading of the time values for all plotted points on the curves.
10. When more than one curve appears on a chart, each curve should be clearly identified by an appropriate label or key.
11. The title of a diagram should be made as clear and complete as possible. The main title should give the reader a quick understanding of what the chart is about. Material serving to complement or supplement the main title should be placed in a subtitle.[5]

---

[5] For a detailed statement of principles of preferred practice in graphic presentation the reader should consult the manual on *Time Series Charts* prepared by the Committee on Standards for Graphic Presentation, which is published by the American Society of Mechanical Engineers, New York. These standards have the approval of the American Standards Association. See also Mudgett, Ref. 114, and Smart and Arnold, Ref. 144.

The eleven principles listed above are based on the recommendations of the Committee on Standards for Graphic Presentation. The wording has been modified in a few cases, since the recommendations have been lifted out of context.

REFERENCES

Allen, R. G. D., *Mathematical Analysis for Economists*, Chaps. 1, 2, 3, 9.

Committee on Graphics, "A Guide for Preparing Technical Illustrations for Publication and Projection," *American Standards Association*.

Committee on Standards for Graphic Presentation, "Time Series Charts, A Manual of Design and Construction," *American Standards Association*.

Croxton, F. E. and Cowden, D. J., *Applied General Statistics*, Chaps. 4–6.

Federal Reserve System, Board of Governors, *Charts on Money, Bank Credit, Money Rates and Business*, Washington, D.C. (monthly).

Fowler, C. B., Griffin, J. I., Cohen, J. B., Cropsey, J., Greenwald, W. I., and Sethur, F., *Economic Handbook: A Visual Survey*.

Goulden, C. H., *Methods of Statistical Analysis*, 2nd ed., Chap. 1.

Livingston, J. A., "Charts Should Tell a Story," *Journal of the American Statistical Association*, Sept. 1945.

Lutz, R. R., *Graphic Presentation Simplified*.

Mudgett, B. D., *Statistical Tables and Charts*.

Riggleman, J. R. and Frisbee, I. N., *Business Statistics*, 3rd ed., Chaps. 5, 6.

Smart, L. E. and Arnold, S., *Practical Rules for Graphic Presentation*.

Spear, Mary E., *Charting Statistics*.

Spurr, W. A., Kellogg, L. S. and Smith, J. H., *Business and Economic Statistics*, Chaps. 7–8.

Tintner, G., *Mathematics and Statistics for Economists*, Chaps. 1, 2.

Walker, Helen M., *Mathematics Essential for Elementary Statistics*, 2nd ed.

The publishers and the dates of publication of the books named in chapter reference lists are given in the bibliography at the end of this volume.

CHAPTER **3**

•
•
•

The Organization of Statistical
Data: Frequency Distributions

Our systematic discussion of statistical procedures opens here, with the investigator possessed of the body of observations that make up a sample. It is assumed that these observations relate to a quantity that may take different numerical values — that is, that we are dealing with a *variable*. The data may have been compiled in the first instance by the statistician himself,[1] or they may have been obtained from primary or secondary sources. Before generalizations or tests may be based upon these materials, organization of the observations is usually necessary.

Preliminary Considerations and Operations

At the outset we should distinguish between problems arising in the analysis of observations ordered in time and problems involved in the treatment of observations not so ordered, or for which the time order is not relevant to the object of inquiry. In studying a time series the primary object is to measure and analyze the chronological variations in the value of the variable. Thus one may study variations in sales over a period of years, fluctuations in the production of bituminous coal, changes in the level of wholesale prices, or the movements of national income from year to year. Quite different is the procedure in the study of such a problem as income distribution at a given time. Here we are desirous of knowing how many income recipients in the United States fall in each of a num-

---

[1] Practices employed in the field work of sampling, and some sampling principles, are treated in Chapter 16.

ber of income classes. The general problem of organization in this latter class of cases is to determine how many times each value of a variable is repeated and how these values are distributed. Data of this sort, when organized, constitute a *frequency series*, as opposed to the *time* or *historical series*. The methods appropriate to these two types of data differ fundamentally and will therefore be treated separately. In the present section we are concerned with the organization and preliminary treatment of data not arranged in order of time.

We may here recall the distinction drawn in Chapter 1 between statistical description and statistical inference. The present chapter and the two next following are concerned solely with problems of description. In the consideration of these problems, however, we should bear in mind their relation to the processes of inference that constitute the heart of statistical method. We shall open the discussion of these processes in Chapter 6. One minor but practical aspect of the distinction between description and inference should be noted here, since it bears upon the language and symbols we shall employ. We shall speak of a measure derived from a sample as a *statistic*. Such a statistic may be an end in itself, as a quantitative description of an attribute of the sample. More often the statistic is of use to us as a basis for an estimate of the corresponding attribute of the parent population. A measure defining such a population attribute is called a *parameter*. It is a useful general rule (although there are exceptions to it) to use Latin letters as symbols for statistics, Greek letters as symbols for parameters.

Raw data. When quantitative data of the type with which the statistician works are presented in a raw state they appear as masses of unorganized material, without form or structure. They may have been drawn from the records of family saving, or from the production or sales records of a business establishment; they may represent a miscellaneous collection of price quotations. If the data have been gathered by other agencies they may already have been arranged in the form of a general table, but this form may be entirely unsuited to the particular object in the mind of the investigator. The first task of the statistician is the organization of the figures in such a form that their significance, for the purpose in hand, may be appreciated, that comparison with masses of similar data may be facilitated, and that further analysis may be possible. Data, the results of *observation*, must be put into definite form and given coherent structure before the generalizations and tests that constitute the process of *inference* are possible.

The figures that follow, representing the earnings during a given week of 220 individuals engaged in piece work in textile manufacturing, will serve as an example of such data in their raw state.

Weekly Earnings of 220 Textile Workers

$49.85	$59.85	$44.40	$57.10	$44.70	$48.80	$44.55	$50.10
48.65	50.50	53.80	51.05	46.85	46.20	47.40	48.30
50.55	48.40	50.40	45.10	48.50	52.05	55.10	43.85
50.10	51.65	55.40	50.30	45.65	45.55	46.65	51.75
53.20	60.50	48.35	48.50	46.20	52.05	52.70	51.20
47.55	42.50	52.65	45.30	58.60	67.60	49.55	48.25
51.45	46.05	46.95	46.40	49.25	47.95	41.05	47.40
45.30	48.65	50.15	51.35	50.05	49.95	49.05	46.65
49.20	50.45	56.90	49.55	52.85	45.40	45.25	49.00
49.60	54.50	50.45	45.85	46.70	50.65	51.30	61.25
52.25	54.10	50.20	51.25	49.25	47.35	59.95	56.40
50.35	50.60	49.45	58.15	39.55	47.85	49.55	48.70
45.55	55.65	43.30	47.70	47.10	51.55	53.00	38.80
52.00	49.65	48.65	52.60	45.85	54.70	44.10	53.65
48.10	45.00	52.95	51.25	50.15	50.80	51.65	56.70
45.45	50.70	40.40	50.30	48.60	51.85	49.75	51.10
50.00	46.60	47.60	53.10	51.25	50.70	63.85	62.10
55.70	55.25	52.30	41.85	50.55	51.95	49.45	48.35
42.20	50.25	47.00	55.95	48.15	50.75	47.70	52.30
53.45	46.45	49.15	58.95	46.30	53.55	55.30	48.10
64.75	53.35	64.05	49.40	51.90	52.70	49.65	49.70
48.55	48.70	48.45	51.70	59.30	50.95	46.35	46.95
51.70	47.30	54.70	49.30	50.40	44.40	51.10	49.85
54.45	49.75	43.60	44.85	44.75	45.70	49.40	48.45
49.45	50.70	46.50	50.00	52.40	57.30	44.25	49.50
45.75	46.45	40.10	54.65	47.70	49.65	47.75	49.00
61.90	52.90	57.30	57.75	60.40	46.15	47.15	49.60
46.80	50.85	42.95	51.95				

The array. If these figures are arranged in order of magnitude something will have been done toward securing a coherent structure. The range covered and the general distribution throughout this range will then be clear, and the way will be prepared for further organization. When so arranged the *array* on page 43 is secured.

The Construction of Frequency Tables

General Features. While the array presents the figures in a shape much more suitable for study than is the haphazard distribution first shown, there is still something to be desired before the mind can readily grasp the full significance of the data. The factory manager may see that the smallest amount earned during the week was

Array: Weekly Earnings of 220 Textile Workers

$38.80	$45.55	$47.35	$48.70	$49.85	$50.75	$52.25	$55.30
39.55	45.65	47.40	48.70	49.85	50.80	52.30	55.40
40.10	45.70	47.40	48.80	49.95	50.85	52.30	55.65
40.40	45.75	47.55	49.00	50.00	50.95	52.40	55.70
41.05	45.85	47.60	49.00	50.00	51.05	52.60	55.95
41.85	45.85	47.70	49.05	50.05	51.10	52.65	56.40
42.20	46.05	47.70	49.15	50.10	51.10	52.70	56.70
42.50	46.15	47.70	49.20	50.10	51.20	52.70	56.90
42.95	46.20	47.75	49.25	50.15	51.25	52.85	57.10
43.30	46.20	47.85	49.25	50.15	51.25	52.90	57.30
43.60	46.30	47.95	49.30	50.20	51.25	52.95	57.30
43.85	46.35	48.10	49.40	50.25	51.30	53.00	57.75
44.10	46.40	48.10	49.40	50.30	51.35	53.10	58.15
44.25	46.45	48.15	49.45	50.30	51.45	53.20	58.60
44.40	46.45	48.25	49.45	50.35	51.55	53.35	58.95
44.40	46.50	48.30	49.45	50.40	51.65	53.45	59.30
44.55	46.60	48.35	49.50	50.40	51.65	53.55	59.85
44.70	46.65	48.35	49.55	50.45	51.70	53.65	59.95
44.75	46.65	48.40	49.55	50.45	51.70	53.80	60.40
44.85	46.70	48.45	49.55	50.50	51.75	54.10	60.50
45.00	46.80	48.45	49.60	50.55	51.85	54.45	61.25
45.10	46.85	48.50	49.60	50.55	51.90	54.50	61.90
45.25	46.95	48.50	49.65	50.60	51.95	54.65	62.10
45.30	46.95	48.55	49.65	50.65	51.95	54.70	63.85
45.30	47.00	48.60	49.65	50.70	52.00	54.70	64.05
45.40	47.10	48.65	49.70	50.70	52.05	55.10	64.75
45.45	47.15	48.65	49.75	50.70	52.05	55.25	67.60
45.55	47.30	48.65	49.75				

$38.80, that the largest amount earned was $67.60, and that most of the employees earned between $46.00 and $53.00, but this is still a vague description of the data. By a process of grouping, that is, by putting into common classes all individuals whose earnings fall within certain limits, a simplified and more compact presentation of the wage distribution may be obtained. Table 3–1 shows the results of this grouping process when the range of each class (the *class-interval*) is five dollars.

This table presents a condensed summary of the original figures, a summary which not only gives us the approximate range of the earnings, but shows, also, how the earnings of the 220 workers are distributed throughout this range. There has been a considerable loss of detail, it will be noted. From the table we may learn that there are 58 persons who earned, during the given week, between $43.00 and $48.00 (the class extends to but does not include $48.00), but we cannot learn how the earnings of the 58 individuals were distributed throughout this range of five dollars. All may have earned exactly $43.00, so far as we may know from the figures shown in the table. This loss of detail is an inevitable accompaniment of the condensation and simplification which the process of classification involves.

If the size of the class-interval be decreased the loss of detail is less pronounced, though the increase in the number of classes means a more cumbersome table and one that presents a more complex picture to the eye. Tables 3-2, 3-3, and 3-4 present the same data, classified with intervals of three dollars, two dollars, and one dollar.

TABLE 3-1

Frequency Distribution of Employees
(Classified on the basis of weekly earnings; class-interval = $5)

Weekly earnings	Number earning stated amount (frequency)
$38.00 to $42.99	9
43.00 to 47.99	58
48.00 to 52.99	110
53.00 to 57.99	28
58.00 to 62.99	11
63.00 to 67.99	4
	220

The four tables we have thus constructed represent four different degrees of condensation of the same data. Tables 3-1, 3-2, and 3-3 present the same general characteristics: a small number of cases in the extreme classes and a more or less regular increase in the frequencies as the center of each of the distributions is approached. The departure from regularity becomes greater the greater the number of classes. Table 3-4, in which the class-interval is one dollar, has 30 classes. In this table the distribution of cases throughout the range is irregular, with noticeable departures from symmetry. The structure of each of the other tables is orderly and approaches more closely a condition of symmetry. Each presents the wage data in condensed and compact form, so that one consulting the tables may learn of the size and distribution of weekly earnings in the factory in question much more readily than by reference to the chaotic collection of figures first shown. Such organized collections of data are termed *frequency distributions*, and their purpose, as the term implies, is to show in a condensed form the nature of the distribution of a variable quantity throughout the range covered by the values of the variable. The construction of

Frequency Distributions of Employees
(Classified on the basis of weekly earnings)

| **TABLE 3–2** | | **TABLE 3–3** | | **TABLE 3–4** | |
| (Class-interval = $3) | | (Class-interval = $2) | | (Class-interval = $1) | |
Weekly earnings	Fre-quency	Weekly earnings	Fre-quency	Weekly earnings	Fre-quency
$38.00 to $40.99	4	$38.00 to $39.99	2	$38.00 to $38.99	1
41.00 to 43.99	8	40.00 to 41.99	4	39.00 to 39.99	1
44.00 to 46.99	40	42.00 to 43.99	6	40.00 to 40.99	2
47.00 to 49.99	63	44.00 to 45.99	22	41.00 to 41.99	2
50.00 to 52.99	62	46.00 to 47.99	33	42.00 to 42.99	3
53.00 to 55.99	21	48.00 to 49.99	48	43.00 to 43.99	3
56.00 to 58.99	10	50.00 to 51.99	48	44.00 to 44.99	8
59.00 to 61.99	7	52.00 to 53.99	22	45.00 to 45.99	14
62.00 to 64.99	4	54.00 to 55.99	13	46.00 to 46.99	18
65.00 to 67.99	1	56.00 to 57.99	7	47.00 to 47.99	15
	220	58.00 to 59.99	6	48.00 to 48.99	20
		60.00 to 61.99	4	49.00 to 49.99	28
		62.00 to 63.99	2	50.00 to 50.99	28
		64.00 to 65.99	2	51.00 to 51.99	20
		66.00 to 67.99	1	52.00 to 52.99	14
			220	53.00 to 53.99	8
				54.00 to 54.99	6
				55.00 to 55.99	7
				56.00 to 56.99	3
				57.00 to 57.99	4
				58.00 to 58.99	3
				59.00 to 59.99	3
				60.00 to 60.99	2
				61.00 to 61.99	2
				62.00 to 62.99	1
				63.00 to 63.99	1
				64.00 to 64.99	2
				65.00 to 65.99	0
				66.00 to 66.99	0
				67.00 to 67.99	1
					220

such a table is the first step to be taken in the organization and analysis of quantitative data of the type represented above.

This general introduction to the subject of frequency tables has left untouched many important matters in connection with their construction. It remains to present a summary statement of these details. It will be clear that the first step here taken, the arrangement of the items in order of magnitude, is unnecessary in the actual construction of such a table. Having determined the upper and lower limits through an inspection of the data, one has but to decide on the number of classes desired, write the class-intervals on an appropriate blank sheet, and proceed to tally the cases falling in each of the classes thus set off. When this process is completed the frequencies are computed and the totals arranged in tabular form of the type illustrated above. These simple operations involve decisions on a number of points, however.

Size of Class-Interval. In deciding upon the size of the class-interval (which is equivalent to deciding upon the number of classes) one fundamental consideration should be borne in mind, namely, that classes should be so arranged that there will be no material departure from an even distribution of cases within each class. This arrangement is necessary because, in interpreting the frequency table and in subsequent calculations based upon it, the mid-value of each class (the *class mark*) is taken to represent the values of all cases falling in that class. Thus, in basing calculations upon Table 3–3, it is assumed that the 33 cases falling between $46.00 and $48.00 may all be represented by the mid-value of that class, $47.00. This assumption will seldom be strictly valid. In the case just cited reference to the original figures will show that it is not a correct assumption. Absolute accuracy would only be obtained by having a class for every value represented in the original figures. Since condensation is necessary, an arrangement of classes should be secured which will minimize the error involved, without transgressing other requirements. Table 3–1 furnishes an example of class-intervals too wide for the material.

The requirement that has just been described clearly calls for a large number of classes. A second requirement, which ordinarily conflicts with this, is that the number of classes should be so determined that an orderly and regular sequence of frequencies is secured. If the classification is too narrow for the data, regularity will not be attained in this respect, and a table without structure or order will be secured. It is desirable, also, that the number of classes be limited in order that the data may be easily manipulated and their significance readily grasped.

A useful procedure for approximating a suitable class-interval has been suggested by H. A. Sturges (Ref. 154). Given a series of N items of which the *range* (the difference between the smallest item and the largest item) is known, a suitable class-interval i may be approximated from the formula

$$i = \frac{\text{Range}}{1 + 3.322 \log N}$$

The specific figure secured in a given instance is likely to be a fractional value, quite unsuited to actual use. An appropriate round number close to the theoretical value, may be chosen.[2] Thus, in the example cited above, with a range of $28.80 and N equal to 220, the use of a class-interval of $3.28 is indicated by the formula. The nearest round number, suitable with reference to other considerations as well, is $3.00. Table 3–2, in which this class-interval is employed, seems to conform most thoroughly to all the requirements we have set forth.

Location of Class Limits. The location of class limits is a matter of considerable importance, for attention to this matter will simplify tabulation and facilitate later calculation. Tabulation of data is easiest when class limits are integers and the class-interval itself is a whole number. Calculation of averages and other statistical measures is facilitated when the mid-values of classes are integers.

Some types of data show a tendency to cluster or concentrate about certain values on the scale along which they are distributed. This is illustrated by the following figures, which form part of a table showing business loans outstanding on the books of a comprehensive sample of member banks of the Federal Reserve System on November 20, 1946. The loans are distributed according to the rate of interest charged.

Interest rate (percent per annum)	Number of loans (in thousands)
2.1 to 2.9	13.7
3.0	34.8
3.1 to 3.9	13.2
4.0	117.2
4.1 to 4.9	26.6
5.0	141.1
5.1 to 5.9	3.6

Here is quite obvious bunching about the integers. The original classified data would show, also, a secondary concentration at each half of one percent. It is clear that in classifying measurements of this sort the midpoints of the various classes should fall at those values about which the observations are concentrated, and class limits must be located with this end in view. For in calculations

[2] The use of this formula rests on the assumption that the proper distribution into classes is given, for all numbers that are powers of 2, by a series of binomial coefficients. The relation of the terms in the binomial expansion to the theory of frequency distributions is discussed below, in Chapter 6.

based upon a frequency table the assumption is made that all the items in each class are concentrated at the midpoint of that class. Thus if a standard class-interval of one half of one percent were to be employed in classifying data of the type represented above, the classes should extend from $1\frac{3}{4}$ to (but not including) $2\frac{1}{4}$, $2\frac{1}{4}$ to $2\frac{3}{4}$, $2\frac{3}{4}$ to $3\frac{1}{4}$, rather than from 2 to $2\frac{1}{2}$, $2\frac{1}{2}$ to 3, etc.

Accuracy of observations and the definition of classes. In the construction of frequency tables it is essential that there be a clear definition of classes, so that there may be no uncertainty as to their range and no question as to the precise class in which a given case falls. A table with an arrangement similar to the following is sometimes encountered:

Class-interval	Frequency
0 to 10	3
10 to 20	8
20 to 30	15
30 to 40	6
40 to 50	2

In the absence of explanation, a question arises at once as to whether a case with a value of 10 would fall in the first or in the second class. It is highly desirable that the range of each class be indicated in some such way as the following, in order that this ambiguity may be avoided:

Class-interval	Frequency
0 to 9.9	3
10 to 19.9	8
20 to 29.9	15
30 to 39.9	6
40 to 49.9	2

This procedure solves the difficulty, however, only in case the observations are accurate to the nearest tenth. If the observations are accurate only to the nearest unit (that is, if the cases recorded as having a value of 10 actually lie between 9.5 and 10.5) a mere change in the description of the class range does not solve the problem of allocating a case at the class limit. In such a case an observation falling at a class boundary may be cut in two, one half being allocated to each of the adjacent classes.

Yule and Kendall lay down the useful principle that in fixing a class boundary the limit should be carried to a farther place in decimals, or a smaller fraction, than the values of the individual cases as originally recorded. Thus, in the preceding example, if observations were correct to the nearest tenth, it would mean that a value recorded as 9.9 actually lay between 9.85 and 9.95. In accurately describing the classes, therefore, the intervals should be given as 0 to 9.95, 9.95 to 19.95, etc. (Since the observations to be tabulated are recorded only to the first decimal place no ambiguity arises from the apparent overlapping of these class limits.) It should be noted that the values of the midpoints, or class marks, with these class limits, would be 4.95, 14.95, etc. In presenting and using the table as given above the real meaning of the class limits should be borne in mind. In all cases class boundaries must be fixed with reference to the accuracy of the observations, and exact class marks must be used to ensure accuracy in subsequent calculations.

The work of tabulation is simplified if, in designating a class, both limits are stated, as above. Errors are likely if only the lower limit of each class is given, or if the midpoint alone is designated. It is desirable, however, particularly if calculations are to be based upon the table, to include a separate column showing the values of the midpoints of the various classes.

Other requirements. Class-intervals should be uniform throughout the table in order that all classes may be comparable. Occasionally tables are published with varying class-intervals, so that on one section of the scale the number of items falling within a class having an interval of 5 is given, and on another section of the scale the number of items falling within a class having a range of 10 is given. Obviously, comparison of classes is impossible. It may be desirable to show in more detail the cases falling within certain ranges on the scale, but this end is best achieved by the construction of a supplementary table relating only to the cases falling within this restricted section. The utility of the main table is not lessened thereby.

Similar in nature is the requirement that there should be no indeterminate classes, that is, classes the ranges of which are not defined. Had all the individuals making $50.00 and over in the illustration of piece-work earnings been entered in a class with the designation "$50.00 and over," the upper limit of this class would have been quite uncertain. This fault in a table is a vital one when it is desired to base calculations upon the data contained in the table. When there are several extreme cases the inclusion of such classes is sometimes unavoidable, but when this is done the actual values of the cases included in such "open end" classes should be given in a footnote to the table.

The errors described in the two preceding paragraphs are exemplified in Table 3–5.

TABLE 3–5

Frequency Distribution of Rented Dwellings in Reno, Nevada, 1934*
(Classified on the basis of rental value)

Monthly rental	Number of dwellings in each class (frequency)
Under $10.00	327
$10.00 to $14.99	349
15.00 to 19.99	521
20.00 to 29.99	1,039
30.00 to 49.99	1,075
50.00 to 74.99	189
75.00 to 99.99	24
$100.00 and over	9
	3,533

* The table is taken from *Real Property Inventory, 1934. Summary and Sixty-Four Cities Combined*, Department of Commerce, Washington. Figures for 255 rented dwellings in Reno were not reported.

In this case the ranges of the two "open end" classes are not known. The ranges of the intermediate classes vary, being $5.00 for two classes, $10.00 for one class, $20.00 for one class, and $25.00 for two classes. The purposes of a special investigation may sometimes be served by the use of such a form, but a table of this type is poorly adapted to the requirements of statistical calculation.

A statistical table, in the form presented to users, should be adapted to the special purpose it is designed to serve. It is not enough that it should meet technical requirements of the kind outlined in the preceding pages. It should have an orderly structure and clear and unambiguous column headings and title; it should be self-sufficient and self-explanatory.

Graphic Representation of Frequency Distributions

Frequency distributions of the type illustrated above serve a very important statistical function in presenting a compact summary of data, and in preparing these data for further manipulation. Such distributions may be presented not only in tabular form, but graphically, utilizing the general principles of the coordinate system which were explained above. Many of the characteristic features of a frequency distribution are most clearly revealed when the graphic method is adopted.

Table 3-1, presenting the weekly earnings of 220 employees, with a class-interval of five dollars, is depicted graphically in Fig. 3.1. In this figure class-intervals are plotted along the x-axis and the corresponding class-frequencies along the y-axis, appropriate scales being selected. The fact should be noted that the scale of abscissas starts not with zero, but with $33. For convenience in presentation, that part of the scale extending from 0 to $33 is

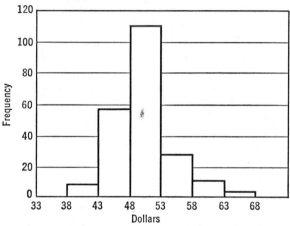

FIG. 3.1. Column Diagram: Distribution of 220 Employees Classified on the Basis of Weekly Earnings (Class-interval = $5.00).

omitted. The student should bear this in mind in seeking to secure a correct impression of the relations between the two variables plotted. In constructing such a figure, which is termed a *column diagram* or *histogram*, short horizontal lines are drawn connecting the points plotted to represent the upper and lower limits of each class-interval. In interpreting this diagram it should be noted that the areas of the different rectangles are proportional to the number of cases represented, the total area representing the entire 220 cases. This device thus presents to the eye a very clear picture of the distribution, showing quite unmistakably the relative number of workers falling in each of the wage classes.

The classes in this case are so large, however, that some violence is done to the facts. So many details are lost that a true conception of the disposition of the items is not given. Fig. 3.2 is a histogram depicting the distribution of cases when a class-interval of three dollars is used. In this case, with smaller steps, we approach more

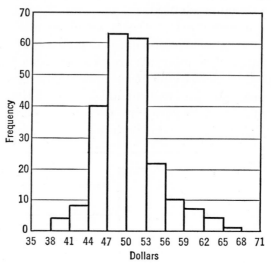

FIG. 3.2. Column Diagram: Distribution of 220 Employees Classified on the Basis of Weekly Earnings (Class-interval = $3.00).

closely an orderly and symmetrical distribution. The same is true of Fig. 3.3, which shows the distribution when the class-interval is two dollars. The distribution represented in Fig. 3.4 has a class-interval of one dollar which, as has been pointed out, is too narrow for the data, with the result that a somewhat irregular structure is

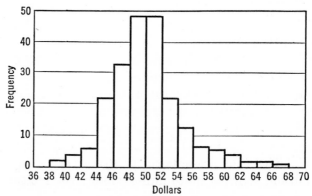

FIG. 3.3. Column Diagram: Distribution of 220 Employees Classified on the Basis of Weekly Earnings (Class-interval = $2.00).

FIG. 3.4. Column Diagram: Distribution of 220 Employees Classified on the Basis of Weekly Earnings (Class-interval = $1.00).

secured. (It should be noted that the vertical scale is not the same in these four figures, so that comparison with respect to class frequencies is only possible by reference to the scale figures.)

Frequency polygons corresponding to the histograms of Figs. 3.1 and 3.4 are shown in Figs. 3.5 and 3.6. Each of these polygons has been constructed by plotting as abscissas the midpoints of the class-intervals, and as ordinates the class frequencies, the points thus secured being connected by a broken line. In completing such a

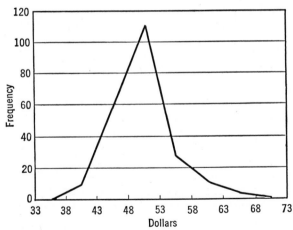

FIG. 3.5. Frequency Polygon: Distribution of 220 Employees Classified on the Basis of Weekly Earnings (Class-interval = $5.00).

figure the class next below the lowest one on the scale and the class next above the highest one on the scale are included, the class frequency being zero in each case. The ends of the polygon thus connect with the base line at the midpoints of these two extra classes. For the frequency polygon the entire area under the curve represents the entire number of cases, but the area of a given interval cannot be taken to be proportional to the number of cases in that interval, because of irregularities in the distribution on either side of the given class. The heights of the ordinates at the midpoints of the various classes are, of course, scaled to represent the class frequencies.

FIG. 3.6. Frequency Polygon: Distribution of 220 Employees Classified on the Basis of Weekly Earnings (Class-interval = $1.00).

The Smoothing of Curves. Attention is again called to the results secured with varying class-intervals. As the class-interval is decreased, up to a certain point, the histograms and polygons become smoother and more regular. Beyond that point breaks begin to appear in the data; the regular change in class frequencies which was found when the classes were larger is broken by the appearance of irregular classes which seem to depart from the rule. Fig. 3.4 reveals some of these breaks. Such irregularities, it is obvious, are exceptions to a general rule which seems to prevail, the rule that the numbers of workers falling within the different wage classes increase from the lower limit of earnings up to a maximum in the neighborhood of $50.00 and then decrease till, in the topmost class from $67.00 to $67.99, but one worker is found. Since all the 220 individuals are engaged in the same work, and since their earnings depend only upon their rapidity and skill, one would expect a quite regular increase and decrease. If we had figures not for one week only, but for 52 weeks, and took the average weekly earnings of each of the 220 workers for the year, we should expect greater regularity with the smaller class-intervals than is actually found, since the accidental fluctuations peculiar to one week alone would thus be eliminated. Or, if we had earnings during one week for 11,440 workers (52 times 220), the same result would be secured. Thus, if regularity and smoothness are to be secured, it is essential not only to decrease the size of the classes but also to increase the number of cases, in order that the accidental irregularities that affect a small number of observations may be eliminated. A refined classification with a small number of cases leads to the condition exemplified in Figs. 3.4 and 3.6. But such an increase in the number of cases is, in general, a practical impossibility. We wish, if possible, to develop a feasible method of approximating the distribution that would be secured with very small class-intervals and a very large number of cases. Such an approximation is possible through the device of curve smoothing. By this method we may secure a smooth *frequency curve* that lacks the irregularities occasioned by minor fluctuations.

Such a smooth frequency curve represents what is taken to be the true underlying distribution of the members of the population from which the sample was drawn. It was pointed out that areas in the frequency polygon are not proportional to the number of cases included, the cause lying in the irregularities of the data. In a smoothed frequency curve these irregularities have been eliminated, and the area between ordinates erected at given points on the scale of abscissas is assumed to be proportional to the theoretical frequency of cases between the given values. Moreover, a smooth progression having been established, frequencies for intermediate values not shown in the original table may be determined by interpolation.[3]

The data of Table 3–6 representing the distribution in 1918 of

---

[3] The limitations of practical statistical work are such that there must of necessity be many gaps in the data. The given values of the variables are not continuous. Interpolation is the process of estimating values of a variable quantity between given values, or of locating a point on a curve between given points. That interpolation is most accurate which leads to estimated values having the highest degree of consistency with the given values.

personal incomes below $4,000, will serve to exemplify the smooth-
ing process.[4]

TABLE 3–6

Distribution of Income among Personal Income Recipients in 1918
(Including all personal incomes below $4,000)

Income class *	Number of persons †
$ 0 to $ 100	62,809
100 to 200	103,704
200 to 300	209,087
300 to 400	489,963
400 to 500	961,991
500 to 600	1,549,974
600 to 700	2,154,474
700 to 800	2,668,466
800 to 900	3,013,034
900 to 1,000	3,144,722
1,000 to 1,100	3,074,351
1,100 to 1,200	2,850,526
1,200 to 1,300	2,535,285
1,300 to 1,400	2,205,728
1,400 to 1,500	1,832,230
1,500 to 1,600	1,512,649
1,600 to 1,700	1,234,397
1,700 to 1,800	999,996
1,800 to 1,900	811,236
1,900 to 2,000	663,789
2,000 to 2,100	549,787
2,100 to 2,200	463,222
2,200 to 2,300	395,115
2,300 to 2,400	340,141
2,400 to 2,500	295,490
2,500 to 2,600	258,650
2,600 to 2,700	227,731
2,700 to 2,800	201,488
2,800 to 2,900	178,901
2,900 to 3,000	154,499
3,000 to 3,100	142,802
3,100 to 3,200	128,217
3,200 to 3,300	115,583
3,300 to 3,400	104,504
3,400 to 3,500	94,803
3,500 to 3,600	86,405
3,600 to 3,700	79,023
3,700 to 3,800	72,562
3,800 to 3,900	66,900
3,900 to 4,000	61,894

* The definition of classes used is equivalent to "$0 to and not including $100," etc.
Thus an individual with an income of $100 would fall in the second class.
† Mitchell's report states "The numbers below are given to the nearest unit. It is not
pretended that such arithmetic accuracy is anything more than technical."

[4] From Mitchell, King, Macaulay and Knauth, Ref. 108. The graduated income estimates
are those of Frederick R. Macaulay.

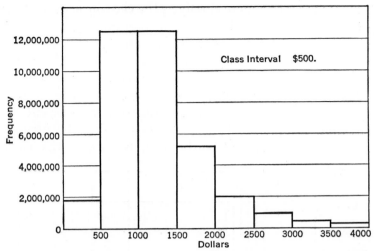

FIG. 3.7. Column Diagram: Distribution of Personal Income Recipients in the United States, 1918. Including All Recipients of Incomes Below $4,000 (Class-interval = $500).

Figures 3.7, 3.8, and 3.9 present column diagrams of these income data, grouped with class-intervals of $500, $200, and $100. As the class-interval is decreased the histograms become more regular and uniform, but our original data permit us to carry this process only to the point where the class-interval is $100. Our problem is to determine the underlying distribution which the data

FIG. 3.8. Column Diagram: Distribution of Personal Income Recipients in the United States, 1918. Including All Recipients of Incomes Below $4,000 (Class-interval = $200).

approximate more and more closely as the class-interval is lessened. If we replace the broken line of the histogram by a smooth curve *enclosing the same total area* as the histogram and so drawn through the points of the histogram that *the area cut from each rectangle is approximately equal to the area added to the same rectangle by the curve,* we will have a frequency curve representing the desired distribution. The requirement that the same total area be enclosed is fundamental. Exceptions to the rule concerning the area of individual rectangles will frequently occur because of the existence

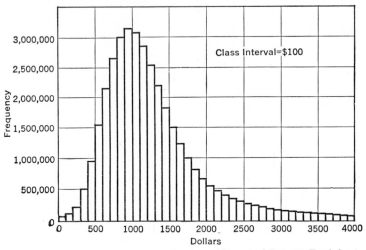

FIG. 3.9. Column Diagram: Distribution of Personal Income Recipients in the United States, 1918. Including All Recipients of Incomes Below $4,000 (Class-interval = $100).

of quite irregular classes, but as a general working principle it is helpful. (More refined methods of fitting a smooth curve to data will be discussed at a later point, but a process of smoothing by inspection such as that described above gives a fairly close approximation to the required curve.)

Figure 3.10 illustrates the result of smoothing the histogram of income distribution shown in Fig. 3.9. Here the quite artificial jumps between income classes are smoothed out, and we secure the graduation by infinitesimal increments which we should expect to find when the incomes of so many millions of persons are included. Here we have that which we desired — an approximation to the true underlying distribution, with the sharp breaks resulting from the method of classification eliminated.

Note on the contemporary distribution of income. The preceding detailed estimates of income distribution in the United States for 1918 serve well the immediate purpose — that of exemplifying the passage from a broken column diagram to the smooth curve approximating the distribution of incomes in the parent population. Macaulay's figures constitute, indeed, the most comprehensive set of graduated income estimates available. They do not, however, provide an accurate representation of income distribution in the United States today. The economic changes of the last thirty years

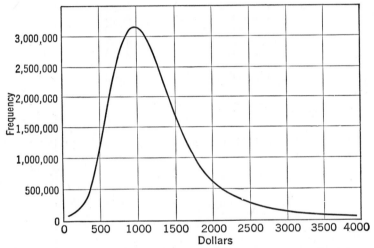

FIG. 3.10. Frequency Curve: Distribution of Personal Income Recipients in the United States, 1918. Including all Recipients of Incomes Below $4,000. (Derived from the column diagram with class-interval of $100.)

have brought major shifts in the division of income by size-classes. Estimates of income distribution in a more recent year, 1950, are given in Table 3–7.

In this discussion of curve smoothing we have been dealing with a major aspect of statistical work — the estimation of the attributes of a population. In particular, we have here been concerned with the manner in which the members of a population of income recipients are distributed, with reference to income size. The present quite preliminary approach to this problem, through the smoothing of an observational distribution, is essentially mechanical. But the problem is one that will enter into much of the subsequent discussion. The precise definition of the manner in which the values of a variable are distributed — the determination of the

Distribution of Family Personal Income
by Families and Unattached Individuals, United States, 1950 *
(Incomes before deduction of income taxes)

Income class	Number of families and unattached individuals (in thousands)
Less than $1,000	3,704
$ 1,000 to 1,999	7,328
2,000 to 2,999	8,044
3,000 to 3,999	8,463
4,000 to 4,999	6,980
5,000 to 5,999	4,459
6,000 to 6,999	2,909
7,000 to 7,999	2,036
8,000 to 8,999	1,212
9,000 to 9,999	728
10,000 and over	2,727
Total	48,590

* Source: "Income Distribution in the United States," a supplement to the *Survey of Current Business*, Office of Business Economics, U.S. Department of Commerce, 1953. Table 3–7 is derived from the absolute and relative frequencies given in Appendix Tables 2 and 24 of this publication.

The estimates in Table 3–7 are based upon Federal income tax returns (projected from earlier years, since 1950 returns were not available when these estimates were prepared) and on sample field surveys of 1950 family income conducted by the Census Bureau and the Board of Governors of the Federal Reserve System. These returns were related to estimates of total family personal income made by the Office of Business Economics as a part of the national income accounts.

The reader will note that the income-receiving unit in Table 3–7 is the family. In preceding income tables in the text it was the individual income recipient. (In the Commerce Department definition, a "family" is a group of two or more related persons living in the same household. An "unattached individual" is a person living alone or with persons not related to him.) Table 3–7 differs, also, from the preceding text tables in that the entire range of incomes is included.

law of distribution prevailing in the case in question — is the objective of scientific work in many fields. Statistics as a scientific discipline has developed and strengthened as our knowledge of the sampling distributions of statistical characteristics has grown. With this we shall deal in greater detail at later points.

Continuous and Discrete Variables. The logical validity of the smoothing process is dependent on the nature of the data being manipulated. From this point of view frequency series of the type discussed above may be divided into two classes, those that relate to continuous variables and those that relate to discontinuous variables. A continuous variable is one that may take any numerical value within a specified range. When observations on such a variable are ranked in order of magnitude, successive values may differ by infinitesimal increments. A discontinuous variable takes only discrete values. Observations on such a variable, ranked in order, change in value only by definite amounts. The curve of underlying values does not rise smoothly, as for the continuous series, but by jumps.

The fact should be emphasized that in making this distinction we are speaking of the values as they would be found in the underlying universe of phenomena from which the actual bodies of material we study are drawn. Any given sample, whether representing continuous or discrete series, will be marked by breaks in the values of the variable. This will be true, in the case of a continuous series, because of the limitations of the instruments and senses we use in measuring. Thus if we measure the heights of individual persons, we may do so to the nearest inch, or perhaps to the nearest eighth or sixteenth of an inch. Yet if ten million men were arranged in order of height the differences between successive individuals would be much smaller than the smallest measurable interval. Height is a continuous variable, even though the observations that enter into a given sample are marked by discontinuity.

Quite different is the distribution of such a variable as interest or discount rates. If one were to secure 100 such quotations and rank them in the order of size the variations would be discontinuous, as in a sample of men whose heights are measured. But in the case of heights the underlying values, if they could be determined for a large population, would be marked by continuous variation, whereas, were an infinite number of discount rate quotations secured, there would still be breaks in the sequence. Discount rates increase or decrease by one quarter or one half of one percent, not by infinitesimal amounts. Such a series is termed discrete, or noncontinuous.

A good example of a discrete series, which also serves as an example of a J-shaped distribution, is provided by Table 3–8 (see Fig. 3.11). This is a classification of machine-tool makers, based upon the number of types of machine tools produced by each.

The series is, of course, discrete since the number of types of tools made by each producer is necessarily defined by an integer. The high degree of specialization in the industry is shown by the concentration of machine-tool makers at the lower end of the scale.

FIG. 3.11. Column Diagram: Distribution of 137 Machine Tool Builders, Classified by Number of Tool Types Produced.

More than half of the total number made but one style of machine tool.

The smoothing process provides a means of securing an approximation to the distribution of values as they would be found if a sample could be increased indefinitely in size. It is based upon the assumption that the irregularities found in the sample actually studied are accidental, and that the underlying values would show

TABLE 3–8

Classification of Membership of National Machine Tool Builders' Association according to Number of Types of Machine Tools Produced *

Types of tools Number	Number of manufacturers
1	80
2	33
3	13
4	8
5	2
More than five	1
	137

* From "Trends in Manhours Expended per Unit, Selected Machine Tools, 1939–1945." U.S. Bureau of Labor Statistics, June, 1947, p. 44.

continuous and unbroken variation. Obviously, therefore, it is only fully justified when applied to a continuous series. A histogram of human heights may be smoothed in order to secure a representation of the true underlying distribution in the population at large, and interpolation based upon this smoothing process is valid. But smoothing is quite illogical for a markedly discontinuous series. It would be meaningless to construct a smooth curve showing the distribution of discount rates for the purpose of securing the theoretical frequency of rates between 4.3675 percent and 4.3850 percent. In practical statistical work, however, it is frequently helpful to handle discrete series as though they were continuous, and in these cases the smoothing device may be employed. But in the interpretation and use of the smoothed curve the logical distinction between continuous and discontinuous variation should be kept in mind.

A U-shaped frequency distribution. In sharp contrast to the customary frequency distributions, in which frequencies increase to a maximum and then decline, is the type represented by the data in Table 3–9. In this distribution commodities are classified on

TABLE 3–9

Distribution of 206 Commodities Classified according
to Frequency of Monthly Price Changes
in Wholesale Markets, 1890–1925 *

Class limits Measure of frequency of change †	Number of commodities
.00– .10	45
.11– .20	25
.21– .30	16
.31– .40	19
.41– .50	14
.51– .60	7
.61– .70	6
.71– .80	15
.81– .90	15
.91–1.00	44
	206

* Excluding 1914–21
† The range of the first class in the above table (in actual values .00 to .105, the original measures being recorded to the second decimal place) is slightly greater than the range of any other class, and the range of the last class (in actual values .905 to 1.000) is slightly less than the range of any other class. The error introduced is negligible, however.

the basis of the frequency of price change, in wholesale markets. An index of frequency of change was constructed for each of 206 commodities for which average monthly prices were available for the period 1890–1925 (the disturbed years 1914–21 were omitted). The index was simply the ratio of the number of months in which prices changed (from the price of the preceding month) to the total number of months less one covered by a continuous price record. Thus for a record covering 120 successive months, the index would be 0 (0/119) for a commodity marked by no price changes; the

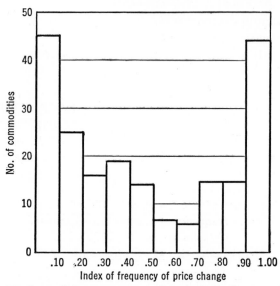

FIG. 3.12. Column Diagram Showing Distribution of Measures of Frequency of Price Changes, 1890–1925 (1914–1921 excluded).

index would be 1.00 (119/119) for a commodity for which the price changed every month.[5] The graphic representation of this distribution, in Fig. 3.12 reveals the remarkable clustering of commodities at the two extremes of the x-scale, with frequencies at a minimum near the median position on the scale. This rather rare distribution type has special interest for economists, in this case, for the light it throws on the movement of prices. High inflexibility and high flexibility were the two dominant types of price behavior in the period covered by this record.

[5] See Mills, Ref. 100, pp. 56–60, 379–81 for a fuller discussion.

Cumulative Arrangement of Statistical Data

For certain purposes it is desirable to arrange data cumulatively, rather than in exclusive classes of the type illustrated in the frequency tables presented above. The accompanying tables will illustrate some of the advantages of this arrangement.

In a study by Kurtz of the durability of telephone poles the results given in Table 3–10 were secured. The table shows that 1,150

TABLE 3–10

Frequency Distribution of 248,707 Telephone Poles, Classified according to Length of Life

Length of life (years)	Number of poles (frequency)
0– 0.9	1,150
1– 1.9	4,221
2– 2.9	10,692
3– 3.9	13,966
4– 4.9	16,633
5– 5.9	18,211
6– 6.9	19,011
7– 7.9	19,260
8– 8.9	20,909
9– 9.9	19,879
10–10.9	20,764
11–11.9	15,454
12–12.9	14,237
13–13.9	13,779
14–14.9	9,764
15–15.9	8,534
16–16.9	7,659
17–17.9	6,918
18–18.9	4,591
19–19.9	1,798
20–20.9	815
21–21.9	313
22–22.9	102
23–23.9	47

poles were scrapped during the first year of use, that 4,221 were scrapped after reaching the age of one year and before reaching the age of two years, and so on. This is simply a frequency table of the ordinary type. A much more significant arrangement for many purposes is secured when the figures are assembled cumulatively, as in Table 3–11.

TABLE 3–11

TABLE 3–11

Cumulative Distribution of 248,707 Telephone Poles, Classified
according to Length of Life
(Cumulated upward with reference to life scale)

Length of life	Number of poles surviving (frequency)
Less than 1 year	1,150
" " 2 years	5,371
" " 3 "	16,063
" " 4 "	30,029
" " 5 "	46,662
" " 6 "	64,873
" " 7 "	83,884
" " 8 "	103,144
" " 9 "	124,053
" " 10 "	143,932
" " 11 "	164,696
" " 12 "	180,150
" " 13 "	194,387
" " 14 "	208,166
" " 15 "	217,930
" " 16 "	226,464
" " 17 "	234,123
" " 18 "	241,041
" " 19 "	245,632
" " 20 "	247,430
" " 21 "	248,245
" " 22 "	248,558
" " 23 "	248,660
" " 24 "	248,707

We should note that it is possible to cumulate a frequency series
in two different ways. From Table 3–11 we may determine readily
the number failing to attain any given age. It is often more convenient to reverse the process, so that the table will enable the
total number above any given value to be immediately determined.
When the telephone pole figures are thus *cumulated downward* Table
3–12 is secured.

Cumulative tables such as those given above have distinct advantages in the handling of many types of data. Life tables are
generally presented in this form. The scientific study of deprecia-
tion will lead to the construction of elaborate "mortality tables"
for various types of equipment, and these will be most useful in the
cumulative form. It is frequently desirable to reduce the frequencies to percentages, as in column (3) of Table 3–12. Cumulated

TABLE 3–12

Cumulative Distribution of 248,707 Telephone Poles, Classified
according to Length of Life
(Cumulated downward with reference to life scale)

(1) Length of life	(2) Number of poles surviving frequency	(3) Percent
0 and more	248,707	100.0
1 year " "	247,557	99.5
2 years " "	243,336	97.8
3 " " "	232,644	93.6
4 " " "	218,678	88.0
5 " " "	202,045	81.2
6 " " "	183,834	73.8
7 " " "	164,823	66.3
8 " " "	145,563	58.5
9 " " "	124,654	50.1
10 " " "	104,775	42.1
11 " " "	84,011	33.8
12 " " "	68,557	27.6
13 " " "	54,320	21.8
14 " " "	40,541	16.3
15 " " "	30,777	12.4
16 " " "	22,243	8.9
17 " " "	14,584	5.9
18 " " "	7,666	3.1
19 " " "	3,075	1.2
20 " " "	1,277	0.5
21 " " "	462	0.2
22 " " "	149	0.06
23 " " "	47	0.02
24 " " "	0	0.00

percentages are particularly helpful when frequency distributions
are to be compared.

The Ogive, or Cumulative Frequency Curve. The general utility
of such cumulated data is limited by the classification system necessarily adopted in condensing the material. Unless we interpolate
mathematically we are limited to the points on the scale actually
noted in Tables 3–11 and 3–12. For this reason, a generalized cumulative curve similar to the smoothed frequency curve described
in the preceding section is desirable. If the values given in Table
3–11 be plotted on coordinate paper (the length of life in each case
as abscissa, and the corresponding number of poles as ordinate)
and a smooth curve drawn through the points thus plotted, the

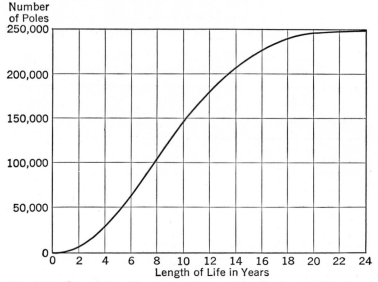

FIG. 3.13. Cumulative Frequency Curve: Distribution of Telephone Poles Classified according to Length of Life (cumulated upward).

FIG. 3.14. Cumulative Frequency Curve: Distribution of Telephone Poles Classified according to Length of Life (cumulated downward).

cumulative frequency curve shown in Fig. 3.13 is secured. In Fig. 3.14 the data of Table 3–12 are plotted.

Such a curve constitutes one of the most effective and useful representations of a frequency series. It is obvious that the limitations of the particular class-interval adopted are in large part removed; the shape of the curve will be fundamentally the same, though the class-interval and number of classes may vary. Frequency curves of the usual type may not be compared unless the groupings are the same, but cumulative frequency curves are subject to no such restriction. Moreover, uneven class-intervals do not distort the *ogive*, or cumulative curve, as they do the ordinary frequency curve.

The cumulative curve is particularly well adapted to interpolation. Thus if it is desired to know the number of poles surviving less than $15\frac{1}{2}$ years, the value of the ordinate of the curve having $15\frac{1}{2}$ as abscissa may be approximated from Fig. 3.13. A value of 222,000 is secured. If the number surviving $8\frac{1}{2}$ years or more is desired, a similar estimate may be made from Fig. 3.14. The interpolated figure in this case is 135,000.

Another type of interpolation possible with such a curve is the determination of the number of cases falling within any given interval. One is not limited to the class-intervals marked out in the original tables. For instance, it may be desirable to know the number of poles surviving more than $10\frac{1}{2}$ but less than 15 years. Reading from the table or from the chart we find that 217,930 poles survived less than 15 years. Interpolating on the chart in the manner described above a figure of 154,000 is secured for the number surviving less than $10\frac{1}{2}$ years. Subtracting the latter figure from the former we have 63,930 as the number of poles falling within the $10\frac{1}{2}$ to 15 years interval. The figure is, of course, an approximation to the true value, as are all values secured through such smoothing and interpolation.

It should be noted that the ogive may be derived directly from the array, without the formation of a frequency table as an intermediate step. This curve, in fact, may be looked upon as merely a graphic representation of the array. It represents one of the simplest forms of statistical organization, as well as one of the most effective methods of manipulating quantitative data.

Relation between the ogive and the frequency curve. The ogive and the frequency curve are merely two different arrangements of precisely the same material, each arrangement having certain distinctive advantages. The characteristics of each may be more clearly apparent if the structural relationship between these two curves is understood. This relationship is graphically portrayed in Fig. 3.15.

FIG. 3.15. Distribution of Bricks Classified according to Transverse Strength. Illustrating the Structural Relation between the Ogive and the Frequency Curve.

This figure is based upon the data in Table 3–13, showing the results of certain tests of the transverse strength of bricks. The upper part of Fig. 3.15 indicates the method by which the ogive is built up. Just as in the histogram, the area of each rectangle is proportional to the number of cases falling in the given class. Since the operation is a cumulative one, however, the base of each rectangle is the cumulated frequencies of all preceding classes. Thus

TABLE 3–13

Frequency Distribution of Bricks Classified
according to Transverse Strength *

Transverse strength (lbs. per sq. inch)	Number of bricks having strength within given limits (frequency)
225– 374.9	1
375– 524.9	1
525– 674.9	6
675– 824.9	38
825– 974.9	80
975–1124.9	83
1125–1274.9	39
1275–1424.9	17
1425–1574.9	2
1575–1724.9	2
1725–1874.9	0
1875–2024.9	1
Total	270

* The data are from the *A.S.T.M. Manual on Presentation of Data*, published by the American Society for Testing Materials, Philadelphia, 1933.

the y-value (frequency) of the first rectangle is 1, erected from 0 as a base, the y-value of the second class is 1, erected from 1 as a base, the y-value of the third class is 6, erected from 2 as a base, and so on. The slope of the curve connecting these rectangles is gradual at first when the frequencies are low, then steeper as the frequencies become greater, and finally tapers off as the frequencies decrease near the upper limit of the distribution.

When the various rectangles representing the class frequencies are dropped to the zero line as a common base, the x-values remaining the same throughout, the histogram or column diagram described in an earlier section is secured. From this the frequency polygon or smoothed frequency curve may be derived.

The Lorenz Curve. Another arrangement of cumulative frequencies is particularly useful in studying income distribution. The data recorded in Table 3–14, taken from the 1949 midyear report of the President's Council of Economic Advisors, will serve to exemplify the procedure.

This arrangement, in which the basis of classification (column 1) and the frequencies (columns 2 and 3) are in corresponding rela-

TABLE 3–14

Cumulative Distribution of Spending Units in the United States Ranked according to Percentage of Total Money Income Received in 1948 before and after Deduction of Federal Income Tax *

Spending units † ranked by size of income	Cumulative percentage of total money income received	
(1)	(2) Before tax	(3) After tax
Lowest tenth	1	1
Second tenth	4	5
Third tenth	9	10
Fourth tenth	15	17
Fifth tenth	22	25
Sixth tenth	31	34
Seventh tenth	41	44
Eighth tenth	53	56
Ninth tenth	68	71
Highest tenth	100	100

* Based on data from the 1949 Survey of Consumer Finances, conducted for the Board of Governors of the Federal Reserve System by the Survey Research Center of the University of Michigan. The figures given are, of course, estimates. They are based on a sample survey covering 3000 to 3500 spending units. For an account of the methods used see the *Federal Reserve Bulletin*, June 1949.
† A spending unit consists of related persons who live together and pool their incomes for their major items of expense.

tive terms, permits the type of graphic portrayal illustrated by Fig. 3.16. An absolutely equal distribution of income, cumulatively expressed, would be represented by a straight line inclined at an angle of 45 degrees. One tenth of the number of spending units would receive one tenth of the income, three tenths of the number of spending units would receive three tenths of the income, etc. The greater the departure from equality (the greater the concentration of income in upper income groups) the more widely will the curve of cumulative relative frequencies depart from the line of equal distribution. Effective comparison of degrees of concentration at different times or under different conditions is facilitated by the use of such graphs as these, which are known as Lorenz curves. Of the two distributions here compared, one relating to the distribution of income before deduction of Federal income taxes, one to income distribution after taxes, the latter shows a closer approach to equality of distribution. This is, of course, the natural result of the application of a graduated income tax.

FIG. 3.16. Lorenz Curves Showing the Distribution of Income in the United States in 1948 before and after Deduction of Federal Income Tax.*

*As estimated by the Survey Research Center for the Board of Governors of the Federal Reserve System,

REFERENCES

Croxton, F. E. and Cowden, D. J., *Applied General Statistics*, Chap. 8.

Dixon, W. J. and Massey, F. J. Jr., *Introduction to Statistical Analysis*, Chap. 2.

Goulden, C. H., *Methods of Statistical Analysis*, 2nd ed., Chap. 2.

Kendall, M. G., *The Advanced Theory of Statistics*, 3rd ed., Vol. I, Chap. 1.

Riggleman, J. R. and Frisbee, I. N., *Business Statistics*, 3rd ed., Chap. 7.

Rosander, A. C., *Elementary Principles of Statistics*, Chap. 3.

Simpson, G. and Kafka, F., *Basic Statistics*, Chaps. 8, 9.

Spurr, W. A., Kellogg, L. S. and Smith, J. H., *Business and Economic Statistics*, Chap. 9.

Waugh, A. E., *Elements of Statistical Method*, 3rd ed., Chap. 3.

Wilks, S. S., *Elementary Statistical Analysis*, Chap. 2.

Yule, G. U. and Kendall, M. G., *An Introduction to the Theory of Statistics*, 14th ed., Chap. 4.

The publishers and the dates of publication of the books named in chapter reference lists are given in the bibliography at the end of this volume.

CHAPTER 4

.
.
.

Some Characteristics of Frequency Distributions: Averages

The classification of quantitative data and the construction of a frequency distribution are a first stage in the task of organization and examination. By means of classification the underlying structure of the data may be revealed and the essential unity of a mass of material may be brought out. But this is only the beginning of the processes of description and inference. It remains to develop methods of measuring and expressing more concisely the significant characteristics of a body of data. For certain purposes the frequency distribution itself must be summarized and condensed, must be boiled down until its essence has been distilled into three or four significant figures.

If each frequency distribution constituted a novel and unique phenomenon, obeying a law peculiar to itself, the task of studying and describing such distributions would be a difficult one. Fortunately this is not so. Quantitative data in widely different fields, when assembled in frequency distributions, show certain common characteristics, obey certain general laws. Experience in one field, therefore, constitutes a guide to work in others. Uniformity in the behavior of masses of data makes possible the development of a generalized method of organizing, analyzing, and comparing measurements drawn from many fields of scientific study.

Examples of Frequency Distributions from Diverse Fields

This fact of a common law of arrangement running through the universe of quantitative facts may be brought home most effec-

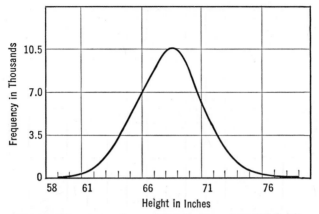

FIG. 4.1. Frequency Curve: Distribution of 67,995 Soldiers Classified by Height.

tively by a comparison of distributions illustrative of various types of data. The characteristics of the frequency distributions and of the frequency curves which follow should be noted, and the distributions compared.

TABLE 4–1

Distribution of Soldiers Classified by Height, 1943 *

Height in inches	Number of soldiers
60	136
61	340
62	748
63	1,632
64	3,264
65	5,576
66	8,227
67	9,791
68	10,675
69	9,519
70	7,343
71	5,100
72	3,060
73	1,428
74	680
75	272
76	136
77	68
Total	67,995

* Source: *Report No. 1–BM*, Army Service Forces, Office of Surgeon General, Medical Statistics Division, "Height and Weight Data for Men Inducted into the Army and for Rejected Men." Classification of inductees by height is based on the whole number of inches reported, disregarding any fractional parts of an inch.

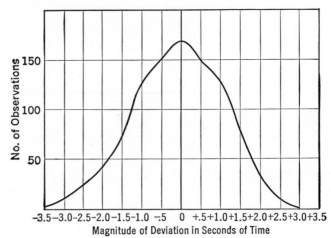

FIG. 4.2. Frequency Curve: Distribution of Errors of Observation in Astronomical Measurements.

The curve in Fig. 4.1 is based upon the data classified in Table 4–1, relating to the heights of a sample of 67,995 men inducted into the U.S. Army in 1943.

Figure 4.2 depicts a frequency curve based upon 1,000 observations made at Greenwich, of the right ascension of Polaris.[1] The

TABLE 4–2

Distribution of Errors of Observation in Astronomical Measurements
(1,000 observations of the Right Ascension of Polaris)

Magnitude of deviation, in seconds of time, from origin	Number of observations
− 3.5	2
− 3.0	12
− 2.5	25
− 2.0	43
− 1.5	74
− 1.0	126
− 0.5	150
0	168
0.5	148
1.0	129
1.5	78
2.0	33
2.5	10
3.0	2
	1,000

[1] From Whittaker and Robinson, Ref. 190.

values on the abscissa define deviations, in seconds of time, from an origin near the mean of all the observations. Frequencies of occurrence of given values on the x-scale are measured, of course, as ordinates on the y-scale. The distribution plotted in Fig. 4.2 is given in Table 4–2.

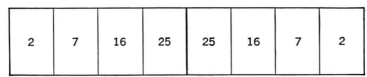

| 2 | 7 | 16 | 25 | 25 | 16 | 7 | 2 |

FIG. 4.3. Zone of Dispersion, Artillery Firing, Showing the Theoretical Percentage Distribution of Shots.

If a piece of artillery be accurately adjusted on a given target (a point) and 100 shots be fired, it will be found that the points of impact of the hundred shots will be dispersed about the target. No

TABLE 4–3

Distribution of 1,000 Shots from a Single Gun

Division	Number of shots recorded
1 (top)	1
2	4
3	10
4	89
5	190
6	212
7	204
8	193
9	79
10	16
11 (bottom)	2
	1,000

matter how accurate the piece or the adjustment only a small percentage of the shots will fall upon the exact point at which they were directed. The points of impact will be scattered about the target in a quite regular fashion, however. If a rectangle be so drawn as to include all the points of impact, and this rectangle (or *zone of dispersion*) be divided into eight equal parts, the distribution of shots within these sections will be as indicated in Fig. 4.3. (In any given case there are likely to be slight departures from this order, but in the long run this distribution will prevail.)

This general rule holds for all classes of guns. The more accurate the gun the smaller will be the zone of dispersion, but the distribution within this zone is theoretically the same in all cases. Rules of fire used in artillery adjustment are based upon this fact.

The results of actual firing may be contrasted with this theoretical distribution. Table 4–3 presents a record of one thousand shots fired from a battery gun at the middle of a stationary target 200 yards distant.[2] The target was divided by horizontal lines into eleven equal divisions. These results are presented graphically in Fig. 4.4.

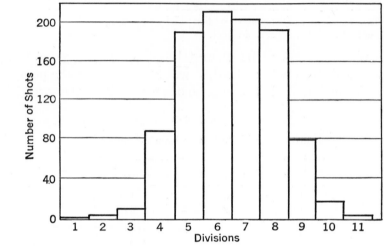

FIG. 4.4. Column Diagram: Distribution of 1,000 Shots from a Single Gun.

The zone of dispersion being divided into eleven divisions instead of the eight referred to in describing the theoretical distribution, a direct comparison cannot be made. We have here, however, the same general type of distribution found in the other examples given. A tendency toward concentration in the lower half of the target reflects a slight departure from symmetry.

When coins are tossed the distribution of heads and tails is assumed to be determined by pure chance. In a single experiment ten coins were tossed 100 times. Table 4–4 shows the frequencies with which given numbers of heads appeared. (The greatest number of heads possible in a given throw under such conditions is, of course, 10; it is also possible that no heads should appear.) Figure 4.5 depicts the corresponding frequency distribution.

[2] From Merriman, Ref. 98.

TABLE 4–4

Distribution of Results in Coin Tossing Experiment
(Ten coins tossed 100 times)

Number of heads	Frequency of occurrence
10	0
9	1
8	4
7	7
6	23
5	30
4	20
3	9
2	5
1	1
0	0
	100

We find in these four widely different fields something approaching a uniform law of arrangement of quantitative data. Do economic data show the same general characteristics? If reference be made to examples given in Chapter 3, comparisons with the four preceding illustrations may be made. The frequency distributions referred to are those relating to weekly earnings of employees, the

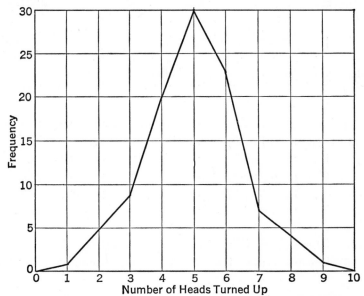

FIG. 4.5. Frequency Polygon: Distribution of Heads in a Coin Tossing Experiment.

length of life of telephone poles, and the size-distribution of income in the United States. (The curve of the 1918 distribution, it should be noted, would show a long tail extending far to the right if the incomes above $4000 were included.) Several additional examples of economic data may be given.

Figure 4.6 illustrates the order in which price variations are distributed. It is based upon a study made by W. C. Mitchell of 5,578 individual cases of change in the wholesale prices of commodities from one year to the next.[3] Thus, for example, the average price of

FIG. 4.6. Frequency Polygon: Distribution of 5,540 Cases of Change in Wholesale Prices of Commodities from One Year to the Next (after Mitchell).

middling upland cotton in New York in a given year was $0.115 per pound. In the following year the average price was $0.128 per pound, an increase of 11.3 percent. This would constitute one entry in the table of rising prices, falling in the class "10–11.9%." The entire table consists of 5,578 such entries. These data are presented in Fig. 4.6 in the form of a frequency polygon, no attempt being made to smooth the curve.

Table 4–5 shows the distribution of London-New York exchange rates (sterling exchange) from 1882 to 1913, inclusive. This was a

---

[3] From Mitchell, Ref. 106. The figure shows the price changes only within the range of a 51 percent fall and a 51 percent rise. One case of a price fall of 55 percent is not shown, and 37 cases of price increases ranging from 52 percent to 104 percent have not been included.

TABLE 4–5

Distribution of London-New York Exchange Rates as Recorded by Months during the Period 1882–1913

Class-interval	Frequency (number of months given rate prevailed)
$4.8275–$4.8324	1
4.8325– 4.8374	6
4.8375– 4.8424	11
4.8425– 4.8474	21
4.8475– 4.8524	23
4.8525– 4.8574	24
4.8575– 4.8624	25
4.8625– 4.8674	40
4.8675– 4.8724	45
4.8725– 4.8774	49
4.8775– 4.8824	35
4.8825– 4.8874	45
4.8875– 4.8924	33
4.8925– 4.8974	16
4.8975– 4.9024	8
4.9025– 4.9074	1
4.9075– 4.9124	1
	384

FIG. 4.7. Frequency Polygon: Distribution of London-New York Exchange Rates (as recorded over a period of 384 months).

period when both currencies were freely convertible into gold, at fixed ratios, with customary market forces operating to keep exchange rates between the two "gold points." Observations covering recent decades would show quite different characteristics. In the distribution shown graphically in Fig. 4.7 monthly rates have been classified according to the frequency of their occurrence over the 32 years of prewar experience.[4]

A distribution of slaughtering and meat-packing plants, classified according to the average hourly earnings of employees, is shown in Table 4–6 and graphically in Fig. 4.8. The data relate to 309 estab-

FIG. 4.8. Frequency Polygon: Distribution of Establishments Engaged in Slaughtering and Meat Packing, by Average Hourly Earnings of Employees, March, 1946.

lishments, employing 122,269 production workers in 1946. There is a clear concentration of frequencies between 80 and 120 cents on the scale of hourly earnings, with the heaviest grouping between 100 and 110 cents. As is customary in income and wage distributions this one is skew, with a tail extending to the right. The range of hourly earnings, like that of incomes in general, is greater above the mode than below.

The frequency curves and histograms based upon economic data, it will be noted, do not all show the symmetry and regularity that seem to characterize the curves representing physical data. Some are nonsymmetrical, showing a preponderance of cases on one side

---

[4] "The figures are . . . the averages of those quoted at the beginning of each month in the *Economist;* on and after July, 1886, the exchange is the 'telegraphic transfer,' before that date, 'short at interest.'" The data are taken from Peake, Ref. 125.

TABLE 4–6

Frequency Distribution of Establishments Engaged in Slaughtering
and Meat Packing, by Average Hourly Earnings of Employees
in March, 1946 *

Hourly Earnings Plant Average	Number of Reporting Establishments
50– 59.9 cents	4
60– 69.9 cents	12
70– 79.9 cents	17
80– 89.9 cents	41
90– 99.9 cents	63
100–109.9 cents	73
110–119.9 cents	37
120–129.9 cents	25
130–139.9 cents	10
140–149.9 cents	14
150–159.9 cents	6
160–169.9 cents	5
170–179.9 cents	1
180–189.9 cents	0
190–199.9 cents	0
200–209.9 cents	1
Total	309

* Reports cover any part of the pay period ending nearest March 15, 1946, on both full-time and part-time basis.

of the point of greatest concentration. In some there are breaks in the regularity of the increase or decrease of frequencies. But in spite of these differences there is obviously a family resemblance between the measurements drawn from the fields of economics, astronomy, anthropometry, ballistics, and pure chance.[5] Certain of the common characteristics may be noted.

Some General Characteristics. There is, in the first place, *variation* in the values of the measurements secured. Human heights vary, astronomical measurements of the same quantity differ, projectiles fired under conditions as nearly constant as it is humanly possible to make them fail to land at the same spot, incomes vary as between individuals, and hourly earnings vary from man to man and from plant to plant. The various observations or values

[5] Examples of more extreme deviations from standard types have been cited. Thus there are J-shaped distributions with maximum frequencies at one end of the scale of x-values; there are U-shaped distributions in which the concentrations of frequencies come at the tails rather than toward the center of the range of x-values. For distributions of these types the descriptive measures to be discussed in this and the following chapter lose some of their power and significance. But such distributions, although of special interest when they occur, are rare.

secured in a given case are distributed along a scale, between two extreme values.

The distribution of these values along the scale (the x-axis) is such that, moving from one extreme value towards the other, the number of cases found at successive points along the scale (the successive class frequencies) increases with more or less regularity up to a maximum, and then decreases in much the same way. In spite of variation, therefore, we find a *central tendency*, a massing of cases at certain points on the scale of values. This is the second notable characteristic that all the frequency distributions appear to possess in common.

FIG. 4.9. The Normal Curve of Error.

If we measure, for each of the successive classes, the amount of deviation along the scale from the point of greatest concentration it will be noted that small deviations are much more frequent than large ones, that extreme deviations are rare, and that deviations on both sides of the point of concentration reach perfect (or almost perfect) equality in the examples taken from the physical sciences and from the field of pure chance, and approximate equality in the economic distributions. (Exceptions to this rule of approximate equality on the two sides of the point of greatest concentration are not infrequent, the example of income distribution being a striking case in point.)

Figure 4.9 is a graph of what is called the normal distribution. The traditional term for the curve is "normal curve of error." Its characteristics, and the nature of the scales used in its representation, will be discussed in greater detail in a later section. At this point it is presented merely as a basic type which some of the above examples approach closely, and from which others represent more or less pronounced deviations. Departures from this type, let it be emphasized, are numerous and significant, but as a basic form this normal curve of error is extremely important in statistical work. Its existence and our knowledge of its qualities are a main justification for the use of a generalized method of describing frequency distributions. Distributions of quantitative data vary, and their variations from each other and from certain standard types are of the greatest significance, but in spite of their variations a family resemblance runs through them all. Each new frequency distribution is not an isolated phenomenon, but a member of a large family. Accordingly, the task of describing a given distribution and generalizing from it may be approached with confidence in methods that have been found applicable in other cases.

Given this more or less common type, how may a given distribution be described and differentiated from others? Certain methods will have been suggested by the preceding discussion.

Descriptive Measures: General

The values of all the observations, it has been noted, are spread along a scale. The frequency distribution may be described by the selection of a single value on that scale which is thoroughly representative of the distribution as a whole. Since the frequencies vary, an obvious choice is the selection of that value which occurs the greatest number of times, or, in other words, that point on the scale at which the concentration is greatest. This value constitutes a *measure of the central tendency* of the distribution. Thus, one might find the income class in which the greatest number of families fall, and let the midpoint of that class (which is $3,500 in the distribution presented in Table 3–7) serve as the representative of the distribution. This most common value, it should be noted, is only one of several possible measures of the central tendency of a given distribution. All such measures are termed *averages*. They are sometimes spoken of as measures of *location*, since they locate the distribution, or important elements of it, on the x-scale.

A single representative value of this type has many uses but, by itself, it obviously leaves out many facts concerning the distribution. Of great importance is the character of the distribution about the average. Are the values of all tabulated cases closely concentrated, or is there pronounced dispersion over a wide range? The representative character of any average depends upon how closely the other values cling to it, upon the degree of concentration about the central tendency. The average, therefore, must be supplemented by a *measure of variation*, a measure of the "scatter" about the central value.

An adequate description should include also an account of the degree of symmetry of the distribution. It is highly important to know whether there are equal distributions of cases on the two sides of the point of greatest concentration, or whether the frequency curve is skewed to one side, as in the case of income distribution illustrated above. If the curve is not symmetrical the degree of a symmetry should be determined, and for this purpose *measures of skewness* have been developed.

Statisticians have employed, also, a measure of the degree of peakedness of frequency curves, derived by comparing given curves with the normal curve of error as a standard. It is obvious that the frequency polygon representing price changes from year to year (Fig. 4.6) would, if smoothed, yield a curve much more peaked than the normal curve, and this fact of pronounced concentration at the central value is highly significant. This characteristic of frequency curves is called *kurtosis*, or *peakedness*, or *excess*. The measurement of kurtosis, when suitable, constitutes the final step in the description of the frequency distribution.

When these various measures have been secured the task of statistical inquiry will be well under way. The chaotic assortment of data with which we started will have been reduced to workable form in the shape of a frequency table, and the essential facts that the table reveals will have been distilled into three or four significant measures. This process not only reveals the characteristics of the given distribution, but also facilitates comparison with similar distributions. For example, it is impossible to compare some tens of millions of unorganized personal income figures for the United States with similar data for Great Britain. But if we secure a value for the average or most representative income for each country, together with a description of the distribution of personal incomes about that central value, we have a legitimate basis for comparative study. Finally, by the determination of these descriptive measures a foundation will have been laid for the processes of inference

— whether the purpose be to estimate population characteristics or to test hypotheses — that are usually the main concern of scientific inquiry.

The succeeding section is devoted to a discussion of one phase of this descriptive process, that involving the measurement of central tendencies. After the development of this subject of averages, problems relating to measures of variation and of skewness will be dealt with.

Measures of Central Tendency

We have seen that the representation of a frequency distribution by an average, a single typical figure, is justified because of the tendency of large masses of figures to cluster about a central value, from which the values of all observed cases depart with more or less regularity and smoothness. It is because of the concentration of cases about a central point on the scale that such representative figures have significance. The average represents the distribution as a whole because it is a typical value. If the individual items entering into a distribution vary widely in value and show no tendency toward concentration, no single value can represent them. Thus the arithmetic mean of the three numbers 3, 125, 1,000 is 376, but 376 is of limited usefulness as a substitute for the three values on which it is based. This fundamental requirement, that there be a tendency toward concentration about a central value, should be met if an average is to be representative.

If the general character of a frequency distribution be recalled, the logic of one sort of average will be clear at once. It was suggested above that that point on the x-scale at which the concentration is greatest, the value that occurs the greatest number of times, might be taken as typical of the entire distribution. This value is termed the *mode*, and the group in which it falls is called the *modal group*. If a frequency curve be drawn to represent a given distribution, the mode will be the *x-value corresponding to the maximum ordinate*.[6] The maximum ordinate itself measures the frequency of the modal group. Students frequently confuse these two values in determining the mode. It is not the distance along the y-scale but the distance along the x-scale that defines the value of the mode. Each ordinate merely measures the number of cases falling in a given class, not the value of the cases falling in that class.

---

[6] Strictly speaking, the mode is the x-value corresponding to the maximum ordinate of the ideal frequency curve that has been fitted to the given distribution.

As typical of a given distribution we might also select that point on the scale of x-values on each side of which one half the total number of cases falls. This value, which is called the *median*, is that which exceeds the values of one half the cases included, and is in turn exceeded by the values of one half the cases. Thus it has been estimated that in 1947 the median family income in the United States was $3,027; one half of the 37,000,000 families received less than this sum, while one half received more. When a distribution is represented by a frequency curve, the area under the curve is divided into two equal parts by an ordinate erected at that point on the x-axis corresponding to the median value. This follows, of course, from the definition of the median, and from the fact that the area under a frequency curve represents the total number of cases included in the distribution.

The *arithmetic mean* is a third type of average that may be used to represent a distribution. This is a *calculated* average, affected by the value of every item in the distribution. Herein, obviously, it differs from the mode and median, which depend primarily upon the relative position of the items in the frequency table and are not affected by the values of all individual items. The arithmetic mean is the center of gravity of a distribution; it would be the x-value of the point of balance of a frequency curve, if the curve could be blocked out and manipulated in solid form.

The *geometric mean* and the *harmonic mean* are two other averages; the characteristics of these will be discussed at a later point.

Notation. The computation or location of these various averages may involve somewhat lengthy processes if the number of cases included is great. If appropriate methods are employed, however, the labor of computation may be materially cut down. The use of the following symbols will simplify the explanation of these methods:

X: the value of an individual observation; a series of observations on a variable quantity is represented by X_1, X_2, $X_3 \cdots X_n$; x is also used as a general symbol for a variable

M, $\overline{X}$ or $\overline{x}$: the arithmetic mean of a sample [7]

---

[7] In later sections use will also be made of the symbol μ (the Greek letter *mu*) to represent the arithmetic mean. As has been noted, letters from the English alphabet are conventionally used to represent attributes of a sample, Greek letters for the corresponding attributes of the population that is being sampled. Thus M, the mean height of a sample of male college students, might be 5 feet 10 inches. This is taken to be an estimate of μ, the unknown mean height of the entire population of male college students.

d or x: the deviation of an individual observation from the mean; the deviation of a class midpoint from the mean

A or M': an arbitrary origin other than the mean

c: the deviation of the mean of a sample from the arbitrary origin

d' or x': the deviation of an individual observation or a class midpoint from an arbitrary origin

f: the number of items (observations) in a given class in a frequency distribution

N: the total number of items in a given series, or in a frequency distribution

Mo: the mode

Md: the median

M_g: the geometric mean

H: the harmonic mean

h: class-interval

Σ (Sigma): a symbol for the process of summation, meaning "the sum of"

The Arithmetic Mean. Using the above notation, the formula for the arithmetic mean is:

$$\overline{X} = \frac{\Sigma X}{N} \tag{4.1}$$

Thus the mean of the measures 2, 5, 6, 7, is equal to the sum of these measures divided by 4, which is $\frac{20}{4}$ or 5. The computation of the arithmetic mean when each measure is reported at its true value is thus a simple process of summation and division. The weekly earnings of 220 textile workers were listed in an earlier section. If these figures be added and the total divided by 220, the mean weekly wage is found to be $50.16841. In this case the task of adding 220 items is somewhat tedious; it is a task which would become almost impossible if one were dealing with the 37,000,000 family income figures, for example. For practical reasons, therefore, it is usually necessary to compute the required averages from the frequency distribution rather than from the original ungrouped data. To exemplify this process we may utilize data relating to the hourly earnings of workers in industrial chemical plants in 1946.

The importance of certain of the precautions mentioned in the section on classification, in connection with the choice of a class-interval, will be clear from this example. When the mean of a distribution is calculated from classified observations, we must assume an even distribution of cases within each class. The class-interval should be selected with this in mind, in order that errors introduced by the assumption may be minimized. If the items in each class are evenly distributed, the mid-value of each class may be taken as representative of all the observations included; when such a mid-value is multiplied by the number of items in the class, the product is approximately equal to the sum of all the individual items in the class. The formula for the mean thus becomes $\overline{X} = \dfrac{\Sigma(fX)}{N}$. Table 4–7 illustrates the procedure in detail.

TABLE 4–7

Calculation of the Arithmetic Mean of Straight-Time Average
Hourly Earnings of Workers in Industrial Chemical Plants
in the Southeastern States, January, 1946 *

Class-interval (cents per hour)	Midpoint X	Frequency f	fX
40– 49.9	45	2	90
50– 59.9	55	326	17,930
60– 69.9	65	500	32,500
70– 79.9	75	368	27,600
80– 89.9	85	202	17,170
90– 99.9	95	174	16,530
100–109.9	105	150	15,750
110–119.9	115	154	17,710
120–129.9	125	72	9,000
130–139.9	135	22	2,970
140–149.9	145	6	870
150–159.9	155	4	620
160–169.9	165	8	1,320
170–179.9	175	4	700
180–189.9	185	2	370
		1,994	161,130

$$\overline{X} = \frac{\Sigma(fX)}{N} \qquad\qquad (4.2)$$
$$= \frac{161,130}{1,994} = 80.8074 \text{ cents}$$

* These figures and similar data appearing in subsequent tables were compiled by the Wage Analysis Branch of the United States Bureau of Labor Statistics. See *Monthly Labor Review*, November, 1946. The detailed statistics were provided through the courtesy of Dr. Ewan Clague, Commissioner of Labor Statistics, and Mr. H. M. Douty, Chief of the Wage Analysis Branch, Bureau of Labor Statistics.

The value secured in this way is sometimes called a weighted arithmetic mean. What we do, in effect, is to secure the arithmetic mean of the 15 figures in the column headed X. We do not take a simple average of these figures, however, but *weight* each one in proportion to the number of cases falling in the class-interval of which it is the mid-value. It is precisely the procedure we should follow in calculating the mean of five men's incomes, two of whom, let us say, have incomes of $2,000 and three of whom have incomes of $3,000. Clearly it would not do to add the figures $2,000 and $3,000, dividing the sum by two. The figure $2,000 is given a weight of two, the figure $3,000 is given a weight of three, and the resultant sum, $13,000, is divided by five. Though the procedure in working from the frequency distribution is thus a form of weighting, the term "weighted average" has in general a more restricted meaning, to be explained at a later point, and should not be applied to an average computed from a frequency distribution.

Short method of computing the arithmetic mean. The calculation of the arithmetic mean from the frequency table is much easier, in general, than from the ungrouped data, but when the number of cases included is large even the computation from the frequency table by the method illustrated above may be laborious. The procedure may be greatly simplified.

From the method of computing the arithmetic mean it follows that the algebraic sum of the deviations of a series of individual magnitudes from their mean is zero. This may be readily demonstrated. We represent the series of magnitudes by $X_1, X_2, X_3, \ldots X_n$, their arithmetic means by $\overline{X}$, and the deviations of the various magnitudes from the mean by $d_1, d_2, d_3, \ldots d_n$. Then

$$\frac{X_1 + X_2 + X_3 + \cdots + X_n}{N} = \overline{X} \tag{4.3}$$

and

$$X_1 + X_2 + X_3 + \cdots + X_n = N\overline{X} \tag{4.4}$$

The number of terms, of course, is equal to N. Therefore, subtracting $\overline{X}$ N times from each side of the equation,

$$(X_1 - \overline{X}) + (X_2 - \overline{X}) + (X_3 - \overline{X}) + \cdots + (X_n - \overline{X}) = 0 \tag{4.5}$$

But

$X_1 - \overline{X} = d_1$, $X_2 - \overline{X} = d_2$, etc., and formula (4.5) may be written

$$\Sigma d = 0 \tag{4.6}$$

Knowing this to be true we may measure the deviations of a series of magnitudes from any arbitrary origin, secure the algebraic sum of the deviations, and from this sum ascertain the difference between the arbitrary origin and the actual mean of the distribution. In effect, a constant has been added to (or subtracted from) each deviation, when the deviation is measured from the arbitrary origin instead of from the actual mean. This constant is the difference between the mean and the arbitrary origin. Since the constant is introduced N times, its value may be readily determined by dividing by N the sum of the deviations from the arbitrary origin.

If we let A represent the arbitrary origin, while $c = \overline{X} - A$, and d_1', d_2', d_3', ... d_n' represent the deviations of the various magnitudes from A (i.e., $d_1' = X_1 - A$, $d_2' = X_2 - A$, etc.) then

$$d_1' = d_1 + c,\ d_2' = d_2 + c,\ d_3' = d_3 + c,\ \dots\ d_n' = d_n + c$$

and

$$\Sigma d' = \Sigma d + Nc$$

But

$$\Sigma d = 0$$
$$\therefore \Sigma d' = Nc$$

and

$$c = \frac{\Sigma d'}{N}$$

From the known values of A and c the value of the actual mean may be obtained, for $\overline{X} = A + c$. The procedure is illustrated in the simple example given in Table 4–8.

TABLE 4–8

Computation of the Arithmetic Mean (Short Method)
(Ungrouped data)

X	f	d'	
5	1	− 15	$A = 20$
15	1	− 5	$c = \dfrac{\Sigma d'}{N} = \dfrac{+\,25}{5} = +\,5$
25	1	+ 5	
35	1	+ 15	$\overline{X} = A + c = 20 + 5 = 25$
45	1	+ 25	
	5	+ 25	

The work of computation may be still further abbreviated, for observations arranged in the form of a frequency distribution, by measuring the deviations in terms of the class-interval as a unit. Then, in finally applying the necessary correction, the difference between the true mean and the arbitrary origin may be again expressed in terms of the original units. The method may be illustrated in detail with reference to the wage data for which the mean has already been calculated (see Table 4–9).

TABLE 4–9

Calculation of the Arithmetic Mean of Straight-Time Average Hourly Earnings of Workers in Industrial Chemical Plants in the Southeastern States, January, 1946 (Short method)

Class-interval (cents per hour)	Mid-point X	Frequency f	d' (in class-interval units)	fd' $-$	fd' $+$	
40– 49.9	45	2	− 4	8		Calculations
50– 59.9	55	326	− 3	978		$A = 85¢$
60– 69.9	65	500	− 2	1,000		
70– 79.9	75	368	− 1	368		1. Algebraic sum of devia-
80– 89.9	85	202	0			tions from A
90– 99.9	95	174	+ 1		174	− 2,354
100–109.9	105	150	+ 2		300	+ 1,518
110–119.9	115	154	+ 3		462	− 836
120–129.9	125	72	+ 4		288	
130–139.9	135	22	+ 5		110	2. Calculation of c (in
140–149.9	145	6	+ 6		36	class-interval units)
150–159.9	155	4	+ 7		28	
160–169.9	165	8	+ 8		64	$c = \dfrac{-836}{1,994} = -.41926$
170–179.9	175	4	+ 9		36	
180–189.9	185	2	+ 10		20	3. Reduction of c to origi-
Total		1,994		− 2,354	+ 1,518	nal units

Class-interval = 10¢
c (in original units)
$= -.41926 \times 10¢$
$= -4.1926¢$

4. Determination of $\overline{X}$
$\overline{X} = A + c$
$= 85 - 4.1926$
$= 80.8074¢$

The steps in this process of calculating the arithmetic mean by the short method may be briefly summarized:

1. Organize the data in the form of a frequency distribution.
2. Adopt as the arbitrary origin the midpoint of a class near the center of the distribution.
3. Arrange a column showing the deviation (d') of the items in each class from the arbitrary origin, in terms of class-interval units. This deviation will be zero for the items in the class containing the arbitrary origin, − 1 for the items in the next lower class, + 1 for the items in the next higher class, and so on.

4. Multiply the deviation of each class by the frequency of that class, taking account of signs. These products are entered in the column fd'.
5. Get the algebraic sum of the items entered in the column fd'.
6. Divide this sum by the total frequency (N). The quotient is the correction (c) in class-interval units.
7. Multiply the correction (c) by the class-interval. The product is the correction in terms of the original units.
8. Add this correction (algebraically) to the arbitrary origin (A); the sum is the mean ($\overline{X}$).

Location of the Median. The median is a value of a variable so selected that 50 percent of the total number of cases, when arranged in order of magnitude, lie below it and 50 percent above it. For many frequency distributions this is a useful and significant figure.

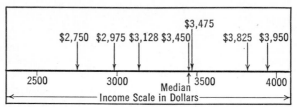

FIG. 4.10. Illustrating the Location of the Median with Ungrouped Data (personal incomes of seven individuals).

Ungrouped data. When an investigator is handling unclassified observations the location of the median is a simple matter. The data having been arranged in order of magnitude, it is necessary only to count from one end until that point on the scale of values is reached that divides the number of cases into two equal parts. As a simple example we may assume that the following seven figures represent the annual incomes of seven individuals:

$2,750 \quad \$2,975 \quad \$3,128 \quad \$3,450 \quad \$3,475 \quad \$3,825 \quad \$3,950$

The scale of values extends from $2,750 to $3,950, and seven items are arranged along this scale. The value $3,000 has two items on one side and five items on the other, so obviously does not conform to our definition of the median. The value $3,450, which coincides with the income of one of the seven individuals, is the median in this case. Three items lie on each side of this value; or, if we assume the central item to be cut in two, $3\frac{1}{2}$ items lie on each side of this point. This case is illustrated in Fig. 4.10. This diagram may help to bring out the fact that the median is a point on a scale so located that it cuts the frequencies in two.

The problem is slightly different when an even number of cases is included. This condition is exemplified in Table 4–10 which shows

TABLE 4–10

Average Hourly Earnings in Selected Industries, January, 1947 *

Industries	Cents per hour
Hotels (year-round)	64.8
Fertilizers	81.0
Cotton manufactures, except smallwares	91.4
Sawmills and logging camps	93.6
Retail trade	95.1
Canning and preserving	97.5
Silk and rayon goods	97.5
Boots and shoes	99.8
Cigarettes	104.1
Furniture	104.5
Cement	107.9
Radios and phonographs	108.4
Flour	110.1
Clocks and watches	110.6
Paper and pulp	112.9
Telephone	113.3
Leather	117.4
Paints, varnishes, and colors	118.1
Wholesale trade	119.7
Slaughtering and meat packing	120.3
Aluminum manufactures	121.3
Textile machinery	122.7
Electrical equipment	123.2
Machinery and machine-shop products	126.2
Refrigerators and refrigeration equipment	126.7
Steel castings	129.8
Machine tools	132.6
Blast furnaces, steel works, and rolling mills	133.3
Aircraft engines	135.8
Engines and turbines	136.8
Automobiles	138.9
Locomotives	139.7
Shipbuilding and boatbuilding	142.1
Forgings, iron, and steel	143.0
Petroleum refining	146.3
Bituminous coal mining	149.0
Newspapers and periodicals	157.2
Anthracite coal mining	158.9

* From *Monthly Labor Review*, April, 1947.

the average earnings per manhour in each of 38 selected industries in January 1947.

In this case the median must be a value on each side of which 19 industries lie. Therefore any value exceeding 119.7 cents (average earnings in wholesale trade) and less than 120.3 cents (average earnings in slaughtering and meat packing) will satisfy the definition of a median. Under these conditions, where the median is really indeterminate, a value half-way between two limiting values is accepted, by convention. The median of the 38 figures would thus be 120.0 cents.

Grouped data. The task of locating the median is essentially the same when the data are in the form of a frequency distribution. The fact that the real values of the individual items are not known, because of the groupings by classes, complicates the problem slightly. We may illustrate the procedure with reference to data on the distribution of family income, as classified in Table 4–11.

TABLE 4–11

Distribution of Money Income among Families in 1947 *

Income class	Number of families (in thousands)	
Under $500	1,640	$\frac{N}{2} = \frac{37,279}{2} = 18,639.5$
$ 500 to $ 999	2,386	
1,000 to 1,499	2,908	
1,500 to 1,999	3,280	$Md = \$3,000 + \left(\frac{223.5}{4,213} \times \$500\right)$
2,000 to 2,499	4,213	
2,500 to 2,999	3,989	$= \$3,000 + \$27$
3,000 to 3,499	4,213	$= \$3,027$
3,500 to 3,999	3,131	
4,000 to 4,499	2,572	
4,500 to 4,999	1,752	
5,000 to 5,999	2,870	
6,000 to 9,999	3,318	
10,000 and over	1,007	
Total	37,279	

* U.S. Bureau of the Census. Current Population Reports: *Consumer Income*, Series P–60, No. 5, Feb 7, 1949. The present table is derived from the percentage distribution given in the Census publication.

This example is especially appropriate because the median may be accurately determined, whereas the mean could not be.

In the present case the location of the median involves the determination of that value on each side of which 18,639.5 items lie. We may assume that we start at the lower end of the scale and move through the successive classes. When we reach the upper limit of the first class (that including items having values from 0 to $500) we have left behind us 1,640 cases, while 35,639 lie in front of us. (The counting unit is 1,000 families). When the upper limit of the second class is attained, 4,026 items have been passed. The upper limit of the sixth class has below it, 18,416 items while below the upper limit of the seventh class are 22,629 items. Somewhere between the lower and upper limits of this seventh class lies the desired point, that which has 18,639.5 items on each side of it. How far must we move through this class, from $3,000 to $3,500 in order to reach this point?

It will be recalled that, for purposes of calculation, the assumption is made that there is a uniform distribution of the items lying within any given class. Since before we reach the seventh class 18,416 cases have been counted, only 223.5 of the 4,213 included in this class are needed to complete the desired number, 18,639.5. On the assumption of even distribution the required 223.5 cases will lie within a distance on the scale equal to $\frac{223.5}{4213}$ of the class-interval. The class-interval is $500; $\frac{223.5}{4213}$ of $500 is equal to $27. As we move up the scale, then, having reached $3,000, we proceed an additional distance equal to $27. At a point on the scale having a value of 3,027 is the dividing line on each side of which lie 18,639.5 cases. This is the value of the median.

The process of computation is shown at the right of the frequency table. The following is a summary of the steps involved in the location of the median:

1. Arrange the data in the form of a frequency distribution.
2. Divide the total number of measures by 2; this gives the number that must lie on each side of the point to be located.
3. Begin at the lower end of the scale and add together the frequencies in the successive classes until the lower limit of the class containing the median value is reached.
4. Determine the number of measures from this class which must be added to the frequencies already totaled to give a number equal to $N/2$.
5. Divide the additional number thus required by the total number of cases in the class containing the median. This indicates the fractional part of the class-interval within which the required cases lie.
6. Multiply the class-interval by the fraction thus set up.
7. To the lower limit of the interval containing the median add the result of the multiplication process indicated in (6). This gives the value of the median.

The last three steps constitute merely a simple form of interpolation.

The entire process may be reversed by beginning at the upper end of the scale and counting downwards. In this case the final operation is one of subtraction from the upper limit of the interval containing the median.

$N/2$ may be a fractional value, as in the example given, or a whole number. The operation is precisely the same in the two cases.

Location of the Mode. The mode is the value of the x-variable corresponding to the maximum ordinate of a given frequency curve. The concept of a modal value is a thoroughly easy one to grasp. It is the most common wage, the most common income, the most common height. It is the point where the concentration is greatest, a characteristic which is effectively brought out by Fechner's term for this average, *dichtester wert*, or *thickest value*. It is not so easy, however, to locate the true mode in a given case. In general statistical work an approximate value only is secured for the mode.

The method of determining this approximate modal value may be illustrated by reference to the distribution shown in Table 4–12.

TABLE 4–12

Frequency Distribution of 5-Percent Bonds
(This table is based upon quotations on the New York Stock Exchange on December 31, 1948, on domestic bonds with coupon rate of 5 percent) *

Quoted price Class-interval	Midpoint X	Frequency f
Less than 80		11
80– 89.9	85	7
90– 99.9	95	14
100–109.9	105	29
110–119.9	115	7
120–129.9	125	3
130 and more		2
		73

* Bonds of corporations in default or in bankruptcy or receivership are excluded.

There is wide dispersion of the 11 cases falling below 80; the existence of this "open-end" class and another at the top of the scale makes it impossible to compute the mean, as the table stands. The mode is therefore an appropriate average to employ.

The class having limits of 100–109.9 contains the greatest number of cases. This appears to be the modal group, and the midpoint of this class, 105, may be tentatively accepted as the value of the approximate mode. But with different classifications quite different values might be secured for the mode. When the original bond quotations are tabulated with varying class-intervals the results in Table 4–13 are secured. (Only the frequencies of the central classes

TABLE 4–13

Selected Class Frequencies
Distribution of 5-Percent Bonds

(a)		(b)		(c)		(d)	
Class-interval = 5		Class-interval = 5		Class-interval = 2.5		Class-interval = 1	
Class-interval	f	Class-interval	f	Class-interval	f	Class-interval	f
85– 89.9	4	82.5– 87.4	4	97.5– 99.9	5	100–100.9	3
90– 94.9	7	87.5– 92.4	3	100.0–102.4	9	101–101.9	5
95– 99.9	7	92.5– 97.4	7	102.5–104.9	8	102–102.9	2
100–104.9	17	97.5–102.4	14	105.0–107.4	8	103–103.9	5
105–109.9	12	102.5–107.4	16	107.5–109.9	4	104–104.9	2
110–114.9	3	107.5–112.4	7	110.0–112.4	3	105–105.9	3
						106–106.9	5
						107–107.9	4

are shown. It is not necessary, for this purpose, to present each of the tables as a whole.) With a class-interval of 5 a value of 102.5 is secured for the mode; a class-interval of 5, again, but with different class limits, yields a mode of 105. With a class-interval of 2.5 a value of 101.25 is obtained. Finally, a class-interval of 1 gives three modes: 101.5, 103.5, and 106.5. Further changes in classification would give still other values. The mode thus appears to be a curiously intangible and shifting average. Its value, for the same data, seems to vary with changes in the size of the class-interval and in the location of the class-limits.

These difficulties arise primarily from limitations to the size of the sample being studied. The true mode, that value which would occur the greatest number of times in an infinitely large sample, could be located exactly if we could increase indefinitely the number of cases included. For, given sufficient cases, the approximate mode approaches the true mode as the class-interval decreases. Grouping in large classes obscures details, and as these classes are reduced in size more of the details are seen and a truer picture of the actual distribution is secured. But since most practical work is necessarily based upon relatively small samples, the increase in the number of classes reveals gaps and irregularities, and causes such a loss of symmetry and order that doubt arises as to where the point of greatest concentration really lies. The different tabulations of bond prices furnish an excellent example of this.

By mathematical methods it is possible to estimate the value of the true mode without securing an infinite number of cases. The smoothing process has been briefly explained. One sort of smoothing involves the fitting of an appropriate type of ideal frequency curve to the data of a given frequency distribution. This gives, theoretically, the distribution which would be secured by the process first indicated, that of decreasing indefinitely the size of the class-interval and increasing indefinitely the number of cases. The value of the x-variable corresponding to the maximum ordinate of this ideal fitted curve is the estimated mode.[8]

For most practical purposes approximate values of the mode are adequate, and these may be secured by much simpler methods. A first and rough approximation may be obtained by taking the mid-value of the class of greatest frequency, a method suggested above. If the general rules for classification which were outlined in an earlier section have been followed, this procedure will not generally involve a gross error.

It is possible, given a fairly regular distribution, to secure, by a process of interpolation within the modal group, a closer approximation than is obtained by accepting the mid-value of this group as the mode. Referring again to the tabulation of bond prices in Table 4–12 it will be noted that the distribution on the two sides of the modal class is not symmetrical. The modal class is that with a mid-value of 105. The class next below, with a mid-value of 95, contains 14 cases, while that next above, with a mid-value of 115, contains but 7 cases. The disproportion is continued in the succeeding classes below and above, more cases being bulked below the modal class than above. For other purposes we have assumed an even distribution of cases between the upper and lower limits of each class, but it is probable that this is not true of the modal class in the present case. Judging from the distribution outside this class, it is likely that the concentration is greater in the lower half of the class-interval, that is, between 100 and 105. The mode, therefore, probably lies below the mid-value 105, rather than precisely at that point. We may attempt to locate it within the group by

[8] A method of approximating the true mode is discussed in Chapter 6.

weighting, assuming a pull toward the lower end of the scale equal to 14 (the number in the class next below) and a pull toward the upper end of the scale equal to 7 (the number in the class next above). This may be expressed by a formula, employing the following symbols:

l = lower limit of modal class
f_1 = frequency of class next below modal class in value
f_2 = frequency of class next above modal class in value
h = class-interval

The interpolation formula is

$$Mo = l + \left(\frac{f_2}{f_2 + f_1} \times h \right) \tag{4.7}$$

Applying this formula to the bond price data presented in Table 4–12, we have

$$Mo = 100 + \left(\frac{7}{21} \times 10 \right) = 100 + 3.33 = 103.33$$

A closer approximation may sometimes be secured by basing the weights (represented by f_2 and f_1) upon the total frequencies of the two or three classes next above the modal class and the same number below. If two classes on each side are included in the present case, a value of 103.23 is secured for the mode of bond prices.

In some cases the problem of locating the mode is complicated by the existence of several points of concentration, rather than the single point which has been assumed in the preceding explanation. A distribution of this type is called bi-modal; when plotted, a frequency curve having two humps is obtained. If the data are homogeneous such a distribution is the result of paucity of data and of the method of classification employed. It may be due to the use of a class-interval too small, with respect to the number of cases included in the sample. An approximate mode may be determined in such cases by shifting the class-limits and increasing the class-interval, carrying on this process until one modal group is definitely established. This reverses the process by which the true mode may be located when the number of cases is infinitely large. With a limited number of cases the location of the point where the concentration is greatest necessitates increasing the size of the class-interval, in order to get away from the irregularities due to the smallness of the sample.

If the distribution remains bi-modal in spite of changes in the class-intervals and class-limits, it is probable that the data reflect the influence of quite different sets of forces. Thus if hourly wage data for a sample of anthracite coal miners and for a sample of hotel workers were combined in a single frequency distribution, two modal points would be expected (see averages in Table 4–10, p. 95). The significance of a frequency distribution is lost if it contains a mixture of observations relating to essentially different groups.

Determination of modal value from mean and median. Another method of securing an approximate value for the mode, a method based upon the relationship between the values of the mean, median, and mode, may be employed in certain cases. In a perfectly symmetrical distribution mean, median, and mode coincide. As the distribution departs from symmetry these three points on the scale are pulled apart. If the degree of asymmetry is only moderate the three points have a fairly constant relation. The mode and mean lie farthest apart, with the median one third of the distance from the mean towards the mode. (If the asymmetry is marked, no such relationship may prevail.) Having the values of any two of the averages in a moderately asymmetrical frequency distribution, therefore, the other may be approximated. In fact, however, the method should only be employed in determining the value of the mode, as the other two values may be computed more accurately by other methods. The value of the mode itself should only be determined in this way when more exact methods are not applicable or are not called for.

The following formula is based upon this relationship:

$$Mo = \text{Mean} - 3(\text{Mean} - Md) \tag{4.8}$$

Applying this formula to the telephone pole data shown in Table 3–10, the following result is secured:

$$Mo = 9.33 - 3(9.33 - 9.015) = 8.385$$

This value is slightly below the mid-value of the modal class, 8.5, and is also less than the value 8.49 which is secured by weighting within the modal group (using four classes on each side).

For some purposes, particularly those that involve the averaging of *rates* or *ratios* rather than quantities, none of the averages that have been described is suitable. The geometric and the harmonic means are types of averages that should be familiar because they are particularly appropriate for such purposes.

The Geometric Mean. The geometric mean is the nth root of the product of n measures; its value thus is represented by:

$$M_g = \sqrt[n]{a_1 \cdot a_2 \cdot a_3 \cdots a_n} \qquad (4.9)$$

The geometric mean of the numbers 2, 4, 8, is

$$\begin{aligned} M_g &= \sqrt[3]{2 \times 4 \times 8} \\ &= \sqrt[3]{64} \\ &= 4 \end{aligned}$$

It is obvious from the method of computation that if any one of the measures in the series has a value of zero the geometric mean is zero.

The actual computation of the geometric mean is greatly facilitated by the use of logarithms. In this form

$$\text{Log } M_g = \frac{\log a_1 + \log a_2 + \log a_3 + \cdots + \log a_n}{N} \qquad (4.10)$$

The logarithm of the geometric mean is equal to the arithmetic mean of the logarithms of the individual measures.

When the measures, of which the geometric mean is desired, are to be weighted, the separate weights are introduced as exponents of the terms to which they apply. Thus if we represent the sum of the weights by N and the weights corresponding to the terms a_1, a_2, a_3, ... a_n, respectively, by w_1, w_2, w_3, ... w_n, the formula for the geometric mean is

$$M_g = \sqrt[n]{a_1^{w_1} \cdot a_2^{w_2} \cdot a_3^{w_3} \cdots a_n^{w_n}} \qquad (4.11)$$

This is equivalent to repeating each term a number of times, the number corresponding to the amount by which it is weighted. (This, of course, is precisely what is done in securing a weighted arithmetic mean.) When logarithms are employed the formula for the weighted geometric mean becomes

$$\text{Log } M_g = \frac{w_1 \log a_1 + w_2 \log a_2 + w_3 \log a_3 + \cdots + w_n \log a_n}{N} \qquad (4.12)$$

A method of computing the geometric mean may be illustrated with reference to Table 4–14, which shows the distribution of the

TABLE 4–14

Computation of the Geometric Mean of Preferred Stock Prices

Class-interval	X	f	$\log X$	$f \log X$
\$ 20–\$ 39.9	30	3	1.47712	4.43136
40– 59.9	50	5	1.69897	8 49485
60– 79.9	70	10	1.84510	18.45100
80– 99.9	90	18	1.95424	35.17632
100– 119.9	110	19	2.04139	38.78641
120– 139.9	130	3	2.11394	6.34182
		58		111.68176

$$\text{Log } M_g = \frac{111.68176}{58} = 1.92555$$
$$M_g = \$84.25$$

prices of 58 preferred stocks with a 5-percent dividend rate. The table is based upon closing prices on the New York Stock Exchange and the New York Curb Exchange on December 31, 1948.

Characteristics of the geometric mean. The nature of the geometric mean may be understood by considering its relation to the terms it represents, as an average.

If the arithmetic mean of a series of measures replace each item in the series, the *sum* of the measures will remain unchanged. Thus, the sum of the numbers 2, 4, 8 is 14. The arithmetic mean of these three numbers is $4\frac{2}{3}$; if this value be inserted in the place of each of the three measures the sum remains 14. It is characteristic of the geometric mean that the *product* of a series of measures will remain unchanged if the geometric mean of those measures replace each item in the series. Thus the product of 2, 4, 8 is 64. The geometric mean of the three numbers is 4; if this value replace each of the three measures the product remains 64.

Again, it is true of the arithmetic mean that the sum of the deviations of the items above the mean equals the sum of the deviations of the items below the mean (disregarding signs). The sums of the differences between the individual items and the mean are equal. In the case of the geometric mean the products of the corresponding ratios are equal. If the ratios of the geometric mean to the measures which it exceeds be multiplied together, the product will equal that secured by multiplying together the ratios to the geometric mean of the measures exceeding it in value. For example, the geometric mean of the numbers 3, 6, 8, 9 is 6. The following equation may be set up:

$$\frac{6}{3} \times \frac{6}{6} = \frac{8}{6} \times \frac{9}{6}$$

The last example brings out the most important characteristic of the geometric mean. It is a means of averaging ratios. Its chief use in the field of economic statistics has been in connection with index numbers of prices, where *rates* of change are of major concern, and where equal *relative* changes should usually be regarded as of equal importance. An example frequently cited is that of two cases of price change, one a ten-fold increase, from 100 to 1,000, the other a fall to one tenth of the old price, from 100 to 10. The arithmetic mean of 1,000 and 10 is 505, the geometric mean is $\sqrt{1,000 \times 10}$, or 100. When the average is of the latter type it is seen that the two equal ratios of change have balanced each other. The arithmetic mean, 505, is quite incorrect as a measure of average ratio of price change. This subject is discussed at greater length in the chapter on index numbers.

What has been said in an earlier section in regard to the advantages of logarithmic charting for certain purposes bears upon the use of the geometric mean. This average is sometimes called the logarithmic mean, as its logarithm is simply the arithmetic mean of the logarithms of the constituent measures. Wherever percentages of change are being averaged, where ratios rather than absolute differences are significant, the use of the geometric mean is advisable.

A problem involving the use of the geometric mean arises in computing the average rate of increase of any sum at compound interest. If p_o represent the principal at the beginning of the period, p_n the principal at the end of the period, r the rate of interest, and n the number of years in the period, the sum to which p_o will amount at the end of the n years, if interest is compounded annually, is represented by the equation:

$$p_n = p_o(1 + r)^n \tag{4.13}$$

It follows from this that:

$$r = \sqrt[n]{\frac{p_n}{p_o}} - 1 \tag{4.14}$$

Thus, if $1,000 at compound interest amounts to $1,600 at the end of 12 years, there has been an increase of 60 percent. The arithmetic mean is 5 percent, but this is not the rate at which the money increased. The true rate is:

$$r = \sqrt[12]{\frac{1,600}{1,000}} - 1$$
$$= \sqrt[12]{1.60} - 1$$
$$= 1.04 - 1$$
$$= .04, \text{ or } 4\%$$

Precisely the same problem arises whenever rates of increase or decrease are to be averaged. The use of the arithmetic mean gives an incorrect result.

The geometric mean as a measure of central tendency. A question arises as to the type of frequency distribution the central tendency of which would be best represented by the geometric mean. When the absolute measures, plotted on the arithmetic scale, give a fairly symmetrical distribution, the arithmetic mean is clearly preferable to the geometric mean. But when the absolute figures thus plotted give an asymmetrical frequency curve of such a type that the asymmetry would be removed and a symmetrical curve secured by plotting the logarithms of the measures, the geometric mean would appear to be preferable. Such a distribution would be one in which not the absolute deviations about the central tendency but the *relative* deviations, the deviations as ratios, were symmetrical. The arithmetic mean of the logarithms of the various measures (which value is, as has been shown, the logarithm of the geometric mean of the original measures) would be the best representative of the central tendency in such a distribution. The curve thus plotted would be symmetrical about the logarithm of the geometric mean. A frequency curve representing the logarithms of percentage changes in prices would tend to show this symmetry about the logarithm of the geometric mean of these changes. These percentage changes, as natural numbers, group themselves in an asymmetrical form, with the range of deviations above the arithmetic mean greatly exceeding the range below. This arises, of course, from the fact that prices of given commodities may increase 1,000 percent or more from a given base, but cannot fall more than 100 percent from any given base. The section on index numbers contains a fuller discussion of this particular phase of the subject.[9]

[9] Walsh, Ref. 187, lays down the following criteria for the use of averages:

(a) When there are no conceivable or assignable upper or lower limits to the values of the terms in a series, the arithmetic average should be employed.

The construction of a frequency distribution in which logarithms are tabulated would be laborious, if the logarithm of each item to be entered had to be determined, before tabulation. It is possible, however, with no great trouble to construct a true logarithmic distribution, with class-interval constant in terms of logarithms. The 58 quotations on preferred stocks tabulated in Table 4–14, range from $23.00 to $124.50. The logarithm of 23.00 is 1.36173; the logarithm of 124.50 is 2.09517. The range in logarithms is 0.73344. We may select 0.12 as a suitable logarithmic class-interval for the present purpose. For convenience in tabulating the data we set up two series of class limits, one in terms of logarithms, one in terms of the corresponding natural numbers. In constructing the distribution natural numbers may be tabulated, utilizing the class limits defined in natural terms. All subsequent calculations may be carried through in terms of logarithms. The distribution appears in Table 4–15.

If the geometric mean is considered appropriate for a given series, the type of distribution represented by Table 4–15 is more logical than that shown in Table 4–14, and the descriptive measurements secured from Table 4–15 have correspondingly greater va-

TABLE 4–15

Distribution of 5-Percent Preferred Stocks on the Basis of Market Price

Class-interval (natural numbers)	Class-interval (logarithms)	Midpoint (logarithms) X	Frequency f	fX
$ 22.39–$ 29.51	1.35–1.46999	1.41	1	1.41
29.52– 38.90	1.47–1.58999	1.53	1	1.53
38.91– 51.28	1.59–1.70999	1.65	3	4.95
51.29– 67.60	1.71–1.82999	1.77	10	17.70
67.61– 89.12	1.83–1.94999	1.89	12	22.68
89.13– 117.49	1.95–2.06999	2.01	27	54.27
117.50– 154.88	2.07–2.18999	2.13	4	8.52
			58	111.06

(b) When there is a definite lower limit at or above zero and no upper conceivable or assignable limit, the geometric average should be employed. Because this is true of price changes Walsh believes the geometric average to be the correct one to use in making index numbers of prices.

(c) When in practice, or in the nature of things, certain upper and lower limits are found to exist and the above criteria cannot be employed, a study of the actual dispersion of the data is necessary. In this case, if the mode is found nearer to the arithmetic average, that average should be employed; if the mode is found nearer to the geometric average, that average should be used.

lidity. We may derive the mean of the logarithms of the preferred stock prices by dividing ΣfX of Table 4–15 (111.06) by 58. The derived value is 1.91483. The antilog of this is $82.19, which is the geometric mean of the distribution. This differs somewhat from the value $84.25 secured from Table 4–14. The difference is due, in part, to the use of different class-intervals and class limits in the two cases. With a relatively small number of observations such differences would be expected to lead to different results. Differing assumptions concerning the internal distribution of items within the several classes would also contribute to a discrepancy between the two results. The value obtained from Table 4–15 is probably a closer approximation to the actual geometric mean than is that obtained from Table 4–14.

A frequency curve based upon the logarithms of the measures included, rather than upon the natural numbers, has been employed to advantage in plotting data relating to income distribution. When natural numbers are plotted, the range of income distribution is so large that it is physically impossible to prepare a chart that will reveal the characteristic features of all sections of the curve. The process of plotting on double logarithmic paper (which is, of course, equivalent to plotting the logarithms of both x's and y's) meets this difficulty, giving a true impression of the whole distribution and the relations between its parts, and, at the same time, brings out certain important features that are obscured in the natural scale chart. In particular, this device appears to smooth into a straight line that part of the curve lying above the mode, a fact which led Vilfredo Pareto to enunciate what has been known as Pareto's Law concerning income distribution. An intensive study of the distribution of income in the United States has led the staff of the National Bureau of Economic Research to call into question certain conclusions drawn from Pareto's generalizations, though the value of the double logarithmic scale for the presentation of income data has been recognized.

The Harmonic Mean. The harmonic mean is a type of average capable of application only within a restricted field, but which should be employed to avoid error in handling certain types of data. It must be used in the averaging of time rates and it has distinctive advantages in the manipulation of some types of price data. As will be seen in Chapter 13, on Index Numbers, the harmonic mean is subject to certain biases that correspond inversely to those to which the arithmetic mean is subject. A mutual offsetting of biases is thus possible. The following example will illustrate the method of employing the harmonic mean.

A given commodity is priced, in three different stores, at "four for a dollar," "five for a dollar," and "twenty for a dollar." The average price per unit is required. The arithmetic average of the figures given (4, 5, and 20) is $9\frac{2}{3}$. If we take this to be the average number sold per dollar, the average price would appear to be \$1.00 $\div$ $9\frac{2}{3}$, or $10\frac{10}{29}$ cents each. But the original quotations are equivalent to unit prices of 25 cents, 20 cents, and 5 cents; the arithmetic average of these prices is $16\frac{2}{3}$ cents apiece. The discrepancy between $10\frac{10}{29}$ cents and $16\frac{2}{3}$ cents is due to a faulty use of the arithmetic mean in averaging quotations in the "so many per dollar" form. Such a mean is, in effect, a weighted average, with greater weight being given to quotations involving a larger number of commodity units.

The correct result may be secured by taking the harmonic mean of the three original quotations. *The harmonic mean of a series of numbers is the reciprocal of the arithmetic mean of the reciprocals of the individual numbers.* Thus if we represent the numbers to be averaged by $r_1, r_2, \ldots r_n$, the formula for the harmonic mean, H, is

$$\frac{1}{H} = \frac{\dfrac{1}{r_1} + \dfrac{1}{r_2} + \dfrac{1}{r_3} + \cdots + \dfrac{1}{r_n}}{N} \qquad (4.15)$$

Using the figures just quoted:

$$\frac{1}{H} = \frac{\dfrac{1}{4} + \dfrac{1}{5} + \dfrac{1}{20}}{3}$$

$$= \frac{10}{60} = \frac{1}{6}$$

$$H = 6$$

The harmonic mean of 4, 5, and 20 is 6, the average number of units sold per dollar. The average price per unit is $16\frac{2}{3}$ cents.

The computation of the harmonic mean of a series of magnitudes is greatly facilitated by the use of prepared tables of reciprocals.[10]

---

[10] *Barlow's Tables of Squares, Cubes, Square Roots, Cube Roots and Reciprocals*, New York, Spar and Chamberlain.

Relations among Different Averages

When different averages are located or computed for a given series of observations, certain relationships are found to prevail among them.

1. The arithmetic mean, the median, and the mode coincide in a symmetrical distribution.
2. In a moderately asymmetrical distribution the median lies between the mean and the mode, approximately one third of the distance along the scale from the former towards the latter. Hence, for this type of distribution there is an approximation to the following relationship:

$$Mo = M - 3(M - Md)$$

3. The arithmetic mean of any series of magnitudes is greater than their geometric mean.
4. The geometric mean of any series of magnitudes is greater than their harmonic mean. The only exception to the last two rules is found when all the measures in the series are equal, in which case arithmetic mean, geometric mean, and harmonic mean are equal.
5. The geometric mean of any two terms is equal to the geometric mean of the harmonic and arithmetic means of those terms. Thus if the terms be 2 and 8, the harmonic mean is $3\frac{1}{5}$, the geometric mean 4, and the arithmetic mean 5. But 4 is also the geometric mean of $3\frac{1}{5}$ and 5. This relationship does not hold when the series includes more than two terms, unless the terms constitute a geometric series.
6. If the dispersion of data tends towards symmetry when the data are plotted on an x-scale in natural numbers, the mode and median will generally be found closer to the arithmetic than to the geometric average. If the dispersion tends toward symmetry when data are plotted on a logarithmic (or ratio) x-scale, the mode and median will generally be found closer to the geometric than to the arithmetic average.

Characteristic Features of the Chief Averages

The arithmetic mean

1. The value of the arithmetic mean is affected by every measure in the series. For certain purposes it is too much affected by extreme deviations from the average.
2. The arithmetic mean is easily calculated, and is determinate in every case.
3. The arithmetic mean is a computed average, and hence is capable of algebraic manipulation.
4. The arithmetic mean is a stable statistic, in a sampling sense. (The meaning of this important statement will be developed more fully at a later point.)

The median

1. The value of the median is not affected by the magnitude of extreme deviations from the average.
2. The median may be located when the items in a series are not capable of quantitative measurement.
3. The median may be located when the data are incomplete, provided that the number and general location of all the cases be known, and that accurate information be available concerning the measures near the center of the distribution.

The mode

1. The value of the mode is not affected by the magnitude of extreme deviations from the average.
2. The approximate mode is easy to locate but the determination of the true mode requires extended calculation.
3. The mode has no significance unless the distribution includes a large number of measures and possesses a distinct central tendency.
4. The mode is the average most typical of the distribution, being located at the point of greatest concentration.

The geometric mean

1. The geometric mean gives less weight to extremely high values than does the arithmetic mean.
2. It is strictly determinate in averaging positive values.
3. The geometric mean is the form of average to be used when rates of change or ratios between measures are to be averaged, as equal weight is given to equal ratios of change. It is particularly well adapted to the averaging of ratios of price change.
4. The geometric mean is capable of algebraic manipulation.

The harmonic mean

1. The harmonic mean is adapted to the averaging of time rates and certain similar terms. It has been employed in the field of economic statistics in the measurement of price movements.
2. The harmonic mean is capable of algebraic manipulation.

This summary has been designed to show that each type of average has its own particular field of usefulness. Each one is best for certain purposes and under certain conditions. The characteristics and limitations of each one should be understood in order that it may be appropriately employed. A complete description of a frequency distribution often calls for the determination of two or three of the chief averages, as well as other statistical measurements. The arithmetic mean is perhaps the most useful single average. The simplicity of its computation, the possibility of employing it in algebraic calculations and the fact that its meaning is perfectly definite and familiar make it highly serviceable in statistical work. Its sphere of usefulness is not universal, however, and it should only be employed when the given conditions render it suitable. A fuller appreciation of the distinctive virtues of the geometric mean is leading to a wider employment of that measure in many types of statistical work.

REFERENCES

Croxton, F. E. and Cowden, D. J., *Applied General Statistics*, Chap. 9.

Dixon, W. J. and Massey, F. J. Jr., *Introduction to Statistical Analysis*, Chap. 3.

Freund, J. E., *Modern Elementary Statistics*, Chap. 4.

Lewis, E. E., *Methods of Statistical Analysis in Economics and Business*, Chap. 3.

Riggleman, J. R. and Frisbee, I. N., *Business Statistics*, 3rd ed., Chap. 8.

Rosander, A. C., *Elementary Principles of Statistics*, Chap. 4.

Simpson, G. and Kafka, F., *Basic Statistics*, Chaps. 10, 11, 12.

Spurr, W. A., Kellogg, L. S. and Smith, J. H., *Business and Economic Statistics*, Chap. 10.

Treloar, A. E., *Elements of Statistical Reasoning*, Chap. 3.

Waugh, A. E., *Elements of Statistical Method*, 3rd ed., Chaps. 4, 5.

Wilks, S. S., *Elementary Statistical Analysis*, Chap. 3.

Yule, G. U. and Kendall, M. G., *An Introduction to the Theory of Statistics*, 14th ed., Chap. 5.

The publishers and the dates of publication of the books named in chapter reference lists are given in the bibliography at the end of this volume.

•
•
•

Some Characteristics of Frequency Distributions: Measures of Variation and Skewness

In the preceding chapters we have been concerned, first, with methods of reducing a mass of quantitative data to a form in which the characteristics of the mass as a whole may be readily determined and, in the second place, with methods of describing the assembled data. The first object is accomplished with the formation of a frequency distribution. The second is partially accomplished when there has been obtained a single significant value in the form of an average which represents the central tendency of the distribution. But any average, by itself, fails to give a complete description of a frequency distribution. Other values are needed before the chief characteristics of a given distribution have been defined and effective comparison with other distributions made possible. The first of these is a measure of the degree to which the items included in the original distribution depart or *vary* from the central value, the degree of "*scatter*," *variation* or *dispersion*. The second is a measure of the degree of symmetry of the distribution, of the balance or lack of balance on the two sides of the central value. A third measure sometimes employed to define the pattern of variation takes account of the distribution of observations as between classes near the mean and classes at the tails of a distribution. This attribute, termed *kurtosis*, will be discussed at a later point. The present chapter deals with measures of variation and skewness.

Nature and Significance of Variation

The fact of variation in collections of quantitative data has been pointed out in earlier sections and the bearing of this fact upon the work of the statistician indicated. Practically every collection of quantitative data, consisting of measurements from the social, biological, or economic field, is characterized by variation, by quantitative differences among the individual units. And this fact of variation is as important as the fact of family resemblance. Biological variation has been a fundamental factor in the evolutionary process. No measurement of a physical characteristic of a racial group, such as height, is complete without an accompanying measure of the average variation in the group in this respect. The material well-being of the people of a country depends upon the degree of variation in income among income recipients, as well as upon the size of the average income. The price movements that are characteristic of economic changes are not uniform throughout the price system. They are unequal from sector to sector, and it is the inequalities that both reflect and necessitate economic adjustments.

The whole body of statistical methods may, indeed, be regarded as a set of techniques for the study of variation. It is variation that creates various types of frequency distributions. The powerful tools of correlation analysis have been constructed for studying relations among variations in different quantities. Comparisons of measures of variation provide means of testing hypotheses. When we generalize statistical measures we attempt to define the limits of accuracy of such generalizations, and for this purpose use still other measures of variation. When we deal with observations that are ordered in time, and for which the chronological sequence is significant, we face new aspects of variation. Changes from month to month and from year to year in national income, in the level of wholesale prices, in the physical volume of production, have profound economic significance. Products of a manufacturing process are marked by variation, no matter how fine the tolerance limits imposed. A new and important body of statistical techniques has been developed to distinguish between those variations in quality that are due to assignable causes (and are thus open to control) and those that are due to chance — "chance" meaning the mass of floating or random causes that cannot be separately defined.

Accurate and sensitive measures of variation are thus necessary at all levels and for all types of statistical work. For our immediate purposes, which have to do with the description of observations organized in frequency distributions, the need of such measures as supplements to measures of central tendency is to be emphasized. An average by itself has little significance unless the degree of variation in the given frequency distribution is known. If the variation is so great that there is no pronounced central tendency an average has limited significance. With a decrease in the degree of variation an average becomes increasingly meaningful.

Variation may be expressed in terms of the units of measurement employed for the original data, or may be expressed as an abstract figure, such as a percentage, which is independent of the original units. When the original units are employed *absolute variability* is measured; when an abstract figure is secured we have a measure of *relative variability*, more suitable for comparison than the former type. Measures of absolute variability are first considered.

Notation. A few symbols not hitherto employed will be used in this chapter. Explanations will come later, but it may be helpful to present the more important of these at this point:

s: the standard deviation of a sample

s^2: the variance of a sample

s_a^2: the mean-square deviation from an arbitrary origin

s': an estimate of the standard deviation of a population (this symbol used chiefly with small samples)

s'^2: an estimate of the variance of a population (this symbol used chiefly with small samples)

σ: the standard deviation of a population

σ^2: the variance of a population

$M.D.$: the mean deviation

Q_1: the first quartile

$Q.D.$: the quartile deviation

D_8: the eighth decile

V: the coefficient of variation

sk: the skewness of a distribution

Measures of Variation

The Range. A rough measure of variation is afforded by the *range*, which is the absolute difference between the value of the smallest item and the value of the greatest item included in the distribution. From the array in Chapter 3, showing the weekly earnings of textile workers, we may note that the smallest observation is

$38.80, the largest $67.60. The range, therefore, is $67.60 − $38.80, or $28.80. If the original data were not to be had the range could be approximated from the frequency table. It would be the difference between the lower limit of the lowest class and the upper limit of the highest class. Thus for bricks classified according to transverse strength (Table 3–13 in Chap. 3), the range is from 225 to 2025, or 1800 (pounds per square inch).

The magnitude of the range, it is obvious, depends upon the values of the two extreme cases only. A single abnormal item would change the range materially. It is, therefore, a somewhat erratic measurement, likely to be unrepresentative of the true distribution of items. For small samples, however, particularly when the sampling operation is repeated and an average of successive results utilized, the range has certain distinct advantages. These have led to its rather extensive employment in inspections designed to maintain the quality of industrial products.

The Standard Deviation and the Variance. The standard and most widely used measure of variation, the *standard deviation*, is the square root of the mean of the squared deviations of the individual observations from their mean. Such deviations are termed *residuals*. The deviations are always measured from the arithmetic mean, since the sum of their squares is a minimum under these conditions. We may note that in statistical work extensive use is made also of the square of the standard deviation (i.e., s^2 for a sample, σ^2 for the population). This quantity is termed the *variance*.

The standard deviation of a sample. The procedure employed in computing s^2 and s is illustrated by a simple example in Table 5–1.

TABLE 5–1

Computation of the Standard Deviation

X	d	d^2		
3	− 6	36	$\overline{X} = 9$	
6	− 3	9	$s^2 = \Sigma d^2/N$	(5.1)
9	0	0	$= \frac{90}{5} = 18$	
12	+ 3	9	$s = \sqrt{\Sigma d^2/N}$	(5.2)
15	+ 6	36	$= \sqrt{18} = 4.24$	
		90		

The sum of the squared deviations from the mean of the five observations here shown is 90. The mean of this quantity is 18, the variance. The square root of 18 is 4.24, the standard deviation.

The symbol s will be used throughout to represent the standard deviation of a sample, taken as the square root of $\Sigma d^2/N$. However, the student should at this stage be introduced to a slight modification of this procedure which yields a measure we may represent by s', derived from

$$s' = \sqrt{\frac{\Sigma d^2}{N-1}} \qquad (5.3)$$

In the present case $s' = \sqrt{\dfrac{90}{4}} = 4.74$. This quantity is of importance in the theory of sampling, and becomes of practical concern when samples are small. It is to be preferred to s when the investigator is using sample results as bases for estimates concerning the population from which the sample was drawn. To make the distinction clear we may at this point briefly anticipate certain ideas which will be discussed more fully in later chapters.

Estimating the standard deviation of a population. In general, in deriving a statistical measurement from a sample, we do so as a step preliminary to an estimate of a population characteristic. The mean of a sample is of value to us as an approximation to the mean of a parent population; the standard deviation of a sample is an approximation to the population σ. Our problem, in the latter case, is that of estimating the variation prevailing in a population of which both the mean and the standard deviation are unknown to us. Regarding the problem in this light, let us consider the nature of the information provided by successive observations. A single observation provides the basis of an estimate of the mean of the parent population. It provides no basis for an estimate of the degree of variation in that population. For all that we know when we have but one observation, all the members of the parent population may have a single uniform value. When we have *two* observations, however, we have a basis for an estimate of the variation in the population; when we have three observations we have an added basis for such an estimate. In the language of Statistics, two observations provide us with one *degree of freedom* for estimating the variation in the parent population, three observations provide us with two degrees of freedom for such an estimate, etc. One degree of freedom is lost, for an estimate of variation, when we have only the information about the parent population that is provided by the observations in our sample. If, in some independent way, we knew the mean of the parent population, there would be no loss of degrees of freedom for such an estimate. A single observation, the deviation of which from the known mean of the parent population could be measured, would provide the basis for an estimate of variation. But we seldom have such independent information. In effect, in default of such information, we use up one degree of freedom in estimating the mean. This leaves $N - 1$ degrees of freedom for the estimate of the standard deviation. The sum of the squared deviations is divided, thus, not by N, but by the number of degrees of freedom available for the given purpose. (As we shall see, the problem of determining degrees of freedom enters in various forms into later procedures.) When this is done in deriving s', we are said to have an *unbiased* estimate of σ.[1]

For practical purposes it is convenient and permissible to use N as the divisor, rather than $N - 1$, when N is large, say in excess of 100. The difference between N and $N - 1$ is then negligible; either s or s' provides a satisfactory estimate of σ. (In general, with large samples we shall make no distinction between s and s'.) Even with a small sample N may be used as the divisor of Σd^2 if the derived measure is to be thought of as simply *descriptive* of a given set of observations, rather than as an estimate of a population characteristic.

Computation of the standard deviation. In the example given in Table 5–1 the five observations were ungrouped. When data are grouped in a frequency distribution the task of computing the standard deviation takes a slightly different form. The measurement of deviations from an arbitrary origin is essential in this case, as it greatly simplifies the calculations. In this process, the sample being quite large, the formula for an estimate of the standard deviation may be written

$$s = \sqrt{\frac{\Sigma f d^2}{N}} \tag{5.4}$$

where f represents a class-frequency, d the deviation of the midpoint of that class from the arithmetic mean, and N the total number of cases included. For the square of the standard deviation we have, of course,

$$s^2 = \frac{\Sigma f d^2}{N}$$

---

[1] The problem of estimation is discussed more fully in Chapter 7.

If a deviation from an arbitrary origin be represented by d' and the mean-square deviation from this origin be represented by s_a^2, we have

$$s_a^2 = \frac{\Sigma f(d')^2}{N}$$

The mean-square deviation from the mean (s^2) is less than the mean-square deviation from any other point on the scale. Hence s_a^2 is greater than s^2. We may represent by c the difference between the true mean and the arbitrary origin. It may be readily established [2] that

$$s^2 = s_a^2 - c^2 \tag{5.5}$$

The value of the standard deviation may be most easily determined, therefore, by computing s_a^2 and c^2. The operations involved are illustrated in detail in Table 5–2, showing the distribution of 83,114 chemical workers, classified on the basis of average hourly earnings in January 1946.

The entire calculation, it will be noted, is carried through in terms of class-interval units, the result being reduced to the original units in the final operation. In computing c, the difference between the true mean and the arbitrary origin, the algebraic sum of the deviations is divided by the number of cases. The arithmetic mean could be determined by reducing c to original units and adding this value (algebraically) to the value of the arbitrary quantity selected as origin, but this is not an essential step. The actual value of the mean need not be known in the computation of the standard deviation.

The *variance* of the distribution in Table 5–2 is, of course,

$$s^2 = (23.5357)^2 = 553.93$$

This can be obtained directly from the figures given below Table 5–2, by multiplying s^2 in class-interval units (5.5393) by the square of the class-interval (100).

[2] For $s^2 = \dfrac{\Sigma d^2}{N}$

$s_a^2 = \dfrac{\Sigma (d')^2}{N}$

$d' = d + c$

$(d')^2 = d^2 + 2cd + c^2$

$\Sigma (d')^2 = \Sigma d^2 + 2c\Sigma d + Nc^2$

but $\Sigma d = 0$

$\therefore \Sigma (d')^2 = \Sigma d^2 + Nc^2$

$\dfrac{\Sigma (d')^2}{N} = \dfrac{\Sigma d^2}{N} + c^2$

$s_a^2 = s^2 + c^2$

$s^2 = s_a^2 - c^2$

TABLE 5–2

Computation of Standard Deviation
Straight-Time Average Hourly Earnings of Workers in Industrial
Chemical Plants, United States, January, 1946

(1) Class-interval (cents per hour)	(2) Mid-point (cents) X_m	(3) Fre-quency f	(4) Deviation from arbitrary origin d'	(5) fd'	(6) $f(d')^2$	(7) $(d'+1)^2$	(8) $f(d'+1)^2$
30.0– 39.9	35	1	– 8	– 8	64	49	49
40.0– 49.9	45	5	– 7	– 35	245	36	180
50.0– 59.9	55	422	– 6	– 2,532	15,192	25	10,550
60.0– 69.9	65	1,600	– 5	– 8,000	40,000	16	25,600
70.0– 79.9	75	3,661	– 4	– 14,644	58,576	9	32,949
80.0– 89.9	85	6,004	– 3	– 18,012	54,036	4	24,016
90.0– 99.9	95	10,564	– 2	– 21,128	42,256	1	10,564
100.0–109.9	105	13,136	– 1	– 13,136	13,136	0	0
110.0–119.9	115	15,048	0	0	0	1	15,048
120.0–129.9	125	13,116	1	13,116	13,116	4	52,464
130.0–139.9	135	8,219	2	16,438	32,876	9	73,971
140.0–149.9	145	4,565	3	13,695	41,085	16	73,040
150.0–159.9	155	4,519	4	18,076	72,304	25	112,975
160.0–169.9	165	1,051	5	5,255	26,275	36	37,836
170.0–179.9	175	988	6	5,928	35,568	49	48,412
180.0–189.9	185	82	7	574	4,018	64	5,248
190.0–199.9	195	91	8	728	5,824	81	7,371
200.0–209.9	205	17	9	153	1,377	100	1,700
210.0–219.9	215	10	10	100	1,000	121	1,210
220.0–229.9	225	6	11	66	726	144	864
240.0–249.9	245	2	13	26	338	196	392
250.0–259.9	255	2	14	28	392	225	450
270.0–279.9	275	1	16	16	256	289	289
310.0–319.9	315	2	20	40	800	441	882
340.0–349.9	345	2	23	46	1,058	576	1,152
		83,114		– 3,210	460,518		537,212

$N = 83,114$

Class-interval $= 10$ cents

c (in class-interval units) $= \dfrac{-3210}{83114} = -.03862$

c^2 (in class-interval units) $= .00149$

s_a^2 (in class-interval units) $= \dfrac{460518}{83114} = 5.54080$

s^2 (in class-interval units) $= s_a^2 - c^2 = 5.54080 - .00149 = 5.53931$

s (in class-interval units) $= 2.35357$

s (in original units) $= 2.35359 \times 10$ cents $= 23.5357$ cents

Correction for errors of grouping. We have pointed out in an earlier section that in basing computations on a frequency table we usually assume that the observations in each class may be treated as though they were concentrated at the midpoint of that class or, which is equivalent to this, that the observations grouped in a given class are distributed evenly between the class limits. Of course, this assumption is not strictly true. If one considers the structure of Table 5–2 it will be clear that the density of the items increases as one moves from either tail toward the modal class. It is a fair inference that, if the data relate to a continuous variable, this increase in density will characterize the observations *within* any class, as well as the items grouped in different classes. In general, that half of each class-interval that lies toward the mode will contain more observations than the other half, lying away from the mode. Thus the actual mean of the observations in a given class will not usually coincide with the midpoint of that class, but will deviate from the midpoint in the direction of the mode.

If the distribution is reasonably symmetrical, this fact will not lead to a systematic bias in the calculation of the mean, for there will be a tendency for positive errors in deviations measured in one direction from the mean to be offset by negative errors in deviations on the other side. But when the deviations are squared, as they are in computing the standard deviation and the variance, the error is systematic. The square of the deviation (from the mean of the total distribution) of a class midpoint will in general be greater than the square of the deviation of the actual mean of the observations in the given class from the mean of the distribution. Under these conditions the sum of the squared deviations derived from the grouped items, as in Table 5–2, will be greater than the true sum of the squared deviations, as this sum might be derived from ungrouped data.

W. F. Sheppard (Ref. 139) has established that the error in the variance due to the use of grouped data in computations amounts to about one twelfth of the square of the class-interval. This will be the case when two conditions prevail:

1. When the data tabulated are observations on a continuous variable.
2. When the frequencies taper off gradually at the two extremes. This latter condition is often defined as one in which the frequency curve fitted to the given distribution is characterized by "high contact" at both tails.

The application of Sheppard's correction is a simple process. If s^2 is the uncorrected variance derived from deviations in class-interval units (the variance thus measured is 5.53931 for the data in Table 5–2), we may write

$$\text{Corrected variance} = s^2 - \frac{1}{12} \qquad (5.6)$$

When the deviations are in original units of measurement, and h is the class-interval in such units, we have

$$\text{Corrected variance} = s^2 - \frac{h^2}{12} \qquad (5.7)$$

Applying this correction to the measures given in Table 5–2 we obtain a corrected variance, in class-interval units, of 5.45598, a corrected standard deviation, in original units, of 23.3580 cents.

The point should be stressed that the application of Sheppard's correction when the basic conditions are not fulfilled (e.g., when a U-shaped distribution, a J-shaped distribution, or any very skew distribution is being studied) may lessen rather than increase the accuracy of the estimate of the variance or the standard deviation. Moreover, the correction should be avoided when the number of observations tabulated is small, say below 500, with customary grouping.

The Charlier check. A check upon the accuracy of the calculations in Table 5–2 (the *Charlier check*) is afforded by the figures in columns (7) and (8). If deviations be measured, not from the arbitrary origin employed in computing the standard deviation, but from an origin one class-interval below, we secure a set of values equal to $d' + 1$. The squares of these values are given in column (7). Multiplying by the corresponding frequencies we have the quantities recorded in column (8), the sum of which is 537,212. This total stands in a definite relationship to the values secured in computing the standard deviation. For

$$\Sigma f(d' + 1)^2 = \Sigma f[(d')^2 + 2d' + 1]$$
$$= \Sigma f(d')^2 + 2\Sigma fd' + \Sigma f$$

or $\qquad \Sigma f(d' + 1)^2 = \Sigma f(d')^2 + 2\Sigma fd' + N \qquad (5.8)$

Inserting in this last equation the values secured from the calculations shown in Table 5–2, we obtain this check:

$$537{,}212 = 460{,}518 - 6{,}420 + 83{,}114$$
$$= 537{,}212$$

The following is a summary of the steps in the process of computing the standard deviation of items grouped in a frequency distribution:

1. Select as arbitrary origin the midpoint of a class near the center of the distribution.
2. Measure the deviations from this point of the items in each class, in class-interval units. Multiply the deviations by the corresponding class frequencies.
3. Divide the algebraic sum of the deviations by N. This gives c, in class-interval units. Compute c^2.
4. Square the deviations and multiply by the corresponding class frequencies.
5. Divide the sum of the squared deviations by N. This gives s_a^2, in class-interval units.
6. From the formula, $s^2 = s_a^2 - c^2$, compute s^2. Extract the square root of this value, securing s in class-interval units.
7. Multiply s, as thus computed, by the class-interval. The result is s in the original units of measurement.

If the population variance is to be estimated, derive the estimate from the relation

$$s'^2 = \frac{\Sigma d^2}{N-1}$$

Alternatively the estimate may be made from

$$s'^2 = s^2 \frac{N}{N-1}$$

Certain of the characteristics of the standard deviation and its relation to other measures of dispersion are described in a later section.

The Mean Deviation. An alternative but less useful measure of the dispersion of items about the central value of a sample is

TABLE 5–3

Computation of Mean Deviation

X	f	d	
3	1	6	$M = 9$
6	1	3	
9	1	0	$M.D. = \dfrac{18}{5} = 3.6$
12	1	3	
15	1	6	
		$\overline{18}$	

afforded by the device of measuring the deviation of each item from this central value, in absolute terms, and averaging these deviations. A simple example is given in Table 5–3. The average (the mean and median coincide in this case) is 9. The deviations are added, taking no account of algebraic signs, and the total divided by the number of items. This procedure is described by the expression

$$M.D. = \frac{\Sigma|d|}{N} \qquad (5.9)$$

where | | indicates that no account is taken of signs.

In general terms, the *mean deviation* of a series of magnitudes is the arithmetic mean of their deviations from an average value, either mean or median. In the process of summation and averaging the algebraic signs of the deviations are disregarded. It is good practice to take the deviations from the median when the mean deviation is to be used as a measure of dispersion, for the mean deviation is a minimum when the median is the point of reference.

When the observations are many the task of computing the mean deviation is less simple. With the data grouped in a frequency distribution, deviations may be measured from the median (or mean) and multiplied by class frequencies. Alternatively, deviations may be measured from the midpoint of the class containing the median (or mean), a later correction being made to offset the error resulting from the use of the class midpoint as origin, rather than the median (or mean). The mean deviation is useful in dealing with small numbers of observations when no elaborate analysis is called for. For extensive use it has certain logical and mathematical limitations (e.g., the disregard of plus and minus signs in adding the deviations is algebraically illogical). It is seldom employed when data have been organized in a frequency distribution.

Quantiles. The character of the variation characteristic of a given distribution of the variable x may be effectively indicated by selected *quantiles*. This is a general term for quantities defining points on the x-scale which divide the total frequencies in specified proportions. The median is a central quantile which, as we have seen, divides the total frequencies into two equal groups. *Quartiles*, as the term implies, are values which divide the total number of observations in a distribution into four equal groups. Thus the first quartile is that point on the scale of x-values below which lie one quarter of the total number of cases and above which lie three quarters of the total. (The second quartile and the median are, obviously, identical). The *deciles* divide the total frequencies into 10 equal groups; the *percentiles* divide them into 100 equal groups. Quantiles are simple and easily understood measures which may be used effectively in defining the degree and character of dispersion. In studies of the distribution of price relatives and other variables Wesley C. Mitchell made extensive use of such measures (Refs. 105 and 106).

In locating quantiles the count begins in all cases at the lower end of the x-scale. The two following examples will illustrate the procedure:

Location of the First Quartile (Q_1), *Family Incomes* (See Table 4–11)

$$N/4 = 9,319.75$$
$$Q_1 = \$1,500 + (2,385.75/3,280) \times \$500$$
$$= \$1,863.68$$

Location of Eighth Decile (D_8), *Family Incomes* (See Table 4–11)

$$N/10 = 3,727.9 \qquad D_8 = \$4,500 + (1,491.2/1,752) \times \$500$$
$$8N/10 = 29,823.2 \qquad = \$4,925.57$$

As is true of the median, the other quantiles will be indeterminate when a quantile value falls between given (ungrouped) values of the variable. In such a case, a value half-way between the two limiting values is conventionally employed.

The Quartile Deviation. In studying dispersion by means of quantiles one does not have a single measure, such as the standard or mean deviation. Such a single measure of variation may be computed readily from the quartiles, however. Within the range between the two quartiles, of course, one half of all the measures are included. The greater the concentration the smaller this interval, hence a fairly accurate measure of dispersion may be obtained from the relationship between these two quartiles. The quartile deviation is the *semi-interquartile range*, half the distance along the scale between the first and third quartiles. Thus if $Q.D.$ represent the quartile deviation, Q_1 the first quartile and Q_3 the third quartile,

$$Q.D. = \frac{Q_3 - Q_1}{2} \qquad\qquad (5.10)$$

If the value of a point on the scale half-way between the first and third quartiles is represented by K, one half of all the measures in a frequency distribution will fall within the range $K \pm Q.D.$ For the data in Table 5–2, relating to the hourly earnings of workers in industrial chemical plants in 1946, we have (in cents):

$$Q_1 = 98.60$$
$$Q_3 = 129.07$$
$$Q.D. = \frac{129.07 - 98.60}{2}$$
$$= 15.235$$
$$K = 98.60 + 15.235$$
$$= 113.835$$

Thus one half of all the measures lie within the range 113.835 ± 15.235. This statement, together with the arithmetic mean of the hourly earnings of chemical workers in the year in question, constitutes a useful description of the distribution. In a perfectly symmetrical distribution the value of K will coincide with the value of the median (that is, the median will lie half-way along the scale from Q_1 to Q_3). The distribution of wage rates is almost symmetrical, the value of the median being 113.89 cents, as compared with 113.835 cents for K.

The probable error. In studying the results of astronomical and other physical measurements it has been found that the values secured by different observers for the same constant quantity vary. In such cases there is an obvious need of a measure of variation which may be used as an index of the reliability of given results. The traditional measure employed in such cases is termed the *probable error*. The probable error (or *P.E.*) is that amount which, in a given case, is exceeded by the errors of one half the observations.

For the normal distribution, which is the ideal type to which many observed distributions of errors of measurement tend to conform, the probable error is equal to 0.6745σ. For the normal distribution, that is, a distance equal to the probable error laid off on each side of the arithmetic mean will define limits within which one half of the total number of cases will fall.

This measure of variation has been employed in fields other than that in which it was originally applied, fields in which the name *probable error* is somewhat misleading. In such cases it is better to think of it as the *probable deviation*, that distance from the mean which will be exceeded by one half of the total deviations.

The probable error is a measure of dispersion which is fully significant only when it applies to a distribution following the normal law of error. In such cases it has a definite and precise meaning.

This is not so when it is applied to skew distributions, and its use in such cases is not advisable.

Relations among Measures of Variation

An understanding of the significance of the various measures of dispersion described above may be facilitated by a general comparison and a summary statement of the relations among them.

1. The *range* is a distance along the scale within which all the observations lie.
2. The *quartile deviation* or *semi-interquartile range* is a distance along the scale which, when laid off on each side of the point midway between the two quartiles, includes one half the total number of observations.
3. The *mean deviation* from the mean, in a normal or slightly skew distribution, is equal to about $\frac{4}{5}$ of the standard deviation. A range of $7\frac{1}{2}$ times the mean deviation, centering at the mean, will include approximately 99 percent of all the cases.
4. When a distance equal to the *standard deviation* is laid off on each side of the mean, in a normal or only slightly skew distribution, about two thirds of all the cases will be included. (In the normal distribution 68.27 percent of the observations will be included.) When a distance equal to twice the standard deviation is laid off on each side of the mean approximately 95 percent of the cases will be included (95.45 percent in a normal distribution). When a distance equal to three times the standard deviation is laid off on each side of the mean about 99 percent of all the observations will be included (99.73 percent in a normal distribution). This general rule that a range of six times the standard deviation, centering at the mean, will include about 99 percent of all the measures furnishes a useful check upon calculations.

    A study of Fig. 6.5 may help to make clear the significance of the standard deviation in a normal distribution.
5. The *probable error*, in a normal distribution, is equal to 0.6745σ. A range of twice the probable error, centering at the mean, will include 50 percent of all the observations. A range of eight times the probable error, centering at the mean, will include approximately 99 percent of all the observations.

Characteristic Features of the Chief Measures of Variation

The range

1. The range is easily calculated and its significance is readily understood. As a rough measure of the degree of variation the range is useful.
2. The value of the range is determined by the values of the two extreme cases. It is thus a highly unstable measure, the value of which may be greatly changed by the addition or withdrawal of a single figure.
3. This measure gives no indication of the character of the distribution within the two extreme observations.

The quartile deviation

1. The quartile deviation is a measure of dispersion that is easily computed and readily understood. It is superior to the range as a rough measure of variation.
2. The quartile deviation is not a measure of the variation from any specific average.
3. This measure is not affected by the distribution of the items between the first and third quartiles, or by the distribution outside the quartiles. The values of the quartile deviation might be the same for two quite dissimilar distributions, provided the quartiles happened to coincide. Because it is not affected by the deviations of individual items it cannot be accepted as an accurate measure of variation.
4. The quartile deviation is not suited to algebraic treatment.

The mean deviation

1. The mean deviation is affected by the value of every observation. As the *average difference* between the individual items and the median (or mean) of the distribution it has a precise significance.
2. The mean deviation is less affected by extreme deviations than the standard deviation.
3. Mathematically, the mean deviation is not as logical or as convenient a measure of dispersion as the standard deviation.

The standard deviation

1. The standard deviation is affected by the value of every observation.
2. The process of squaring the deviations before adding avoids the algebraic fallacy of disregarding signs.
3. The standard deviation has a definite mathematical meaning and is perfectly adapted to algebraic treatment.
4. The standard deviation is, in general, less affected by fluctuations of sampling than the other measures of dispersion.
5. The standard deviation is the unit customarily used in defining areas under the normal curve of error. (See Chapter 6.) The standard deviation has, thus, great practical utility in sampling and statistical inference.

The probable error

1. The probable error has a definite meaning in the case of a distribution following the normal law. It has not this precise meaning for other distributions, and should not be employed in describing them.
2. The definite relationship between the probable error and the standard deviation, for a normal distribution, permits the value of the probable error to be readily determined.
3. Traditionally, the probable error has been used as an index of the magnitude of sampling errors. It has now been generally displaced by the standard error (which will be discussed in Chapters 7 and 8). Its use is not recommended.

All the measures of variation described above may be utilized for particular purposes. The standard deviation, however, is the best general measure and should be employed in all cases where a high degree of accuracy is required. The probable error is, in effect, merely a fractional part of the standard deviation, with a definite but restricted field of usefulness.

The Measurement of Relative Variation

We have been dealing in the preceding section with absolute variability. The various measures of dispersion secured by the methods outlined describe the variability of the data in terms of absolute units of measurement. The standard deviation of a distribution of workers classified according to hourly wage rates would be in cents; that of a distribution of steel plants according to the tonnage of steel produced would be in tons. If the object in a given case is the description of a single frequency distribution it is desirable that the original unit be employed throughout, but if measures of variation of two different distributions are to be compared, difficulties are encountered. This is clear if the units are unlike, but even if the units are identical the same difficulty arises. Thus measures of variation in the weights of dogs and in the weights of horses might both have been computed in pounds. Because the standard deviation of horse weights is greater than the standard deviation of dog weights, it does not follow that the degree of variability is greater in the former case. A measure of absolute variation is significant only in relation to the average from which the deviations are measured. For comparison, therefore, it must be reduced to a relative form, and the obvious procedure is to express a given measure of variation as a percentage of the average from which the deviations have been measured. The quantity thus becomes an abstract number, a measure of the relative variability of the given observations, and may be compared with similar terms computed from other distributions.

The Coefficient of Variation. The measure of relative variation most commonly employed is that developed by Pearson, termed the *coefficient of variation*, and represented by the letter V. It is simply the standard deviation as a percentage of the arithmetic mean. Thus

$$V = \frac{\sigma}{M} \times 100 \qquad (5.11)$$

Applying this formula to the results secured from the analysis of the distribution of workers in industrial chemical plants in 1946, classified according to average hourly earnings (Table 5–2), we have

$$V = \frac{23.54}{114.61} \times 100$$
$$= 20.54 \text{ percent}$$

This measurement may be compared with a similar coefficient relating to the distribution of steel workers in open hearth furnaces in 1933, classified according to average hourly earnings. For steel workers the standard deviation of hourly earnings was 18.68 cents. This indicates smaller dispersion than that found among chemical workers in 1946. However, the average hourly earnings of steel workers in 1933 (a depression year) was 50.14 cents. For the coefficient of variation we have

$$V = \frac{18.68}{50.14} \times 100$$
$$= 37.26 \text{ percent}$$

The relative variation of hourly earnings for steel workers in 1933 was substantially greater than that of hourly earnings for chemical workers in 1946, although the absolute variation was much smaller for the steel group.

The coefficient of variation is affected, of course, by the value of the mean, as well as by the size of the standard deviation. If the mean should coincide with the origin (i.e., if $M = 0$), V would be equal to infinity for all values of the standard deviation other than zero. For distributions with mean values close to zero (e.g. distributions of corporations, in a year of depression, classified on the basis of net operating revenue) V is thus a somewhat ambiguous statistic.

When the median is the average employed, a measure of relative variation analogous to V may be obtained from the relation $M.D./Md;$ similarly, when the quantity K is used to define central tendency, relative variation may be measured by $Q.D./K$. These measures may be put in percentage terms if desired.

Measures of Skewness

Methods have been developed in the preceding sections for describing the central tendency of a frequency distribution and for measuring the degree of concentration, or degree of dispersion, about that central tendency. One further measure is needed, and that is one which indicates the degree of skewness or asymmetry of a given distribution. For it is essential to know, in regard to a given distribution, whether the observations are arranged symmetrically about the central value, or are dispersed in an uneven, asymmetrical fashion about that value. Having such a figure it will be possible effectively to summarize the characteristics of a frequency distribution in three simple terms — an average, a measure of dispersion, and a measure of skewness. There are two measures of skewness in current use.

If a frequency curve is perfectly symmetrical, mean, median, and mode will coincide. As the distribution departs from symmetry these three values are pulled apart, the difference between the mean and the mode being greatest. This difference may be used, therefore, as a measure of skewness. It is desirable in this case, as in measuring relative variability, to secure an index in the form of an abstract number, which may be compared with similar figures derived from other distributions. To this end, Pearson has proposed dividing the absolute difference between mean and mode by the standard deviation of the given distribution. His formula for the measure of skewness is

$$sk = \frac{M - Mo}{s} \qquad (5.12)$$

In a symmetrical distribution, where mean and mode coincide, the value of this measure will be zero. Under other conditions the value may be positive or negative, depending upon the relative positions of the two averages on the scale.

For moderately skew distributions the degree of skewness may be estimated more readily from the formula

$$sk = \frac{3(M - Md)}{s} \qquad (5.13)$$

This corresponds approximately to the other formula, because of the fact that in a moderately asymmetrical distribution the median lies between the mean and the mode, about one third of the distance from the former towards the latter.

Because it is difficult to locate the mode by simple methods, a measure of skewness more easily computed than Pearson's is desirable in some cases. Bowley has proposed such a method, based upon the relationship between the first and third quartiles and the median. If the distribution is symmetrical these two quartiles will be equidistant from the median; with an asymmetrical distribution this is not so. Therefore, if we let q_2 represent the difference between the upper quartile and the median and q_1 represent the difference between the median and the lower quartile, we may use the formula

$$sk = \frac{q_2 - q_1}{q_2 + q_1} \tag{5.14}$$

as a means of securing a measure of skewness. This value will vary between 0 and $\pm$ 1. For with perfect symmetry $q_2 = q_1$, and the measure is 0; with asymmetry so pronounced that the median and one of the quartiles coincide, either q_2 or q_1 becomes equal to 0, and the formula gives a value of $+$ 1 or $-$ 1. Bowley suggests that a value of 0.1 indicates a moderate degree of skewness, while a value of 0.3 indicates marked skewness.

The values secured from this measure are not, of course, comparable with the values secured from the application of Pearson's formula for measuring skewness.

Peakedness, or " Excess." Reference has been made (page 86) to a fourth measurable characteristic of grouped data. This characteristic has to do with the degree to which observations are concentrated in the neighborhood of the mean and at the tails of a given distribution. The measurement of peakedness involves the use of "moments." Discussion of this topic lies beyond the scope of the present volume.

REFERENCES

Croxton, F. E. and Cowden, D. J., *Applied General Statistics*, Chap. 10.
Dixon, W. J. and Massey, F. J. Jr., *Introduction to Statistical Analysis*, Chap. 3.
Freund, J. E., *Modern Elementary Statistics*, Chap. 5.
Kendall, M. G., *The Advanced Theory of Statistics*, 3rd ed., Vol. I, Chap. 3.
Lewis, E. E., *Methods of Statistical Analysis in Economics and Business*, Chap. 4.
Mills, F. C., *The Behavior of Prices*, Chap. 3, sec. 4.
Riggleman, J. R. and Frisbee, I. N., *Business Statistics*, 3rd ed., Chap. 9.
Rosander, A. C., *Elementary Principles of Statistics*, Chap. 4.
Spurr, W. A., Kellogg, L. S. and Smith, J. H., *Business and Economic Statistics*, Chap. 11.

Treloar, A. E., *Elements of Statistical Reasoning*, Chap. 4.
Waugh, A. E., *Elements of Statistical Method*, 3rd ed., Chap. 6.
Wilks, S. S., *Elementary Statistical Analysis*, Chap. 3.
Yule, G. U. and Kendall, M. G., *An Introduction to the Theory of Statistics*, 14th ed., Chap. 6.

The publishers and the dates of publication of the books named in chapter reference lists are given in the bibliography at the end of this volume.

CHAPTER 6

Introduction to Statistical Inference and Probability: Binomial and Normal Distributions

In the opening chapter of this book we emphasized the significant distinction between *sample* and *population*, and noted that the central concern of statistics, as a method of inquiry, is with inferences that go beyond the observations that make up a given sample. In dealing with the organization and description of frequency distributions in the three preceding chapters, only incidental mention has been made of populations and their characteristics. These chapters dealt, in the main, with the problems faced in reducing masses of quantitative data to orderly form and in defining the attributes of the resulting distributions. But the organization and description are but a beginning of the statistician's task. These steps merely pave the way for processes of generalization aimed at knowledge transcending the immediate observations. We turn now to this central problem.

Deduction and Induction

The logical process by which one arrives at generalizations from a study of particular cases is termed *induction*, as opposed to *deduction*, which involves the drawing of specialized conclusions from general propositions. The distinction is familiar, but its bearing on the logical issues we here face is so direct as to warrant a brief review of the subject.

The syllogism of *deductive* reasoning, running from major premise and minor premise to conclusion, takes such a form as the following (to cite an example that is sanctified by immemorial usage):

Major premise: All men are mortal
Minor premise: Socrates is a man
Conclusion: Socrates is mortal.

Or the following

Major premise: All the beans in this (specified) bag are white
Minor premise: These beans (i.e., a specific handful) are from this bag
Conclusion: These beans (the specific handful) are white.

In noting the necessary formal validity of such syllogisms, three points may be made:

1. There is complete internal consistency
2. The conclusions flow from the premises; they are consequences of universal propositions
3. In employing such a syllogism we are working with a closed system. All the relevant circumstances are before us, or are implied in the premises.

Inductive arguments corresponding, in subject matter, to the above illustrations would take the following form:

Premise: Socrates, Xenophon, Democritus (*et al*)—are men
Premise: Socrates, Xenophon, Democritus (*et al*)—are mortal
Conclusion: All men are mortal.

Or:

Premise: These beans (a specific handful) are from this (specified) bag
Premise: These beans (the specific handful) are white
Conclusion: All the beans in this (specified) bag are white.

One sharp contrast between the two modes of reasoning is to be emphasized. The conclusions of the deductive arguments are implied in the two statements that introduce each argument. If the premises are true, the conclusion may not be questioned. Nothing is added by the conclusion, although the chains of reasoning may be highly valuable in revealing truths that are only implicit in the premises. The conclusions of the inductive arguments, however, are broader than the premises. Something new has been added. If the conclusions are true, human knowledge has been extended. But there is a price to be paid for this potential extension of knowledge. Inductive reasoning may be fruitful, but it is dangerous. There can be no certainty that the conclusions of inductive reasoning are true. Invalid, indeed quite false, conclusions may be drawn by the inductive process.

Certain of the essential qualities of inductive reasoning are summarized by the following statements:

1. The conclusions of an inductive argument hold only in terms of probabilities, never with certainty. For such conclusions, by the very definition of induction, apply to cases not included in the observations. When all the cases to be covered by a conclusion are included in the observations, the conclusion ceases to be an induction. Accordingly, although induction is a highly fruitful means of adding to human knowledge, it is always hazardous. A leap in the dark is always involved when we apply conclusions to cases not yet observed.

2. There is a necessary reference to circumstances outside the facts inherent in the premises. We are not working with a closed system, but with an open system, only part of which has been directly observed. Many of the unobserved parts are relevant to our argument and conclusions. Facts not always set forth in the premises are relevant to our confidence in the conclusions, e.g., the method employed in making the observations that enter into the premises. (How were the beans making up the handful selected?) Since no comprehensive account of all the circumstances that bear upon an inductive argument is ever possible, one who accepts the conclusions of inductive reasoning places dependence on the personal discernment and integrity of the persons making the observations and completing the argument. One may with justice paraphrase the advertising slogan, and say, "The priceless ingredient of every induction is the honor and integrity of its maker." One might be tempted to go further and say that it is less dangerous to have a scoundrel among deductively reasoning mathematicians than to have a scoundrel among statisticians!

3. We must assume that there exists some uniformity in the system of facts to which the premises and the conclusion of inductive reasoning relate. Here is the rational justification for the leap in the dark that induction always entails. This assumption, which has been termed, variously, the uniformity of nature, the routine of experience, "a limitation to the amount of independent variety" found in nature, is always present as an unspoken premise in induction. If there were not some uniformity in natural processes, if nature were marked by utter chaos, no amount of piling-up of evidence could justify an induction. We could say nothing about conditions beyond the limits of observation. It is clear that we must go beyond the immediate evidence in accepting this assumption of uniformity. That compound of judgment and of accumulated but unspecified experience that we use in distinguishing the "rational" from the "irrational," and which may give us confidence in the assumption of uniformity in a given situation, contains *a priori* elements. It is here that deduction (which is never really divorced from induction) enters into our empirical reasoning.

4. The verification of induction calls for objective reference. The formal validity of deduction (e.g., of a chain of mathematical reasoning) rests purely on internal consistency. "Mathematical truth," it has been said, "is the absence of contradiction." But the conclusions of inductive reasoning must be tested finally against observation; if they stand, it must be on the basis of consistency with the facts of nature in the given sphere.

Statistical Inference

The statements just made relate to induction as a general logical process. Our concern here is with *statistical induction*, or *statistical inference*. Such inference, which involves the generalization of statistical results, is akin to the more general process, in all respects covered by the four summary statements. It has, in addition, distinctive characteristics of its own. The problems with which it deals take two forms—*estimation*, and the *testing of hypotheses*.

Estimation. The problem of estimation may be put in the following form: A statistical measurement—an arithmetic mean, a standard deviation, a coefficient of variation—has been derived from the study of sample data drawn from a given population. At an earlier point the reader was introduced to the concept of a "population," as the statistician employs that term. In general, let us recall, a sample is assumed to have been drawn not from a finite population—the population that might be covered by actual enumeration—but from the infinite population, or universe, that would be generated if the forces or system of causes that brought this sample into being were to operate without limit. A population may be an aggregate of persons, things, or measurements; R. A. Fisher speaks of a population of "possibilities," referring to the possible results of an experiment many times repeated. The measurement derived from the sample—such a measurement is termed a *statistic*—defines some characteristic of that sample. The task of inference, in such a case, is to provide us with an estimate of the measurement defining the corresponding characteristic of the population. The measurement relating to the population is termed a *parameter*. Such an estimate may specify a particular value of the parameter (this is *point-estimation*). Alternatively, this form of inference may take the form of a statement defining limits within which the parameter may be expected to lie, together with a measure, in probability terms, of the reliability of this conclusion (this is *interval-estimation*). A significant feature of interval-estimation is this: The uncertainty that attaches to the conclusions of all inductions holds for the conclusion of such an inference, but in basing estimates upon statistical data we are able to provide a measure of the degree of uncertainty attaching to the conclusion. How this is done will be our concern in the following chapter. At this point we reiterate: Our certain knowledge is limited to *statistics* —to measurements of the characteristics of samples. We use this knowledge to the best of our ability to provide us with approximations to the true *parameters* which we can never know.

The other general statements made about inductive reasoning apply, also, to statistical inference. The assumption of uniformity in nature, or of a limited amount of independent variety in nature, is usually spoken of in the statistical world as the stability of large numbers. Regularities in birth rates and death rates, in price movements, and in seasonal processes are familiar examples of such stability.

The uniformity that statistical stability indicates is, of course, of supreme practical importance. If we could not be assured of a certain degree of stability in the results obtained from successive samples it would be quite invalid to generalize from the examination of a limited number of cases. No weight would attach to any study except one covering the entire universe of things or measurements composing the given population. Yet such all-inclusive studies are practically impossible. Index numbers of prices, of wages, of living costs, and of production; monthly counts of the labor force; surveys of corporate profits and of consumer spending —all must of necessity be based on the study of samples, and all must postulate stability. Therefore, when we generalize such a measure as an index of wholesale prices we do so on some such assumption as this: It is reasonable to suppose that, in the larger population to which this result is to be applied, there exists uniformity with respect to the characteristic we have measured. As a result of this uniformity we should expect that inferences based upon successive samples of the same size drawn from this population would belong to a family with common, stable, and definable characteristics. On this assumption we are able to attach measures of reliability to statistical inferences.

It is evident that in making this assumption, in saying "It is reasonable to suppose . . . ," we are introducing a hypothesis that is incapable of complete verification by purely statistical methods. There is thus, as we have already pointed out, an *a priori* element in every statistical induction. The statistical conclusion can never stand completely on its own feet. It must be endorsed by reason and judgment if it is to carry conviction.

The problem of statistical inference, in the words of Oskar Anderson, is that of so utilizing samples as to arrive at the best possible approximation to the characteristics of universes. In the task of estimation that is here entailed we must assume that these universes are stable, and that all their attributes are stable. Of course, an attribute of such a stable universe may not be exactly determined from the attribute of a single sample. However, measures defining the attributes of numerous samples drawn from the same universe (i.e., the same parent population) will be distributed in a systematic fashion about the universe parameter of which they are estimates. The precise determination of the characteristics of such a distribution of estimates is essential to the determination of the reliability of estimates. The power of statistical techniques has grown as our detailed knowledge of such distributions has expanded.

Tests of hypotheses. In testing hypotheses, the other form of statistical inference, there is also reference to a "population," but here the task is that of determining whether a sample yielding a given *statistic* (e.g., a stated arithmetic mean) could have been drawn from a population for which the corresponding *parameter* is known, or is given by hypothesis. Is the difference between the actual statistic and this parameter one that the chance fluctuations of sampling might bring about, or is the difference too great to be attributed to sampling fluctuations? This is the form taken by most tests of hypotheses, or *tests of significance*. The question is one that is always answered in terms of probability. If the probability that chance factors could account for the observed difference is very slight, the hypothesis is rejected. The difference is significant. If the probability is great enough to justify an explanation in terms of chance, we say that the observations are not inconsistent with the hypothesis. The difference is not significant. The hypothesis is not rejected.

These rather abstract statements will become much more definite when we discuss concrete instances of statistical inference, in Chapters 7 and 8. At this stage we would emphasize the following in summary of part of the preceding argument:

The conclusions of all inductive reasoning hold in terms of probability. The logician Charles S. Peirce used the words "uncertain inference" to describe induction—a suggestive phrase that points to a key aspect of induction.

Statistical inference, which is concerned with the generalization of quantitative results, is distinctive in that it is possible in such inference to provide measures of the probabilities attaching to conclusions. This is true whether the conclusions are estimates of limits within which population parameters fall, or statements relating to tests of significance. The task of the statistician in this major field of statistical endeavor is to provide the tools for defining these probabilities, and to set up working rules for the use of these tools.

It is clear that the concept of probability lies at the very heart of the theories and practices of modern statistics. We turn now to a discussion of some elementary principles of probability. A detailed treatment of the theory of probability would carry us beyond the limits of the present volume. The discussion that follows is presented only as an introduction to the subject, with emphasis on certain ideas and distributions having a special bearing on statistical procedures.

Notation. For convenience of reference we here list the symbols that will be introduced in this chapter. Explanations will be given in the text.

p: the probability of the successful outcome of an event

q: the probability of the unsuccessful outcome of an event

n: the number of ways in which an event can occur; the number of events in a trial

$n!$: factorial n; the product of the integers from 1 to n

μ (mu): the mean of a population

μ': the mean of a population of relative frequencies

σ' (sigma): the standard deviation of a population of relative frequencies

y: an ordinate of a frequency curve

y_0: the maximum ordinate of a frequency curve

Elementary Theorems in Probability

If an event can occur in n mutually exclusive and equally likely ways, a of which are to be considered as successful and b as unsuccessful, the probability p of a successful outcome may be written

$$p = \frac{a}{n}$$

and the probability q of an unsuccessful outcome may be written

$$q = \frac{b}{n}$$

It will be understood that the words "successful" and "unsuccessful" are used in a neutral sense. (Alternatively we might say that we include in the a group only outcomes marked by the possession of a certain property, in the b group outcomes marked by the absence of this property. But it will be convenient to use the traditional terms.) Since the sum of the successful and unsuccessful outcomes is equal to the total number of events, we have

$$a + b = n$$

Dividing by n,

$$\frac{a}{n} + \frac{b}{n} = 1$$

so that

$$p + q = 1$$

A probability, therefore, may be written as a ratio. The numerator of the fraction corresponding to this ratio represents the number of successful (or unsuccessful) outcomes, while the denominator represents the total number of possible outcomes. If the outcome or outcomes represented by a should be, in fact, impossible, this ratio would be zero. On the other hand, if only the outcome or outcomes represented by a were possible, a would equal n, and the ratio would be unity. The scale of probability thus extends from zero, representing the impossible, to unity, representing certainty.

The idea that a "probability" corresponds to a *frequency ratio* is one that is generally accepted today. However, for purposes of mathematical reasoning it is desirable that the concept have a precision and a generality that would be denied it if it were tied to empirically observable ratios. These purposes are served if a probability number be regarded, in Cramér's words, as "the conceptual counterpart" of an empirical frequency ratio. A probability is, in the last analysis, an abstract conception. Perhaps no die could be so flawlessly constructed that the probability of getting a 6 spot on a given throw is exactly 1/6. But we may conceive of, and build theorems on, an abstract entity for which p is exactly

1/6. It is these abstract entities, and the abstract probabilities attaching to them, that provide the foundation of the theory of probability. This theory in turn provides the conceptual framework for the study of the results of random experiments which are the direct concern of modern statistics.

If we toss a coin there are two possible outcomes, the turning up of a tail and the turning up of a head. If we regard these two possibilities as equally likely (as they are if we think of the conceptual counterparts of the frequency ratios we should get from numerous tossings) we have, as the probability of a tail

$$p = \tfrac{1}{2}$$

and of a head

$$q = \tfrac{1}{2}$$

If we roll a die, regarding a 6 spot as a favorable outcome,

$$p = \tfrac{1}{6}$$

and

$$q = \tfrac{5}{6}$$

If a card be drawn from a pack of 52 the chance of drawing the ace of spades is $\tfrac{1}{52}$, of failing in that endeavor, $\tfrac{51}{52}$.

The addition of probabilities. What is the chance of securing *either* an ace of spades *or* a two of spades in a single draw from a pack of 52 cards? *In such a case, where any one of several mutually exclusive outcomes will be considered favorable, the probability of a success is the sum of the separate probabilities.* In this example

$$p = \tfrac{1}{52} + \tfrac{1}{52} = \tfrac{1}{26}$$

The chance of drawing either a heart or a spade from a pack of playing cards is given by

$$p = \tfrac{13}{52} + \tfrac{13}{52} = \tfrac{1}{2}$$

The multiplication of probabilities. Two events are said to be independent when the outcome of one does not affect the outcome of the other. Thus the result of one throw of a die does not, presumably, affect the result of the next toss. *The probability of a compound event (i.e., a combination of two events, independent of one another) is the product of the probabilities of the separate events.* Thus the chance of securing an ace, followed by a 2 spot, in two successive throws of a die, is given by

$$p = \tfrac{1}{6} \times \tfrac{1}{6} = \tfrac{1}{36}$$

In computing the probability of a given outcome it is frequently necessary both to multiply and to add probabilities. For example, we wish to determine the chance of securing the total 5 from two dice thrown simultaneously. We may label the dice *a* and *b* to distinguish them. This total may be secured from any one of the four following combinations:

Die a	Die b
1	4
2	3
3	2
4	1

The chance of securing an ace with die a is $\frac{1}{6}$, of securing a 4 with die b is $\frac{1}{6}$. The chance of the two in combination is $\frac{1}{36}$. Similarly, the probability of each of the other three combinations is $\frac{1}{36}$. But any one of these four results will give a total of 5, and will be considered successful. Hence

$$p = \tfrac{1}{36} + \tfrac{1}{36} + \tfrac{1}{36} + \tfrac{1}{36} = \tfrac{1}{9}$$

We have in this example answered the question: What is the probability of securing exactly 5 in the toss of two dice? We might put the question: What is the chance of securing *at least* 5 in the toss of two dice? In this case a total of 5 or more will be considered a favorable outcome. Just as in the preceding example, we may work out the probability of securing each of the results that will be accepted as successful. The following summary indicates the probability of each of these totals:

Probability of throwing 12 with two dice $= \dfrac{1}{36}$

"   "   "   11   "   "   " $= \dfrac{2}{36}$

"   "   "   10   "   "   " $= \dfrac{3}{36}$

"   "   "   9   "   "   " $= \dfrac{4}{36}$

"   "   "   8   "   "   " $= \dfrac{5}{36}$

"   "   "   7   "   "   " $= \dfrac{6}{36}$

"   "   "   6   "   "   " $= \dfrac{5}{36}$

"   "   "   5   "   "   " $= \dfrac{4}{36}$

Sum of above probabilities $= \dfrac{30}{36}$

The chance of throwing at least 5 in the toss of two dice is, therefore, $\frac{30}{36}$ or $\frac{5}{6}$.

The Binomial Expansion and the Measurement of Probabilities. It is possible to express certain of these fundamental relations in a generalized form. A simple illustration may be employed to exemplify the derivation of the desired general expression.

If two coins are tossed simultaneously there are four possible outcomes

a	b	a	b	a	b	a	b
T	T	T	H	H	T	H	H

(The two coins are represented, respectively, by the letters a and b.) In the first of these possible outcomes we get two tails (TT). This, which we may here regard as two successes, represents the compound probability $p \cdot p = p^2$. In the present case, where $p = \frac{1}{2}$, the probability of this compound event is $\frac{1}{2} \cdot \frac{1}{2} = \frac{1}{4}$. The fourth of the four possible outcomes (HH) represents two failures (i.e., no tail with either coin). The probability of this result is also $\frac{1}{4}$ $(= q \cdot q = \frac{1}{2} \cdot \frac{1}{2})$. Each of the two other outcomes (the second and third) represents a combination of one success (T) and one failure (H). The probability of the second of these combinations, TH, is $\frac{1}{4}$ $(= p \cdot q = \frac{1}{2} \cdot \frac{1}{2})$; the probability of the third outcome, HT, is $\frac{1}{4}$ $(= q \cdot p = \frac{1}{2} \cdot \frac{1}{2})$. For the probability of such mixed result, one success and one failure (the order being here of no concern), we must add the probabilities of the separate outcomes, getting, in the present case, $2pq$, or $\frac{1}{2}$.

The generalization of this process of estimating the probabilities of various combinations of independent events, when the probabilities of these events are known, rests upon the fact that the probabilities of the several combinations are given by the successive terms of a binomial expansion. Thus, for the simple case of two events, we have

$$(p + q)^2 = p^2 + 2pq + q^2$$

The student will note that p^2 is the probability of two successes as has been demonstrated above; $2pq$ is the probability of a combination of one success and one failure; q^2 is the probability of two failures. For the case in which p (e.g., the probability of throwing a tail) $= q = \frac{1}{2}$, the probabilities of the several different outcomes are given by

$$(\tfrac{1}{2} + \tfrac{1}{2})^2 = \tfrac{1}{4} + \tfrac{1}{2} + \tfrac{1}{4}$$

If three coins, represented by the letters a, b, and c, are tossed simultaneously, we have eight possible outcomes

| abc | abc | abc | abc | abc | abc | abc | abc |
| TTT | TTH | THH | THT | HTT | HTH | HHT | HHH |

A count of the possible outcomes will show that the chance of getting 3 tails in a single toss of 3 coins is 1/8. The chance of getting 2 tails (combined with 1 head) is 3/8; the chance of getting 1 tail (combined with 2 heads) is 3/8; the chance of getting no tails is 1/8. Here, since we have three independent events, the exponent of the binomial is 3. The probabilities of the several possible outcomes are given by the successive terms of

$$(p + q)^3 = p^3 + 3p^2q + 3pq^2 + q^3$$

With $p = q = \frac{1}{2}$, we have

$$(\tfrac{1}{2} + \tfrac{1}{2})^3 = \tfrac{1}{8} + \tfrac{3}{8} + \tfrac{3}{8} + \tfrac{1}{8}$$

These are the probabilities shown by direct count in the example cited above.

This procedure applies generally. It may be shown that if there are n independent chance events, the probability of a "successful" outcome of a given event being p and the probability of an "unsuccessful" outcome being, q the probabilities of n successes, of n-1 successes, of n-2 successes, etc. are given by successive terms in the binomial expansion $(p + q)^n$.

If we wish to know not the separate probabilities but the probable frequencies of the various outcomes in a given number of trials, these may be computed from the expression

$$N(p+ q)^n \tag{6.1}$$

where N represents the number of trials and n the number of independent events in a trial. Thus if there are 200 trials and there are two independent events in each trial, the probable frequencies are given by

$$200(p + q)^2 = 200(p^2 + 2pq + q^2)$$

With $p = q = \frac{1}{2}$ this gives us

$$200\left(\frac{1}{4}\right) + 200\left(\frac{1}{2}\right) + 200\left(\frac{1}{4}\right) = 50 + 100 + 50$$

which indicates the probable frequencies of 2 successes, 1 success, and no successes.

If there are three independent events, the probable frequencies in N trials are determined from the binomial expansion of

$$N(p + q)^3$$

If N equals 200, we have

$$200(p^3 + 3p^2q + 3pq^2 + q^3)$$

If p equals $\frac{1}{2}$, we have

$$200\left(\frac{1}{8}\right) + 200\left(\frac{3}{8}\right) + 200\left(\frac{3}{8}\right) + 200\left(\frac{1}{8}\right) = 25 + 75 + 75 + 25$$

These terms indicate, in order, the probable frequencies of 3 successes, 2 successes, 1 success, and no successes. The total frequencies secured by carrying through the process of multiplication will be equal to the number of trials, for all possible outcomes are covered by the expansion.

Thus when we know in advance[1] the probabilities attaching to similar but independent events, we may determine the probable frequencies of any given number of successes or failures. This is true whether p and q be equal or unequal. It is necessary only that p and q remain constant. There is here a fact of great significance in the development of statistical theory.

The Binomial Distribution

Certain points of importance may be made clear by comparing some experimental results with the theoretical frequencies given by the binomial expansion. Twelve dice were thrown a number of times. Each 4, 5, or 6 spot appearing was considered to be a success, while a 1, 2, or 3 spot was a failure. (In a typical throw we might have the following spots up: 3, 1, 5, 1, 2, 4, 4, 6, 3, 2, 3, 5. In this lot there are five successes, and the result is so tallied.) In a classical example recorded by W. F. R. Weldon[2] twelve dice were thrown in this way 4,096 times, a success being defined as above. The results are recorded in Col. (2) of Table 6.1, and the distribution is shown in Fig. 6.1. By computation we find the arithmetic mean and the standard deviation of this distribution to be, respectively, 6.139 and 1.712.

Let us compare with these results those we might expect, from given conditions, with 12 flawless (i.e., evenly balanced) dice.

---

[1] A distinction is sometimes drawn between *a priori* probabilities of the type described above, which are assumed to be known apart from experience, and *empirical* probabilities, which are derived from observation. As an example of the latter type we have, as the probability that a man aged 35 will live 10 years, the ratio 74,173/81,822. This is based upon the American Experience Table of Mortality, which shows that of 81,822 men living at age 35, there are 74,173 living 10 years later. (This particular table, we should note, is now somewhat out-dated, as a result of recent improvements in mortality experience.) Since the idea of *a priori* probabilities is a somewhat nebulous one, it would be preferable to distinguish between *conceptual* probabilities and *empirical* probabilities, the former being the conceptual counterparts of the frequency ratios that provide measures of empirical probabilities. (Cf. Cramér, Refs. 22, 23 and Neyman, Refs. 118, 119).

[2] Cited by F. Y. Edgeworth, *Encycl. Brit.*, 11th ed., Vol. XXII, 394.

Twelve dice were thrown each time, hence we are dealing with 12 independent events. There were 4,096 trials. Since either a 4, 5, or 6 is considered a success, $p = q = \frac{1}{2}$.

For the terms in the binomial expansion we have

$$(p + q)^n = p^n + np^{n-1}q + \frac{n(n-1)}{1 \cdot 2} p^{n-2}q^2$$
$$+ \frac{n(n-1)(n-2)}{1 \cdot 2 \cdot 3} p^{n-3}q^3 + \ldots + q^n$$

In the present case we have

$$4,096\left(\frac{1}{2} + \frac{1}{2}\right)^{12}$$

Expanding

$$4,096 \left(\frac{1}{4,096} + \frac{12}{4,096} + \frac{66}{4,096} + \frac{220}{4,096} + \frac{495}{4,096} + \frac{792}{4,096} + \frac{924}{4,096}\right.$$
$$\left. + \frac{792}{4,096} + \frac{495}{4,096} + \frac{220}{4,096} + \frac{66}{4,096} + \frac{12}{4,096} + \frac{1}{4,096}\right)$$

Completing the indicated multiplication we have the theoretical frequencies of the various possible successes in 4,096 throws of 12 dice. These are shown in column (3) of Table 6.1.

The distribution of the theoretical frequencies is shown in Fig. 6.1, with that of the observed frequencies. The relationship

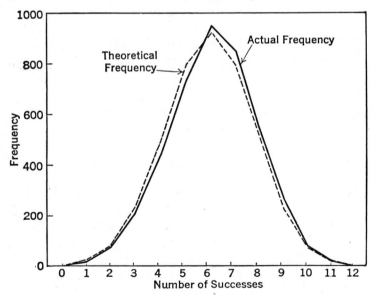

FIG. 6.1. A Comparison of Actual and Theoretical Frequencies in a Dice-Rolling Experiment.

of the two distributions appears to be close. (What is a "close" relationship will be considered at later points.)

TABLE 6–1

Comparison of Actual and Theoretical Frequencies in Dice-Rolling Experiment

(1) Number of successes	(2) Observed frequencies	(3) Theoretical frequencies
0	0	1
1	7	12
2	60	66
3	198	220
4	430	495
5	731	792
6	948	924
7	847	792
8	536	495
9	257	220
10	71	66
11	11	12
12	0	1
	4,096	4,096

The distribution defined by the entries in columns (1) and (3) of Table 6.1, and shown graphically by the broken line in Fig. 6.1, is a *binomial distribution*, one of central importance in statistical theory and in the applications of statistical methods. The general formula for the binomial distribution is

$$y = \frac{n!}{x!(n-x)!} p^x q^{n-x} \tag{6.2}$$

where n is the number of independent events in a trial, p is the probability of success in a single event, q is the probability of a failure, x is a stated number of successes, and y is the probability of obtaining the stated number of successes. The symbol $n!$ stands for "factorial n", which is the product of the integers from 1 to n; $x!$ is factorial x. To exemplify the use of this formula: we wish to determine the probability of obtaining just 3 heads n a single trial consisting of the toss of 4 coins. Substituting in the above equation the given values (i.e., for n substitute 4; for x, 3; for p, 1/2; for q, 1/2), we have

$$y = \frac{4 \cdot 3 \cdot 2 \cdot 1}{(3 \cdot 2 \cdot 1)(1)} \{(\tfrac{1}{2})^3 \cdot (\tfrac{1}{2})^1\} = \frac{24}{6} (\tfrac{1}{8} \cdot \tfrac{1}{2}) = 4/16$$

The probability of getting 3 heads in a toss of 4 coins is 4/16.

Certain of the characteristics of the binomial distribution may be briefly summarized:

It is a discrete distribution. Its graphic representation is marked by discontinuities of the type shown in Fig. 6.1.

Its form depends, in a particular case, on the parameters p and n (q, being equal to $1 - p$, is not counted as a separate parameter). The parameter n is always a positive integer.

The distribution will be symmetrical if p and q are equal, asymmetrical if p and q are unequal. However, as n increases, p and q (unequal) being unchanged, the degree of skewness decreases sharply. This approach to symmetry as n increases is graphically portrayed in Fig. 6.2. Here we have plotted the distributions derived by expanding (0.8 + 0.2), i.e., $(q + p)$ with n equal, successively, to 6, 12, and 48. The frequencies shown on the y-axis are percentages of the total, for each distribution. With increasing values of n there is a notable increase in symmetry, even though p and q

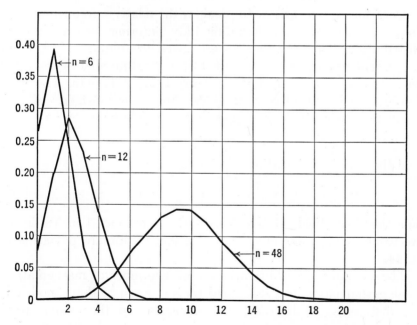

FIG. 6.2. Binomial Distributions. Graphic Representation of the Binomial $(0.8 + 0.2)^n$ for $n = 6$, $n = 12$, and $n = 48$.

are far from equal. There is also apparent a decline in the discontinuities that are so marked with low values of n. This point will call for further comment in the next section.

For the mean of a binomial distribution we have

$$\mu = np \tag{6.3}$$

The variance of a binomial distribution is given by

$$\sigma^2 = npq \tag{6.4}$$

and the standard deviation by

$$\sigma = \sqrt{npq} \tag{6.5}$$

Substituting in the above equations the values of n, p, and q for the theoretical distribution represented in Table 6.1, we have

$$\mu = 12 \times 0.5 = 6$$

and

$$\sigma = \sqrt{12 \times 0.5 \times 0.5} = \sqrt{3} = 1.732$$

These may be compared with the mean of the observed frequencies, which is 6.139, and with the standard deviation of these frequencies, which is 1.712. The differences may reflect the influence of sampling fluctuations, or imperfections in the dice actually used by Weldon. At a later point we shall discuss methods by which these two effects may be distinguished.

Occasion often arises to deal with relative frequencies, or frequency ratios, when handling data entering into a binomial distribution. Thus the "successes" listed in column (1) of Table 6-1, might be measured as ratios to the total number of events in each throw of 12 dice, i.e., as 0/12, 1/12, 2/12, etc. The class frequencies would, of course, be the same. The mean (μ') of such frequency ratios binomially distributed, would be given by

$$\mu' = p$$

and the standard deviation (σ') by

$$\sigma' = \sqrt{\frac{pq}{n}} \tag{6.6}$$

For the theoretical relative frequencies represented in Table 6.1 we would have, therefore, a mean of 0.5, a standard deviation of 0.144.

The binomial distribution is one of a number of mathematical models that enter into statistical theory. Each of these models is an abstract generalization; its attributes and the axioms from which its qualities may be deduced may be defined with precision. These abstract conceptions may be built up without reference to events in the real world, and may have no bearing on such events. Of course, it may be found that natural events in some spheres correspond in some degree to a model thus built up. In the latter case, the model may contribute materially to an understanding of these events and to generalizations concerning such events. As the preceding example will have suggested, distributions of data in a number of fields correspond closely to the model provided by the binomial expansion. Such models, accordingly, provide working tools of high value in dealing with observational material.

The Normal Distribution

We may return to a consideration of the curve in Fig. 6.1 which represents the theoretical frequencies in the dice-throwing experiments. It is a perfectly symmetrical 12-sided polygon, the number of sides (excluding the base) corresponding to the number of independent events in the particular problem considered. With 6 events we should have a 6-sided figure, with 20 events a 20-sided figure, and so on. It is obvious that, as n increases, the number of sides to the polygon increasing correspondingly in number, the graph representing the expansion of the binomial $(p + q)^n$ approaches more and more closely a smooth curve.

This approach to continuity in binomial distributions as n increases will be found whether p and q be equal, as in the distributions represented in Fig. 6.1, or unequal, as in the distributions represented in Fig. 6.2. Moreover, if p and q be unequal, the skewness marking distributions corresponding to low values of n will decline as n increases. We have already noted (Fig. 6.2) the movement toward symmetry as n increased from 6, to 12, to 48, with p and q constant. As n approaches infinity, such a graph approaches a smooth, symmetrical curve. The limit which the binomial distribution thus approaches is called the *normal distribution*. Its graphic representation, which is called the *normal curve of error*, is shown in Fig. 6.5, on page 158.

The normal distribution has long occupied a central place in the theory of statistics and in applications of this theory. It was first defined over 200 years ago by De Moivre, who recognized it as a continuous form marking the limit of the discrete binomial distribution. It was independently rediscovered by C. F. Gauss and P. S. Laplace in the early years of the nineteenth century. The rediscovery, which came from work on the distribution of errors of observation, led to great emphasis in the succeeding half century on the normal "law" as a model to which distributions of observations on all natural phenomena were supposed to conform. Correction of this excessive emphasis (a correction largely due to Karl Pearson and his co-workers in the Galton Laboratory of the University of London) served to place the normal distribution in proper perspective, as one among many distribution types occurring in nature. However, as Kendall remarks, "as the importance of the (normal) distribution declined in the observational sphere it grew in the theoretical, particularly in the theory of sampling." And as the theory of sampling has developed, to become the fundamental concern of statisticians, the normal distribution has retained its place as one of the pillars of modern statistics.

In writing the equation to this curve we express the frequency y as a function of the variable x. For convenience, the origin of the independent variable is taken at the mean; a given x stands, therefore, for a stated value of that variable expressed as a deviation from the mean x. This equation is written in several forms. The expression

$$y = \frac{1}{\sigma\sqrt{2\pi}} \, e^{-x^2/2\sigma^2} \qquad (6.7)$$

is a basic form, relating to a curve having unit area. In this equation σ is the standard deviation of the given normal distribution, π is the constant 3.14159, and e is the constant 2.71828 (the base of the system of natural logarithms). When we say that the curve has unit area we mean that the total frequency, N, is equated to 1, for convenience in representation and calculation. To obtain ordinates for a particular distribution, the ordinates given by formula (6.7) are multiplied by N. The equation to a normal curve corresponding to a particular distribution is thus given by

$$y = \frac{N}{\sigma\sqrt{2\pi}} \, e^{-x^2/2\sigma^2} \qquad (6.8)$$

We may note that the quantity $\dfrac{N}{\sigma\sqrt{2\pi}}$ in formula (6-8) is equal to the maximum ordinate (y_0) of the normal curve corresponding to a distribution of stated total frequency (N) and stated standard deviation (σ). Thus if N is 1000 and σ is 10, we should have

$$y_0 = \frac{1000}{10\sqrt{2\pi}}$$

Substituting 3.14159 for π we derive the value 39.894 for y_0. Having y_0 we may use the following form of the equation to the normal curve

$$y = y_0 e^{-x^2/2\sigma^2} \tag{6.9}$$

Thus the ordinate at any stated distance x from the maximum ordinate may be determined by multiplying the maximum ordinate by the quantity $e^{-x^2/2\sigma^2}$. (In a normal distribution mean, median and mode coincide. The maximum ordinate is, therefore, the ordinate at that point on the X-scale at which these three identical values fall). An ordinate 20 units above the mean, on the X-scale, would, for the above distribution, have the value

$$y = 39.894 \times 2.71828^{-400/200}$$

$$= 39.894 \times \frac{1}{2.71828^2}$$

$$= 5.399*$$

Finally, we may have an equation that refers to a curve of unit area, and with deviations from the mean of the X-variable expressed not in the original X-units, as in formulas (6.7), (6.8), and (6.9), but in units of the standard deviation of X. That is, the unit of measurement on the X-scale will be x/σ, where x is the deviation $(X - \mu)$. We obtain then an equation like (6.7) above, but with σ equal to 1. That is

$$y = \frac{1}{\sqrt{2\pi}}\ e^{-x^2/2} \tag{6.10}$$

This gives us an expression for the normal distribution in standard form, with zero mean, unit standard deviation, and unit area. Reversion to the original units of measurement for any variable, and to absolute frequencies, may be accomplished by simple adjustments, using given values of σ and N.

The curve plotted in Fig. 6.5 on p. 158, which shows frequencies rising to a maximum at the mean (which is also the mode and median) and declining symmetrically for values of x above the mean, is called the *normal frequency function*. The corresponding cumulative distribution (cp. Fig. 3.13, p. 68), with frequencies cumulated upward, is termed the *normal distribution function*.

---

* Tabled values greatly facilitate the calculation of ordinates. See Pearson and Hartley, Ref. 126; Fisher and Yates, Ref. 51.

This is shown graphically in Fig. 6.3. The cumulated frequency is,

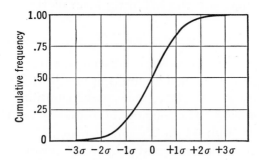

FIG. 6.3. The Cumulative Normal Curve:
The Normal Distribution Function.

of course, zero at the lower end of the range, N (or unity, for the standardized normal form) at the upper end.

Properties of the Normal Distribution. Some of the major properties of this distribution have already been noted. The distribution is symmetrical (skewness = 0) and continuous. The range extends theoretically from an x of $-\infty$ to an x of $+\infty$. Actually, 0.997 of the area under the curve falls between ordinates at $x = -3\sigma$ and $x = +3\sigma$. The general distribution is completely defined by the parameters μ and σ. That is, when the location of the mean has been established (as a base from which x is measured) and the standard deviation has been specified, the distribution of frequencies for a curve having unit area (i.e., with $N=1$) may be determined. (See formula 6.7 above.) To determine the absolute frequencies corresponding to a specific set of observations the quantity N must be known, in addition to μ and σ (see equation 6.8 above).

If the normal curve be regarded geometrically, we may note that points of inflection occur at $\mu + \sigma$ and at $\mu - \sigma$.

The usual representation of the normal curve of error in its standard form gives the impression that all normal frequency curves are exactly alike (apart from variations in N). It is useful to consider the effect on the curve of changes in the two parameters μ and σ (N being constant). The effect of a change in μ is merely to shift the curve along the x-scale, with no change in form. A change in σ affects the representation on both scales, and thus modifies the relative proportions of the plotted curve. The effect on the x-scale is obvious. But the y-scale is also affected, because the value of the maximum ordinate in a curve of unit area depends

on the value of σ (for $y_0 = \dfrac{1}{\sigma\sqrt{2\pi}}$). The effect of varying σ from

6 to 10, and then to 20, with N constant at unity and with μ constant at 0, is shown by the curves plotted in Fig. 6.4.

FIG. 6.4. Comparison of Normal Frequency Curves with Varying Standard Deviations.

The equation to the normal curve of error may be derived in several ways. It can be obtained as the equation to the limit curve of the binomial distribution. Gauss's deduction of the error equation may be found in standard works on least squares. We have given the equation here without proof. At this stage the student will, perhaps, accept this model on an intuitive basis, as the limit of the binomial distribution. We may, however, throw light on reasons for the emergence of the normal distribution in varying observational fields by noting four basic conditions that must prevail among the factors affecting the individual events that make up a given population, if the distribution of observations is to be normal:

1. The causal forces must be numerous and of approximately equal weight.
2. These forces must be the same over the universe from which the observations are drawn (although their incidence will vary from event to event). This is the condition of homogeneity.
3. The forces affecting individual events must be independent of one another.
4. The operation of the causal forces must be such that deviations above the population mean are balanced as to magnitude and number by deviations below the mean. This is the condition of symmetry.

Areas Under the Normal Curve. Practical applications of our knowledge of the normal distribution are greatly facilitated by prepared tables giving ordinates of the standardized normal curve for stated values of x/σ, and specifying fractional parts of the total area under the curve that lie between ordinates erected at stated distances from the mean. By simple computations these standard values of ordinates and areas may be modified for the N and the σ of any given distribution. Greater use is made of the tabulated areas than of the tabulated ordinates. Selected values from a table of areas are given in Table 6.2. The more detailed measurements needed for accurate computation are given in Appendix Table I. Areas as well as ordinates of the normal curve are given in Pearson and Hartley (Ref. 126) and Fisher and Yates (Ref. 51).

TABLE 6–2

Areas under the Normal Curve, in Terms of Abscissa
(Giving fractional parts of the total area between y_o and ordinates erected at varying distances from y_o)

x/σ	a	x/σ	a
0.0	.00000	2.0	.47725
0.1	.03983	2.1	.48214
0.2	.07926	2.2	.48610
0.3	.11791	2.3	.48928
0.4	.15542	2.4	.49180
0.5	.19146	2.5	.49379
		2.5758	.49500
0.6	.22575	2.6	.49534
0.7	.25804	2.7	.49653
0.8	.28814	2.8	.49744
0.9	.31594	2.9	.49813
1.0	.34134	3.0	.49865
1.1	.36433	3.1	.49903
1.2	.38493	3.2	.49931
1.3	.40320	3.3	.49952
1.4	.41924	3.4	.49966
1.5	.43319	3.5	.49977
1.6	.44520	3.6	.49984
1.7	.45543	3.7	.49989
1.8	.46407	3.8	.49993
1.9	.47128	3.9	.49995
1.96	.47500	4.0	.49997

Since the normal curve is symmetrical about the maximum ordinate, the values given in Table 6-2 apply to observations on either side of the mean. In using such a table, deviations from the mean are first expressed in units of the standard deviation. (The term *normal deviate* is applied to such a quantity, that is, to a deviation from the mean of a normal distribution expressed in units of the standard deviation of that distribution.) The proportion of the total area lying between any two ordinates may then be readily determined. For example: What proportion of the cases in a normal distribution lies between the maximum ordinate and an ordinate erected at a distance from the mean equal to $+ 1\sigma$? Reading down the x/σ column to 1.0, we find the value .34134 opposite it. This, in ratio form, is the proportion of cases falling within the limits indicated. Expressing this ratio as a percentage, we have 34.134 percent as the answer to our question.

Fig. 6.5 shows the relation of this area (the shaded area A) to

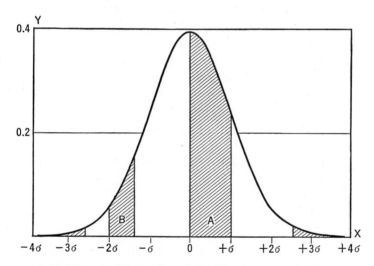

FIG. 6.5. An Illustration of the Measurement of Areas Under the Normal Curve.

the total area under the curve. (The ordinate values measured on the y-scale of Fig. 6.5 are those given by the standard formula (6.10), when $N = 1$ and $\sigma = 1$.)

What proportion of the total number of cases in a normal frequency distribution will fall between an ordinate erected at a distance from the mean equal to $- 1.4\sigma$ and one erected at $- 2\sigma$?

From the table we find that 41.924 percent of the total area will lie between y_0 and the ordinate at -1.4σ; 47.725 percent will lie between y_0 and the ordinate at -2σ. The difference, 5.801 percent, will fall between the ordinates at -1.4σ and at -2σ. This may be converted into actual frequencies by taking this proportion of the total number of cases in the given distribution. The shaded segment B in Fig. 6.5 represents the area thus marked off.

For certain purposes we wish to know the proportion of the total number of cases deviating by a stated amount or more *in either direction* from the mean of a normal distribution. If we wish to know the proportion of all cases deviating from the mean by 1.96σ or more, we must add to the area between $+1.96\sigma$ and the upper limit of the curve the area between -1.96σ and the lower limit of the curve. Each of these areas equals $0.50000 - 0.47500$, or 0.025. The percentage of cases deviating from the mean by $+1.96\sigma$ or more is 2.5; the percentage deviating by -1.96σ or more is 2.5. The percentage deviating above or below the mean by 1.96σ or more is 5.0. Similarly, it may be determined from the entries in Table 6-2 that just one percent of all the cases in a normal distribution will deviate from the mean, positively or negatively, by 2.5758σ, or more. This "one percent" area is represented by the sum of the shaded portions at the two tails of Fig. 6.5. The ordinates defining the inside limits of these segments are erected at $+2.5758\sigma$ and at -2.5758σ, while the outer limits are at infinity.

Special significance attaches to the two limits last mentioned, because of the uses made of them in interpreting errors of sampling. This topic is developed at a later point. Here we may note that the figures defining proportions of the total area under the normal curve falling in given areas may also be interpreted as probabilities. The probability that a given observation, made at random in a population distributed according to the normal law of error, will fall between the mean and a value one standard deviation above the mean is 0.34134; the probability that a given observation will deviate from the mean by 1.96σ or more is 0.05; the probability that a given observation will deviate from the mean by 2.5758σ or more is 0.01.

The method by which probabilities of occurrence may be determined from a table of areas under the normal curve, and by which the significance of a given normal deviate may be established, should be clearly understood. These methods enter in many ways into the work of a statistician.

The uses of the normal curve of error, and of the table of areas based thereon, are too varied to be enumerated at length here. A simple example may serve to introduce the subject.

Fitting a Normal Curve. The process of fitting a normal curve to a set of observations involves the computation of theoretical frequencies corresponding to the observed frequencies. This may be done from a table of areas under the normal curve (see Appendix Table I). Using such a table, in the manner indicated in the preceding section, the areas between the maximum ordinate and ordinates erected at the various class limits may be determined. By the simple process of subtraction the area within each class, and hence the theoretical frequencies, may then be computed.

To illustrate the fitting procedure we make use of a frequency distribution based upon the annual number of telephone calls made by members of a sample of 995 residence telephone subscribers in Buffalo, New York.[3] It is a tenable preliminary assumption that the conditions giving rise to a normal distribution prevail among a population of residence telephone subscribers, although this assumption must be tested against the actual observations. Of course, the actual range of message use is not infinite; there is, indeed, a definite lower limit at zero on the scale of message use. But within the actual range of the observations the tailing off of frequencies is so pronounced that the existence of a boundary at zero does not, in fact, conflict with the theoretical conditions.

The actual distribution of telephone subscribers is given in Table 6-3. We shall require estimates of the mean and standard deviation of the assumed parent population; calculations of these two quantities are shown below the table.

The computations shown in Table 6-3 yield 476.96 as the sample mean, 147.65 as the standard deviation of the sample. The sample mean may be used as an estimate of the population mean μ, but, as we have seen, the sample standard deviation s requires a modification if we are to have an unbiased estimate of the population σ

---

[3] The study from which this distribution was derived was made by the statistical division of the American Telephone and Telegraph Company. See "Introduction to Frequency Curves and Averages." *Statistical Bulletin, Statistical Methods Series, No. 1.* Issued by Chief Statistician, American Telephone and Telegraph Co.

TABLE 6–3

Annual Message Use of 995 Telephone Subscribers
Illustrating the Computation of Mean and Standard Deviation

(1)	(2)	(3)	(4)	(5)	(6)
Interval of message use*	Mid-point	Fre-quency	Deviation of class midpoint from arbi-trary origin in class-interval units		
		f	x'	fx'	$f(x')^2$
0– 50	25	0	– 10	0	0
50– 100	75	1	– 9	– 9	81
100– 150	125	9	– 8	– 72	576
150– 200	175	19	– 7	– 133	931
200– 250	225	38	– 6	– 228	1,368
250– 300	275	50	– 5	– 250	1,250
300– 350	325	95	– 4	– 380	1,520
350– 400	375	85	– 3	– 255	765
400– 450	425	115	– 2	– 230	460
450– 500	475	132	– 1	– 132	132
500– 550	525	144	0	0	0
550– 600	575	116	1	116	116
600– 650	625	79	2	158	316
650– 700	675	54	3	162	486
700– 750	725	31	4	124	496
750– 800	775	11	5	55	275
800– 850	825	5	6	30	180
850– 900	875	6	7	42	294
900– 950	925	2	8	16	128
950–1,000	975	1	9	9	81
1,000–1,050	1,025	1	10	10	100
1,050–1,100	1,075	1	11	11	121
		995		– 956	9,676

CALCULATIONS

$M' = 525$

$c = -\dfrac{956}{995}$

$\quad = -0.9608$

c (in original units)

$\quad = -0.9608 \times 50$

$\quad = -48.04$

$M = M' + c$

$\quad = 525 - 48.04$

$\quad = 476.96$

$s^2 = \dfrac{9676}{995} - (-0.9608)^2$

$\quad = 9.7246 - 0.9231$

$\quad = 8.8015$

Applying Sheppard's corrections†

$s^2 = 8.8015 - 0.0833$

$\quad = 8.7182$

$s = 2.953$

s (in original units)

$\quad = 2.953 \times 50$

$\quad = 147.65$

* As here classified an item having a value of 50 was put in the class having 50 as an upper limit. Items falling on other class limits were similarly disposed of.

† At this point we use the same symbol s^2 for the uncorrected and corrected variances.

(see p. 117 above). The correction is made in the variance. For an unbiased estimate of the population variance we have

$$s'^2 = \frac{N}{N-1} s^2$$

In the present case s^2, in class-interval units, is 8.7182. Thus

$$s'^2 = \frac{995}{994} \times 8.7182 = 8.7270$$

$$\text{and } s' = 2.954$$

To obtain s' in original units we multiply this value by the class-interval, 50. The unbiased estimate of the standard deviation of the population is then 147.70. (With a sample as large as the present one there is no difference, for practical purposes, between s and s'. With small samples s' is definitely superior to s.)

Our next task is to determine theoretical class frequencies, i.e., the frequencies to be expected for class-intervals of 0-50, 50-100, etc., in a distribution of 995 observations drawn from a normal population having a mean of 476.96 and a standard deviation of 147.70. The computations shown in Table 6-4 are based upon a table of areas under the normal curve similar to that given in Appendix Table I. (Sheppard's table, which was used, gives areas to two more decimal places than does Appendix Table I.) The procedure employed should be clear from the previous illustration. For the lower limit of the class falling between 50 and 100 on the x-scale, the deviation from the mean in standard deviation units is $\frac{50 - 476.96}{147.70}$, or -2.89. From the table of areas we find that the proportion of the total area falling between an ordinate at the mean and an ordinate 2.89 standard deviations below the mean is .4980738. Multiplying by 995, this proportion is expressed in terms of total frequencies for a sample of 995 cases drawn from the assumed normal population. This gives 495.58 cases as the number to be expected between the mean and an ordinate at 50 on the x-scale. A similar calculation gives us 492.14 as the number of cases to be expected between the mean and an ordinate at 100 on the x-scale. The difference between 495.58 and 492.14, or 3.44, is the theoretical frequency in the class whose limits are 50 and 100 on the x-scale. This process, repeated for each of the other classes, gives us the theoretical distribution by classes shown in column (5) of Table 6-4.

TABLE 6–4

Illustrating the Computation of Theoretical Frequencies from a Table of Areas

(1) Class limit	(2) Deviation from mean in units of σ $\dfrac{x}{\sigma}$	(3) Proportion of area between y_0 and ordinate at $\dfrac{x}{\sigma}$	(4) Number of cases between y_0 and ordinate at $\dfrac{x}{\sigma}$	(5) Theoretical frequencies, by classes		
0	− 3.23	.4993810	496.88			
50	− 2.89	.4980738	495.58	0–	50	1.92*
100	− 2.55	.4946139	492.14	50–	100	3.44
150	− 2.21	.4864474	484.02	100–	150	8.12
200	− 1.88	.4699460	467.60	150–	200	16.42
250	− 1.54	.4382198	436.03	200–	250	31.57
300	− 1.20	.3849303	383.01	250–	300	53.02
350	− .86	.3051055	303.58	300–	350	79.43
400	− .52	.1984682	197.48	350–	400	106.10
450	− .18	.0714237	71.07	400–	450	126.41
500	+ .16	.0635595	63.24	450–	500	134.31
550	+ .49	.1879331	186.99	500–	550	123.75
600	+ .83	.2967306	295.25	550–	600	108.26
650	+ 1.17	.3789995	377.10	600–	650	81.85
700	+ 1.51	.4344783	432.31	650–	700	55.21
750	+ 1.85	.4678432	465.50	700–	750	33.19
800	+ 2.19	.4857379	483.31	750–	800	17.81
850	+ 2.53	.4942969	491.83	800–	850	8.52
900	+ 2.87	.4979476	495.46	850–	900	3.63
950	+ 3.20	.4993129	496.82	900–	950	1.36
1,000	+ 3.54	.4997999	497.30	950–1,000		.48
1,050	+ 3.88	.4999478	497.45	1,000–1,050		.15
1,100	+ 4.22	.4999878	497.49	greater than 1,050		.05
						995.00

* The theoretical distribution shows .62 of a case below − 3.23σ. To preserve formal consistency this amount has here been added to the theoretical frequency between 0 and 50.

This theoretical distribution may be compared, class by class, with the distribution of actual frequencies as given in column (3) of Table 6-3. Or the comparison of the actual distribution and fitted curve may be made graphically, as shown in Fig. 6.6. It is apparent by inspection that the normal curve gives a fairly good fit to the data, although there are several classes in which the differences are marked. A natural question arises as to the reason for the failure of the normal curve to fit at all points. There are two possible answers to such a question. The failure to fit may be

FIG. 6.6. Illustrating the Fitting of a Normal Curve to Frequency Distribution of Telephone Subscribers, Classified according to Message Use.

due merely to chance fluctuations such as are found in any sample. We may have an underlying law of distribution of residence subscribers, classified by message use, which accords perfectly with the normal law of error, but the particular sample selected may be marked by certain irregularities which would be ironed out if a very large number of cases were included. On the other hand, the differences may be due to the fundamental failure of such a distribution to accord with the normal law of error. Such a law may not describe the distribution of telephone calls, in which case the normal curve should not be employed.

At this stage we may note, without discussion, that the differences between theoretical and observed frequencies in the present example are small enough to be attributed to chance fluctuations of sampling. The evidence is clear, however, that the discrepancies between the observed frequencies and those in the corresponding normal distribution are not excessively large. The observed facts are not inconsistent with the hypothesis that residential telephone subscribers, classified according to frequency of telephone use, are distributed in accordance with the normal law of error.

This conclusion gives generality to the results of our study. We know the attributes of distributions following the normal law of error, and once the identification of an actual distribution with this standard type has been effected we may draw upon this knowledge. In using the original frequency table we are limited to the classes there established. We may now go beyond this and determine how many cases may be expected within stated limits. We may compute the probability of a case falling between any two points on the x-scale, or above or below any given value. The observed results, standing alone, are restricted in their significance to the particular observations recorded, but the theoretical frequencies have no such limitations. They apply generally, to the entire population from which the sample was drawn. In so far as we are assured of the representative character of our sample we have a basis for inference that would be afforded by no amount of study of the particular distribution as a thing apart. This fact, that a knowledge of the theoretical frequencies permits *generalization* beyond the limits of direct observation, is perhaps the most important of the advantages derived from the identification of an actual distribution with an ideal type, such as the normal distribution.[4]

REFERENCES

Anderson, R. L. and Bancroft, T. A., *Statistical Theory in Research*, Chaps. 2, 3.

Clark, C. E., *An Introduction to Statistics*, Chaps. 2, 3, 4.

Cramér, H., *The Elements of Probability Theory and Some of its Applications*, Part I.

Cramér, H., *Mathematical Methods of Statistics*, Chaps. 13, 15, 17.

David, F. N., *Probability Theory for Statistical Methods*, Chaps. 1-5.

Dixon, W. J. and Massey, F. J. Jr., *Introduction to Statistical Analysis*, Chaps. 4, 5.

Elderton, W. P., *Frequency Curves and Correlation*, 4th ed., Chap 3.

Feller, W., *An Introduction to Probability Theory and its Applications*, Vol. I, Chaps. 1-7.

Goulden, C. H., *Methods of Statistical Analysis*, 2nd ed., Chap. 3.

Hoel, P. G., *Introduction to Mathematical Statistics*, 2nd ed., Chaps. 2, 5.

Kelley, T. L., *Fundamentsls of Statistics*, Chap. 8.

[4] In this chapter we have discussed only two of a number of theoretical distributions that are used by statisticians. Other distributions of special importance in the theory of sampling will be discussed in subsequent chapters. Explanations of the Poisson distribution will be found in standard works. A comprehensive system of ideal frequency distributions, developed by Karl Pearson, is described by Elderton, Ref. 35. For a discussion of the Pearson and other distribution functions see also Kendall, Ref. 78, Vol. I, Chapters 5-6 and Mood, Ref. 109, Chapter 6.

Kendall, M. G., *The Advanced Theory of Statistics*, 3rd ed., Vol. I, pp. 116-120, 128-133, 164-183.

Marschak, J., "Probability in the Social Sciences," Chap. 4 of Lazarsfeld, P. F., ed., *Mathematical Thinking in the Social Sciences*.

Mather, K., *Statistical Analysis in Biology*, 2nd ed., Chaps. 2, 3.

Mood, A. M., *Introduction to the Theory of Statistics*, Chap. 2.

Neyman, J., *First Course in Probability and Statistics*, Chap. 2.

Rosander, A. C., *Elementary Principles of Statistics*, Chaps. 5, 7, 13, 25, 26.

Tintner, G., *Mathematics and Statistics for Economists*, Chaps. 20, 23.

Tippett, L. H. C., *The Methods of Statistics*, 4th ed., pp. 48-78.

Treloar, A. E., *Elements of Statistical Reasoning*, Chaps. 5, 6.

Walker, H. M. and Lev, J., *Statistical Inference*, Chap. 2.

Waugh, A. E., *Elements of Statistical Method*, 3rd ed., pp. 155-211.

Wilks, S. S., *Elementary Statistical Analysis*, Chaps. 4, 5, 6, 8.

Yule, G. U. and Kendall, M. G., *An Introduction to the Theory of Statistics*, 14th ed., Chaps. 7, 8.

The publishers and the dates of publication of the books named in chapter reference lists are given in the bibliography at the end of this volume.

CHAPTER **7**

•
•
•

Statistical Inference: Problems of Estimation

At various stages in the preceding discussion we have spoken of the problems involved in passing from the known facts provided by a sample to generalizations about the population from which the sample was drawn. In particular, our concern in such generalizations is with the unknown values of the *parameters* that define attributes of such a parent population. In estimating a parameter (a mean, a median, a standard deviation) we may wish to obtain a single figure which, in some sense, represents the best guess we can make as to the actual value of the parameter in question. Alternatively, our estimate may take the form of a statement specifying limits within which, with a given degree of confidence, we may expect the actual value of the parameter to fall. The estimate of a single figure is called a *point estimate*; the statement that presents limits, rather than a single figure, is called an *interval estimate*. In the present chapter we shall deal with certain criteria and methods that have to do with point estimation, and shall then proceed to a more extended discussion of interval estimates and of the probabilities that attach thereto. But first the basic idea of randomness calls for brief discussion. For the samples to which the theory of probability may be applied must be random samples.

Random Variables and Random Samples

We think of a variable as a quantity that may take any of a number of different values. The addition of the word *random* modifies the concept materially. A *random variable* may take any of a number of values; the individual values will be marked by irregularity in their occurrence, but when many individual values are brought together regularity of arrangement will appear. The regularity may be of many types, for different random variables, but for any one such variable there is orderliness in its mass behavior. Another way of putting this is to say that when many individual values of a random variable are organized (as in a frequency distribution) orderliness that takes the form of a definite distribution function will emerge. The separate values will be members of a "population" with definable attributes.

We should stress that randomness is the key to the orderliness that thus appears. The practical importance of this fact is very great. As Shewhart has said, "The ability to randomize a set of numbers or a set of objects by means of some distinguishable physical operation provides the scientist with a powerful technique for making valid predictions." For the prediction that is impossible with reference to individual members of a population of random variables is possible with reference to members of such a population in the mass. Some of the conditions under which random series appear have been suggested in discussing the normal distribution. Here the forces affecting individual events must be independent; each event must be affected by a multiplicity of forces; there must be equality of forces tending to generate values above and below the mean value. Such a distribution is, of course, just one of many possible random distributions. The conditions noted may be modified rather substantially, and randomness may remain. The regularities represented by distribution functions are of diverse types. In all cases individual events are unpredictable, but the stability of large numbers generates regularity, and makes possible prediction (in probability terms) concerning mass behavior.

As we shall see, deliberate achievement of the randomness that makes valid prediction possible calls for design and most careful planning (see Chapter 16). At this stage we may note that if we are to have a *random sample*, which is the necessary basis of a valid inference, we must have a sample the elements of which are independent events, that all these events must come from the same population, and that the method of drawing the sample must be such that the probability of being chosen is definable for each member of the population (by "element of a sample" we here mean a single observation). In the actual field work of sampling elaborate techniques are often necessary to ensure that these conditions are in fact met in a given case.

We may here note a special term used for distributions of random variables. When we have specified for any distribution the relative frequency with which values of a random variable fall within each of a number of defined classes, we have a *probability distribution*. (Relative frequencies, as we have seen, may be interpreted as probabilities.) The binomial and normal distributions are probability distributions; there are many others. Every random variable has its distinctive probability distribution. Such a distribution may be defined by a *frequency function* of the familiar type, with frequencies rising to a maximum and then declining, or by a *distribution function* showing cumulative frequencies or probabilities.

Notation. The symbols employed in this chapter accord in general with the system previously outlined. We may note the following:

s': an unbiased estimate of σ

m: the mean of a distribution of sample means

σ_m: the standard deviation of a distribution of sample means; the standard error of a mean; also written $\sigma_{\bar{x}}$

s_m: the estimated standard error of a sample mean; also written $s_{\bar{x}}$

θ (theta): a population parameter (a general symbol)

t_e: a statistic regarded as an estimate of θ

σ_s: the standard deviation of a distribution of sample s's; the standard error of the standard deviation

s_s: the estimated standard error of a sample s

σ_{md}: the standard error of the median

s_{md}: the estimated standard error of a sample median

σ_{q_1}: the standard error of the first quartile

σ_{d_1}: the standard error of the first decile

f_s: the number of successful outcomes out of n events

$n-f_s$: the number of unsuccessful outcomes out of n events

s_p: the estimated standard error of a proportion, or of a relative frequency

pe: a percentage

s_{pe}: the estimated standard error of a percentage

N_p: the total number of cases in a finite population

Sampling Distributions: Preliminary Discussion

When a sample has been drawn, by random processes, from a given population, we may from the sample (which is composed of X_1, X_2, X_3, . . . X_n) estimate any characteristic of the parent population. The mean of the sample is an estimate of the mean of the population; the standard deviation of the sample can be corrected to give an unbiased estimate of the standard deviation of the population; a measure of skewness of the sample provides an estimate of the skewness of the population. If we should draw many random samples from a given population, all samples being of the same size, the means of the various samples ($\overline{X}_1$, $\overline{X}_2$, $\overline{X}_3$, etc.) would give us a series of varying estimates of the population mean. These varying estimates would constitute a random variable. Every sample mean may be regarded as an observed value of this new random variable (new in that the unit of observation here is not one member of the original population of X's, but one member of a new population of $\overline{X}$'s). These means may be organized in a frequency distribution. Similarly, a series of standard deviations derived from successive samples may be put in the form of a frequency distribution. Such a distribution, composed of the means of successive samples, or of the standard deviations of successive samples, would have the general characteristics of the distributions discussed in earlier chapters. In each distribution observations would tend to concentrate about a central value; frequencies would tail off, symmetrically or asymmetrically, about this central value. As the number of observations was increased, discontinuities that might be present when the number of observations was small would be reduced; there would be a clear tendency toward a continuous frequency curve as the total frequencies increased. The smooth frequency curve which would thus be approached would be the graphic representation of what is called a *sampling distribution*.

The attributes of such sampling distributions are of supreme importance in the theory and practice of statistics. The power of statistical inference derives from the knowledge we now possess of the sampling distributions of standard deviations, coefficients of correlation, and other statistical measurements. For knowledge of such distributions—which are probability distributions—enables us to specify the probabilities that attach to the conclusions of statistical inferences. To understand how this is done we must know something about the sampling distributions of the chief statistical measurements. As a basis for the discussion that is to follow we first briefly note the characteristics of the sampling distribution of the arithmetic mean.

We have seen above that the means of successive random samples of size N, all drawn in the same way from the same parent population, constitute a random variable. Observations on this random variable (i.e., the various mean values) can be organized in a frequency distribution. This distribution—and this is a fact of central importance in theoretical and practical statistics—will be normal, or will tend toward the normal type, whether the population from which the samples have been drawn be normally distributed or not. If the parent population is normal, the distribution of sample means will be normal; if the parent population is not normal, the distribution of sample means will be asymptotically normal, that is, will approach the normal form as N increases.[1] Moreover, the mean and the standard deviation of the distribution of means will bear definite relations to the parameters of the parent population. The mean of the sampling distribution, which we may represent by the symbol m_m, will be equal to μ, the population mean. Or, more precisely, as the number of samples increases the mean of the distribution of means will approach μ or converge in probability[2] to μ. The standard deviation of the sampling distribution, which we may represent by s_m or, in the limit, σ_m, will in the same sense be equal to the population σ divided by the square root of the number of observations in each sample; that is $\sigma_m = \sigma/\sqrt{N}$. The mean and the standard deviation completely define a normal distribution; the sampling distribution

[1] This approach to normality of distributions of means has been established for samples drawn from infinite populations with finite standard deviations, regardless of distribution type; it holds also for samples drawn from finite populations under quite general conditions. For a discussion of the validity of the normal approximation see Cochran, Ref. 17, pp. 22-28, and the references there cited.

W. A. Shewhart gives a striking illustration of the emergence of the normal distribution among means of samples drawn from parent distributions of diverse types. Shewhart drew many samples, each containing four observations, from a normal parent population, from a rectangular parent population (i.e., one for which the frequency distribution was rectangular in shape), and from a right triangular parent population (i.e., one for which the frequency distribution took the form of a right triangle). In each of the three cases the distribution of sample means was acceptably normal. See Shewhart, Ref. 140, pp. 179-184.

[2] For the mathematical meaning of convergence in probability see Cramér, Ref. 23, p. 252.

of means of samples drawn from a population of given mean and standard deviation is thus completely determined.

Since we are usually concerned about the degree of dispersion to be found among a series of means, standard deviations, or other statistics derived from successive samples from a given parent population, our chief interest, in respect of measures descriptive of sampling distributions, is usually in those that define the degree of variation in such distributions. For the sampling distribution of the mean this, as just noted, is σ_m. The knowledge that $\sigma_m = \sigma/\sqrt{N}$ suffers from one important practical limitation. We do not usually know σ, the standard deviation of the parent population. However, for large samples the standard deviation s of the sample may be accepted as a good estimate of σ, for s tends to approach σ (i.e., "converge in probability" to σ) for such samples. (For small samples it is well to use s', the unbiased estimate of σ, in preference to s. See p. 118.) If we use s or s' as an approximation to σ we employ the symbol s_m, instead of σ_m, for the standard deviation of the sampling distribution of the mean. (We may note that this measure, σ_m or s_m, is called the *standard error of the mean*.) Having s_m and knowing that it measures the dispersion of sample means in a distribution that is normal, or acceptably so, we may interpret it with confidence as a measure of sampling reliability. We shall see shortly how such measures are used in estimation.

Each sampling distribution may be thought of as a population of estimates. We are interested in such distributions because of their basic role in the process by which we estimate population parameters, or seek to define the limits within which such param- may be expected to fall. It is the process of estimation which is our central concern.

Point Estimation

The problem of point estimation, we may recall, is that of determining (from the observations in a sample) a single number which may be regarded as an acceptable estimate of the unknown value of a specified population parameter. Thus from the data of an actual sample we may wish to estimate the arithmetic mean of the population from which the sample has been drawn. There are open to the statistician several methods of estimation, involving different procedures and resting on different concepts of "acceptability."

Of these we shall here deal with one that is widely used, and which lends itself to simple arithmetic procedures.

The nature of *the method of least squares* is suggested by its name. When we employ this method for estimating, say, a population mean, we find that value for which the sum of the squares of the residuals is a minimum (a residual being, in such a case, the deviation of an observed value from the estimate of the mean). The arithmetic mean of a series of observations meets this condition; the mean of a sample is a least squares estimate of the mean of the population from which the sample has been drawn. A least squares fit of a straight line to scattered points is that line for which the sum of the squares of the deviations is a minimum. The least squares principle is one with a long tradition, and one that has been extensively employed in practice. As we have noted, the procedures followed in applying it are relatively simple. For normally distributed observations the results obtained from least squares estimates have full logical validity. For nonnormal distributions other methods yield more satisfactory estimates, but even in such cases (except when the departure from normality is very great) the method of least squares gives estimates that are fully acceptable for most statistical purposes.

Other procedures used in point estimation employ the *method of moments* or the *method of maximum likelihood*.[3] The latter, which has the sounder logical foundation and the wider applicability, was developed by R. A. Fisher (Ref. 47, papers 10, 11, 24, 26). We should emphasize that, for samples drawn from normal parent populations, maximum likelihood estimates are identical with least squares estimates for arithmetic means, standard deviations, and measures of correlation.

The student may well ask, at this point, "How may we distinguish good methods of estimation from poor ones? What standards of judgment are appropriate?" The answer is that statisticians have developed certain criteria that are applied in the appraisal of estimates and in the evaluation of methods of estimation. Thus they distinguish *unbiased* from biased estimating methods, *consistent* methods from those that are not consistent, *efficient* from inefficient methods. We do not here attempt to present the mathematical reasoning behind these various criteria. Our purpose

---

[3] These methods are discussed in Mills, *Statistical Methods*, Third Edition, Chapters 6 and 7.

will be served by brief statements of the nature of these criteria and by a summary indication of the considerations that have led students of the logic of statistics to define these principles.

A given statistic t_e is an *unbiased* estimate of the corresponding population θ if θ is the mathematical expectation of t_e. To say that θ is the mathematical expectation of t_e is to say that as the number of samples increases the arithmetic mean of the t_e values obtained from the samples approaches (or converges in probability to) θ. (It is here assumed that all the t_e's are derived from samples of fixed size N.) A sample mean $\overline{X}$ is an unbiased estimate of μ, the corresponding population parameter. A sample variance s^2, computed from $s^2 = \Sigma(X - \overline{X})^2/N$, is not an unbiased estimate of the population variance σ^2, for the mean of the sampling distribution of s^2 will be smaller than σ^2. (This fact has been noted in Chapter 5 in discussing the method of deriving from a sample an estimate of the population σ.) An unbiased estimate of σ^2 may be obtained by dividing $\Sigma(X - \overline{X})^2$ by $N - 1$ instead of by N.

A given statistic t_e is a *consistent* estimate of the parameter θ if, as the sample size N increases without limit, the values of t_e converge in probability to θ. This criterion differs from the preceding in that N was taken to be fixed in the preceding case, whereas N is thought of as tending to infinity in the present case.

A sample mean $\overline{X}$ is a consistent, as well as an unbiased, estimate of μ, the population mean. The sample statistic s^2, computed from $s^2 = \Sigma(X - \overline{X})^2/N$, is a consistent although not an unbiased estimate of the population variance σ^2. For as N gets larger and larger the difference between s^2 and σ^2 tends to get smaller and smaller; s^2 approaches σ^2. This is not incompatible with the fact that from samples of fixed size we would get a distribution of s^2 values the mean of which would not be σ^2, but something less than σ^2.

In considering the idea of *efficiency* in estimates we may revert to the concept of sampling distributions. Estimates such as sample means or standard deviations, when derived from many samples of the same size drawn from the population whose parameters are to be estimated, form frequency distributions. In the limit, each of these constitutes a population of estimates. In the long run we may expect to get better estimates from statistics the distribution of which is concentrated about the parameter we are estimating, than from statistics having a distribution marked by extreme dispersion. For the reliability of the estimate (if it be an unbiased estimate) depends on the degree of concentration found in its sampling distribution. This concentration, as measured by the variance (σ^2) of the sampling distribution, a quantity which is termed the *sampling variance*, is the quality to which the term efficiency applies. Of two estimates, that with the smaller variance is the more efficient. An estimate marked by minimum variance is an *efficient* estimate.

When we consider the attributes of specific sampling distributions we shall be particularly interested in their variances, or their standard deviations. These indexes of efficiency and of reliability are of central importance in statistical inference.

In point estimation we seek to pick out a single value which, in some specified sense, may be regarded as the "best" estimate of some unknown parameter. But an estimate of this sort, while pinpointed on a unique value, is quite unlikely to coincide with the true value of the parameter that concerns us. If we are dealing with a continuous variable there is an infinity of possible wrong estimates, and but one right estimate. Perhaps we have studied a sample of income recipients in the United States in a given year, and on the basis of the information provided by the sample reach the conclusion: The true mean income of income recipients in the United States in the year X was $4,244. Although this may be the "best" estimate that we can make, it is almost certainly not the correct figure (which may fall at any point over a wide range). To the conclusion as it stands no probability statement may be attached. But for logical and practical reasons the information given by our sample will be of greatest use to us if a conclusion summarizing the relevant information given by the sample can be put in a form to which a probability statement may be attached. Since we shall be generalizing from a sample the conclusion will be an uncertain one, in any event, but we should like to be able to put some measure to the degree of uncertainty involved.

Interval Estimation: Confidence Limits

The theory of interval estimation leads to a conclusion of the following sort: The true mean income of income recipients in the United States in the year X lay between $4,146 and $4,342. This is a statement that may be true or false, for the true mean income of the population in question was either between the stated limits or it was not. Whether it is true or false we do not know. But the merit of the method of interval estimation is that it enables us to attach a specific probability to a family of statements of the type just cited, and thus to define the degree of confidence we may have in any single statement of this sort.

An Example : estimation of μ when σ is known. The method of interval estimation now generally employed may be explained, first, in terms of a hypothetic example. We shall assume that an investigator is seeking to estimate the mean μ of a normal population having a standard deviation σ equal to 40. That is, the investigator knows that the distribution is normal, and knows the standard deviation of the distribution, but does not know its mean. We assume now that the investigator has drawn 1,000 samples from this population, each including 400 observations. For each of these samples he has calculated $\bar{X}$. Let us say that the calculated values of $\bar{X}$ are 99.5, 102.1, 95.8, 98.7, 101.4 . . . , etc., to a total of 1,000 figures. We have seen above that the means of samples of fixed size N, drawn from a given population, will be distributed normally, with a standard deviation equal to $\sigma/\sqrt{N}$. Thus we know that the 1,000 means, of which 5 have been given above, will make up a normal distribution, with standard deviation $40/\sqrt{400}$, or 2. We know, therefore, that the investigator is drawing from a population that may be represented by the graph shown in Fig. 6.5. The mean of this population, μ, is unknown to the investigator, but he does know the limits within which stated proportions of the population of means will fall. Sixty-eight percent will fall within $\mu \pm 2$; 95.45 percent will fall within $\mu \pm 4$; 99.7 percent will fall within $\mu \pm 6$.

We must now permit the investigator to draw the inference that is possible on the basis of the information given him by each successive sample. We do so at this point without explanation, other than to note that 95 percent of the area under a normal curve falls within ordinates erected 1.96σ below the mean and 1.96σ above the mean. This is to say that in using the multiples of σ indicated below, the investigator is working with a 95 percent "confidence interval," a phrase that will be explained shortly.

After drawing the first sample, of which the mean is 99.5, our investigator makes the statement:

1. "The mean μ of the population from which I am drawing falls between 95.58 and 103.42."

After drawing each of the succeeding samples he makes a statement similar in form, but different in the limits it specifies. The four succeeding statements, corresponding to the second, third, fourth, and fifth sample means given above, are:

2. "The mean μ falls between 98.18 and 106.02."
3. "The mean μ falls between 91.88 and 99.72."
4. "The mean μ falls between 94.78 and 102.62."
5. "The mean μ falls between 97.48 and 105.32."

The reader will observe that the limits set in each statement are derived by subtracting 3.92, i.e., 1.96 × 2, (2 being the standard deviation of the distribution of means), from the given sample mean, and by adding 3.92 to the given sample mean. Thus 95.58 = 99.5 − 3.92; 103.42 = 99.5 + 3.92.

If, now, we may assume that we (the author and the reader) have a piece of information not available to the investigator, we may check the accuracy of his several statements. This added information is that the true mean of the population from which the samples have been drawn is exactly 100. We note that four of the five statements are true, and that one (the third) is false. The mean μ does not fall between 91.88 and 99.72. The relation of each statement to the facts may be more clearly apparent in Fig. 7.1.

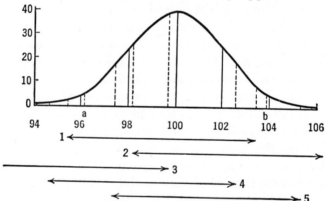

FIG. 7.1. Normal Curve Showing Distribution of Sample Means, with 0.95 Confidence Intervals Based on Five Samples.*

* Parameters of population from which samples were drawn: Mean = 100 (not known to investigator). Standard deviation = 40 (known to investigator). Each sample N = 400.

The statements, in order, are represented by the numbered lines drawn below the graph of the normal curve representing the distribution of means. Each of these lines indicates the location of ordinates at the limits of the specified interval. Four of these intervals include the true mean, μ; one does not.

The ordinates a and b are erected at points on the x-scale falling 1.96σ below and 1.96σ above the mean μ. The area between them is 95 percent of the area under the curve. It will be noticed that if a point corresponding to a sample mean falls anywhere within the area between ordinates a and b, the interval $\overline{X} \pm 1.96\sigma$ will include the mean μ. In all such cases statements of the type given on page 187 will be true. If a sample point falls outside ordinate a or ordinate b, the interval $\overline{X} \pm 1.96\sigma$ will not include the mean μ. In all such cases, statements of the type cited in the examples above will be false. But since $\overline{X}$'s of the type here considered will be normally distributed, 95 percent of them, in the long run, will fall within the limits $\mu \pm 1.96\sigma$. Thus for 95 percent of all cases, statements of the type here discussed will be true, while 5 percent will be false. If our investigator were to base upon each of his 1,000 $\overline{X}$'s statements similar to the 5 cited above, we should expect that about 950 of them would be true, while about 50 would be false. (We say "about," because 1,000, although a large number, is finite, and the chances of sampling could easily lead to some departure from these figures.) In an actual inquiry the investigator would probably draw but one sample. Thus the only generalization he would make would be, say, "The mean μ falls between 95.58 and 103.42." This is true or false. The investigator does not know which. He does not say that the probability is 0.95 that it is true. The actual probability that it is true is either 1 (i.e., the statement is in fact true) or 0 (i.e., the statement is in fact false). But he does know that of many statements of this type, based upon operations of the same kind, 95 out of 100 would be true. In other words, this particular statement belongs to a family of statements of which 95 out of 100 would be true. His confidence in the statement is measured by a "probability coefficient" of 0.95. Hence the term *confidence interval*, used to describe the interval between 95.58 and 103.42.

This mode of phrasing a statistical inference departs from the method that was prevalent several decades ago. In particular, the reader will note, the parameter μ, which is to be estimated, is regarded as a *constant*, not as a variable quantity. In most practical problems we are trying to estimate a value that is clearly a constant, although an unknown one. Thus we may not use language (such as, "The probability is 0.50 that the true mean falls between such and such limits") that implies that a parameter is variable.

Since the parameter is a constant, statements specifying limits within which it is said to lie are either true or false. *Probabilities attach to the family of statements*, all made in the same way, but specifying varying intervals. What is variable in such a family of statements is the *location of the interval*, not the parameter that is being estimated.

We must note, finally, that the example cited above illustrates a special situation—that in which the σ of the parent population is known. Because σ is known, the intervals specified in the various statements are all of the same width. Where σ is not known the procedure and the interpretation of the conclusions are similar, but the ranges set forth in different statements will be unequal. This case calls for brief attention.

An example : estimation of μ when σ is not known. We shall now assume that an investigator has drawn ten samples, with $n = 101$ in each case, from a given population, which may or may not be normal. The population mean and standard deviation, which are not known to the investigator, are, in fact, 80 and 20, respectively. From the observations in each sample the investigator computes the mean, $\overline{X}$, and the standard deviation, s' $\{s'$ being regarded as an estimate of σ, is derived from $s' = \sqrt{\Sigma x^2/(N - 1)}$ $\}$. The several values of $\overline{X}$ and of s' are given in Table 7-1. The standard error of the mean of each of the ten samples is now estimated (from

TABLE 7–1

Illustrating the Estimation of a Population Mean
Means and Standard Deviations derived from Ten Samples from a given
Population, with 0.95 Confidence Intervals Based Thereon

(1) Sample number	(2) Mean	(3) Standard deviation	(4) Estimated standard error of $\overline{X}$	(5) Confidence interval for $P = 0.95$
	X	s'	$s_{\overline{x}}$	$\overline{X} \pm 1.96\ s_{\overline{x}}$
1	81.2	19.8	1.98	77.32 to 85.08
2	79.6	21.4	2.14	75.41 to 83.79
3	84.0	19.2	1.92	80.24 to 87.76
4	82.1	22.6	2.26	77.67 to 86.53
5	80.6	20.2	2.02	76.64 to 84.56
6	78.2	17.3	1.73	74.81 to 81.59
7	78.8	20.9	2.09	74.70 to 82.90
8	81.4	18.5	1.85	77.77 to 85.03
9	79.1	19.5	1.95	75.28 to 82.92
10	80.3	21.1	2.11	76.16 to 84.44

(Population parameters: $\mu = 80$, $\sigma = 20$. Each sample $N = 101$)

$s_{\bar{x}} = s'/\sqrt{N}$). On the basis of the information given by each sample the investigator now estimates an interval within which the mean may be expected to fall. Since he has decided to work with a confidence coefficient of 0.95 the confidence limits are derived, in each case, by subtracting from and by adding to the sample mean the quantity $1.96s_{\bar{x}}$. Thus from the data of sample No. 1 the conclusion reached is:

"The mean μ falls between 77.32 and 85.08."

(The lower limit, 77.32 is, of course, $81.2 - (1.96 \times 1.98)$ while the upper limit, 85.08, is $81.2 + (1.96 \times 1.98)$. These limits appear as the entries in column (5) of Table 7-1. This statement may be true or it may be false. On the theory of interval estimation the investigator believes that of 100 statements, each based on an operation similar to that which yields the first statement, 95 will be true and 5 false. The "confidence intervals" specified in 10 such statements, each based on the information given by a sample of 101 observations drawn from the same parent population, are shown in column (5) of Table 7-1. They are shown graphically in Fig. 7.2.

The ten confidence intervals thus set forth differ in location. The central point of each is the mean of one of the ten samples. In this respect they are like the confidence intervals cited in the preceding example (p. 176). But they differ from those previously cited in that their ranges differ. Thus the range of the first confidence interval in Table 7-1 is 7.76, that of the second is 8.38. The smallest interval is 6.78, given by sample No. 6; the greatest is 8.86, given by sample No. 4. The ranges differ, of course, because the investigator has to use the standard deviations of the several samples as estimates of the population σ, which he does not know. Some of these sample standard deviations are below the true σ (in sample No. 6, s' is but 17.3, as compared with the σ value 20); some are above. There are two factors, therefore, in the variations among the confidence intervals estimated from the several samples —varying central points and varying ranges. But the notable fact is that in spite of the two varying factors, 95 percent of the ranges thus specified will in the long run include the true mean. In the illustration here given, in Table 7-1 and Fig. 7.2, nine of the ten confidence intervals cited do in fact include the mean, 80. Only for sample No. 3, which gave a mean value well in excess of the

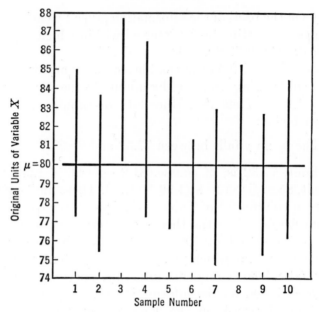

FIG. 7.2. Showing the Range of Each of Ten Interval Estimates of a Population Mean, with Confidence Coefficient of 0.95 (Population parameters, $\mu = 80$, $\sigma = 20$, not known to investigator. Each sample $N = 101$).

population μ, does the confidence interval fail to include μ. It will be understood, of course, that in both this example and the one preceding, the investigator who is estimating the location of the population mean is without the information we possess, in studying Fig. 7.1 and Fig. 7.2. He does not know where any interval falls, with respect to the true mean μ. To make clear what is actually happening, the reader has here been given information not available to the investigator. The latter possesses only the information needed for defining each of the confidence intervals and the corresponding probability coefficient, together with the knowledge that each statement (asserting that μ falls within a given confidence interval) belongs to a family of statements of which, in the long run, 95 percent will be true. In a particular case this is not exact information, it is true, but it is information of high practical importance, and information on the basis of which decisions may be made and action taken.

We should note that the choice of the confidence coefficient 0.95 is in some respects arbitrary. If the investigator chooses to make statements that he would expect to be true, in the long run, only 1 time out of 2, he would choose a confidence coefficient of 0.50. The multiplier of the standard error of the mean (see heading to column (5), Table 7-1) would then be 0.6745 instead of 1.96. If he chose to make statements that he would expect to be true, in the long run, 99 times out of 100, he would choose a confidence coefficient of 0.99, and use a multiplier of 2.576. Thus, with the coefficient 0.99, the conclusion reached on the basis of the first sample drawn, for which the mean is 81.2 and the standard deviation 19.8, would be:

"The mean μ falls between 76.1 and 86.3."

Raising the confidence coefficient in this way, from a level of 0.95 to 0.99, increases the range of the confidence interval, of course, thus making the conclusion less precise. But it raises one's confidence in the truth of the statement, elevating it into a family of statements which may be expected to be correct 99 times out of 100. In defining confidence limits we may choose to have greater precision with less confidence, or less precision with greater confidence. The choice of confidence coefficients in given cases will depend on the nature of the problem faced, and to some extent on the temperament of the investigator. Coefficients of 0.95 and 0.99 are most commonly used.

In practical employment of the method of interval estimation the essential element is knowledge of the sampling distribution of the particular statistic—mean, standard deviation, coefficient of correlation—that is to be generalized. Is the sampling distribution normal for such a measure (e.g., a mean) computed from samples drawn from a normal parent population? for a measure computed from samples drawn from non-normal populations? Most important in such knowledge of sampling distributions is knowledge of the *character* of dispersion to be expected and of means of estimating the *degree* of dispersion. If we know that a given distribution is normal, or not too far removed from the normal type, and if we may make a reasonable estimate of the standard deviation of such a distribution, the specific information to be had from a single sample will give us the basis for setting the limits of a confidence interval and for asserting with a specified degree of confidence that the population parameter falls within this interval. If the sampling distribution departs significantly from the normal type the procedure is somewhat less simple, but inference is still possible. Important non-normal sampling distributions have been defined in detail, often in tabular form. Such tables, to which we shall have later reference, make it possible to estimate parameters and to test hypotheses with definable degrees of precision.

Some Standard Errors and Their Uses in Estimation

In the present section we shall give examples of procedures employed in defining confidence intervals, setting forth at the same time characteristics of the sampling distributions of various statistical measures.

The Arithmetic Mean. Table 5-2 in Chapter 5 shows the distribution of 83,114 workers in industrial chemical plants, classified according to their average hourly earnings in January, 1946. The arithmetic mean of this distribution is 114.61 cents; the standard deviation s is 23.54 cents. Accepting this standard deviation as an approximation to the standard deviation of the population from which this sample was drawn,[4] we have

$$s_m = \frac{s}{\sqrt{N-1}} = \frac{23.54}{\sqrt{83,113}} = 0.082$$

The true mean of the hourly earnings of wage workers in industrial chemical plants in January, 1946, is not known. The figure 114.61 cents is our best approximation to it. If we should draw many samples, each the size of the one we have here, we should have many mean values normally distributed and centering, we may assume, at the true value. The standard deviation of this normal distribution we estimate as 0.082 cents. If we wish to work with a probability coefficient of 0.95 we have as the lower limit of the desired confidence interval $114.61 - (1.96 \times 0.082)$, or 114.45. As the upper limit we have $114.61 + (1.96 \times 0.082)$, or 114.77. Our statistical inference, therefore, takes the following form: "The mean hourly earnings of the universe of industrial chemical workers

---

[4] We have derived s from the formula $s = \sqrt{\dfrac{\Sigma d^2}{N}}$. Accordingly, in estimating the standard error of M it is logical to use the formula $s_m = s/\sqrt{N-1}$. That is, N should be reduced by 1 either in the estimation of σ or in the derivation of s_m. (For samples as large as the one here considered the reduction of N by 1 is purely formal. It does not affect the result significantly.) If s_m is derived from the d's of the original data, the single operation is summed up in Bessel's formula

$$s_m = \sqrt{\frac{\Sigma d^2}{N(N-1)}}$$

in January, 1946, lay between 114.45 cents and 114.77 cents." This particular statement may be true or false. Of an infinitely large number of such statements, based upon similar operations, 95 percent will be true, 5 percent false.

If we should choose to work with a probability coefficient of 0.99 we should set the lower limits of the confidence interval at a point 2.576 s_m below the sample mean, the upper limit at a point 2.576 s_m above the sample mean. In this case our conclusion would be: "The mean hourly earnings of the universe of industrial chemical workers in January, 1946, lay between 114.40 cents and 114.82 cents."

The confidence intervals are narrow, of course, with samples as large as the one here considered. Means of samples of this size would be very closely concentrated—a fact that permits very accurate estimation.

When a measure derived from a sample is presented as an estimate of a population parameter it is customary to give the statistic in question with its standard error, rather than to write out the formal conclusion. Thus we would write, for the estimated mean of hourly earnings of industrial chemical workers, $M = 114.61$ cents ± 0.08. The user of the statistic may then set up his own confidence interval, choosing the probability coefficient that he deems appropriate. It was the practice in earlier years to present the probable error of a statistic (i.e., 0.6745 the standard error) in this fashion, but the standard error is now generally employed. To avoid confusion, however, it is well to indicate that it is the standard error which is given.

In setting up confidence intervals for population means on the basis of information derived from samples, we have made use of three important facts—that the sampling distribution of $\bar{X}$'s is normal, or asymptotically normal, that the standard deviation of the sampling distribution of means may be defined in terms of the standard deviation of the parent population and of the sample N, and that when a sample is large the standard deviation of the parent population may be estimated with confidence from the standard deviation of the sample. By procedures somewhat similar to those that lead to the standard error of the mean, the standard errors of a number of other statistical measurements have been derived. It is true, under very general conditions, that the distributions of sample characteristics computed from sample moments tend toward normality as n approaches infinity. The standard deviations of such sampling distributions are usually definable, as was true in the case of the mean, in terms of the parameters of the parent population and of sample N's. The standard errors of these measurements are generally approximated by substituting the known sample characteristic (e.g., the standard deviation of the sample, as in the preceding example) for the corresponding unknown population parameter. Thus it is true, remarkably, that by virtue of behavior characteristics of large numbers we are able to utilize information given by samples themselves in generalizing the results obtained from samples.[5]

Sampling a finite population. The procedures discussed above all relate to samples drawn from infinite populations. This is the assumption usually made in statistical inference. Even when the population sampled is in fact limited in size, we usually take our results to apply to the infinite population that would be generated if the forces that gave rise to the population actually in existence were to operate indefinitely without change in character. But the investigator sometimes wishes to work in terms of a population of limited and known size. The standard error of the mean of a sample drawn from such a population may be estimated from a modification of the customary formula. Using N as the number of cases in the sample and N_p for the total number in the population, we may write

$$s_m = \frac{s'}{\sqrt{N}} \sqrt{\frac{N_p - N}{N_p}} \qquad (7.1)$$

The effect of the modification is to reduce the sampling error of the mean. If N_p is very much greater than N the reduction is very slight; in effect the drawing in such a case has been made from an infinite population. If the sample has covered every case in the population, N_p and N will be equal and the standard error of the mean will be zero.

The Standard Deviation. The standard deviation s, treated as a random variable as was $\overline{X}$ above, has an asymptotically normal distribution. (For small samples, as we shall see, the departure from normality is great enough to call for distinctive treatment.) For large samples, say with N in excess of 100, we may treat it as

---

[5] The procedures here discussed are applicable to large samples. For most purposes a sample of 100 may be considered "large." Samples for which N is less than 30 are always considered "small." (Special procedures appropriate to small samples are discussed in Chapter 15.)

a normally distributed variate. If the parent population is normal, the standard deviation of a distribution of s's will be given by

$$\sigma_s = \sigma/\sqrt{2N} \qquad (7.2)$$

Not knowing the standard deviation of the population we substitute for σ (in the right-hand term above) the sample s. (No distinction is drawn between s and s', for we are dealing with large samples.) Thus we have

$$s_s = s/\sqrt{2N} \qquad (7.3)$$

As an illustration of the process of estimating the standard deviation of a normal population we may use the data on residence telephone subscribers (see Table 6-3). As an estimate of σ we have $s = 147.7$; $N = 995$. We have, therefore,

$$s_s = \frac{147.7}{\sqrt{1,990}} = 3.31$$

If we wish to work with a confidence interval of 0.99, we set confidence limits below and above 147.7 by 2.576 × 3.31, or 8.5. Thus our conclusion is: "The standard deviation of the population of residence telephone subscribers lies between 139.2 and 156.2." The coefficient 0.99 is a measure of our confidence that this statement is true.[6]

The Quantiles. We have used quantile as a generic term for measures such as the median, the quartiles, or the deciles, that divide the total frequencies in a distribution into specified proportions. Since every sample quantile may be regarded as an estimate of a corresponding population quantile, the usual problems of inference arise in the use of such measures in research. The sampling distributions of all quantiles tend toward normality as the sample size N increases. Thus for large samples we regard such sampling distributions as effectively normal, with means equal to the population quantiles that correspond to given sample quantiles. The standard deviations of the sampling distributions of the various quantiles (i.e., the standard errors of the quantiles) vary, as is to be expected. The following summary gives the standard errors of various quantiles, derived from samples drawn from normal parent populations. If the samples are large, the stated measures give good approximations to the standard errors

[6] In dealing with samples drawn from nonnormal universes, the estimate given by formula (7.3) may be improved upon by using a quantity derived from the fourth powers of deviations from the sample mean, as well as the standard deviation of the sample. See p. 198 of Mills, *Statistical Methods*, Third Edition, and the discussion of moments in Chapter 6 of that book.

of quantiles for samples from nonnormal parent populations, provided that the parent distributions are not extremely skew.

Quantile	Standard error
Median	$\sigma_{md} = 1.2533\sigma/\sqrt{N}$
First quartile	$\sigma_{q_1} = 1.3626\sigma/\sqrt{N}$ (σ_{q_3} identical)
First decile	$\sigma_{d_1} = 1.7094\sigma/\sqrt{N}$ (σ_{d_9} identical)
Second decile	$\sigma_{d_2} = 1.4288\sigma/\sqrt{N}$ (σ_{d_8} identical)
Third decile	$\sigma_{d_3} = 1.3180\sigma/\sqrt{N}$ (σ_{d_7} identical)
Fourth decile	$\sigma_{d_4} = 1.2680\sigma/\sqrt{N}$ (σ_{d_6} identical)

The σ of each formula stands, of course, for the standard deviation of the parent population. If this is not known the sample s (or s') will be substituted for it, with a corresponding change in the symbol for the standard error.

It will be noticed that the sampling error of the median is some 25 percent greater than the sampling error of the mean of a sample of similar size. The mean is, ordinarily, a more stable statistic than the median. (For a distribution with heavy concentration of observations near the modal value, i.e., a very peaked distribution, the stability of the median would be greater.) Quantiles near the center of the scale of x-values are marked by sampling errors smaller than those characteristic of quantiles near the limits of the range.

The Standard Error of a Proportion. In discussing the binomial distribution (Chapter 6) we noted that the standard deviation of a distribution of relative frequencies is given by $\sqrt{\dfrac{pq}{n}}$. This fact is very useful in generalizing results that take the form of frequency ratios, or relative frequencies, whether these are cited as proportions (e.g., 8/12) or as percentages. If we let f_s represent the number of "successful" outcomes out of n events, the relative frequency or proportion of successes will be f_s/n; the proportion of nonsuccesses will be $\dfrac{n - f_s}{n}$. Since f_s/n corresponds to p, of the general formula given above, and $\dfrac{n - f_s}{n}$ corresponds to q, the formula for the standard error of the proportion f_s/n may be written

$$s_p = \sqrt{\dfrac{\dfrac{f_s}{n} \cdot \dfrac{n - f_s}{n}}{n}} \qquad (7.4)$$

which reduces to

$$s_p = \sqrt{\dfrac{f_s(n - f_s)}{n^3}} \qquad (7.5)$$

Thus we may regard f_s/n as a random variable, normally distributed with standard deviation given by formula (7.5) above. For accurate approximation by these processes n should not be small, and neither p nor q should be very small.

To illustrate this procedure we shall assume that a sample poll has been taken of election preferences in a given community. Of 400 voters interviewed 320 $(= f_s)$ favor candidate A, while 80 $(= n - f_s)$ favor candidate B. We are required to estimate the proportion of all the voters favoring A. The sample proportion, p, of successes is 320/400 or 0.80. The standard error of this proportion is

$$s_p = \sqrt{\dfrac{320(400 - 320)}{400^3}}$$

$$= \dfrac{16}{800} = 0.02$$

The proportion and its standard error may be presented thus:

$$f_s/n = 0.80 \pm 0.02$$

If we wish to generalize, using 0.95 as the probability coefficient, the limits of the desired confidence interval will lie 1.96 s_p below and above the given proportion, 0.80. The product 1.96 s_p is equal to 0.0392, which we round off to 0.04. We may then say "The proportion of all voters favoring candidate A falls between 0.76 and 0.84." We make this assertion with confidence measured by the indicated probability coefficient.

For proportions, as for arithmetic means, standard errors vary inversely with the square root of n. Thus if we had covered only

100 cases in the above poll, the proportions being as they were in the larger sample, we should have

$$s_p = \sqrt{\frac{80(100 - 80)}{100^3}}$$

$$= 0.04$$

In the first example cited n was four times as great as in the second; the standard error in the first case was one half as large as in the second case.

It is frequently convenient to work with percentages, rather than with frequency ratios or proportions. When this is done, the standard error of the percentage is derived from a slight modification of equation (7.4). If we let $P_e = 100(f_s/n)$ and $100 - P_e = 100(n - f_s)/n$, equation (7.4) becomes

$$s_{pe} = \sqrt{\frac{P_e(100 - P_e)}{n}} \tag{7.6}$$

For the first example cited we should have $P_e = 100 \times \frac{320}{400} = 80$. For the standard error of P_e we should have

$$s_{pe} = \sqrt{\frac{80 \times (100 - 80)}{400}} = 2$$

The result would be given as

$$P_e = 80 \pm 2$$

Sampling errors and significant figures. In deciding upon the number of figures to be recorded as significant, measures of sampling errors are, of course, pertinent. A useful general rule laid down by Truman L. Kelley follows: *In a final published constant, retain no figures beyond the position of the first significant figure in one third of the standard error; keep two more places in all computations.* Its application may be illustrated with reference to the figures on hourly earnings of 83,114 chemical workers (Table 5-2). The mean, to four places, is 114.6138 cents. The standard error of the mean is .082 cents. One third of this is .0273. The first significant figure is in the column of hundredths. By the rule, therefore, the arithmetic mean should be given as 114.61 cents. Two more places, or four decimal places in all, should be retained in calculations.

Some Limitations to Measures of Sampling Errors. The importance of such measures of reliability as have been discussed above is, of course, great. With their aid we may give precision to our judgments concerning the margins of error involved in extending statistical results beyond the limits of actual observation. Yet limitations attach to them, and these must not be forgotten in a purely mechanical application of statistical tests.

Reference has been made to limitations arising out of the size of samples. We have noted the striking fact that many of the sampling distributions that concern statisticians are only "asymptotically normal," tending toward normality as n increases. When this is the case procedures that may be justified in handling large samples may be invalid for small samples. ". . . asymptotic expressions," as Cramér says, "are sometimes grossly inadequate when we are dealing with small samples."[7] Here we should like to have knowledge of the exact form of sampling distributions. However, knowledge of *exact* sampling distributions is limited. The exact distribution of the mean, $\overline{X}$, has been established for very general conditions. Distributions of other statistical measures defining attributes of samples from normal universes have been systematically studied, and some generally applicable findings obtained. For measures other than the mean, derived from samples drawn from non-normal universes, knowledge of exact distributions is limited. Fortunately, however, the tendency toward normality as n increases enables us to generalize with a fairly high degree of confidence when we are dealing with many of the statistics that are currently employed in handling mass data, *provided* that our samples be large. When this is so, the methods discussed in the present chapter may be used in drawing warranted conclusions. Moreover, exact distributions have been defined for certain small sample characteristics, and techniques have been developed for the practical application of this information. These will be discussed in the following chapter.

In deriving and using the measures of sampling error discussed in this chapter we make certain assumptions about the character of the samples employed and about the nature of the sampling process that has generated these samples. A basic assumption is that our samples are *random*. Only when we generalize from

---

[7] In general, as we have noted, we should regard a sample as small when N is less than 30; we regard a sample as large when N is greater than 100. Under certain circumstances, however, (see Chapter 9 on correlation for examples) a sample of 100 may not be considered large.

random samples may we speak in terms of probabilities. (Means of assuring randomness have been mentioned in Chapter 1; they are more fully discussed in Chapter 16.) A sample is drawn under *random* conditions if the separate events (the selections, or drawings of sample elements) are independent, and the probability of inclusion in the sample is known, or definable, for all members of the population. We have conditions of *simple random sampling* if the events (the selections) are independent and if the probability of inclusion in the sample is the same for all members of the population. (The condition of independence, strictly interpreted, would mean that in sampling from a finite population a given drawing would have to be replaced before the next drawing were made. If the finite number is reasonably large such replacement may be neglected.) The various measures of sampling error described in this and the following chapter are applicable when the conditions of simple random sampling have been realized.[8]

The degree to which the stated conditions of random sampling are fulfilled, in a given case, is in part subject to conscious control. Elaborate techniques have been developed to improve the approximations to these conditions that are achieved in actual field investigations. In particular, much may be done to ensure randomness in the sample, and something can be done to ensure the independence of individual events. Perfect fulfillment of all the conditions is, however, difficult to realize in the handling of social and economic data. The standard errors we have discussed in this chapter, we must emphasize, can give no indication of the possibility of fluctuations in successive samples arising from errors unrelated to random sampling. Fluctuations due to bias and faults arising from lack of representativeness of the sample quite elude this method of measuring the reliability of statistical inferences. The reduction of such biases and the avoidance of such faults must be the constant concern of the statistical investigator.

The element of time adds one serious difficulty to the problem of statistical induction in the realm of economics, and in the social sciences generally. A universe that extends over time is subject to elements of change that are not present among data relating to a cross-section of time. Conditions of pig iron production, of banking,

---

[8] In Chapter 16 we develop an additional, though related, condition, bearing on sample design in simple random sampling. If a sample of n elements is to be regarded as a simple random sample, the conditions of selection must be such that every possible set of n elements in the population has the same chance of being chosen.

of foreign trade, of income distribution change from year to year, even from month to month. We may hardly assume that data relating to different time periods reflect the play of identical forces. When we deal with data from different periods we are, as Oskar Anderson has pointed out, drawing from different universes. The structural changes that occur in economic organization are manifestations of this state of never-ending transition. Accordingly the homogeneity of all populations extending over time is suspect. In particular are hazards faced when an induction extends to a time period not covered by the data of observation.

In the application of statistical methods proper choice of objectives, wise planning, and effective field work are of at least equal importance with skill in the use of statistical techniques. This is especially true as regards problems of sampling. Here chief emphasis falls on soundness and accuracy in the field work. The problems of field work are specialized and particular, arising out of specific problems and conditions. Appropriate special knowledge is needed for the selection and validation of the sample.

Much may be done to strengthen a statistical induction by making actual statistical tests of the homogeneity of the population and of the stability of sampling results. By the study of successive samples the representativeness of statistical measures may be determined; and by testing the subordinate elements of a given sample, when broken up into significant subgroups, the inherent stability of a sample may be checked. The uniformity of nature in a given field is assumed in every induction. The induction is strengthened by every piece of evidence that supports the assumption.

REFERENCES

Anderson, R. L. and Bancroft, T. A., *Statistical Theory in Research,* Chaps. 9, 10.

Clark, C. E., *An Introduction to Statistics,* Chap. 5.

Cramér, H., *Mathematical Methods of Statistics,* Chaps. 32, 34.

Fisher, Sir Ronald (R. A.)., *Contributions to Mathematical Statistics,* Papers 10, 11, 25, 26, 27.

Johnson, P. O., *Statistical Methods in Research,* Chap. 6.

Mood, A. M., *Introduction to the Theory of Statistics,* Chap. 11.

Neyman, J., "Outline of a Theory of Statistical Estimation based on the Classical Theory of Probability," *Philosophical Transactions of the Royal Society,* 1937.

Neyman, J., *Lectures and Conferences on Mathematical Statistics and Probability*, 2nd ed., Chap. 4.

Rosander, A. C., *Elementary Principles of Statistics*, Chaps. 15, 16, 17.

Shewhart, W. A., *Economic Control of Quality of Manufactured Product*, Chap. 13.

Shewhart, W. A., *Statistical Method from the Viewpoint of Quality Control*, pp. 92-110.

Waugh, A. E., *Elements of Statistical Method*, 3rd ed., Chap. 9.

Wilks, S. S., *Elementary Statistical Analysis*, Chaps. 9, 10.

Wilks, S. S., *Mathematical Statistics*, Chap. 6.

Yule, G. U. and Kendall, M. G., *An Introduction to the Theory of Statistics*, 14th ed., Chaps. 17, 18.

The publishers and the dates of publication of the books named in chapter reference lists are given in the bibliography at the end of this volume.

CHAPTER 8

Statistical Inference: Tests of Hypotheses

In introducing the subject of statistical inference we drew a distinction between estimation, the object of which is to locate a population parameter at a point or within stated limits, and the testing of hypotheses. We concern ourselves now with the theory of such tests and with their application.

The testing of hypotheses that refer to the actual world involves, in one form or another, the setting of hypotheses against data of observation. If observed facts are clearly inconsistent with a given hypothesis, it must be rejected. If the facts are not inconsistent with the hypothesis, the hypothesis is tenable. These simple statements require elaboration, of course, but they contain essential truths about the process by which scientific theories are tested, prior to acceptance or rejection. So far as the immediate evidence is concerned acceptance is always qualified; rejection often is. In the tests here in question decisions are made in terms of probabilities.

The procedures here to be discussed relate to statistical hypotheses. A *statistical hypothesis* is one that specifies properties of a distribution of a random variable. These properties (or parameters) are the hypothetical values with which we compare measures derived from an actual sample. The difference between an observed statistic and the corresponding hypothetical parameter is the central quantity with which the test deals. If this difference is small (what constitutes a "small" difference will be considered below) we may say that the facts are not inconsistent with the hypothesis; if the difference is great, we conclude that the facts are not consistent with the hypothesis.

The techniques and theory of statistical tests have been developed over the last half century, the greatest progress having been made in the last thirty years. Karl Pearson, "Student," R. A. Fisher, Jerzy Neyman and E. S. Pearson have made major contributions. The argument that is here briefly sketched deals with the theories of Neyman and E. S. Pearson.[1]

Notation. Certain symbols not hitherto used will be introduced in this discussion. The more important of these are given below:

H, H_0, H_1: hypotheses

T: a deviation from the mean of a normal distribution expressed in units of the standard deviation; a normal deviate

D: the difference between two arithmetic means

s_D: the standard error of the difference between means; written also as $s_{\bar{x}_1 - \bar{x}_2}$

$s_{s_1 - s_2}$: the standard error of the difference between two standard deviations

$s_{p_1 - p_2}$: the standard error of the difference between two proportions

t: the ratio of a normally distributed variable with zero mean to the square root of an independently distributed estimate of the variance of that variable

On the Theory of Statistical Tests

The theory of statistical tests may be introduced by citing two general principles:

1. In testing a particular statistical hypothesis H_0 we imply that it may be wrong. That is, we admit that there are hypotheses alternative to the one being tested. These alternative hypotheses should be considered explicitly in choosing an appropriate test.

2. When we test a hypothesis we should like to avoid errors. In the choice of a test we therefore try to minimize the frequency of errors that may be committed in applying it.

The Neyman-Pearson theory thus recognizes the hypothesis H_0,

---

[1] See Neyman and Pearson, Refs. 122, 123; Neyman, Refs. 116, 121.

the one explicitly defined as the subject of the test, and a family of alternative hypotheses, a member of which may be represented by H_1. When a test has been chosen (on principles to be referred to below) and applied, the investigator faces the possibility of two kinds of errors:

1. *An error of the first kind* (Type I) is committed when two conditions prevail:

    (a) The hypothesis H_0, which is being tested, is in fact true;

    (b) The result of the test leads to the rejection of the hypothesis H_0.

2. *An error of the second kind* (Type II) is committed when two conditions prevail:

    (a) The hypothesis H_0, which is being tested, is in fact false (some alternative hypothesis H_1 is true);

    (b) The result of the test leads to the acceptance of the hypothesis H_0.

The existence of two kinds of possible errors is distinctive of the problems faced in testing hypotheses. In *interval estimation,* one of the forms of statistical inference discussed in the preceding chapter, the investigator makes the flat statement that a given parameter falls within stated limits. The statement is false if the parameter in question does not fall within those limits. The investigator faces the possibility of but one type of error. A new theoretical problem is faced, thus, when we pass from interval estimation to the testing of hypotheses. The solution of this problem gave new power to statistical tools. In the present discussion we deal briefly with the general nature of the solution, before passing to applications.

In general terms, it is obviously desirable that tests should be employed that make the chances of both kinds of errors as small as possible. Since it is generally considered more important to avoid an error of the first kind than it is to avoid an error of the second kind, the test employed should be one that leads very infrequently to the rejection of a true hypothesis. This leads to the following working principle, in selecting among possible tests: An attempt is made, first, to control errors of Type I. That is, the probability of a Type I error is fixed arbitrarily at a level of significance, say α (alpha), which would ordinarily be one of the conventional limits 0.05 or 0.01. In comparing two tests for both of which the probability of a Type I error is α, we would choose that one for which the probability of a Type II error is the smaller.

A test of this sort rests upon the following reasoning: The observations included in any sample will define a *sample point E*. The whole sample space (or region) within which, in a given instance, points derived from all possible samples must fall is represented by the symbol W. (This region may be a straight line, a two-dimensional surface, or a more complex space, the number of dimensions depending upon the number of coordinates of the sample point E.) The whole region, W, is divided into two complementary spaces, one being the *region of rejection* (for which the symbol w is used) the other the *region of acceptance* $(W - w)$. As these terms suggest, the hypothesis being tested in a given instance is accepted if the sample point E falls in the region $W - w$; it is rejected if it falls in w. As we have noted, the probability that E will fall within w, the region of rejection, when the hypothesis is in fact true is called the *significance level* of the test. Where the significance level is to be set in a given case must be determined by the investigator, with reference to the possible consequences of errors of each of the two types.[2]

An example. We may illustrate the procedure by reference to a simple example (after Mood), involving a choice between two alternative hypotheses. The test will be based upon a single observation. Let us assume that a given population of x's is described by either the frequency curve A or the curve B, which are shown in Fig. 8.1. We are to test H_0, which is the hypothesis that the population in question has the distribution A. We set the significance level at 0.05. The single alternative hypothesis is H_1, which specifies that the population has the distribution B. One or the other is true.

The single observation x_1 on which the test is to be based will give us a point on the x-axis. Our problem is to define on this axis *intervals of acceptance* and of *rejection* (these correspond, of course,

[2] A logical burglar, pondering possible professional operations on a certain bank, might set up the hypothesis:

The bank is equipped with a burglar alarm.

He commits an error of Type I if, the hypothesis being in fact true, he rejects it and tries to rob the bank. The consequence is his arrest. If the hypothesis is, in fact, false, and he accepts it, abstaining from the attempt, he commits an error of Type II. In consequence he foregoes a possibly fruitful operation. An error of Type I might well seem to him to be more serious in its adverse consequences.

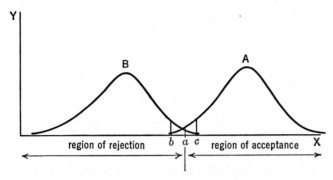

FIG. 8.1. An Illustration of Tests of Hypotheses Location of Regions of Acceptance and Rejection in a Simple Test.

to the *regions* set up for tests involving more dimensions). Having the information here assumed, i.e., information concerning the two distributions A and B, the problem is solved by locating on the x-axis the point a at which an ordinate of distribution A will divide the area under curve A into two segments including, respectively, 0.05 and 0.95 of the total (see Fig. 8.1). The region of acceptance will be the interval on the x-scale lying to the right of the point a; the region of rejection will be the interval to the left of a. H_0 will be accepted if the observation x_1 falls in the interval of acceptance, rejected if it falls in the interval of rejection.

It is clear that if H_0 is in fact true, the probability of x_1 falling to the right of point a is 0.95, of falling to the left, 0.05. Hence the possibility of an error of Type I (i.e., of rejecting H_0 when it is true) is 0.05. The location at point a of the division between the intervals of acceptance and rejection leaves open the possibility of an error of Type II (i.e., the acceptance of a false hypothesis). For if H_0 is in fact false (H_1 being true), there is a probability, though a small one, that an observation which is really drawn from distribution B will fall in the interval of acceptance for H_0. This probability is measured by the proportion of the total area of distribution B that falls in the interval of acceptance shown in Fig. 8.1.

The probability of an error of Type I, in respect of hypothesis H_0, may be modified at will. Thus if we wish to reduce the probability of such an error to, let us say, 0.0001, we could do so by setting at point b on the x-scale the dividing line between the intervals of acceptance and rejection for H_0. Point b has been so located as to divide the area under curve A into segments including, respectively 0.9999 and 0.0001 of the area under the curve. In so doing, of course, we increase the probability of a Type II error, for we increase the portion of the area under curve B that lies in the interval of acceptance for H_0. Conversely, we could move the point of division to c (see Fig. 8.1), which would, under the conditions here pictured, reduce to a negligible figure the probability of an error of Type II, but would increase materially the probability of an error of Type I.

A major criterion for choosing among possible tests has to do with their relative effectiveness in avoiding errors of Type II. It is, of course, desirable that when a given hypothesis H_0 is in fact false, the sample point E should fall in the critical region w, which is the region of rejection. When this occurs, the test is successful in detecting a false hypothesis. The probability that the test will do this is the measure of its *power*. Of two tests that are alike in respect of the probability of a Type I error, that one is the more powerful which is the more effective in detecting false hypotheses.

Neyman and Pearson have stressed one other criterion for use in evaluation of tests of hypotheses—that of bias. A stated hypothesis H_0, being tested, is either true or false. We should not like to reject it if it is true; we should like to reject it if it is false. If a given test is less likely to reject H_0 when it is true than when it is not true, the test is said to be *unbiased*. This is to say, for an unbiased test the probability that a stated hypothesis will be rejected is always a minimum when the hypothesis tested is true.

The object sought in the application of these various criteria is, of course, to minimize the chance of making a mistake, whether of Type I or of Type II. To this end, we wish to employ a technique that has high powers of discrimination—that will enable us to identify and thus to accept true hypotheses, and to identify and thus to reject false hypotheses.

The problem is not a simple one, nor have definitive solutions been reached for all problems of this sort. One important complexity arises out of the fact that in a particular case there may be many alternative false hypotheses, not merely one that may be set against a single true hypothesis. Thus we face a series of comparisons: H_0 the true hypothesis versus H_1' a given false hypothesis; H_0 against H_1'', another false hypothesis; H_0 against H_1''', a third false hypothesis, etc. For a fixed probability of a

Type I error, critical regions may vary from comparison to comparison.

Consider, as an example of this situation, the problem that is faced when one wishes to test the hypothesis that a sample yielding a given mean, say $\overline{X} = 38$, has been drawn from a parent population with mean $\mu = 40$. That is, the hypothesis H_0, which is true, is that $\mu = 40$. Actually there are a great many possible alternative hypotheses—that $\mu = 25$, that $\mu = 39$, that $\mu = 52$, etc. If, in fact, the hypothesis H_0 is true, a Type II error would be committed if the false hypothesis H_1' that $\mu = 25$ were accepted. But the Type II risk is very slight in this case, the difference between the true hypothesis and the false one being great. But for the alternative hypotheses $H_0 = 40$ and $H_1'' = 39$, the situation is different. The difference between the true and the false hypotheses is very small. The danger of a Type II error (which would be committed if the false hypothesis H_1'' were accepted) is very much greater than in the first example. Similarly, for other possible false hypotheses probabilities of a Type II error will vary. Which is to say, the critical region w' for one test will not be the same as the critical region w'' for another test.

The examples that follow illustrate procedures that are employed in testing various statistical hypotheses. (Applications of other tests will be given in later chapters.) These specific examples will give a measure of concreteness to the general statements about the theory of tests of significance. The examples to be cited are simple, intended only to indicate the nature of such tests and to suggest their fruitfulness.

Some Tests of Significance

Significance of a Mean. Weldon's data (see Table 6-1), relating to results obtained from tossing dice, present a typical problem. It will be recalled that since the appearance of a 4, 5, or 6 spot was counted as a success, $p = 0.5$, and $q = 0.5$; 12 dice were tossed on each throw, hence $n = 12$; the number of throws, 4096, gives us the value of N. The theoretical value of the mean result is $6 (= np)$; the theoretical value of the standard deviation is 1.732 $(= \sqrt{npq})$. The actual mean $\overline{X}$ was 6.139. Could this mean value have been obtained if the dice were actually true? Could our sample of 4096 tosses come from a population for which $\mu = 6$ and for which $\sigma = 1.732$?

At an earlier point we have discussed the sampling distribution of the arithmetic mean. We know that many means, derived from samples of size N drawn from a given parent population, will constitute a distribution having a mean (μ) equal to the mean of the parent population, and with standard deviation (σ_m) equal to $\sigma/\sqrt{N}$ (where σ is the standard deviation of the parent population and N is the sample size). With reference to our present problem, we know that the means of many samples drawn from a parent population with $\mu = 6.00$ and $\sigma = 1.732$ would be distributed normally with mean $= 6.00$ and $\sigma_m = 1.732/\sqrt{4096} = 0.027$. May we regard the mean we have actually obtained, 6.139, as a random member of such a distribution of arithmetic means?

The central measure in such a test is $\overline{X} - \mu$, the difference between sample mean and hypothetical mean. We set up the hypothesis H_0 that the true difference is zero. (In this form the hypothesis is often called the *null hypothesis*.) Our question is: Are the observed facts consistent with this hypothesis?

In the application of the test we express the deviation of sample mean from hypothetical mean in units of the standard deviation of the distribution of the means. Thus we have

$$T = \frac{\overline{X} - \mu}{\sigma_m} \tag{8.1}$$

$$= \frac{6.139 - 6.00}{0.027} = 5.1$$

Since the distribution of sample means to which σ_m relates is normal (see p. 170), the quantity T, which measures a deviation from the mean of a normal distribution in units of the standard deviation of that distribution, is to be interpreted as a normal deviate. In the present case we have a deviation (from the mean of a normal distribution) equal to 5.1 standard deviations. Is such a deviation a likely occurrence? The answer, of course, is No. If our sample mean 6.139 is to be regarded as actually a member of a population of means having an average value of 6.00 and a standard deviation of 0.027, it represents an event that is to be expected less than 1 time in 1,000,000. Such an event is so improbable that we must dismiss it as a possibility. Chance could not have accounted for such a large deviation. We conclude: The observed facts are not consistent with the null hypothesis, which must therefore be rejected. This leaves us with the positive conclusion that the mean of the parent population from which the sample was drawn was not 6.00; the dice were not balanced and true. The rejection, it is to be noted, must be in terms of probability. It is not impossible that true dice would, in a very rare combination, yield results of the kind we have observed. But when the probability of such results is so small (if the hypothesis in question were in fact true) that only a miracle, in effect, would account for them, we may with high confidence reject the hypothesis.

A question of central importance must be faced here: How small should be the probability (corresponding to a particular deviate T) to warrant rejection of a stated hypothesis? Where should we set the significance level? We must answer, first, that the setting of such a boundary must be in part arbitrary. What one investigator would regard as highly improbable might be regarded by a temperamentally more optimistic man as not unlikely. However, as we have noted on earlier pages, there is a general consensus that sets the limit of customary rejection at either $P = 0.05$ or $P = 0.01$. In using the lower of the two as the limit, we would say: The event that can happen only 1 time out of 100, or less frequently, does not happen in ordinary experience. Therefore, if T is equal to or greater than 2.576 the hypothesis is to be rejected. The same type of reasoning would be used for a limit set at $P = 0.05$ (for which the normal deviate T would equal 1.96), except that an event happening only 1 time in 20, or less frequently, would be regarded as too unlikely to warrant acceptance of the hypothesis.

When we say that a T of 2.576 represents a deviation that will be reached or exceeded only 1 time in 100, we are taking account of deviations *above and below* the hypothetical true mean. In the particular case we are dealing with, the sample mean 6.139 *exceeds* the hypothetical mean 6.00, but in testing the significance of such a difference it is usually proper to ask whether such an *absolute* difference, regardless of sign, may be attributed to chance. We have no reason in this case to expect bias in one direction, rather than the other, or to formulate a hypothesis involving deviations in one direction only. In other words, the appropriate test in this instance is a two-tailed test, meaning that in interpreting T we take account of areas in both tails of the normal distribution. The region of rejection includes both extremes of that distribution. There are cases in which deviations in one direction only are of concern; in these cases a one-tailed test is appropriate.

We have suggested above that it is well to consider the possible consequences of errors of Type I and Type II, in choosing boundaries of the region of rejection. If one believes that an error of the first kind (i.e., the rejection of a true hypothesis) is particularly undesirable, the significance level of the test may be pushed out. Thus one might decide to reject a stated hypothesis only in case of a divergence between observed and hypothetical values so great that it would occur only 1 time out of 1,000, or less frequently. That is, the value of T in such a test as that cited above would have to be 3.291, or greater, to warrant the conclusion that the observations were inconsistent with the hypothesis. On the other hand, if the danger of accepting a false hypothesis were particularly to be avoided, one might work with a significance level of 0.10 (corresponding to a T of 1.645). By this means we would reduce the likelihood of accepting a false hypothesis, although we should thereby increase the probability of rejecting a true hypothesis. Thus the selection of the significance level is a problem that is in some ways peculiar to each test, to be solved by the individual investigator. The Weldon problem that has served as our illustration above involves no special considerations one way or the other, since its interest is historical. But to one making professional use of dice the matter would be of particular concern. For the acceptance of dice as accurate when they are not (a Type II error) would affect the hazards of play to the presumed disadvantage of one party.

A somewhat different example is provided by data relating to the financial experience of buyers and sellers of securities. Table 8-1, which is taken from the report of an exhaustive study by Paul F. Wendt, shows the distribution of customers of a New York Stock Exchange firm, classified by amounts of realized profits, or losses. The sample here represented was chosen by random processes from among all customers whose invested capital amounted to less than $5,000. The trading experience recorded fell between 1933 and 1938. The mean of the distribution shown in Table 8-1 is $+ \$135.44$. The estimated standard deviation of the population, s', is $1,214.90$.

The universe of which this is a random sample is the total of all small investors (a group defined as those whose capital investment did not exceed $5,000) purchasing securities through member firms of the New York Stock Exchange during the period 1933-38. It is

TABLE 8–1

Frequency Distribution Showing the Investment Experience of 395 Customers
of a New York Stock Exchange Firm, 1933-1938*
(Realized profits and losses in a random sample of accounts having
invested capital of less than $5,000)

Class-interval† (dollars)	Midpoint (dollars)	Frequency
− 9,000 to − 8,000	− 8,500	1
− 4,000 to − 3,000	− 3,500	2
− 3,000 to − 2,000	− 2,500	7
− 2,000 to − 1,000	− 1,500	15
− 1,000 to 0	− 500	147
0 to + 1,000	+ 500	187
+ 1,000 to + 2,000	+ 1,500	23
+ 2,000 to + 3,000	+ 2,500	5
+ 3,000 to + 4,000	+ 3,500	2
+ 4,000 to + 5,000	+ 4,500	3
+ 5,000 to + 6,000	+ 5,500	1
+ 6,000 to + 7,000	+ 6,500	1
+ 9,000 to + 10,000	+ 9,500	1
		395

* Wendt, Ref. 189, p. 31.

† An entry exactly at the upper limit of any class, say with profits of $2,000, was put
in the class next above.

of some interest to know whether such investors gained or lost, on
the whole, in this period. We may set up the null hypothesis that
the true mean of realized profits and losses of this group was zero.
Are the sample results consistent with this hypothesis? It seems
appropriate to use a probability level of 0.01 in this test.

The test to be made is similar in form to that applied in the
preceding case, except that we now have no information about the
degree of dispersion in the parent population except that which is
afforded by the sample. Accordingly, in estimating the standard
error of the mean, we must use s' as an estimate of the population
σ. Thus

$$s_m = \frac{s'}{\sqrt{N}} = \frac{1214.90}{\sqrt{395}} = 61.13$$

For the measure T, which expresses the difference between sample mean and hypothetical mean in units of the standard error of the mean, we have,

$$T = \frac{\overline{X} - \mu}{s_m} = \frac{135.44 - 0}{61.13} = 2.22$$

This is to be interpreted as a normal deviate; a distribution of arithmetic means of samples of the size here considered would be normal. Moreover, we should use a two-tailed test, since in testing the hypothesis we should take account of the possibility of deviations on the loss side as well as on the profit side. A deviation of the magnitude here observed would occur, in a normal distribution, about 2.6 times in 100 trials. At the significance level we have set up, a difference as great as the one here recorded between the sample mean and the hypothetical value zero could occur as the result of random sampling fluctuations. We must conclude that the observations are not inconsistent with the hypothesis that small investors, on the whole, neither gained nor lost in the period 1933-38; we therefore accept the hypothesis.

Significance of a Difference between Two Means. A problem that arises frequently in statistical investigations is that of determining whether two samples could have been drawn from the same parent population, or from parent populations which are alike in respect of some stated parameter. There would, of course, solely as a result of sampling fluctuations, be some difference between corresponding measurements derived from two samples drawn by random methods from the same universe. Arithmetic means would differ; measures of dispersion or of skewness would differ. This problem may be approached by comparing any two statistics (e.g., standard deviations of two samples), or by comparing the frequency distributions of the two samples, in full. Usually interest attaches to particular statistics. Do the mean incomes of doctors and lawyers differ significantly? Is the standard deviation of hourly earnings greater among textile workers than among steel workers? At this point we consider the procedure employed in testing the significance of the difference between two arithmetic means.

The office of the Surgeon General of the United States Army has recorded the heights of a sample of army inductees in 1943 and of a similar sample in 1917.[3] Summary measures follow:

	1943 sample	1917 sample
N	67,995	868,445
Mean height	68.11 inches	67.49 inches
Standard deviation	2.59 inches	2.71 inches

Are these results consistent with the hypothesis that the 1943 and the 1917 samples came from parent populations with equal arithmetic means? The null hypothesis is a statement, in effect, that no change occurred between 1917 and 1943 in the average height of American males of service age.

The measure that concerns us is D, the difference between the two arithmetic means. In the present case $D = 68.11 - 67.49$, or $+ 0.62$. The null hypothesis specifies that the true difference between the means is zero. If we were in fact drawing successive pairs of samples from parent populations with the same mean we should obtain a series of values of D, some plus, and some minus. The sampling distribution of D's thus derived has been established. The D's would be distributed in accordance with the normal law about a mean value zero. The parameter of this sampling distribution of immediate concern to us is its standard deviation. How great would the dispersion of these sample D's be? It has been determined that under these conditions the dispersion of D's would be measured by

$$\sigma_D = \sqrt{\frac{\sigma_1^2}{N_1} + \frac{\sigma_2^2}{N_2}} \qquad (8.2)$$

where σ_1 is the standard deviation of the population from which the first sample comes, σ_2 is the standard deviation of the population from which the second sample comes, and the two N's define the numbers of observations in the two samples. In fact we do not know the two σ's. We substitute for them the s's of the corresponding samples. We have, therefore, as our estimate of σ_D

$$s_D = \sqrt{\frac{s_1^2}{N_1} + \frac{s_2^2}{N_2}} \qquad (8.3)$$

---

[3] "Height and Weight Data for Men Inducted into the Army and for Rejected Men." *Report No. 1-BM*, Army Service Forces, Office of the Surgeon General, Medical Statistics Division.

(In view of the size of the samples we may neglect the loss of one degree of freedom in estimating s.) Formula (8.3) may be put in the form

$$s_D = \sqrt{s_{m_1}^2 + s_{m_2}^2} \tag{8.4}$$

where each s_m is the standard error of the mean of a given sample.

In testing the null hypothesis in this case we shall use a confidence level of 0.01. The measurement needed for this test, derived from formula (8.3), is

$$s_D = \sqrt{\frac{2.59^2}{67,995} + \frac{2.71^2}{868,445}}$$
$$= \sqrt{0.000106}$$
$$= 0.01$$

The test is made in terms of T, the discrepancy between the observed D and the hypothetical value zero, expressed in units of the standard error of D. Thus we have

$$T = \frac{D - 0}{s_D} \tag{8.5}$$
$$= \frac{0.62 - 0}{0.01}$$
$$= 62.0$$

This value of T, regarded as a normal deviate, represents an infinitely small probability. The observed difference between the sample means of 1943 inductees and 1917 recruits is far too great to be attributed to the play of chance. We may reject the null hypothesis with a very high degree of confidence. The two samples did not come from populations with equal arithmetic means.[4]

In the example just cited the test relates to the standard error of the difference between independent random variables. As in earlier illustrations, we treat the mean of the 1943 sample as one value of a random variable. Other values of the variable would be the means of similar samples drawn from the same parent population. Similarly, the mean of the 1917 sample is regarded as

---

[4] If we had been testing the hypothesis that the two samples came from the same parent population, we should have regarded the two sample variances s_1^2 and s_2^2 as estimates of the same population variance. It would be appropriate in this case to use deviations from the two sample means as bases for a single pooled estimate of the population variance, using this single variance as the numerator of each of the terms under the radical sign in formula (8.3). See formulas (15.7) and (15.8) for a similar procedure with small samples.

a member of a series of random variables. The following general rule holds: *The standard error of the difference between two independent random variables is equal to the square root of the sum of their variances.* This is precisely what we have in formula (8.4). (The standard error of the *sum* of two independent random variables is also equal to the square root of the sum of their variances.) Emphasis should be placed on the word *independent*. If the random variables compared (in this case the means) are not independent, the standard error of their difference will be reduced by an amount depending on the degree of correlation between the two variables, while the standard error of their sum will be correspondingly increased.[5] In the present instance the variables are completely independent. As an example of related variables we may cite the discount rates of commercial banks and of Federal Reserve banks, discussed in the following chapter. These rates are not independent random variables, for commercial bank rates in a given district are immediately affected by changes in Federal Reserve rates in that district. The standard error of the difference between the means of these two sets of rates would not be given by formula (8.2).

For tests of this sort, when samples are large, it is not necessary that the parent populations from which the samples come be normal in their distribution. For samples of the size here considered the distributions of means would be normal, and the distribution of D's would be normal, whether parent populations were normal or not. For the full accuracy of such tests, equality of the variances of the parent populations from which the samples come is a necessary condition when samples are small and unequal in size. (Other considerations enter also when samples are small, as we shall see.) For large samples, however, a difference between population variances will not invalidate the test.

Significance of a Difference between Proportions. Another test of great practical utility involves the comparison of proportions, or percentages. We may have for samples for each of two industries the percentage of workers unemployed at a given time. Is an observed difference attributable to chance, or does it provide evidence of a real difference between the industries in the incidence

---

[5] The general concept of correlation will be introduced in Chapter 9. In the meantime the student unfamiliar with the concept may simply take the term to be synonymous with nonindependent.

of unemployment? The percentage of short business cycles recorded for the United States is smaller than the percentage of short cycles in the experience of Great Britain. Is the observed difference in relative frequencies indicative of a real difference between the forces determining cycle durations in the two countries?

For the standard error of a proportion, such as f_s/n (f_s being the frequency of successes and n the total number of independent events), we have

$$\sigma_p = \sqrt{pq/n} \tag{8.6}$$

where p is the proportion in question and q is $1 - p$.

In a problem of the type here in question, the critical figure is the difference between relative frequencies, or proportions. If two measures of relative frequency are independent of one another we may apply the general rule cited above for the standard error of the difference between two independent random variables (p. 207). Each of the two proportions is here regarded as a member of a series of random variables. In testing the relevant null hypothesis, the variance of the first random variable is $\bar{p}\bar{q}/n_1$; the variance of the second is $\bar{p}\bar{q}/n_2$. (Here $\bar{p}$, the weighted mean proportion $(n_1p_1 + n_2p_2)/(n_1 + n_2)$, is our best estimate of the population p.) The two variances differ only in respect of n, for by hypothesis the samples come from the same universe. Thus we have

$$s_{p_1-p_2} = \sqrt{\frac{\bar{p}\bar{q}}{n_1} + \frac{\bar{p}\bar{q}}{n_2}} \tag{8.7}$$

where $s_{p_1-p_2}$ is the estimated standard error of the difference between two proportions.

To illustrate the use of this test we may use data cited by Wendt in his study of the financial experience of customers of a Stock Exchange firm for the period 1933-38. Wendt divided the members of a sample of 285 customers into an "investment" group, whose dealings were largely in bonds and in dividend-paying common and preferred stocks, and a "speculative" group, whose dealings were largely in low-priced, speculative shares.[6] Of 98 customers in the investment group 68 showed profits while 30 showed losses. (These are *realized* profits and losses. The record was less favorable after adjustment for book profits and losses.) Thus we have $p_1 = 68/98$, or 0.694; $q_1 = 1 - 0.694 = 0.306$. In the speculative group 105 customers out of 187 showed profits, while 82 showed losses.

[6] Wendt, Ref. 189, pp. 149-158. What I have here termed the "speculative" group is Wendt's "full-lot speculative."

Therefore $p_2 = 105/187 = 0.561$; $q_2 = 0.439$. The investment group, as here sampled, fared better in respect of realized gains than did the speculative group. For the difference between p_1 and p_2 we have $0.694 - 0.561$, or 0.133. Is this difference indicative of a real difference between the "populations" from which the investment and speculative samples come? In this test we shall use an 0.01 level of significance.

On the assumption that the conditions of simple sampling (see p. 203) prevailed in Wendt's operations, we may estimate the standard error of the difference between the two proportions from the relation shown in formula (8.7) on page 208. The weighted mean proportions are $\bar{p} = 0.607$, $\bar{q} = 0.393$. Thus we have

$$s_{p_1-p_2} = \sqrt{\frac{0.2386}{98} + \frac{0.2386}{187}}$$
$$= 0.061$$

The observed difference between the two proportions is 0.133. We set up the null hypothesis, that the true difference between the two relative frequencies in the populations from which they come is zero. In applying the test for significance we are asking, therefore, whether the quantity 0.133 may be regarded as a single observation on a normally distributed variate with a mean of zero and a standard deviation of 0.061. (The distribution of the quantity $p_1 - p_2$ will approach normality for large samples. We may therefore assume normality in the present instance, although with small samples this assumption would not be warranted.) Expressing the deviation of the observed difference from the hypothetical difference in units of the standard error of the difference, we have

$$T = \frac{0.133 - 0}{0.061} = 2.18$$

A deviation as great as this, or greater, might be encountered about 2.9 times in 100 trials as a result of chance fluctuations. Since we are working with an 0.01 criterion in this case, we are not justified in rejecting the hypothesis. The difference is large enough, it is true, to suggest that the parent population of which the investment group was a sample fared somewhat better in realized gains than did the "speculative" population. But the difference is not clearly significant.

In the following example we have "population" values for the p's and q's, together with values from a sample drawn from the parent population. The *World Almanac* has reported that 8.28 percent of all males in the United States are named John; 0.43 percent are named Clarence. Of a sample of 400,000 males having common surnames (such as Smith, Brown, or Jones) 5.48 percent were named John, 1.04 named Clarence. These proportions suggest that parents whose surnames are common are less likely than are parents with uncommon surnames to select a common given name for their sons, and more likely to select a relatively uncommon given name. In this case, since we have a population value, we may estimate the standard error of a proportion from the general expression for the standard deviation of a distribution of relative frequencies, $\sqrt{pq/n}$. We may ask: Does the proportion of males in the sample who are named John, 0.0548, differ materially from the universe proportion, 0.0828? For a sample of this size

$$s_p = \sqrt{\frac{0.0828 \times 0.9172}{400,000}} = 0.000436$$

We here use the universe values of p and of q, and the N of the sample for the n (the number of independent events) of the formula. The test then takes the form

$$T = \frac{p_0 - p_a}{s_p} \tag{8.8}$$

where p_0 is the observed proportion of males named John in the sample of 400,000, p_a is the anticipated proportion, on the hypothesis that the probability of a male having the given name of John is the same in the sample of 400,000 as in the general population, and s_p is the standard error of the proportion in question for samples of 400,000. In this case

$$T = \frac{0.0548 - 0.0828}{0.000436} = -64.2$$

This value of T, interpreted as a normal deviate, represents, of course, a deviation so extreme as to be impossible. The probability of being named John is significantly smaller for the members of the group with common surnames than it is for members of the population of males at large. A similar test applied to the sample proportion named Clarence also indicates a clearly significant difference, the sample proportion this time being in excess of the universe proportion.

Some General Considerations Bearing on Tests of Hypotheses

Our chief concern in this chapter has been with the testing of statistical hypotheses (in dealing with small samples we reverted briefly to an aspect of the subject of estimation). This discussion has touched upon some of the more general aspects of the theory of inquiry, but it has dealt, in the main, with methodology. In concluding the discussion it is proper to stress certain logical considerations that were not fully developed in the preceding pages. Three points of central importance are to be made.

1. A generalization (a hypothesis) suggested by the observations in a given sample cannot be tested against that sample. There must be *predesignation* of the hypothesis, or of the population parameter, that is to be tested.[7] If a given sample of business cycles should suggest that the mean duration of business cycles in the United States is 40 months, we could hardly use the mean of that sample in testing the hypothetical mean of 40 months. The fallacy of such a test is obvious, yet this type of circularity is not uncommon. A technique for forecasting the level of wholesale prices, the prices of securities, or the state of business is often tested against the historical record that suggested the technique. Of course, this is not to say that an investigator should not be open-minded to theories that may be suggested by observations. But when a theory is thus suggested, it must be tested against a new set of observations. (We have already referred to the rule that an investigator should, *before* he applies a test of significance, designate the confidence level according to which he will accept or reject the hypothesis in question. The principle here is the same.)

2. Statistical evidence never provides positive proof of the truth of a hypothesis. The essence of statistical testing is that the

A player might draw (with replacement) from a pack of cards a four of diamonds, a king of spades, a five of clubs, and a nine of clubs, and then exclaim at the remarkable fact that just these four cards should have turned up—a combination to be expected only 24 times in 7,311,616 trials (the order of draw is not assumed to matter). This is not remarkable after the event. It would only have been remarkable had the player predesignated the result by announcing before his draw that these four particular cards would appear. Without this predesignation the player is, in effect, setting up the hypothesis that he will draw a four of diamonds, a king of spades, a five and a nine of clubs *after* he has drawn those precise cards.

In an incident famous in baseball history Babe Ruth, being heckled by the opposing team, pointed to a spot in the right-field bleachers and then proceeded, on the next pitch, to hit a home run to that precise spot. This was predesignation.

facts are given a chance to disprove hypotheses; the facts do not prove hypotheses. The reader will have noticed the form of the conclusion reached after a test is applied. One may say, "The observations are not inconsistent with the hypothesis," or, "The observations are not consistent with the hypothesis." The second statement, it is clear, is more decisive than the first. When we reject a hypothesis we may be able to do so with a high degree of confidence. If the difference between an observed statistic and a hypothetical parameter is so great that chance might be expected to lead to such a divergence only 1 time in 10,000,000 trials, the investigator may be reasonably sure that there is a true difference, and so reject the hypothesis. (But there will always remain a slight probability that the rejection was unjustified.) However, acceptance of a hypothesis can never carry the degree of confidence that would attach to a rejection based on a 1/10,000,000 probability. Indeed, these facts are more likely to be consistent with a false hypothesis (of which there will be legion) than with the true hypothesis. Choice among hypotheses with which the facts are consistent must be based on rational grounds, not on empirical evidence. This last statement carries us to the third of our three points.

3. If we are to have confidence in a hypothesis it must have support beyond the statistical evidence. It must have a rational basis. This phrase suggests two conditions: The hypothesis must be "reasonable," in the sense of concordance with *a priori* expectations. Secondly, the hypothesis must fit logically into the relevant body of established knowledge. Reference to statistical evidence is essential and important in determining the degree of confidence we may have in a hypothesis, but the support we get from this side is of a negative sort. We say of it that it does not disprove the hypothesis. Positive elements of support come from the side of reason.[8]

---

[8] The condition that a hypothesis must have a rational basis is, of course, necessary. Yet the investigator should heed a warning voiced by Lord Russell against excessive emphasis on conformity to expectations and to existing knowledge, in appraising ideas about nature. If hypotheses that do not conform to existing knowledge were to be *ipso facto* rejected, the advance of knowledge would be seriously retarded. Since there is a danger of self-delusion in research, danger of finding only that for which one is looking, the completely unexpected may sometimes have a sounder claim than does that which appears to be perfectly rational because it conforms so nicely to existing patterns of thought. Thus, says Russell, the quantum theory, which broke sharply with the body of traditional thought about the physical world, has for that very reason strong claim to acceptance.

REFERENCES

Anderson, R. L. and Bancroft, T. A., *Statistical Theory in Research*, Chap. 11.

Churchman, C. W., *Theory of Experimental Inference*.

Clark, C. E., *An Introduction to Statistics*, Chap. 6.

Cramér, H., *Mathematical Methods of Statistics*, Chap. 35.

Deming, W. E., *Some Theory of Sampling*, pp. 537-554.

Dixon, W. J. and Massey, F. J. Jr., *Introduction to Statistical Analysis*, Chap. 7.

Fisher, Sir Ronald (R. A.), *The Design of Experiments*, 4th ed.,

Fisher, Sir Ronald (R. A.), *Statistical Methods for Research Workers*, 11th ed., Chap. 5.

Freeman, H. A., *Industrial Statistics*, Chap. 1.

Goulden, C. H., *Methods of Statistical Analysis*, 2nd ed., Chap. 4.

Hoel, P. G., *Introduction to Mathematical Statistics*, 2nd ed., Chap. 10.

Mather, K., *Statistical Analysis in Biology*, 2nd ed., Chaps. 4, 5.

Mood, A. M., *Introduction to the Theory of Statistics*, pp. 245-270.

Neyman, J., "Basic Ideas and Some Recent Results of the Theory of Testing Statistical Hypotheses," *Journal of the Royal Statistical Society*, Vol. 105, 1942.

Neyman, J., *Lectures and Conferences on Mathematical Statistics and Probability*, 2nd ed., Chap. 1, part 3.

Neyman, J., and Pearson, E. S., "Contributions to the Theory of Testing Statistical Hypotheses," *Statistical Research Memoirs*, Vol. 1, 1936; Vol. 2, 1938.

Neyman, J. and Pearson, E. S., "On the Problem of the Most Efficient Tests of Statistical Hypotheses," *Philosophical Transactions of the Royal Society*, Vol. 231, 1933.

Rosander, A. C., *Elementary Principles of Statistics*, Chaps. 24, 27.

Tintner, G., *Mathematics and Statistics for Economists*, Chap. 25.

Tippett, L. H. C., *The Methods of Statistics*, 4th ed., pp. 86-103, 141-149.

Tippett, L. H. C., *Technological Applications of Statistics*, Chaps. 8, 9.

Wald, A., *Statistical Decision Functions*.

Walker, H. M. and Lev, J., *Statistical Inference*, Chaps. 3, 7.

Wilks, S. S., *Elementary Statistical Analysis*, Chap. 11.

Wilks, S. S., *Mathematical Statistics*, Chap. 7.

The publishers and the dates of publication of the books named in chapter reference lists are given in the bibliography at the end of this volume.

CHAPTER 9

:

The Measurement of Relationship:

Linear Correlation

Introduction

The problems we have discussed in the preceding chapters have dealt primarily with the behavior of a single variable. The arrangement of the values of a single variable along a scale may be described by measures of central tendency, or of location, and by accompanying measures that define the pattern of variation about a central value. The examples of statistical inference so far considered have dealt with the estimation of parameter values for a single variable, or to tests involving hypothetical values of such a variable. In dealing with theoretical distributions in Chapter 6 we introduced the concept of frequency, measured along the vertical or y-axis of a coordinate system, as a function of a variable x, usually measured as a deviation along the horizontal axis. That is, the frequency of occurrence of a single value is presented as *dependent* upon the magnitude of the deviation of that value from a specified origin. The mathematical expression for such a theoretical distribution is a statement of a *functional relation* between a dependent and an independent variable. Such relations of a simple type were briefly considered in Chapter 2. We now open a more systematic discussion of methods employed in the measurement of relations among variable quantities. Our concern here will be with the manner in which two (or more) variables fluctuate with reference to one another. A suggestive general term for such joint behavior is *covariation*; the term commonly employed in statistical literature is correlation. In the present chapter we deal with the simplest form of covariation, linear correlation between two variables.

As a familiar example of simple correlation we may refer again to the relation between the number of rings in the trunk of a tree (Y) and the age of the tree (X). For an X-value of 3, Y will be equal to 3; for an X-value of 5, Y will be equal to 5. This relation is shown in Fig. 2.3, on p. 11. Here we have a perfect relationship; X determines Y completely. All the plotted points lie on a straight line that can be drawn through them. Fig. 9.1 (based on Table 9-1)

FIG. 9.1. Personal Net Savings and Disposable Personal Income in the United States, 1948-1953.

TABLE 9–1

Personal Net Savings and Disposable Personal Income in the United States, 1948-1953 (in billions of dollars)

	Personal net savings	Disposable personal income
1948	10.0	188
1949	7.6	188
1950	12.1	206
1951	17.7	226
1952	18.4	237
1953	20.0	250

shows a different situation. Here are plotted aggregate personal net savings, in billions of dollars, as estimated for the United States for the years 1948-53, and corresponding figures for aggregate disposable personal income (i.e., personal income less personal taxes). It is to be expected that personal savings will be affected by the magnitude of personal income. It is also to be expected that the relationship will be imperfect, since factors other than size of income affect consumers' decisions on the division of income between consumption and saving. These expectations are borne out by Fig. 9.1. (The period covered is, of course, too short to provide evidence of anything like a consistent relationship; these fragmentary data are here used merely for illustrative purposes.) The general tendency of savings to rise as disposable income rises may be defined by a line drawn through the plotted points, but it is clear that what is defined is a tendency, not an invariant relationship.

The first task in a problem of this sort is that of defining the relationship between dependent and independent variables, whether it be perfect, as in the tree example, or merely a tendency to which there are exceptions, as in the other example. In general terms, for the linear case, we must establish the values of a and b in the equation to a straight line, $Y = a + bX$. For the first example given above this presents no problem. It is obvious that the equation desired is $Y = X$. The first constant on the right hand side of the general expression disappears, i.e., $a = 0$; the constant b is equal to 1. But the simplicity of this problem is quite exceptional. The situation represented in Fig. 9.1 is the usual one. Any two of the six points here plotted would define a straight line; fifteen different lines might be obtained. But no one of these lines would be accepted as satisfactorily defining the relationship that concerns us. What we want is the single straight line that best describes the *average relationship* between Y and X, that best defines the tendency for Y and X to vary together. We wish to determine values of a and b in the general equation to a straight line that may be regarded as *best* in the light of the evidence we have.

A simple illustration will serve to demonstrate an approximative method and the preferred method of doing this. Nine points (1,3; 2,4; 3,6; 4,5; 5,10; 6,9; 7,10; 8,12; 9,11—the X-value being given first in each pair of coordinates) are plotted in Fig. 9.2. Our problem is the fitting of a straight line to these points. By inspection, rough values of a and b may be determined. A transparent

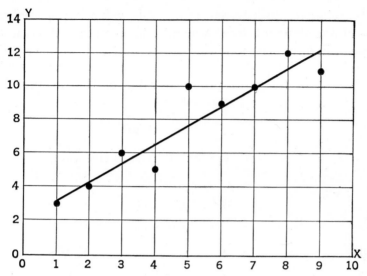

FIG. 9.2. Illustrating the Fitting of a Straight Line to Nine Points.

ruler may be used in approximating the desired function. The slope of the line thus laid out may be measured, the y-intercept determined, and the desired equation thus approximated. Obviously this is a loose and uncertain method; the results obtained by different individuals may be expected to differ widely. We need a more objective procedure for selecting a line that may be considered "best." One such procedure for determining the constants a and b for such a line of best fit is the method of least squares. Reference has been made to this method in preceding chapters, in connection with the problem of estimation. Some of its limitations were there noted. We here deal with it in simple terms as a generally useful procedure for estimating the values of constants when observations conflict.

The Method of Least Squares. Assume that we have a number of observed values of a certain quantity, and that these observed values differ. We wish to obtain the most probable value of the quantity being measured. It is capable of demonstration that the most probable value of the quantity is that value for which the sum of the squares of the residuals is a minimum. (A "residual" is of course a difference between an estimated value and an observed value.) This is true of the arithmetic mean of the observed values. Thus, if a given distance be measured by a number of individuals, with varying results, the most probable value is the arithmetic mean of the different measurements. The process of computing the mean involves the following steps, which are enumerated for the purpose of simplifying the later explanation. We seek a result, a statement of the most probable value of the distance being measured, which will take the form:

$$M = \text{(a constant)}$$

Let us say we have three approximations to this value:

$$M = 5{,}672 \text{ feet}$$
$$M = 5{,}671 \text{ feet}$$
$$M = 5{,}676 \text{ feet}$$

adding, $$3M = 17{,}019 \text{ feet}$$

Since there is but one unknown, M, it may be derived directly from this equation, and we have

$$M = 5{,}673 \text{ feet}$$

This is the value for which the sum of the squares of the deviations is a minimum.

A similar problem arises when the relation between two variables is being measured. Our goal in this case is an equation describing this relationship. However, we have secured varying results that do not agree precisely as to the constants in the equation of relationship.

In other words, our plotted points do not all lie on the same line. What are the most probable values of the constants in the required equation? The answer is analogous to that given when a single quantity was being measured. We seek the constants which, when the resulting equation is plotted, will give a line from which the deviations of the separate points, when squared and totaled, will be a minimum. Assuming that each pair of measurements gives an approximation to the true relationship between the variables, we wish to find the most probable relationship, and this is given by the line for which the sum of the squared deviations is a minimum.

We have, in the present example, nine pairs of values for X and Y. Substituting these values in the generalized form of the linear equation, $Y = a + bX$, we secure the following observation equations:

$$3 = a + 1b$$
$$4 = a + 2b$$
$$6 = a + 3b$$
$$5 = a + 4b$$
$$10 = a + 5b$$
$$9 = a + 6b$$
$$10 = a + 7b$$
$$12 = a + 8b$$
$$11 = a + 9b$$

Any two of these equations could be solved as simultaneous equations, and values of a and b secured. But these values would not satisfy the remaining equations. Our problem is to combine the nine observation equations so as to secure two *normal equations*, which, when solved simultaneously, will give the most probable values of a and b. The first of these normal equations is secured by multiplying each of the observation equations by the coefficient of a, the first unknown in that equation, and adding the equations obtained in this way. Since the coefficient of a in the present case is 1 throughout, the nine observation equations are unchanged by the process of multiplication. The second of the normal equations is secured by multiplying each of the observation equations by the coefficient of b, the second unknown in that equation, and adding the equations obtained. Thus the first equation is multiplied throughout by 1, the second by 2, and so on. The process of securing the two normal equations is illustrated in Table 9-2.

TABLE 9–2

Derivation of Normal Equations from Observation Equations

$3 = a + 1b$	$3 = 1a + 1b$
$4 = a + 2b$	$8 = 2a + 4b$
$6 = a + 3b$	$18 = 3a + 9b$
$5 = a + 4b$	$20 = 4a + 16b$
$10 = a + 5b$	$50 = 5a + 25b$
$9 = a + 6b$	$54 = 6a + 36b$
$10 = a + 7b$	$70 = 7a + 49b$
$12 = a + 8b$	$96 = 8a + 64b$
$11 = a + 9b$	$99 = 9a + 81b$
$70 = 9a + 45b$	$418 = 45a + 285b$

The two normal equations are

$$70 = 9a + 45b$$
$$418 = 45a + 285b$$

It remains to solve these equations for a and b. By multiplying the first equation by 5 and subtracting it from the second, a may be eliminated; a value of $\frac{68}{60}$, or 1.133, is found for b. Substituting this value in either of the equations, a value of 2.111 is secured for a. The equation to the best fitting straight line is, therefore,

$$Y = 2.111 + 1.133X$$

In the actual application of the method it is not necessary to write out and total the equations, as is done above. We need only insert the proper values in the two equations,

$$\Sigma(Y) = Na + b\Sigma(X) \tag{9.1}$$

$$\Sigma(XY) = a\Sigma(X) + b\Sigma(X^2) \tag{9.2}$$

where Σ indicates a summation process.

The work of computation is facilitated by a tabular arrangement similar to that shown in Table 9-3. The normal equations for a

TABLE 9–3

Computation of Values Required in Fitting a Straight Line

X	Y	XY	X^2	
1	3	3	1	$N = 9$
2	4	8	4	$\Sigma(X) = 45$
3	6	18	9	$\Sigma(Y) = 70$
4	5	20	16	$\Sigma(X^2) = 285$
5	10	50	25	$\Sigma(XY) = 418$
6	9	54	36	
7	10	70	49	
8	12	96	64	
9	11	99	81	
45	70	418	285	

specific problem are secured by substituting in the standard equations (9.1) and (9.2) above the values given at the right of that table. The results are of course identical with those obtained from the observation equations.

When the equation to the best fitting straight line has been obtained the values of Y corresponding to given values of X may be computed and compared with the observed values. Table 9-4 presents the results secured.

TABLE 9–4

Comparison of Observed and Computed Values of a Variable Quantity*

X	Y_0	Y_c	v $(Y_0 - Y_c)$	v^2	Xv
	(observed)	(computed)			
1	3	$3.2\frac{4}{9}$	$-\ .2\frac{4}{9}$	.0597	$-\ .2\frac{4}{9}$
2	4	$4.3\frac{7}{9}$	$-\ .3\frac{7}{9}$	.1427	$-\ .7\frac{5}{9}$
3	6	$5.5\frac{1}{9}$	$+\ .4\frac{8}{9}$	.2390	$+\ 1.4\frac{6}{9}$
4	5	$6.6\frac{4}{9}$	$-\ 1.6\frac{4}{9}$	2.7041	$-\ 6.5\frac{7}{9}$
5	10	$7.7\frac{7}{9}$	$+\ 2.2\frac{2}{9}$	4.9381	$+\ 11.1\frac{1}{9}$
6	9	$8.9\frac{1}{9}$	$+\ .0\frac{8}{9}$	.0079	$+\ .5\frac{3}{9}$
7	10	$10.0\frac{4}{9}$	$-\ .0\frac{4}{9}$	.0020	$-\ .3\frac{1}{9}$
8	12	$11.1\frac{7}{9}$	$+\ .8\frac{2}{9}$	.6760	$+\ 6.5\frac{7}{9}$
9	11	$12.3\frac{1}{9}$	$-\ 1.3\frac{1}{9}$	1.7190	$-\ 11.8$
			0.0	10.4885	0.0

* The common fractions are retained in certain columns in order that the sum of the deviations may be exactly zero.

The sum of the deviations of the plotted points from the line is zero. The sum of the deviations when each is multiplied by the corresponding value of X is also zero. The accuracy of the actual calculations involved in fitting may be tested in this way. The sum of the squares of the deviations, 10.4885, is a minimum. Any change in the value of a or b would give a line for which the sum of the squared deviations would exceed 10.4885.

We have discussed the technique of least squares because of its bearing on the problem of defining relations between variables. This problem is faced in all fields of inquiry. In some cases in the realm of the physical sciences the relations that prevail are invariant. Thus the speed of a body falling in a vacuum is a direct function of the time it has fallen. In a perfect vacuum the relationship is perfect; there are no departures from the relation specified by the equation $y = gt$ (where y is the speed, t the time of fall, and g the gravitational constant). But in the social and biological sciences perfect mechanical relationships are not found. We find tendencies, relationships that hold on the average. Observations do not accord without exception to a mathematically definable "law." Causal forces are complex, not single, and isolation of one or two factors is usually impossible. Thus the height and weight of individuals are related, but not in a mechanical way; the price of cotton is related to the supply of cotton, but other factors also influence the price; earnings are influenced by the productivity of labor, but are not determined by this factor alone. In all such cases as these the determination of an equation of relationship calls for an averaging process by which "most probable" values of the constants in the equation may be estimated from varying observations. The method of least squares is an instrument appropriate to this problem. This method, we should note, is fully justified as a means of estimating "most probable" values of desired constants only when the distribution of deviations is normal. Practically, the method is used as a convenient and simple procedure for approximating the desired values even when more complex procedures (maximum likelihood for non-normal cases) would give more defensible results.

Notation. In general the system of notation employed in this chapter on correlation follows the practice of earlier chapters. Certain new symbols are introduced.

$s_{y.x}$: the standard error of estimate of Y, as estimated from X

$s_{x.y}$: the standard error of estimate of X, as estimated from Y

r: the coefficient of correlation; often with subscripts, as r_{yx}, the first subscript indicating the dependent variable, the second the independent variable

ρ (rho): a population value of a coefficient of correlation

b_{yx}: a coefficient of regression, subscripts indicating dependent and independent variables

β_{yx}: (beta with subscript yx) the population value of b_{yx}

Y_c or y_c: a value of Y or of y computed from a regression equation

d_{yc}: the deviation of a value of Y_c from the mean Y

v: a residual; the deviation of Y from Y_c

s_{yc}: the standard deviation of a series of Y_c values

p or p_{xy}: the mean product of the paired values of two variables, the origin being at the point of averages; this quantity is sometimes called the *covariance*

s_{xy}: the covariance of a sample; p_{xy}

σ_{xy}: the population covariance; the population equivalent of p_{xy}

p': the mean product of the paired values of two variables, the origin being elsewhere than at the point of averages

d_{yx}: a coefficient of determination, subscripts indicating dependent and independent variables; a quantity equal to r_{yx}^2

z': a logarithmic transformation of r

ζ (zeta): the population value of z'

s_r: an estimate of the standard error of r; when written σ_r, the population value of s_r

s_z': the estimated standard error of z'

s_b: an estimate of the standard error of the coefficient of regression; when written σ_b, the population of s_b

r_r: a value of Spearman's coefficient of rank correlation obtained from a sample

ρ_r: a population value of Spearman's coefficient

s_{r_r}: the estimated standard error of r_r

As in earlier chapters, capital letters (X, Y) are used to represent original values of the variables, as measured from the zero points on the scale of actual values. Small letters (x, y) are used for values of variables expressed as deviations from their respective arithmetic means. Small letters with prime marks (x', y') are used for deviations from arbitrary origins.

The Relation between Family Expenditures for Current Consumption and Family Income after Taxes: Averages by Cities

As a typical example, illustrating the derivation of descriptive measures, we consider the relation between expenditures for purposes of current consumption and current family income after taxes. The data, which relate to income and expenditures in 1950, are averages for 33 small cities which constitute a representative sample of United States cities with populations from 2,500 to 30,500.[1] These averages are given in columns (2) and (3) of Table 9-5. (In interpreting conclusions the reader will bear in mind that the city, not the individual family, is the unit of observation.)

These data are plotted in Fig. 9.3, each dot defining the position

FIG. 9.3. Family Consumption Expenditures and Family Income: Averages by Cities,* 1950, with Line of Average Relation.

* A sample of 33 cities with populations of 2,500 to 30,500.

[1] The materials are from the Survey of Consumer Expenditures in 1950, conducted by the U. S. Bureau of Labor Statistics. Definitions, details of the sampling procedure, and some preliminary results are given in "Family Income, Expenditures, and Savings in 1950," *Bulletin No. 1097* (Revised) of the Bureau of Labor Statistics, June, 1953.

TABLE 9–5

Average Current Family Income after Taxes and Average Family
Expenditures for Current Consumption in Cities with Populations of
2,500 to 30,500 United States, 1950*
(Both variables in thousands of dollars)

(1)	(2)	(3)	(4)	(5)	(6)
City	Average Current Family Income	Average Family Expenditures for Current Consumption			
	X	Y	XY	X^2	Y^2
Anna, Ill.	3.60	3.40	12.2400	12.9600	11.5600
Antioch, Calif.	5.10	4.52	23.0520	26.0100	20.4304
Barre, Vt.	3.78	3.90	14.7420	14.2884	15.2100
Camden, Ark.	3.04	3.09	9.3936	9.2416	9.5481
Cheyenne, Wyo.	5.04	4.58	23.0832	25.4016	20.9764
Columbia, Tenn.	3.15	3.22	10.1430	9.9225	10.3684
Cooperstown, N. Y.	3.55	3.47	12.3185	12.6025	12.0409
Dalhart, Tex.	4.00	3.55	14.2000	16.0000	12.6025
Demopolis, Ala.	2.93	2.85	8.3505	8.5849	8.1225
Elko, Nev.	5.33	5.05	26.9165	28.4089	25.5025
Fayetteville, N. C.	3.47	3.40	11.7980	12.0409	11.5600
Garrett, Ind.	4.03	3.70	14.9110	16.2409	13.6900
Glendale, Ariz.	3.40	3.69	12.5460	11.5600	13.6161
Grand Forks, N. Dak.	4.02	3.95	15.8790	16.1604	15.6025
Grand Island, Nebr.	3.97	3.96	15.7212	15.7609	15.6816
Grand Junction, Colo.	3.58	3.54	12.6732	12.8164	12.5316
Grinnell, Iowa	3.59	3.28	11.7752	12.8881	10.7584
Laconia, N. H.	3.55	3.78	13.4190	12.6025	14.2884
Lodi, Calif.	4.07	4.10	16.6870	16.5649	16.8100
Madill, Okla.	3.18	3.19	10.1442	10.1124	10.1761
Middlesboro, Ky.	3.02	3.26	9.8452	9.1204	10.6276
Nanty-Glo, Pa.	3.78	3.78	14.2884	14.2884	14.2884
Pecos, Tex.	3.82	3.73	14.2486	14.5924	13.9129
Pulaski, Va.	3.45	3.33	11.4885	11.9025	11.0889
Ravenna, Ohio	3.88	3.72	14.4336	15.0544	13.8384
Rawlins, Wyo.	4.71	4.26	20.0646	22.1841	18.1476
Roseburg, Ore.	4.58	4.04	18.5032	20.9764	16.3216
Salina, Kan.	3.60	3.40	12.2400	12.9600	11.5600
Sandpoint, Idaho	3.28	3.32	10.8896	10.7584	11.0224
Santa Cruz, Calif.	3.69	3.34	12.3246	13.6161	11.1556
Shawnee, Okla.	3.08	3.19	9.8252	9.4864	10.1761
Shenandoah, Iowa	3.97	3.67	14.5699	15.7609	13.4689
Washington, N. J.	4.06	4.15	16.8490	16.4836	17.2225
Total	125.30	121.41	469.5635	487.3518	453.9073

* Readers should note the following comment by the Bureau of Labor Statistics: "Experience suggests that average family income is usually understated. . . . It is therefore quite incorrect to interpret the entire difference between reported income and expenditure as saving or dis-saving."

of a single city in respect of average family expenditure for consumption and average current income. Such a figure is termed a "scatter diagram." It is clear from this diagram that there is a relationship between the two variables. In general, the cities with high average family incomes are also those with high average family expenditures for consumption. The relationship, however, is not perfect. Two cities with almost the same average family income may differ materially in average expenditures for consumption. Thus for Dalhart, Texas, with average family income of $4,000, average consumption expenditures were $3,550, while for Washington, New Jersey, where average family income was $4,060, average expenditures for consumption were $4,150. Were the relation between the two variables perfect, cities having the same average family income would have the same average expenditures for consumption.

The Equation of Average Relationship. Our first problem is the derivation of an equation to describe this relationship which, while not perfect, is clearly existent. We shall assume that the relationship is linear, and shall employ the method of least squares in estimating the best values of the constants a and b in an appropriate equation. This calls for the solution of the normal equations

$$\Sigma(Y) = Na + b\Sigma(X)$$
$$\Sigma(XY) = a\Sigma(X) + b\Sigma(X^2)$$

The values required for the solution of these equations may be derived from the data as arranged in Table 9-5. Substituting, we have

$$121.4 = 33a + 125.30b$$
$$469.5635 = 125.30a + 487.3518b$$

Solving,

$$a = 0.8707$$
$$b = 0.7396$$

The required equation is

$$Y = 0.8707 + 0.7396X$$

This line is plotted in Fig. 9.3.

A mathematical expression has now been secured for the relation between the two variables being studied, average family expenditures for consumption and average family income after taxes. The former is the dependent or Y-variable in the equation, the latter the independent or X-variable. This equation constitutes a measure of the functional relationship between these two variables, but it is only an expression of *average* relationship. How significant is the equation? If the relationship were perfect, and the plotted points all lay on the line describing this relationship, the equation could be used with confidence as an accurate instrument for determining the value of one variable from a value of the other. But a line with a definite equation may be fitted to points that depart very widely from it, that are widely dispersed. In such a case the equation may have the appearance of describing a precise relationship but the variation is so great that it cannot be used with confidence. It is the same problem as that which arises when an average is employed. We must know how significant the average is, how great the concentration about it, before we may use it intelligently. So the equation of relationship between variables means little unless we know to what extent it holds in practical experience. We must have a measure of the dispersion about the line we have fitted.

In describing the frequency distribution, the standard deviation is used as the best general measure of variation. It is, obviously, the measure we need in determining the reliability of the equation of average relationship. The standard deviation about this line will not only serve as a general index of the significance of this equation but will enable us to measure the degree of accuracy of estimates based upon the equation.

Computation of the Standard Error of Estimate. The standard deviation about a line of average relationship, being a measure of the accuracy of estimates, may be termed the *standard error of estimate*. (The term *standard deviation* is generally confined to the root-mean-square deviation about the arithmetic mean.) The standard error of estimate is represented by the symbol $s_{y \cdot x}$, usually written with subscripts to indicate dependent (first subscript) and independent variables.

In the computation of $s_{y \cdot x}$ we must know the computed value of Y that corresponds to each given value of X. By substituting the given values of X in the equation

$$Y = 0.8707 + 0.7396X$$

normal Y values may be computed. The deviations of the actual

Y values from the computed may be determined. The root-mean-square of these deviations, or residuals, which are represented by the symbol v, is the required measure. A method of computation is illustrated in Table 9-6. From this table we have

$$s_{y \cdot x} = \sqrt{\frac{\Sigma v^2}{N}} = \sqrt{\frac{0.8868}{33}}$$

$$= 0.164 \text{ (in thousands of dollars)}$$

The measure $s_{y \cdot x}$ is to be interpreted in precisely the same way as the standard deviation about an arithmetic mean. Given a normal distribution of items about the line of relationship, 68 percent of all the cases will lie within a range of $\pm s$ (in this case 0.164), 95 percent will fall within $\pm 2s$ (in this case 0.328) and 99.7 percent will fall within $\pm 3s$ (here, 0.492). If there were no scatter about the line fitted to the points representing the corresponding values of X and Y, $s_{y \cdot x}$ would have a value of zero, and the value of Y could be estimated from the value of X with perfect accuracy. The less the dispersion about the line, the smaller the value of $s_{y \cdot x}$. The value of $s_{y \cdot x}$ serves, therefore, as an indicator of the significance and usefulness of the line that describes the relation between the two variables. The standard error of estimate, it should be noted, is expressed in the same units as the original Y-values.[2]

The making of estimates. We may, for the moment, consider the significance of these results. Let us assume that, not knowing the average family expenditures for current consumption in a given city, we are under the necessity of estimating it. Two methods are open to us. We may, in the first place, base the estimate upon our knowledge of the Y-variable alone. The arithmetic average of the 33 city entries for Y_0, given in Table 9-6, is 3.679 (the unit, it will be remembered, is \$1,000). With no specific information as to average expenditures for consumption in a particular city, the

---

[2] For descriptive purposes, and for consistency in the various calculations illustrated in this part of Chapter 9, we derive the standard error of estimate from $\sqrt{\Sigma v^2 / N}$. However, if we are thinking of $s_{y \cdot x}$ as an estimate of a population value, $\sigma_{y \cdot x}$, the divisor in the expression under the radical sign should be $N - 2$, not N. The reasoning that justifies this is similar to that which leads to the use of $N - 1$ rather than N in estimating a population σ. In deriving an estimate of the standard error of estimate from observations we use up two degrees of freedom, in effect, when we use these observations in the fitting of the straight line. Hence there are only $N - 2$ degrees of freedom for the observations to deviate from the line. It will be desirable to use $N - 2$ as the divisor in dealing with certain problems of inference in later sections of this chapter.

TABLE 9–6

Illustrating the Computation of Residuals and their Squares

(1)	(2)	(3)	(4)	(5)
	Average Expenditures for Current Consumption (in thousands of dollars)		(2)–(3)	
City	Actual Y_0	Computed Y_c	v	v^2
Anna, Ill.	3.40	3.53	− 0.13	0.0169
Antioch, Calif.	4.52	4.64	− 0.12	0.0144
Barre, Vt.	3.90	3.67	+ 0.23	0.0529
Camden, Ark.	3.09	3.12	− 0.03	0.0009
Cheyenne, Wyo.	4.58	4.60	− 0.02	0.0004
Columbia, Tenn.	3.22	3.20	+ 0.02	0.0004
Cooperstown, N. Y.	3.47	3.50	− 0.03	0.0009
Dalhart, Tex.	3.55	3.83	− 0.28	0.0784
Demopolis, Ala.	2.85	3.04	− 0.19	0.0361
Elko, Nev.	5.05	4.81	+ 0.24	0.0576
Fayetteville, N. C.	3.40	3.44	− 0.04	0.0016
Garrett, Ind.	3.70	3.85	− 0.15	0.0225
Glendale, Ariz.	3.69	3.39	+ 0.30	0.0900
Grand Forks, N. Dak.	3.95	3.84	+ 0.11	0.0121
Grand Island, Nebr.	3.96	3.81	+ 0.15	0.0225
Grand Junction, Colo.	3.54	3.52	+ 0.02	0.0004
Grinnell, Iowa	3.28	3.53	− 0.25	0.0625
Laconia, N. H.	3.78	3.50	+ 0.28	0.0784
Lodi, Calif.	4.10	3.88	+ 0.22	0.0484
Madill, Okla.	3.19	3.22	− 0.03	0.0009
Middlesboro, Ky.	3.26	3.10	+ 0.16	0.0256
Nanty-Glo, Pa.	3.78	3.67	+ 0.11	0.0121
Pecos, Tex.	3.73	3.70	+ 0.03	0.0009
Pulaski, Va.	3.33	3.42	− 0.09	0.0081
Ravenna, Ohio	3.72	3.74	− 0.02	0.0004
Rawlins, Wyo.	4.26	4.35	− 0.09	0.0081
Roseburg, Ore.	4.04	4.26	− 0.22	0.0484
Salina, Kan.	3.40	3.53	− 0.13	0.0169
Sandpoint, Idaho	3.32	3.29	+ 0.03	0.0009
Santa Cruz, Calif.	3.34	3.60	− 0.26	0.0676
Shawnee, Okla.	3.19	3.15	+ 0.04	0.0016
Shenandoah, Iowa	3.67	3.81	− 0.14	0.0196
Washington, N. J	4.15	3.87	+ 0.28	0.0784
Total				0.8868

arithmetic mean of all the city figures would be taken as the most probable value for the city in question. (The most probable value of a series of observations is the mean of the series.) The accuracy of this estimate depends on the degree of dispersion about the mean, which may be defined by the standard deviation. In the present case the standard deviation has a value of 0.468. Here is a measure of the reliability of estimates based on the mean of all the Y's.

Another method of estimating current family expenditures for consumption in a given city is open to us if we have information concerning average family income in that city. For as a result of the study described in the preceding pages we know that the average relationship between consumption expenditures and family income (as averaged by cities) is defined by the equation

$$Y = 0.8707 + 0.7396X$$

If in a given city average current family income, after taxes, is 4.000 (in thousands of dollars), it may be estimated from this equation that current consumption will be 3.8291, or 3,829 to the nearest dollar. This is the most probable value of Y as determined from the equation of average relationship. Is this estimate any better than the previous one, which took the mean Y as the most probable value? Does our knowledge of the average relationship between X and Y aid us in estimating the value of Y from a known value of X?

The answers to these questions are given by the *standard error of estimate*, and by the relation between the standard error of estimate and the standard deviation of Y. The standard error of estimate is 0.164. The standard deviation of Y is 0.468. Clearly the estimate made from the equation is more accurate than the estimate based upon the value of the mean Y. From our knowledge of the relationship between the two variables, even though that relationship is by no means constant or perfect, we are able to reduce materially the errors of estimate. (The reader will be aware that, in working with data obtained from samples, estimates of the mean Y and of the constants a and b in the equation of regression are themselves subject to errors. These errors do not enter into the comparison of the standard deviation of Y and the standard error of estimate.)

The Coefficient of Correlation. We have now secured two measures that aid us in describing the relationship between variable quantities. The first is the fundamental equation of relationship, the expression of the degree of change in one variable associated, on the average, with a given change in the other. The second is the *standard error of estimate*, the measure of the degree of "scatter" about the line of average relationship. The standard error resembles the standard deviation in that it is a measure expressed in absolute terms, in the units employed in measuring the original Y-values. This measure enables us to determine the probability that an observed value will fall within specified limits of an estimate based upon the equation of relationship.

In measuring variation it has been found that an abstract measure of variability is needed, one which is divorced from the absolute terms of the given problem. Such a measure is particularly needed, it was noted, when different distributions are to be compared. So, for measuring the *degree of variability,* a coefficient of variation is employed. There is need of a somewhat similar measure in connection with our present problem. We need a measure of the *degree of relationship* between two variables, an abstract coefficient that is divorced from the particular units employed in a given case. Such a measure is termed a coefficient of correlation.

This measure may be explained in terms of the preceding discussion. It was found that the usefulness of estimates based upon the equation of relationship could be determined by comparing the standard error of estimate of Y (the measure of scatter about the line of relationship) with the standard deviation of Y. If the standard error of estimate be as great as the standard deviation the equation of relationship is of no use to us, but if the standard error be less than the standard deviation the accuracy of estimates may be improved by using this equation. The significance of the equation is thus indicated by the relation between the standard error of estimate and the standard deviation. But these are both in absolute terms, so that by dividing one by the other an abstract measure may be secured. Thus we might write

$$\text{Measure of correlation} = \frac{s_{y \cdot x}}{s_y}$$

A somewhat more useful measure is secured by putting the ratio in this form:

$$\text{Measure of correlation} = r = \sqrt{1 - \frac{s_{y \cdot x}^2}{s_y^2}} \qquad (9.3)$$

This measure, when used in connection with a linear equation, is called the *coefficient of correlation* and, as is indicated in formula (9.3), is represented by the symbol r.

A brief consideration of this formula[3] will help to make clear the

---

[3] In deriving the mean squares $s_{y \cdot x}^2$ and s_y^2 that enter into the formula (9.3), the same N must be used as the divisor of the two relevant sums of squares. That is, there is no reduction of N to take account of degrees of freedom lost. See footnote p. 228.

significance of r. If there is no dispersion about the line of relationship, $s_{y \cdot x}$ will have a value of zero; the equation describes a perfect
relationship between the two variables. In this case, as is clear
from the formula, r must have a value of 1.

The maximum value of $s_{y \cdot x}$ is one that is equal to s_y. Under
these conditions, when the equation of relationship is of no aid in
improving our estimates, the formula will give zero as the value
of r. Such a value indicates that there is no relationship between
the two variables; in other words, that the straight line of best fit
is horizontal, passing through the mean of the Y's. It shows that
there is no tendency for the high values of Y to be associated with
high values of X or for high values of Y to be associated with low
values of X. The two variables fluctuate in absolute independence.
In such a case the deviation of each point from the fitted line is
equal to its deviation from the mean, and the two root-mean-square
deviations are equal, as stated.

Zero and unity are thus the limits to the value of r. The values
found in practical work fall somewhere between these limits,
approaching unity in cases where the degree of relationship is high.
The greater the value of r, the greater the confidence that may be
placed in the equation as an expression of a relation which is
approximated in a high percentage of cases. In the example presented above, dealing with average family expenditures for
consumption and average family income after taxes, we have

$$r = \sqrt{1 - \frac{(0.164)^2}{(0.468)^2}}$$

$$= 0.937$$

This coefficient indicates a definite and fairly close connection
between these two variables for the cities included in the sample.

The coefficient of correlation may be made more meaningful by
giving it the sign of the constant b in the equation of relationship.
This sign indicates whether the slope of the line is positive or
negative and, when attached to r, enables us to tell whether the
relationship is direct or inverse. Thus in the present case high
values of one variable are paired with high values of the other.
The correlation is positive and the coefficient should be written

+ 0.937. As an example of negative correlation we may cite cotton production and cotton prices. Here the relation is inverse: high values of one variable are generally associated with low values of the other.

The Coefficient of Determination. In the preceding pages we sought to measure the relation between two variable quantities by deriving a linear *equation of average relationship*, supplementing this equation by a *standard error of estimate* and a *coefficient of correlation*. The standard error of estimate defines the degree of variation, in absolute terms, about the line of relationship; the coefficient of correlation provides an abstract measure of the degree of relationship between two variables, when this relationship is defined by a straight line. It will be helpful now, in introducing a final relevant measure, to view the problem of correlation in a somewhat different light.

An investigator uses the methods of correlation analysis because he is concerned about the fact of variation in some quantity that interests him. Thus in seeking to understand crop-yield variations from year to year one may study the effect of variations in rainfall on yields. In the example cited on earlier pages, the concern of the investigator is to explain, in some sense, the rather wide variations among the city averages defining family expenditures for current consumption. From this point of view the problem is set by the fact of variation in the dependent variable; the magnitude of the problem, we may say, is indicated by the variance, or the standard deviation, of the dependent variable.

The variance, among small cities, of average family expenditures for consumption is given by $s_y^2 = 0.21907$ (standard deviation $s_y = 0.468$). This is a measure of the dispersion among the observed values of Y, as given in column (2) of Table 9-6 (p. 261) and as plotted in Fig. 9.3 (p. 256). This dispersion among the observed values of Y is what we are seeking to explain. We may compute a similar measure among the computed values of Y, as these are derived from the linear equation of average relationship. These Y_c's are given in column (3) of Table 9-6. The variance of these computed values, which we may represent by $s_{y_c}^2$, is 0.1922. As a final measure, derived from the difference between the members of each pair of observed and computed values (see columns (4) and (5) of Table 9-6), we have $s_{y \cdot x}^2 = 0.0269$. This is the variance of the residuals, the square of the standard error of estimate

$(s_{y \cdot x} = 0.164)$ to which we have already been introduced.
These three variances stand in an interesting relation:

$$s_y^2 = s_{y \cdot x}^2 + s_{y_c}^2 \tag{9.4}$$

$$0.2191 = 0.0269 + 0.1922$$

That is, the original variance of Y is equal to the sum of the
variance of the computed values of Y and the variance of the
residuals, which measure the difference between observed and
computed values.[4] The original variance has been broken into two
components. One of these components, $s_{y \cdot x}^2$, may be taken to
reflect the influence, on average family expenditures for consumption, of factors other than variations in average family income.

---

[4] Following is a proof of this relation:
  A least squares fit to the observed values, Y_0, gives us the equation

$$Y_c = a + bX \tag{1}$$

The series Y_0 and Y_c (Y_c being a computed value) have the same mean, $\overline{Y}$.
  Let
$$d = Y_0 - \overline{Y}$$
$$d_c = Y_c - \overline{Y}$$
$$v = Y_0 - Y_c$$

It follows from the least squares fitting process that

$$\Sigma v = 0 \tag{2}$$
$$\Sigma vX = 0 \tag{3}$$

Since $\qquad\qquad d_c = Y_c - \overline{Y}$

then, from (1)

$$d_c = a + bX - \overline{Y}$$
$$= a - \overline{Y} + bX \tag{4}$$

If we multiply each residual v by the constant $a - \overline{Y}$, and add, we have, from (2)

$$\Sigma(a - \overline{Y})v = 0 \tag{5}$$

If we multiply each vX by the constant b and add, we have from (3)

$$\Sigma(bX)v = 0 \tag{6}$$

Adding (5) and (6),

$$\Sigma(a - \overline{Y} + bX)v = 0 \tag{7}$$

But from equation (4) the quantity in parentheses is equal to d_c.
Hence

$$\Sigma v d_c = 0 \tag{8}$$

  From the initial expressions for d, v, and Y_c it follows that

$$d = v + d_c \tag{9}$$

Hence $\qquad\qquad d^2 = v^2 + 2vd_c + d_c^2 \tag{10}$

and $\qquad\qquad \Sigma d^2 = \Sigma v^2 + 2\Sigma vd_c + \Sigma d_c^2 \tag{11}$

But from (8) $\qquad \Sigma vd_c = 0$

Hence $\qquad\qquad \Sigma d^2 = \Sigma v^2 + \Sigma d_c^2 \tag{12}$

$$\Sigma d^2 / N = \Sigma v^2 / N + \Sigma d_c / N \tag{13}$$

and

$$s_y^2 = s_{y \cdot x}^2 + s_{y_c}^2 \tag{14}$$

These are the factors responsible for "scatter" about the line of average relationship. If we may speak in terms of "explanation," $s_{y \cdot x}^2$ measures the "unexplained variation" in Y. The other component, s_{yc}^2, may be thought of as a measure of the "explained variation" in Y. For, on the assumption that we are dealing here with a truly causal relationship, we may say that these computed values vary among themselves because they are associated with varying average family incomes—i.e., with varying values of X. If consumption expenditures were a rigid function of family income, with no other factors affecting such expenditures, Y and Y_c would be equal for each value of X; $s_{y \cdot x}^2$ would be zero, and s_{yc}^2 would equal s_y^2. In the present case the component representing "explained variation" is much larger than the component representing "unexplained variation." On the assumption that the two variables are causally related we may say that variation from city to city in average family income accounts for the major part of the variation from city to city in average family expenditures for consumption.

Since the variances cited stand in an additive relationship, we may express the "explained variation," as defined by s_{yc}^2, as a fractional part of the original variation of the Y's, as defined by s_y^2. Thus if we use the symbol d_{yx} to represent the proportion of the variation in Y attributable to, or determined by, variations in X, we may write

$$d_{yx} = \frac{s_{yc}^2}{s_y^2} \tag{9.5}$$

$$= \frac{0.1922}{0.2191} = 0.877$$

This is the *coefficient of determination.*

The coefficient of determination stands in a simple relation to the coefficient of correlation. As a general expression for the square of this coefficient we have

$$r_{yx}^2 = 1 - \frac{s_{y \cdot x}^2}{s_y^2} \tag{9.6}$$

This equation may be put in the form

$$r_{yx}^2 = \frac{s_y^2 - s_{y \cdot x}^2}{s_y^2} \tag{9.7}$$

But from equation (9.4) on p. 234 above we have

$$s_y^2 - s_{y \cdot x}^2 = s_{y_c}^2 \tag{9.8}$$

The left hand member of equation (9.8) is the numerator of equation (9.7). Substituting in (9.8) the equivalent value, $s_{y_c}^2$, we have

$$r_{yx}^2 = \frac{s_{y_c}^2}{s_y^2} = d_{yx} \tag{9.9}$$

The coefficient of determination is equal to the square of the coefficient of correlation. This last equation, (9.9), provides an illuminating way of regarding the coefficient of correlation. The coefficient of correlation, squared, is equal to the variance of the computed values of Y (the "explained" variance) divided by the variance of the observed values of Y. With reservations to be noted shortly, r^2 may be said to measure the proportion of the variability of the dependent variable that is attributable to the independent variable.

The coefficient of determination is a highly useful measure, but one that is obviously open to misinterpretation. In the first place, the term itself may be misleading, in that it implies that the variable X stands in a determining or causal relationship to the variable Y. The statistical evidence itself never establishes the existence of such causality. All the statistical evidence can do is to define *covariation*, that term being used in a perfectly neutral sense. Whether causality is present or not, and which way it runs if it is present, must be determined on the basis of evidence other than the quantitative observations. (What constitutes causality in an ultimate sense may, indeed, be beyond the power of an investigator to establish.) Because this is so, the words "explained" and "unexplained" have been set within quotation marks in the preceding discussion.[5] In the present case there is a rational basis for assuming that expenditures for consumption are in part determined, in a meaningful sense, by the size of family income; there is some justification for the use of the term in this instance.

The second qualification has to do with the measure of variation employed. The additive relationship that permits the breaking of total variation into "explained" and "unexplained" components holds only for the variances. It does not hold for the standard

---

[5] Here, as in systematic semantics, quotation marks around a word may be taken to mean "Beware, it's loaded."

deviations. The fact that variation is measured by the square of the standard deviation must be borne in mind when a coefficient of determination is cited.

A third general point applies to all the measures of correlation discussed in the preceding pages. We have dealt only with the linear case—the case in which the function defining average relationship is a straight line. Measures similar to d_{yx} may be computed when other functions are used, but the function employed in a given instance must be specified if the measure is to be unambiguous.

With these reservations in mind, we may say that the evidence of our present sample of 33 small cities indicates that 87.7 percent of the variation from city to city in average family expenditures for consumption is due to variation in average family income, after taxes. Such a statement, properly qualified, is informative and useful.

Details of calculation. In the preceding section an attempt has been made to explain the various measures necessary in studying the relationship between variable quantities without introducing a detailed explanation of procedure. We may now return to a consideration of the details of calculation, including certain methods by which this calculation may be reduced to a minimum.

The procedure followed in the preceding illustration is a logical one to employ in deriving the three required values. This method is capable of general application, but the labor involved may be materially reduced by taking advantage of a short-cut method of deriving $s_{y.x}$. This method may be first explained with reference to data of the type dealt with above. And, for the present, the discussion will be confined to cases in which the relationship between variables may be described by a straight line.

The first problem is the derivation of the equation of relationship. A line of the type

$$Y = a + bX$$

is fitted by the method of least squares.

The next step is the computation of $s_{y.x}^2$, the square of the standard error of estimate. This was done in the above illustration by measuring the deviation of each individual observation from the fitted line, and getting the mean-square of these deviations.

It may be shown[6] that this value can be derived from the following equation:

$$s_{y \cdot x}^2 = \frac{\Sigma(Y^2) - a\Sigma(Y) - b\Sigma(XY)}{N}$$

The quantities a and b are the constants in the equation to the fitted straight line. The other values relate to the original observations. Substituting in this equation a and b and the other necessary values, taken from Table 9-5, we have[7]

$$s_{y \cdot x}^2 = \frac{453.9073 - (0.870745 \times 121.41) - (0.739628 \times 469.5635)}{33}$$

$$= 0.0269$$

$$s_{y \cdot x} = 0.164$$

From this point the procedure may follow that already described, r being computed from the formula

$$r = \sqrt{1 - \frac{s_{y \cdot x}^2}{s_y^2}}$$

The coefficient r may be secured, however, without computing $s_{y \cdot x}$

[6] The general formula for the standard error of estimate is

$$s_{y \cdot x}^2 = \Sigma v^2 / N \qquad (1)$$

where each

$$v = Y_0 - Y_c$$
$$= Y_0 - a - bX \qquad (2)$$

There will be as many equations of this type as there are points. Multiplying each equation by v, and adding, we have

$$\Sigma v^2 = \Sigma v Y_0 - a\Sigma v - b\Sigma v X \qquad (3)$$

But

$$\Sigma v = 0$$

and

$$\Sigma v X = 0$$

and therefore

$$\Sigma v^2 = \Sigma v Y_0 \qquad (4)$$

Returning to equation (2), we multiply throughout by Y_0 and add, securing

$$\Sigma v Y_0 = \Sigma Y_0^2 - a\Sigma Y_0 - b\Sigma(XY_0) \qquad (5)$$

Substituting the equivalent of $\Sigma v Y_0$ in equation (4), we have

$$\Sigma v^2 = \Sigma Y_0^2 - a\Sigma Y_0 - b\Sigma(XY_0) \qquad (6)$$

from which the given formula for $s_{y \cdot x}^2$ is derived. (The symbol Y of the text formula represents, of course, observed values of Y, for which the symbol Y_0 has been used in this note.)

[7] For the sake of formal consistency the values of a and b are here given to a greater number of decimal places than in the equation as first presented.

as an intermediate value. The above formula for r may be reduced to

$$r^2 = \frac{a\Sigma(Y) + b\Sigma(XY) - Nc_y^2}{\Sigma(Y^2) - Nc_y^2} \qquad (9.10)$$

where c_y is the difference between the mean Y and the origin employed in the calculations.[8] If the origin is zero on the original Y scale, c_y will be equal to the arithmetic mean of the Y's.

In the present case, using the data of Table 9-5, we have

$$c_y = \frac{121.41}{33} = 3.67909$$

The other values are the same as those employed above in computing $s_{y \cdot x}^2$. Substituting in formula (9.10), we have

$$r^2 = \frac{6.341362}{7.2292}$$

$$= 0.8772$$

$$r = + 0.937$$

In effect, then, the labor of fitting a straight line by the method of least squares gives us most of the quantities needed in securing s and r, the two other measures necessary for a complete description

---

[8] The formula

$$r^2 = 1 - \frac{s_{y \cdot x}^2}{s_y^2}$$

may be written

$$r^2 = 1 - \frac{\Sigma(v^2)}{\Sigma(y^2)}$$

in which y refers to deviations from the arithmetic mean of the Y's. But

$$\frac{\Sigma(y^2)}{N} = \frac{(\Sigma Y^2)}{N} - c_y^2$$

where Y represents a deviation from an arbitrary origin (in this case zero on the original scale) and c_y represents the difference between this origin and the mean of the Y's.

Therefore

$$r^2 = 1 - \frac{\Sigma(v^2)}{\Sigma(Y^2) - Nc_y^2}$$

Substituting in this equation the equivalent of $\Sigma(v^2)$, as given in footnote 7,

$$r^2 = 1 - \frac{\Sigma(Y^2) - a\Sigma(Y) - b\Sigma(XY)}{\Sigma(Y^2) - Nc_y^2}$$

Simplifying,

$$r^2 = \frac{a\Sigma(Y) + b\Sigma(XY) - Nc_y^2}{\Sigma(Y^2) - Nc_y^2}$$

of the relation between two variable quantities. The only additional quantities required are $\Sigma(Y^2)$ and c_y.

There is a logical validity in the sequence of operations described in the preceding pages, a sequence that yields, first, a least squares equation of average relationship, secondly, a measure of errors involved in basing estimates on such an equation and, thirdly, an abstract measure of degree of correlation. It will be convenient to call this method the "least squares" procedure. An alternative procedure yields the coefficient of correlation as the first measure obtained, with the constants in the equation and the standard error of estimate as supplementary measures. We shall call this latter method the "product-moment" method. (The methods are mathematically equivalent; different terms are employed for convenience of reference.) The arithmetic of the product-moment method is simpler when the number of observations is large and the data are organized in a double frequency table.

The Product-Moment Formula for the Coefficient of Correlation: Ungrouped Data

In the preceding examples the coefficient of correlation has been computed from the formula

$$r^2 = \frac{a\Sigma(Y) + b\Sigma(XY) - Nc_y^2}{\Sigma(Y^2) - Nc_y^2}$$

which is based upon relations involved in fitting a straight line by least squares. We shall show that this reduces to a simpler form often more appropriate in practice.

When a straight line is fitted to data, the origin being at the point of averages, the two normal equations

$$\Sigma(Y) = Na + b\Sigma(X)$$
$$\Sigma(XY) = a\Sigma(X) + b\Sigma(X^2)$$

become

$$\Sigma(y) = Na + b\Sigma(x)$$
$$\Sigma(xy) = a\Sigma(x) + b\Sigma(x^2)$$

where y and x measure deviations from the point of averages. The first of these equations disappears and the second reduces to

$$\Sigma(xy) = b\Sigma(x^2)$$

for

$$\Sigma(x) = 0 \text{ and } \Sigma(y) = 0$$

The slope, b, is the only constant required, and this may be computed from the relationship

$$b = \frac{\Sigma(xy)}{\Sigma(x^2)}$$

Under the same conditions the formula

$$r^2 = \frac{a\Sigma(Y) + b\Sigma(XY) - Nc_y^2}{\Sigma(Y^2) - Nc_y^2}$$

reduces to

$$r^2 = \frac{b\Sigma(xy)}{\Sigma(y^2)}$$

for $c_y = 0$ when the deviations are measured from the mean of the Y's. Substituting for b its equivalent, as just determined, we have

$$r^2 = \frac{\Sigma(xy) \cdot \Sigma(xy)}{\Sigma(y^2) \cdot \Sigma(x^2)}$$

But $\Sigma(y^2) = Ns_y^2$ and $\Sigma(x^2) = Ns_x^2$

Therefore

$$r^2 = \frac{\Sigma(xy) \cdot \Sigma(xy)}{N^2 s_y^2 s_x^2}$$

and

$$r = \frac{\Sigma(xy)}{N s_x s_y} \tag{9.11}$$

in which x and y refer to deviations from an origin at the point of averages.

This formula may be given as

$$r = \frac{p}{s_x s_y} \tag{9.12}$$

in which

$$p = \frac{\Sigma(xy)}{N}$$

The quantity p is the *mean product* of the paired values of x and y, these variables being measured as deviations about their respective means. The mean product, which is sometimes represented by the symbol s_{xy}, is also termed the *covariance*, or the first *product-moment*. Since the first product-moment is one of the quantities entering into the formula given in (9.11) and (9.12) above, this is called the *product-moment formula* for r.

This formula has been given here in terms of statistics derived from samples. With reference to population characteristics we should use symbols for population parameters. Thus we should have

$$\rho = \frac{\Sigma(xy)}{N\sigma_x\sigma_y} \tag{9.13}$$

or

$$\rho = \frac{\sigma_{xy}}{\sigma_x\sigma_y} \tag{9.14}$$

In this last formula the symbol σ_{xy} stands for the population covariance, that is, for the mean product of paired X and Y values making up the parent population. It is the population equivalent of p. (The symbols s_{xy} and σ_{xy} are not to be confused with $s_{x \cdot y}$ and with $\sigma_{x \cdot y}$, the standard error of estimate when X is estimated from Y.

The computation of the coefficient of correlation from this formula proceeds along lines somewhat different from those outlined in the preceding section. As we have seen, both the arithmetic mean and the standard deviation may be readily computed by the selection of an arbitrary origin from which all deviations are measured, a later correction being made to offset the error involved in using this arbitrary origin. Similarly, the mean product p may be computed by a short method, requiring the use of assumed means and the application of a correction at the end of the process.

If x' and y' represent deviations from points arbitrarily selected as assumed means, while p' represents the mean product of such deviations, then

$$p' = \frac{\Sigma(x'y')}{N}$$

The computation of p' is not difficult, for deviations may be measured from central points, and may be expressed in class-interval units. Having p' we may secure the true mean product from the formula

$$p = p' - c_x c_y$$

in which c_x and c_y represent the differences between the true and assumed means of the x's and y's, respectively.[9]

An example. This method may be illustrated with reference, first, to ungrouped data, using the figures for family income (X) and family expenditures for consumption (Y), by cities. The values required for this computation, as given in Table 9-5, are

$$N = 33$$
$$\Sigma(X) = 125.30$$
$$\Sigma(Y) = 121.41$$
$$\Sigma(X^2) = 487.3518$$
$$\Sigma(Y^2) = 453.9073$$
$$\Sigma(XY) = 469.5635$$

The mean product may be computed from the formula

$$p = \frac{\Sigma(xy)}{N} = \frac{\Sigma(x'y')}{N} - c_x c_y$$

We may select as arbitrary origin the actual origin on the two original scales. Hence we have

$$p = \frac{\Sigma(XY)}{N} - c_x c_y \tag{9.15}$$

(When the arbitrary origin is at zero on the original scales, the

---

[9] The following is a proof of this relationship:

$x' = $ deviation of any point from assumed mean of x's
$x = $ deviation of same point from true mean of x's
$c_x = $ difference between true and assumed means of x's
$y' = $ deviation of same point from assumed mean of y's
$y = $ deviation of same point from true mean of y's
$c_y = $ difference between true and assumed means of y's
$x' = x + c_x$
$y' = y + c_y$
$x'y' = (x + c_x)(y + c_y) = xy + c_x y + c_y x + c_x c_y$

For the sum of all such products for N points, we have

$$\Sigma(x'y') = \Sigma(xy) + c_x\Sigma(y) + c_y\Sigma(x) + Nc_x c_y$$

But $\qquad\qquad\qquad \Sigma(y) = 0$ and $\Sigma(x) = 0$.

Therefore $\qquad\qquad \Sigma(x'y') = \Sigma(xy) + Nc_x c_y$

$$\frac{\Sigma(x'y')}{N} = \frac{\Sigma(xy)}{N} + c_x c_y$$

$$\frac{\Sigma(xy)}{N} = \frac{\Sigma(x'y')}{N} - c_x c_y$$

or $p = p' - c_x c_y$

symbol X corresponds to x' and Y corresponds to y', as used in the formulas.)

For the two standard deviations

$$s_x = \sqrt{\frac{\Sigma(X^2)}{N} - c_x^2}$$

$$s_y = \sqrt{\frac{\Sigma(Y^2)}{N} - c_y^2}$$

These measures may be computed readily from the values secured from Table 9-5:

$c_x = 125.30/33 = 3.79697$ $\qquad\qquad$ $c_y = 121.41/33 = 3.67909$
$c_x^2 = 14.41698$ $\qquad\qquad\qquad\qquad$ $c_y^2 = 13.53570$

$$p = \frac{469.5635}{33} - (3.79697 \times 3.67909)$$

$$= +0.25981$$

$$s_x = \sqrt{\frac{487.3518}{33} - 14.41698} \qquad s_y = \sqrt{\frac{453.9073}{33} - 13.53570}$$

$$= 0.5927 \qquad\qquad\qquad\qquad = 0.4680$$

Solving for the coefficient of correlation

$$r = \frac{p}{s_x s_y} = \frac{+0.25981}{0.5927 \times 0.4680}$$

$$= +0.93666$$

The equation to the straight line that describes the average relationship between X and Y may be derived from the values required for the preceding calculations. When the origin is at the point of averages this equation may be written

$$y = \rho \frac{\sigma_y}{\sigma_x} x \qquad\qquad (9.16)$$

or, in terms of sample measures

$$y = r \frac{s_y}{s_x} x \qquad\qquad (9.17)$$

Substituting the proper values,[10] we have

$$y = +0.93666 \frac{0.4680}{0.5927} x$$

$$= 0.7396x$$

---

[10] For purposes of numerical consistency r is carried to five places in this calculation.

This is the equation secured by the method of least squares. The constant term representing the y-intercept disappears, since the origin is at the point of averages, through which the least squares line must pass.[11]

When the product-moment method is employed in computing the coefficient of correlation and in determining the equation of regression, the standard error, $s_{y \cdot x}$, may be derived by a simple change in the formula first presented for r. From the expression

$$r^2 = 1 - \frac{s^2_{y \cdot x}}{s^2_y}$$

we may secure the formula

$$s_{y \cdot x} = s_y \sqrt{1 - r^2} \qquad (9.18)$$

which enables us to compute $s_{y \cdot x}$, if we have s_y and r. In the present case,

$$s_{y \cdot x} = 0.4680 \sqrt{1 - 0.877332}$$
$$= 0.164$$

The Product-Moment Method: Classified Data

In the examples presented above we have had only 33 observations. With a larger number it becomes difficult to retain the individual values in the study of relationships. These individual items must be grouped in significant classes, and all computations

---

[11] That the formula $y = \rho \frac{\sigma_y}{\sigma_x} x$ is equivalent to the formula based upon the method of

least squares may be readily demonstrated. When the line passes through the point of averages, the equation, $Y = a + bX$, becomes $y = bx$.

But $b = \frac{\Sigma(xy)}{\Sigma(x^2)}$. We may write, accordingly, $y_c = \frac{\Sigma(xy)}{\Sigma(x^2)} x$.

This is equivalent to $\qquad y_c = \rho \frac{\sigma_y}{\sigma_x} x$

for the latter may be written

$$(1)\quad y_c = \frac{\Sigma(xy)}{N \sigma_y \sigma_x} \cdot \frac{\sigma_y}{\sigma_x} x \qquad\qquad (3)\quad y_c = \frac{\Sigma(xy)}{N \sqrt{\frac{\Sigma(x^2)}{N}} \cdot \sqrt{\frac{\Sigma(x^2)}{N}}} x$$

$$(2)\quad y_c = \frac{\Sigma(xy)}{N \sigma_x \cdot \sigma_x} x \qquad\qquad (4)\quad y_c = \frac{\Sigma(xy)}{\Sigma(x^2)} x$$

(The symbol y_c is employed for the computed value of y, in these equations, to avoid confusion with the actual y's which appear in the right-hand members of the equations.)

Scatter diagram — Y: Discount Rate (rows), X – Federal Reserve Bank Discount Rate (columns). Cell entries are tally marks.

Discount Rate (Y) \ X – Federal Reserve Bank Discount Rate	1.25 to 1.74%	1.75 to 2.24%	2.25 to 2.74%	2.75 to 3.24%	3.25 to 3.74%	3.75 to 4.24%	4.25 to 4.74%	4.75 to 5.24%	5.25 to 5.74%	5.75 to 6.24%	6.25 to 6.74%	6.75 to 7.24%
7.75 to 8.24%										⦀	⦀	⦀⦀
7.25 to 7.74%										⦀⦀	⦀⦀	⦀
6.75 to 7.24%							⦀	⦀	⦀⦀⦀	⦀⦀⦀⦀⦀⦀⦀	⦀⦀⦀	⦀⦀⦀⦀⦀⦀
6.25 to 6.74%						⦀⦀	⦀⦀⦀	⦀⦀⦀	⦀⦀	⦀⦀⦀	⦀	⦀⦀⦀
5.75 to 6.24%					⦀⦀	⦀⦀⦀	⦀⦀⦀⦀⦀⦀⦀⦀⦀⦀	⦀⦀⦀⦀⦀⦀⦀⦀⦀	⦀⦀	⦀⦀⦀		

FIG. 9.4. Tabulation of Items in a Correlation Table.

Y—Commercial Bank

5.25 to 5.74%

4.75 to 5.24%

4.25 to 4.74%

3.75 to 4.24%

3.25 to 3.74%

TABLE 9–7

Correlation Table Showing the Relation between Federal Reserve Bank Discount Rates and the Discount Rates of Commercial Banks, and Illustrating the Computation of Quantities Needed in the Measurement of Correlation

Y—Discount rates of commercial banks (percent) (rows); *X—Discount rates of federal reserve banks (percent)* (columns)

Class interval	Mid-point	f	d'	fd'	fd'²	1.25–1.74	1.75–2.24	2.25–2.74	2.75–3.24	3.25–3.74	3.75–4.24	4.25–4.74	4.75–5.24	5.25–5.74	5.75–6.24	6.25–6.74	6.75–7.24	Total	Σ(x'y')
7.75–8.24	8.00	4	+5	20	100										+15 / 1 / (+15)	+20 / 1 / (+20)	+25 / 2 / (+50)		85
7.25–7.74	7.50	17	+4	68	272										+12 / 7 / (+84)	+16 / 9 / (+144)	+20 / 1 / (+20)		248
6.75–7.24	7.00	117	+3	351	1,053									+6 / 4 / (+24)	+9 / 63 / (+567)	+12 / 9 / (+108)	+15 / 36 / (+540)		1,254
6.25–6.74	6.50	62	+2	124	248								+2 / 22 / (+44)	+4 / 10 / (+40)	+6 / 22 / (+132)	+8 / 1 / (+8)	+10 / 3 / (+30)		254
5.75–6.24	6.00	366	+1	366	366					−2 / 9 / (−18)	−1 / 21 / (−21)	0 / 146 / (0)	+1 / 150 / (+150)	+2 / 8 / (+16)	+3 / 32 / (+96)				223
5.25–5.74	5.50	475	0	0	0				0 / 1 / (0)	0 / 90 / (0)	0 / 164 / (0)	0 / 175 / (0)	0 / 45 / (0)						
4.75–5.24	5.00	402	−1	−402	402			+4 / 4 / (+16)	+3 / 25 / (+75)	+2 / 111 / (+222)	+1 / 196 / (+196)	0 / 65 / (0)	−1 / 1 / (−1)						508
4.25–4.74	4.50	264	−2	−528	1,056			+8 / 16 / (+128)	+6 / 27 / (+162)	+4 / 122 / (+488)	+2 / 96 / (+192)	0 / 3 / (0)							970
3.75–4.24	4.00	77	−3	−231	693	+18 / 1 / (+18)	+15 / 9 / (+135)	+12 / 19 / (+228)	+9 / 19 / (+171)	+6 / 29 / (+174)									726
3.25–3.74	3.50	16	−4	−64	256	+24 / 4 / (+96)	+20 / 2 / (+40)	+16 / 1 / (+16)		+8 / 9 / (+72)									224
Total		1,800		−296	4,446														4,492

X-axis marginal values (Discount rates of federal reserve banks):

		1.25–1.74	1.75–2.24	2.25–2.74	2.75–3.24	3.25–3.74	3.75–4.24	4.25–4.74	4.75–5.24	5.25–5.74	5.75–6.24	6.25–6.74	6.75–7.24	Total
Mid-point		1.50	2.00	2.50	3.00	3.50	4.00	4.50	5.00	5.50	6.00	6.50	7.00	
f		5	11	40	72	370	477	393	223	22	125	20	42	1,800
d'		−6	−5	−4	−3	−2	−1	0	+1	+2	+3	+4	+5	
fd'		−30	−55	−160	−216	−740	−477	0	223	44	375	80	210	−746
fd'²		180	275	640	648	1,480	477	0	223	88	1,125	320	1,050	6,506

must be based upon these grouped data. This means, merely, that we must handle data organized in frequency distributions. Since we are dealing with two variables, however, the simple frequency table must be modified to meet the needs of the present problem. Such a modified frequency table, arranged to facilitate the computation of the values needed in studying relationship, is termed a *correlation table* or a *bivariate frequency table*. When the investigator is working with such a table, the product-moment method usually offers the simplest and easiest procedure.

Construction of a Correlation Table. As a typical problem involving the construction of a correlation table we may consider the relation between discount rates of commercial banks and the corresponding discount rates of Federal Reserve banks. Since the paper discounted by commercial banks may be rediscounted by Federal Reserve Banks for member banks, some degree of relationship between the rates may be expected. Our present object is the measurement of that relationship.

The first step is the tabulation of the original observations. Monthly values of each variable were secured for each of the twelve Federal Reserve cities over a period of 150 months.[12] In the process of tabulation the items must be combined so that a Federal Reserve bank discount rate is paired with the corresponding rate charged by the commercial banks of the same city. Fig. 9.4 illustrates the method of tabulation.

Tabulation having been completed, a correlation table designed to facilitate later computations may be constructed. Table 9-7 illustrates a suitable form. In this table, it will be noted, an arbitrary origin (M') is employed for each variable. M' is 4.50 for the X's, 5.50 for the Y's. Deviations represented by x' and y' are measured in class-interval units from this origin. In each compartment of the correlation table there are three figures, involved in the computation of $\Sigma(x'y')$. The figure in the center indicates the number of items falling in that compartment. Thus there are seven pairs having X values between 5.75 and 6.25 (midpoint 6.0) and Y values between 7.25 and 7.75 (midpoint 7.5). For each of these pairs x' (the deviation from the assumed mean of the X's)

---

[12] The period covered extended from July, 1920, to December, 1932. For the first part of this period discount rates of the Federal Reserve banks relate to trade acceptances; for later years they are "rates for member banks on eligible paper." The commercial bank rates are those charged on customers' prime commercial paper. The customary rate over a given 30-day period was taken as of the middle of that period.

is $+ 3$, in class-interval units, and y' (the deviation from the assumed mean of the Y's) is $+ 4$, in class-interval units. For each pair, therefore, $x'y' = + 12$. This figure appears at the top of the compartment. But there are seven pairs in this compartment, so the sum of $x'y'$ for this group is $+ 84$. This figure appears in parentheses at the bottom of the compartment. To secure $\Sigma(x'y')$ for the entire table it is necessary to add algebraically the values secured in this way for all compartments. The addition is first carried out for the different rows, the subtotals being given in the column at the right of the table. It is found that $\Sigma(x'y') = + 4,492$, in class-interval units.

TABLE 9–8

Calculation of the Coefficient of Correlation between the Discount Rates
of Commercial Banks and of Federal Reserve Banks*
(Calculations based on the entries in Table 9.7)

$M'_x = 4.50$ $M'_y = 5.50$ $p = \dfrac{\Sigma(x'y')}{N} - c_x c_y$

$c_x = \dfrac{-746}{1,800} = -.414$ $c_y = \dfrac{-296}{1,800} = -.164$ $= \dfrac{+4,492}{1,800} - [(-.414)(-.164)]$

$c_x^2 = (-.414)^2 = .171$ $c_y^2 = (-.164)^2 = .027$ $= +2.4956 - .0679$

$s_{x'}^2 = \dfrac{6,506}{1,800} = 3.614$ $s_{y'}^2 = \dfrac{4,446}{1,800} = 2.470$ $= +2.4277$

$s_x^2 = s_{x'}^2 - c_x^2$ $s_y^2 = s_{y'}^2 - c_y^2$ $r = \dfrac{p}{s_x s_y}$

$\quad = 3.614 - .171$ $\quad = 2.470 - .027$ $= \dfrac{+2.4277}{(1.855)(1.563)}$

$\quad = 3.443$ $\quad = 2.443$ $= \dfrac{+2.4277}{2.8994}$

$s_x = 1.855$ $s_y = 1.563$

$M_x = 4.50 - .5(.414)$ $M_y = 5.50 - .5(.164)$ $r = +.837$

$\quad = 4.293$ $\quad = 5.418$

NOTE: The class-interval unit has been employed in all the computations shown in this table.

* We here use $s_{x'}^2$ to represent the mean square deviation of the x's about the arbitrary origin M'_x, and $s_{y'}^2$ to represent the mean square deviation about M'_y. These symbols correspond to s_a^2 in Chapter 5.

The Computation of r and the Derivation of the Equation of Relationship. Details of the computation of the coefficient of correlation are given in Table 9-8. The standard deviations and the mean product p, all in class-interval units, are obtained by familiar methods. The coefficient r is then determined from the relation

$$r = \frac{p}{s_x s_y} = \frac{+\,2.4277}{1.855 \times 1.563}$$

$$= +\,0.837$$

It is convenient in such an operation to keep all the quantities entering into the final calculation in class-interval units, as is here done. Sheppard's corrections may be used, when appropriate, in estimating the two standard deviations that enter into the calculation of r. They have not been employed in the present example because the discount rates of Federal Reserve banks are not a continuous variable.

In deriving the equation to the straight line that describes the average relationship between x and y from the general equation

$$y = \rho \frac{\sigma_y}{\sigma_x} x \qquad\qquad (9.19)$$

we substitute the sample values s_y and s_x for the population measures σ_y and σ_x. In this use s_y and s_x should be expressed in units of the original scales.[13] This is done by multiplying the present values by the class-intervals.

s_x (in original units) $= 1.855 \times .50 = .9275$
s_y (in original units) $= 1.563 \times .50 = .7815$

Substituting the given values in the formula, we have

$$y = .837 \frac{.7815}{.9275} x$$

$$= .705x$$

The Lines of Regression. In the above discussion certain terms ordinarily employed in the treatment of correlation have been purposely omitted. Several of these should be explained.

The equation to the line of best fit in the preceding illustration was found to be

$$y = .705x$$

when the origin was taken at the point of averages. In this equation y is expressed as a function of x; that is, x is taken to be the

---

[13] When the class-intervals happen to be the same, as in the present case, the change is not necessary, as the relation between numerator and denominator is not altered. In practice it is advisable always to express the two standard deviations in original units at this stage of the calculations.

independent variable and y the dependent variable. The equation expresses the average variation in y (discount rates of commercial banks) corresponding to a change of one unit in x (discount rates of Federal Reserve banks). This line of relationship corresponds precisely to a line of trend, which describes the average change in a given series accompanying a unit change in time. A line which thus describes the average relationship between two variables is termed a *line of regression*. Its equation is termed a *regression equation*, and the quantity $\rho \dfrac{\sigma_y}{\sigma_x}$ (or in sample values $r \dfrac{s_y}{s_x}$) which gives the slope of such a line is called a *coefficient of regression*. The use of these terms dates back to early studies by Galton, dealing with the relation between the heights of fathers and the heights of sons. Sons, Galton found, deviated less on the average from the mean height of the race than their fathers. Whether the fathers were above or below the average, the sons tended to go back or *regress* towards the mean. He therefore termed the line which graphically described the average relationship between these two variables the *line of regression*. The term is now used generally, as indicated above, though the original meaning has no significance in most of its applications.

In any given case equations to two lines of regression may be computed. One is an expression of the average relationship between a dependent Y-variable and an independent X-variable; the other describes the relationship between a dependent X-variable and an independent Y-variable. The significance of the two may be indicated graphically.

Figure 9.5 is derived directly from the correlation table shown in Fig. 9.4. The circle in each column represents the mean Y-value of all the items falling in that column. Thus in the third column there are 40 cases, including all those with X-values falling between 2.25 percent and 2.75 percent. The Y-values vary, however, being distributed as shown in Table 9-9. Similar mean values are obtained for the other columns. These are plotted in Fig. 9.5, together with the line of regression of Y on X.

In Fig. 9.5 the X-variable (Federal Reserve bank discount rates) is independent. As it increases from 4.0 percent to 4.5, 5.0, 5.5 percent, and so on, the average of commercial bank rates increases also. An average commercial bank rate of 4.29 percent was associated with an average Federal Reserve bank rate of 2.5 percent;

1.25 1.75 2.25 2.75 3.25 3.75 4.25 4.75 5.25 5.75 6.25 6.75 7.25
Means of (3.60)(3.90) (4.28)(4.56)(4.86) (5.11)(5.60)(5.96)(6.40) (6.69)(7.25)(7.02)
Columns   Federal Reserve Bank Rates – Percent

FIG. 9.5. Showing the Relation between Discount Rates of Commercial Banks and Federal Reserve Bank Discount Rates. (The broken line connects the means of the columns and the straight line shows the average change in commercial bank rates corresponding to a unit change in Federal Reserve bank rates; i.e., it represents the regression of Y on X.)

TABLE 9–9

Computation of the Arithmetic Mean of an Array

Class-interval	Midpoint m	Frequency f	fm
4.75 − 5.24	5.0	4	20.0
4.25 − 4.74	4.5	16	72.0
3.75 − 4.24	4.0	19	76.0
3.25 − 3.74	3.5	1	3.5
		40	171.5

$$M = \frac{171.5}{40} = 4.2875$$

an average commercial bank rate of 4.56 percent was associated with an average Federal Reserve bank rate of 3.0 percent, and so on. (The commercial bank rates cited are the means of the entries in the columns referred to.) The slope of the straight line, which is the line of regression or the line of average relationship, measures the average increase in commercial bank rates corresponding to a unit increase in Federal Reserve bank rates.

It is possible to view the relationship between these two variables in another light. These questions arise: Given a certain commercial bank discount rate, what is the average Federal Reserve bank rate associated with it? And for a given change in commercial bank discount rates, what is the average change in the corresponding Federal Reserve bank rates? The commercial bank rate is now looked upon as independent, and the Federal Reserve rate as an associated dependent variable. These questions are answered by Fig. 9.6. The points marked by the small circles and connected by

FIG. 9.6. Showing the Relation between Federal Reserve Bank Discount Rates and the Discount Rates of Commercial Banks. (The broken line connects the means of the rows and the straight line shows the average change in Federal Reserve bank rates corresponding to a unit change in commercial bank rates; i.e., it represents the regression of X on Y.)

the broken line show the locations of the arithmetic means of the items falling in the various rows. Thus the 16 X-items in the bottom row have an average value of 2.75 percent. This is the average Federal Reserve bank discount rate associated with a commercial bank rate of 3.5 percent. The average Federal Reserve bank rate associated with a commercial bank rate of 4.0 percent is 2.93 percent, and so on. The straight line fitted to these points indicates the relationship between the two, its slope measuring the average increase (or decrease) in Federal Reserve bank rates associated with a unit change in commercial bank rates.

This is the line of regression of X on Y. The general formula for the equation to this line is:

$$x = \rho \frac{\sigma_x}{\sigma_y} y \qquad (9.20)$$

Substituting the present values, we have

$$x = .837 \frac{.9275}{.7815} y$$

or

$$x = .993y$$

The factors in this equation, it will be seen, are the same as those entering into the formula for the line of regression of y on x.[14] If r is equal to 1 the two lines coincide, and if, in addition, the two standard deviations are equal, the line of regression will bisect the angle formed by the axes. If the points be plotted on a chart scaled in units of the standard deviations, we have $y = rx$; the slope of the line of regression is then equal to the value of r.

The coefficient of regression is represented by the symbol b. In a simple correlation problem there are two such coefficients, representing the slopes of the two lines of regression. These are

$$b_{yx} = r \frac{s_y}{s_x} \qquad (9.21)$$

$$b_{xy} = r \frac{s_x}{s_y} \qquad (9.22)$$

(The subscripts indicate the relation between the two variables. The first subscript refers to the dependent variable in each case.)

[14] The formula

$$x = r \frac{s_x}{s_y} y$$

may be reduced to

$$x = \frac{\Sigma(xy)}{\Sigma(y^2)} y$$

This is the equation to a line fitted to the points plotted in Fig. 9.6 in such a way that the sum of the squares of the *horizontal deviations* is a minimum.
The formula

$$y = \frac{\Sigma(xy)}{\Sigma(x^2)} x$$

is the equation to the line for which the sum of the squares of the *vertical deviations* is a minimum. An understanding of this point may make clear the difference between the two lines of regression.

The coefficient r appears in both formulas. This being so, it is clear that r may be computed from the regression coefficients. For

$$\sqrt{b_{yx} \cdot b_{xy}} = \sqrt{r\frac{s_y}{s_x} \cdot r\frac{s_x}{s_y}} = \sqrt{r^2} = r$$

Thus if we know the slopes of the two lines of regression r may be determined. In the present example

$$r = \sqrt{.705 \times .993} = .837$$

Use of the Equations of Regression. The two equations of regression given above

$$y = .705x$$

and

$$x = .993y$$

describe relations between deviations from the respective arithmetic means. That is, the origin is at the point of averages, and to use the equations we cannot use the original values of X and Y but must express them as deviations from their means. For example, we wish to determine the normal commercial bank rate associated with a Federal Reserve bank rate of 6 percent. The mean value of the X-variable (Federal Reserve bank rates) is 4.293 percent. A rate of 6 percent represents a deviation from the mean of $+1.707$. Substituting this value in the first of the above equations, we have

$$y = .705 (+ 1.707)$$
$$= + 1.203$$

This is the average y-deviation associated with an x-deviation of $+1.707$. To get the normal commercial bank rate associated with a Federal Reserve rate of 6 percent the quantity $+1.203$ percent must be added to the mean commercial bank rate, 5.418 percent. The value we wish is thus 6.621 percent.

This calculation has been rather round-about because of the form of the equation of relationship. This equation can be put in more appropriate form for such computations.

Let

$$\overline{X} = \text{arithmetic mean of the } X's$$
$$\overline{Y} = \text{arithmetic mean of the } Y's$$

Then

$$y = r \frac{s_y}{s_x} x$$

may be written

$$Y - \overline{Y} = r \frac{s_y}{s_x} (X - \overline{X}) \qquad (9.23)$$

In this last equation X and Y represent the values of the variables on the original scales, and not as deviations from their respective means. In terms of the coordinate chart, it means shifting the origin from the point of averages to a point corresponding to zero on each of the original scales.

To illustrate the greater utility of the equation in this form, the equation

$$y = .705x$$

may be changed in the manner indicated. It becomes

$$Y - 5.418 = .705(X - 4.293)$$
$$= .705X - 3.027$$
$$Y = 2.391 + .705X$$

This is the equation with the origin so shifted that the original values may be employed directly. To determine the commercial bank rate normally associated with a Federal Reserve rate of 6 percent we may substitute the latter value in the equation just secured.

$$Y = 2.391 + (.705 \times 6.0)$$
$$= 6.621$$

Precisely the same results are secured as with the equation in the other form, but for many purposes it is preferable to have an equation in which the actual values may be inserted.

The equation

$$x = r \frac{s_x}{s_y} y$$

may be similarly changed to

$$X - \overline{X} = r \frac{s_x}{s_y} (Y - \overline{Y})$$

Zones of estimate. The significance of the standard error of estimate as a measure supplementary to an equation of regression is brought out graphically in Fig. 9.7. Here we have plotted the line of regression of Y on X (i.e., $Y = 2.391 + 0.705X$). "Zones of estimate," whose limits above and below the line of regression are

FIG. 9.7. Scatter Diagram of Federal Reserve and Commercial Bank Rates, with Line of Average Relationship and Zones of Estimate.

set by $s_{y \cdot x}$ or multiples of $s_{y \cdot x}$, are defined by broken lines. Within the zone having a width equal to $2S$, centering at the fitted straight line, 68 percent of all the points should fall, on the assumption that the distribution of y-deviations is normal over the entire range of x-values, and that the dispersion of y-deviations is constant over this range.[15] Within the zone having a width equal to $6S$, centering at the fitted straight line, 99.7 percent of all the points should fall, on the same assumption. The smaller the value of S the narrower these zones, and hence the more accurate the estimates that are based upon the equation of average relationship.

---

[15] The assumptions of normality and of constancy of dispersion restrict the practical use of the concept of zones of estimate. Logarithmic and harmonic transformations of the dependent variable may extend the range of use by yielding normal distributions of deviations, where deviations on the arithmetic scale are non-normal (See Mills (Ref. 102). Mood (Ref. 109, pp. 297-9) outlines a more precise procedure for defining prediction intervals (which are analogous to confidence intervals), but the procedure is restricted to normally distributed variates.)

Summary of Correlation Procedure

In the foregoing pages there have been presented two quite different methods of securing the values required in measuring the relationship between two variables. The steps in the two methods may be briefly summarized. The method of least squares is basic in both cases, but that term may appropriately be employed to describe the first method outlined, for the process of fitting the line is the first and fundamental step in that procedure.

The Least Squares Method.

1. Fit a straight line to the data by the method of least squares. A simple arrangement of the data in columns will permit the ready computation of the required values, $\Sigma(X)$, $\Sigma(Y)$, $\Sigma(X^2)$, $\Sigma(Y^2)$, $\Sigma(XY)$. The equation thus obtained describes the average relationship between the two variables.

2. Compute the standard error of estimate, $s_{y.x}$, from the formula

$$s_{y.x}^2 = \frac{\Sigma(Y^2) - a\Sigma(Y) - b\Sigma(XY)}{N}$$

The quantity $s_{y.x}$ is a measure of the reliability of estimates based upon the equation of relationship, and is to be interpreted in the same way as is the standard deviation about an arithmetic mean.

3. Compute the coefficient of correlation, r, from the formula

$$r^2 = 1 - \frac{s_{y.x}^2}{s_y^2}$$

or from

$$r^2 = \frac{a\Sigma(Y) + b\Sigma(XY) - Nc_y^2}{\Sigma(Y^2) - Nc_y^2}$$

Give r the sign of the constant b in the equation of regression. This coefficient is an abstract measure of the degree of relationship between the two variables, in so far as this relationship may be described by a straight line.

4. If an equation describing the regression of X on Y (X being dependent) is desired, the proper values may be substituted in the two normal equations

$$\Sigma(X) = Na + b\Sigma(Y)$$
$$\Sigma(XY) = a\Sigma(Y) + b\Sigma(Y^2)$$

The equation secured will be of the type

$$X = a + bY$$

The standard error of estimate, $s_{x.y}$, may be computed by making the appropriate changes in the formula as given for $s_{y.x}$. The value of r will be the same as in the preceding case, in which Y is dependent.

The Product Moment Method.

A.   Data to be handled as individual items.

1. Arrange the paired observations in parallel columns and compute the quantities $\Sigma(X)$, $\Sigma(Y)$, $\Sigma(X^2)$, $\Sigma(Y^2)$, $\Sigma(XY)$.

2. Divide these quantities throughout by N. For the first two of these quotients we may use the symbols c_x and c_y (i.e.,

$$\frac{\Sigma(X)}{N} = c_x$$

and

$$\frac{\Sigma(Y)}{N} = c_y)$$

3. Compute the mean product from the formula

$$p = \frac{\Sigma(XY)}{N} - c_x c_y$$

4. Compute the two standard deviations from the formulas

$$s_x = \sqrt{\frac{\Sigma(X^2)}{N} - c_x^2}$$

$$s_y = \sqrt{\frac{\Sigma(Y^2)}{N} - c_y^2}$$

5. Compute the coefficient of correlation from the formula

$$r = \frac{p}{s_x s_y}$$

6. Determine the equations of regression by substituting the proper values in the formulas

$$y = r \frac{s_y}{s_x} x$$

$$x = r \frac{s_x}{s_y} y$$

(Note: For each of these equations the origin is at the point of averages.)

7. If desired, transfer the origin to zero on the two original scales by substituting the arithmetic means in the equations

$$Y - \overline{Y} = r \frac{s_y}{s_x} (X - \overline{X})$$

$$X - \overline{X} = r \frac{s_x}{s_y} (Y - \overline{Y})$$

8. Compute the two standard errors of estimate from the formulas

$$s_{y \cdot x} = s_y \sqrt{1 - r^2}$$

$$s_{x \cdot y} = s_x \sqrt{1 - r^2}$$

B. Data to be classified.
  1. Construct a correlation table.
  2. Select an assumed mean for each variable. Measure the deviations of the various items from the assumed means in class-interval units.
  3. Compute c_x and c_y in class-interval units.
  4. Compute s_x and s_y in class-interval units.
  5. Compute $\Sigma(x'y')$ in class-interval units for each compartment of the correlation table. Total these figures to get $\Sigma(x'y')$ for the whole table.
  6. Determine the value of the mean product in class-interval units from the formula

$$p = \frac{\Sigma(x'y')}{N} - c_x c_y$$

  7. Compute r from the formula

$$r = \frac{p}{s_x s_y}$$

  8. Reduce s_x and s_y to original units.
  9. Determine the equations of regression by substituting the proper values in the formulas

$$y = r \frac{s_y}{s_x} x$$

and

$$x = r \frac{s_x}{s_y} y$$

  10. If desired, transfer the origin to zero on the two original scales from the formulas

$$Y - \overline{Y} = r \frac{s_y}{s_x} (X - \overline{X})$$

$$X - \overline{X} = r \frac{s_x}{s_y} (Y - \overline{Y})$$

11. Compute the two standard errors of estimate from the formulas

$$s_{y \cdot x} = s_y \sqrt{1 - r^2}$$

$$s_{x \cdot y} = s_x \sqrt{1 - r^2}$$

It is advisable, in all cases, to construct scatter diagrams and to plot the lines of regression thereon. It is generally possible to derive from such diagrams a truer idea of the relations involved, and of the adequacy of the methods employed, than may be obtained from a study of the figures alone.

A limitation. A question naturally arises as to the degree of generality attaching to the measures of relationship described in the preceding pages. Are they limited to certain types of distributions, or may they be employed as absolutely general and universally valid measures?

As we have seen, the standard deviation has a precise and definite meaning with respect to distributions following the normal law. Having values of the mean and of the standard deviation, we know, in such instances, the exact percentage of cases in the population that will fall within any stated limits. If the distribution departs from the normal type the standard deviation is still a useful measure, but it cannot be interpreted in the same exact sense. Bearing this in mind, the formula

$$r^2 = 1 - \frac{s_{y \cdot x}^2}{s_y^2}$$

may be considered.

When the distribution of the original values of the dependent variable about their mean is normal and the distribution about the least squares line is normal, both $s_{y \cdot x}$ and s_y have specific and exact meanings, and it is perfectly legitimate to compute such a measure as r, based upon the relation of one to the other. Departures from normality in either case reduce the significance of this comparison. But just as the standard deviation remains a useful measure, even for distributions that depart from normality, so do the standard error of estimate and the coefficient of correlation. Care must be taken in their interpretation in such cases, however. It must be recognized that these measures have their full significance only in cases where the distributions of the two variables and the distributions of deviations from regression lines are normal, or approximately so.

A simple example may make clear the effect upon the value of the coefficient of correlation of an extreme departure from a normal distribution. In this example we shall use figures showing the population of each of ten cities and the number of television sets in each of these cities, in 1953 (see Table 9-10). When the first nine of these cities, omitting New York, are treated as a group, the following values are secured:

TABLE 9–10

Television Sets and Population in Ten U. S. Cities, 1953*
(both variables in tens of thousands)

City	Population X	Number of television sets installed Y
Denver	45	12
San Antonio	46	12
Kansas City	47	29
Seattle	48	25
Cincinnati	51	38
Buffalo	58	35
New Orleans	59	16
Milwaukee	65	43
Houston	67	22
New York City	802	345

* The data tabulated are estimates from the Bureau of the Census, *Sales Management*, and the National Broadcasting Company, as cited in *The Economic Almanac*, 1953-4, National Industrial Conference Board. Estimates of television sets are as of April 1, 1953.

$$s_y = \quad 10.68$$

$$s_{y \cdot x} = \quad 9.78$$

$$r = + \, 0.4027$$

The nine points and the line of regression are plotted in Panel A of Fig. 9.8.

When we include New York City in the group, the values secured for the sample of ten cities are

$$s_y = \quad 96.30$$

$$s_{y \cdot x} = \quad 9.23$$

$$r = + \, 0.9954$$

The ten points and the line of regression are plotted in Panel B of Fig. 9.8.

The reason for the markedly different results is obvious. The inclusion of the one very large city with the nine smaller cities greatly increases the standard deviations of both variables. That of the Y-variable (number of television sets) is raised from 10.68 to 96.30. But $s_{y \cdot x}$, the measure of the scatter about the fitted line, undergoes no such pronounced change in value. For the nine cities

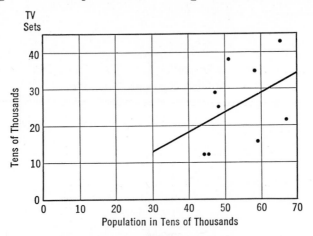

PANEL A. Showing the Relation between Number of Television Sets Installed and Population, in Nine United States Cities, 1953.

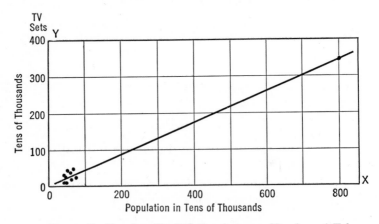

PANEL B. Showing the Relation between Number of Television Sets Installed and Population, in Ten United States Cities, 1953.

FIG. 9.8

it is 9.78; for the ten cities it is 9.23. This is due to the fact that the one exceptional case is given such great weight, in fitting by the method of least squares, that the fitted line must pass through or very near the point representing this observation. Accordingly, $s_{y \cdot x}$ is always affected less than s_y by a single very exceptional case. Since the value of r depends upon the relationship

$$r = \sqrt{1 - \frac{s_{y \cdot x}^2}{s_y^2}}$$

the presence of such a case always tends to increase the value of the measure of correlation. The introduction of the one exceptional case in the above example changes a low and nonsignificant correlation coefficient to one of virtual unity. The result, of course, is meaningless.

While this example represents an extreme instance, the same distortion will be present, in greater or less degree, whenever there is a departure from normality. In practice, use of the various measures of relationship is not restricted to perfectly normal distributions, but the measures we have discussed above lose some degree of significance when derived from non-normal distributions.

The measures of correlation and regression discussed in this chapter have so far been dealt with on the descriptive level only. But such measures, describing relations found in particular samples, are of interest to us primarily as bases for estimates of population parameters, and for tests of hypotheses. We now turn to these problems of inference.

Problems of Inference Involving Measures of Correlation and Regression

Sampling Distribution of the Coefficient of Correlation. The sampling distribution of r varies with the population value of the coefficient of correlation, ρ (rho), and with N, the size of the sample. For samples drawn from normal parent populations the distribution of r tends toward the normal type as N increases; this tendency is much more pronounced for values of ρ close to zero than for values of ρ that depart widely from zero. For ρ close to -1 and $+1$ the value of N must be very large if the distribution of r is to be symmetrical and approximately normal.

The reason for this is clear. If ρ, the population value, is close to unity, say $+ 0.98$, the sample r's have a possible range of only 0.02 in one direction, a possible range of 1.98 in the other direction. But if ρ is equal, say to $+ 0.04$ the range of possible deviation in one direction is very close to the range of possible deviation in the other direction. Under these conditions a distribution of r approaching symmetry is to be expected. This difference is shown graphically in Fig. 9.9. Here we have the sampling distribution of r for $\rho = + 0.10$ and $N = 8$, and the sampling distribution of r for $\rho = + 0.80$ and $N = 8$.

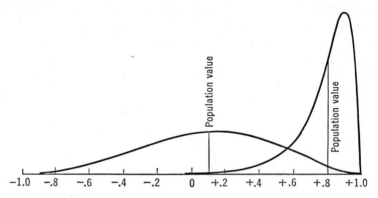

FIG. 9.9. Frequency Curves Showing Sampling Distributions of the Coefficient of Correlation. For Samples with $N = 8$, Drawn from Populations for which $\rho = + 0.10$ and $+ 0.80$.

Using the symbol σ_r for the standard error of r we have, as a general expression holding for samples drawn from normal parent populations,[16]

$$\sigma_r = \frac{1 - \rho^2}{\sqrt{N - 1}}. \tag{9.24}$$

There are two important restrictions on the use of formula (9.24). In the first place, it calls for ρ, the population value of r, and this is not usually known. Investigators frequently use r as derived from a given sample as an approximation to ρ, but the approximation may be a very poor one, especially if N is small. For the special case in which we are testing the hypothesis that a given sample is

---

[16] Since two variables are always involved in samplings of this sort, the term "bivariate normal parent" is often used for such a universe.

drawn from a population for which ρ is zero, formula (9.24) reduces to

$$\sigma_r = \frac{1}{\sqrt{N-1}} \qquad (9.25)$$

For such a test the uncertainty about ρ is, of course, removed.

The second restriction attaches to the interpretation of σ_r as the standard deviation of a normal distribution of sample r's. For samples of small and moderate size the sampling distribution of r may depart widely from the normal type, especially for high values of population ρ. If ρ were at all close to unity, N would have to be quite large if formula (9.24) were to be used with confidence for purposes of statistical inference.

Difficulties arising out of variations in the distribution of r as ρ and N change have been largely overcome. The distribution of r was exactly defined by R. A. Fisher in 1915 (Ref. 49). Tables prepared by F. N. David (Ref. 26) give detailed characteristics of distributions of r for varying values of ρ (0, .1, .2, .3, .4, .5, .6, .7, .8, .9), for N from 3 to 25, and for N of 50, 100, 200, and 400. For the N's and ρ's indicated, these provide more accurate bases for inference than do formulas (9.24) and (9.25).

The Transformation of r**.** Finally, escape from the limitations that grow out of the non-normality of distributions of r, under many conditions, is provided by an ingenious transformation due to R. A. Fisher (Ref. 50). Fisher has shown that a logarithmic function of r, for which the symbol z' may be used, is distributed in a form acceptably close to the normal for samples of quite moderate size. This function tends to normality rapidly as N increases. This is true regardless of the population value of the coefficient of correlation. For the transformation we have

$$z' = \tfrac{1}{2} \{ \log_e(1 + r) - \log_e(1 - r) \} \qquad (9.26)$$

The scales of possible values of r and z' are, of course, quite different. For $r = 0$, $z' = 0$; for $r = 1$, $z' = \infty$. Negative values of r give negative values of z'.

Some of the differences between the distributions of r and of z' are brought out by a comparison of the distributions in Fig. 9.10. The pronounced skewness of the distribution of r's for samples of 12 drawn from a population for which $\rho = -0.80$ stands in sharp contrast to the nearly normal distribution of corresponding z''s.

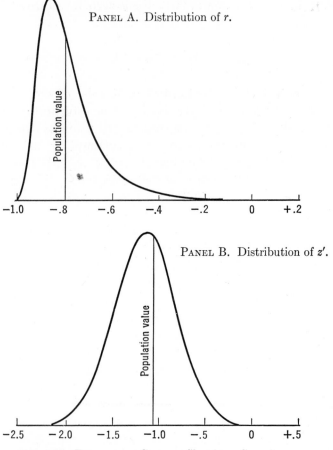

FIG. 9.10. Frequency Curves Showing Sampling Distributions of r and z'. Samples with $N = 12$, Drawn from Populations for which $\rho = -0.80$.

The sample values of z' may be thought of as estimates of a population value ζ (zeta). Close approximations to the mean and the standard deviation of a distribution of z''s are given by

$$\bar{z}' = \zeta + \frac{\rho}{2(N-1)} \qquad (9.27)$$

$$s_{z'} = \frac{1}{\sqrt{N-3}} \qquad (9.28)$$

It is apparent from formula (9.27) that z' has a slight upward bias, that is, that the mean of many sample values of z' would be slightly greater numerically than the population value ζ. This bias is measured by the term $\rho/2(N-1)$. Correction for the bias may be made if necessary, using r as an estimate of ρ. More important is formula (9.28), giving the standard error of z'. This may be taken to be the standard deviation of a normally distributed variate. Its magnitude depends solely on the size of N, not at all on the population ρ. That is, the form of the distribution of z' is virtually independent of the degree of correlation. It does not vary, as does the distribution of r, with variations in the population ρ. As a result, the sampling errors to which z' is exposed may be estimated with considerable accuracy. (For very small samples David's tables are to be preferred to the z' transformation.)

Transformations of r to z', and from z' to r, are effected most readily by prepared tables (see Appendix Table V.) Examples of the use of such tabled values will be given shortly.

Among the advantages of the z'-transformation is that it replaces r by a function with a distribution of values corresponding more closely to the true significance of observed correlations than do those of r. Thus a change in the value of r from .88 to .98 is equivalent, on the r scale, to a change from .20 to .30. But the first of these differences represents, on the z' scale, a change from 1.38 to 2.30 (a range of .92) while the second represents a change in z' from .20 to .31 (a range of .11). The difference in the first case, on the z' scale, is more than eight times that indicated in the second case. In this the z' scale gives a far more accurate representation of the true significance of observed correlations than does the r scale. A difference of a stated number of points on the r scale is more significant for high values of r than for low values.

In dealing with correlation measures derived from samples from non-normal parent populations, the investigator is on less certain ground than when he works with samples from normal universes. For the distributions of such measures have not been defined with accuracy. It is customary in practice to use the measures of sampling error discussed above, without rigorous requirement of parent normality. Investigations of E. S. Pearson, indicating that sampling distributions of r are not greatly affected by departures from normality in the sampled populations, give some justification for this general practice. But in the present state of our knowledge material departure from parent normality must cloud inferences based on coefficients of correlation.

Examples of Inference in Linear Correlation. In illustrating the estimation of the sampling error of a given value of r, we may use the results cited on earlier pages, defining the relation between discount rates of commercial banks and corresponding discount rates of Federal Reserve banks. The value of r is $+ 0.837$, while N is 1,800. The sample is large, and we may use the relation

$$s_r = \frac{1 - \rho^2}{\sqrt{N - 1}}$$

Substituting r as an approximation to ρ, and using the given value of N we have

$$s = \frac{1 - 0.837^2}{\sqrt{1800 - 1}} = \frac{0.299431}{42.41} = 0.007$$

With confidence represented by a probability of 0.99 we may state that the population value of the coefficient of correlation in this case falls between 0.819 and 0.855. The lower of these limits is given, of course, by $+ 0.837 - (2.58 \times 0.007)$, the higher by $+ 0.837 + (2.58 \times 0.007)$.

The first question usually asked when a correlation study has been completed is: Is the value of r significant? More specifically: Is it consistent with the hypothesis that in the population from which the sample has been drawn there is no relation between the two variables here studied? This is, of course, another form of the null hypothesis. In the present case we wish to know whether the facts can disprove this null hypothesis.

In a study of the movements of commodity prices, 1,202 measurements were secured on the timing of advances in the prices of individual commodities during periods of general business revival. Paired with each measurement was a similar observation on the timing of the decline in the price of the given commodity during the succeeding period of general business recession.[17] We desire to know whether there is any relation between the sequence of price revival and the sequence of price recession. Is there a pattern in price movements during business cycles? Evidence of the existence of such a persistent pattern would lend support to the view that cycles represent true regularities in economic life.

These 1,202 pairs of observations yield a correlation coefficient of $+ 0.27$. This does not show a pronounced degree of relationship.

[17] See Mills, Ref. 100, p. 131.

Our chief concern, however, is not with the magnitude of r. We wish to know whether the result is consistent with the hypothesis that the true correlation is zero. For the standard error of r we have

$$s_r = \frac{1}{\sqrt{1{,}202 - 1}} = 0.029$$

By hypothesis, the population value of r is zero, so the numerator of the fraction is 1.

If the true value of r were zero, and the standard error of r were 0.029, what would the probability be that, as a result of chance, we should secure a coefficient of $+ 0.27$ from a given sample? Since this value represents a departure of more than 9 standard deviations from the hypothetical value of zero, the probability that the difference is due to chance is infinitely small. We conclude that the results are not consistent with the hypothesis that the sequence of price change during revival is unrelated to the sequence of decline in a succeeding recession. The null hypothesis is disproved.

Had the value of T $\left(\text{in this case } T = \dfrac{r - 0}{s_r}\right)$ been less than 2.58 the conclusion would of course have been different. In such a case the discrepancy between the sample r and the hypothetical value of zero could be attributed to sampling fluctuations. The result would not be inconsistent with the null hypothesis.

Having established that the results are not consistent with the hypothesis that the true value of r is zero, we may compute the standard error of r as actually derived, and estimate confidence limits for the population value. Using the sample r as an approximation to ρ we have

$$s_r = \frac{1 - 0.27^2}{\sqrt{1{,}202 - 1}} = 0.027$$

Limits derived from the sample r minus and plus 2.58 times s_r are equal, respectively, to $+ 0.20$ and $+ 0.34$. These are the 0.99 confidence limits for ρ.

In the preceding test of significance N was quite large, and it was safe to use formula (9.25), which assumes normality. For small samples tests of the null hypothesis, for r, may be most readily made by means of a table prepared by R. A. Fisher, showing the values of correlation coefficients at stated levels of significance. Selected values from this table are given in Table 9-11 and in Appendix Table IV. In simple correlation problems, this is to be read with n equal to $N - 2$.

The use of the table requires little explanation. If a sample is based on 12 pairs of observations, with n equal to 10, we would require a coefficient at least as high as 0.7079 before we accept it as significant, if our standard of significance is $P = .01$. For only 1 time out of 100 trials would a sample of 12 drawn from an un-

TABLE 9–11

Values of the Correlation Coefficient for Different Levels of Significance*

n	$P = .05$	$P = .02$	$P = .01$
1	.996917	.9995066	.9998766
2	.95000	.98000	.990000
3	.8783	.93433	.95873
4	.8114	.8822	.91720
5	.7545	.8329	.8745
6	.7067	.7887	.8343
7	.6664	.7498	.7977
8	.6319	.7155	.7646
9	.6021	.6851	.7348
10	.5760	.6581	.7079
11	.5529	.6339	.6835
12	.5324	.6120	.6614
13	.5139	.5923	.6411
14	.4973	.5742	.6226
15	.4821	.5577	.6055
16	.4683	.5425	.5897
17	.4555	.5285	.5751
18	.4438	.5155	.5614
19	.4329	.5034	.5487
20	.4227	.4921	.5368
25	.3809	.4451	.4869
30	.3494	.4093	.4487
35	.3246	.3810	.4182
40	.3044	.3578	.3932
45	.2875	.3384	.3721
50	.2732	.3218	.3541
60	.2500	.2948	.3248
70	.2319	.2737	.3017
80	.2172	.2565	.2830
90	.2050	.2422	.2673
100	.1946	.2301	.2540

* This table is printed here through the courtesy of R. A. Fisher and his publishers, Oliver and Boyd, of Edinburgh. The original appears as Table V.A of *Statistical Methods for Research Workers*.

correlated population yield a value of r as great as 0.7079. If our standard of significance is $P = .05$ we would accept as significant of a real relationship an r of 0.5760, or greater, obtained from a sample of 12.

We have noted the great value of Fisher's z'-transformation in increasing the effectiveness of inference involving the coefficient of correlation. This transformation is particularly appropriate in estimating ρ for the population of cities which was sampled in deriving data on average family income and average family expenditures on consumption. Calculations cited on preceding pages give us an r of $+ 0.937$, measuring the relation between these two variables for a sample of 33 cities with populations from 2,500 to 30,500. Here we are dealing with a relatively small sample, drawn from a population for which ρ is, apparently, fairly close to unity. Under such conditions the distribution of r will depart materially from normality. Accordingly we shall transform r to z' in setting confidence limits for our estimate of the population ρ.

From Appendix Table V we determine that the value of z' corresponding to an r of $+ 0.937$ is $+ 1.71$. The sample size is 33. We have

$$s_{z'} = \frac{1}{\sqrt{N-3}} = \frac{1}{\sqrt{33-3}} = \frac{1}{5.477} = 0.1826$$

This may be interpreted as the standard deviation of a normal distribution of z''s. We wish to set for z' population limits corresponding to a probability of 0.99. The lower limit will be $+ 1.71 - (2.58 \times 0.1826)$, or 1.24. The upper limit will be $+ 1.71 + (2.58 \times 0.1826)$, or 2.18. Thus we may make the statement, with a confidence of 0.99, that the population z' falls between 1.24 and 2.18. Transforming these limits back to the r scale (using Appendix Table V) we may, with a confidence of 0.99, set our population ρ between $+ 0.8455$ and $+ 0.9748$.

The null hypothesis, for r, may be tested with accuracy by means of the z'-transformation, for large samples for which prepared tables (such as Table 9-11 above) are not suitable.

The transformation to z' makes possible, also, an accurate test of the significance of the difference between two observed correlations. The standard error of the difference between two values of z is given by

$$s_{D_{z'}} = \sqrt{\frac{1}{N_1 - 3} + \frac{1}{N_2 - 3}} \qquad (9.29)$$

where N_1 is the number of pairs of observations in the first sample, N_2 the number in the second.

This test may be illustrated with reference to observations on the timing of price changes during business cycles. For 111 commodities we have observations on the timing of price declines in two successive periods of business recession occurring in the late 90's and early 1900's. The degree of relation between the time sequences of commodity price changes in these two recessions is indicated by a coefficient of correlation of $+ 0.22$. For two similar (successive) periods in the 1920's the measure of correlation, based on the prices of 121 commodities, has a value of $+ 0.36$. There appears to have been a closer approach to a common pattern in the later period than in the earlier. In testing the significance of the difference between the two results we set up the hypothesis that the two samples were drawn from the same parent population, and that therefore the true value of the difference between the two coefficients is zero.

For the two samples we have

$$r_1 = + 0.22; \ z_1' = + 0.223; \ \frac{1}{N_1 - 3} = \frac{1}{108} = 0.0093$$

$$r_2 = + 0.36; \ z_2' = + 0.377; \ \frac{1}{N_2 - 3} = \frac{1}{118} = 0.0085$$

The difference to be tested is

$$D_{z'} = 0.377 - 0.223 = 0.154$$

The standard error of this difference is

$$s_{D_{z'}} = \sqrt{0.0093 + 0.0085} = 0.133$$

We wish to know whether $D_{z'}$ is significantly different from zero. We compute, therefore,

$$T = \frac{D_{z'} - 0}{s_{D_{z'}}} = \frac{0.154 - 0}{0.133} = 1.16$$

Interpreting 1.16 as a normal deviate, we conclude that the difference is not significant. Dz' differs from the hypothetical value of zero by only slightly more than one standard deviation. The results are not inconsistent with the hypothesis that the two samples are drawings from the same parent population. There is here no clear evidence that the degree of relationship between price movements in successive cycles was closer in the 1920's than in the earlier period.[18]

There is economic significance in another comparison, for which the same test may be used. We have referred above to observations dealing with the relation between the discount rates of commercial banks and of Federal Reserve banks. The sample used in the illustration includes 1,800 observations, covering the period 1920-1932. For this sample $r = + 0.837$. Data from another sample, which includes 735 observations, cover the years 1922-1949. For this sample $r = + 0.936$. There is overlapping in part, but the second sample is drawn in the main from a later period. A comparison of the results indicates that for recent years changes in commercial bank rates have been tied more directly to Federal Reserve bank rates than was true in the earlier period. (The comparison is not perfect, partly because of the overlapping, which would tend to make the sample results agree, and partly because of some technical differences in the data used. These differences do not preclude comparison, but they call for caution in the interpretation of conclusions.) Transforming the r's to z''s, and measuring the difference, we have $D_{z'} = 0.49$. The standard error of $D_{z'}$, derived from formula (9.29), is 0.044. Thus for the normal deviate, defining the difference in units of the standard deviation, we have

$$T = \frac{0.49 - 0}{0.044} = 11.1$$

In spite of the overlapping, the difference is clearly significant. There is here a strong indication that variations in the two discount rates have been more closely related in recent years than they were in the earlier period. The conclusion calls for moderate qualification because of data differences, but the fundamental indication is probably accurate.

Finally, making use of the z'-transformation, we may combine results secured from the measurement of correlation in different samples. If we have two values of r, obtained from samples drawn from the same population, a weighted average of the two will

[18] The time factor enters to cloud statistical inductions relating to samples drawn from different periods. Such an induction should be supported by evidence indicating that fundamental conditions in the field in question have not been altered over the time interval involved. This caution does not, of course, affect the procedure illustrated above.

provide a better estimate of the true correlation than will either of the r's, taken separately. For the averaging process we transform the r's to z''s, weight each z' by the corresponding N, less 3, and average them. For example, we may combine the two coefficients defining relations between the time sequences of price changes in business cycles, since the test has indicated that they do not differ significantly. Here we have

$$\text{Average } z' = \frac{z_1'(N_1 - 3) + z_2'(N_2 - 3)}{(N_1 - 3) + (N_2 - 3)} \tag{9.30}$$

$$= \frac{(+\ 0.223 \times 108) + (+\ 0.377 \times 118)}{226}$$

$$= +\ 0.303$$

The standard error of this weighted average z', we may note, is given by

$$s_{z'} = \frac{1}{\sqrt{N_1 - 3) + (N_2 - 3)}} \tag{9.31}$$

We may wish to transform this weighted z' back to the corresponding r. From Appendix Table V we obtain the value $r = +\ 0.29$. This we may accept as the best estimate we have of the correlation between price declines in successive periods of business recession.

Sampling Errors of the Coefficient of Regression. In certain problems coefficients of regression are more meaningful than coefficients of correlation. For samples drawn from normal universes the standard error of the coefficient of regression b_{yx} may be estimated from

$$s_{b_{yx}} = \frac{s_{y \cdot x}}{s_x \sqrt{N - 1}} \tag{9.32}$$

where $s_{y \cdot x}$ is the standard error of estimate of y.[19] This measure may be used in the usual fashion in problems of estimation and in tests of significance, when the statistics have been derived from large samples.

[19]
$$s_{y \cdot x} = \sqrt{\frac{\Sigma(y - y_c)^2}{N - 2}}$$

where y denotes a given value of the dependent variable and y_c denotes the corresponding value derived from the equation of regression. In the computation of $s_{y \cdot x}$ for this purpose N is reduced by the number of constants in the equation of regression. Two degrees of freedom have been used up, in effect, in computing y_c.

As an example of the procedure employed in testing b for significance, in large samples, we may cite the equation to the trend line for New York City temperature, given in Chapter 10 and plotted in Fig. 10.3. Such a trend line is, in effect, a regression function, temperature being the dependent variable and time the independent variable. For the period 1871-1949 the equation of regression is $Y = 52.482 + 0.0346X$, where X is measured in years from an origin at 1910 and Y is measured in degrees Fahrenheit. The coefficient of regression defines an average annual increase in temperature of 0.0346 degrees. Does this coefficient reflect the play of chance, or is it significant of a real secular increase in the temperature of New York City? From formula (9.32) above we obtain $s_b = 0.006$. The null hypothesis to be tested is that $\beta = 0$. Deriving T, the normal deviate, in the customary fashion we have

$$T = \frac{b - \beta}{s_b} = \frac{0.0346 - 0}{0.006} = 5.77$$

The null hypothesis must be rejected. The evidence indicates that there has been a significant increase in mean annual temperatures in New York City over this period of 78 years. (We should note that a test of this sort would usually be of questionable validity, when applied to a series of observations ordered in time, because of the lack of independence of successive observations. With meteorological data, however, it is not unreasonable to assume that there is independence, apart from the slowly acting secular factor with which the test deals.)

Spearman's Coefficient of Rank Correlation

Limitations arising from non-normality of the populations from which samples are drawn may be avoided, in dealing with certain problems, by the use of what are called *nonparametric* methods. It is the essence of these methods that they involve no assumptions about the parameters of the populations sampled. In certain cases freedom from such assumptions makes possible greater accuracy in the making of inferences—the major objective of most statistical work. In the study of correlation we may escape from parametric assumptions by ordering observations by size, and basing calculations upon the *ranks* thus established. Furthermore, the use of ordered arrangements makes it possible to deal, quantitatively, with individuals or other entities that may be ranked on the basis of qualities not open to exact measurement.

Data to be used in an example of the descriptive application of rank correlation methods are shown in Table 9-12. Here, for ten United States cities with populations of 1,000,000 or over, are given average family income after taxes and average family expenditures for consumption in 1950. These cities are ranked in order of average family income, from the highest to the lowest. In columns (4) and (5) of Table 9-12 the money values of income and consumption expenditures for these cities are replaced by measures of rank.

TABLE 9–12

Illustrating the Computation
of the Spearman Coefficient of Rank Correlation
Family Income after Taxes and
Family Expenditures on Current Consumption, 1950
Averages for Ten Cities with Populations of 1,000,000 and Over*

(1)	(2)	(3)	(4)	(5)	(6)	(7)
	Average	Average	Rank on basis of		Differ-	
	money	expenditures	average	average	ence	
City	income	on	family	consumption	d	
	after taxes	consumption	income	expenditure	(4)−(5)	d^2
Chicago, Ill.	$5,080	$4,905	1	2	− 1	1
Cleveland, Ohio	4,876	4,671	2	3	− 1	1
New York, N. Y.	4,852	4,932	3	1	+ 2	4
Los Angeles, Calif.	4,745	4,661	4	4	0	
San Francisco-Oakland, Calif.	4,584	4,477	5	6	− 1	1
Pittsburgh	4,583	4,506	6	5	+ 1	1
St. Louis, Mo.	4,546	4,251	7	9	− 2	4
Philadelphia-Camden	4,506	4,384	8	7	+ 1	1
Boston, Mass.	4,200	4,300	9	8	+ 1	1
Baltimore, Md.	3,983	3,919	10	10	0	
Total						14

* From *Bulletin 1097* (revised), U. S. Bureau of Labor Statistics, June, 1953.

The degree of correlation is indicated by the degree of concordance between the two rankings. A precise measure of correlation is provided by Spearman's coefficient

$$r_r = 1 - \frac{6\Sigma d^2}{N^3 - N} \tag{9.33}$$

where d is the difference between the ranking of a given city in columns (4) and (5), and N is the number of cities included.[20]

[20] This formula may be derived from the usual product-moment formula, with x and y relating to ranks, not to measurements. In this derivation use is made of the fact that the sums of the squares of the deviations of the first N natural numbers from their mean is equal to $\frac{N^3 - N}{12}$.

The basic quantity needed, Σd^2, is derived as indicated in Table 9-12. Given this quantity and N, the number of cities, we have

$$r_r = 1 - \frac{84}{10^3 - 10}$$
$$= + 0.9152$$

It is clear from formula (9.33) that r_r will be $+1$ if the rankings of cities based on the two variables are identical throughout. For then each d will be zero, and Σd^2 will be zero. It may be shown that when the rankings are exactly inverse r_r will be -1. Thus, as for r, r_r may fall between $+1$ and -1, being 0 when there is no relation between the two rankings.

Tests of Significance of Rank Order Coefficients

We have referred briefly above to problems of inference that are faced in using coefficients of rank correlation. Such problems arise, primarily, in determining whether a given coefficient provides evidence of a significant degree of correlation, in the population, between the attributes on which paired rankings have been based.

Coefficients of rank correlation, r_r, derived from large samples drawn from a universe for which ρ_r is zero are distributed normally, or effectively so. For the standard deviation of such a distribution of r_r's we have

$$s_{r_r} = \frac{1}{\sqrt{N - 1}} \qquad (9.34)$$

This may be applied in testing the null hypothesis when N is large, say 25 or more, and when there are no ties in the rankings of either variable.

For small samples the distribution of r_r is not normal. Kendall (Ref. 78, I, 396-7; Ref. 80, 142) gives tables that may be used in determining the significance of the Spearman coefficient when $N < 9$. For sample sizes between 9 and 25, drawn from uncorrelated parent populations, the distribution of r_r is not known. We should note, also, that the distributions of r_r for samples drawn from correlated parent populations (i.e., $\rho_r \neq 0$) have not been established. Thus there are important areas of indeterminacy in basing inferences on the Spearman coefficient.[21]

[21] M. G. Kendall has devised a coefficient of rank correlation represented by the symbol τ (tau), and has established relevant sampling distributions for various values of N. Kendall's coefficient is not quite so simple in structure as Spearman's, but has distinct advantages when tests of significance are to be applied. See Kendall, Ref. 80. A brief explanation of Kendall's coefficient is given in Mills, *Statistical Methods*, Third Edition, pp. 316-7.

Coefficients of rank correlation, with other nonparametric measures, have a considerable range of usefulness. Their freedom from assumptions concerning the nature of population distributions gives them special validity in situations not infrequently encountered in handling economic and other social data. Series ordered in time, which are of special concern in economic analysis, represent one promising area of use for such methods.

REFERENCES

Clark, C. E., *An Introduction to Statistics*, Chap. 9.

Croxton, F. E. and Cowden, D. J., *Applied General Statistics*, Chap. 22.

Deming, W. E., *Statistical Adjustment of Data*, Chap. 4.

Dixon, W. J. and Massey, F. J. Jr., *Introduction to Statistical Analysis*, Chap. 11.

Ezekiel, M., *Methods of Correlation Analysis*, 2nd ed., Chaps. 3, 5, 7, 18.

Fisher, Sir Ronald (R. A.), *Statistical Methods for Research Workers*, 11th ed., Chap. 6.

Freeman, H. A., *Industrial Statistics*, Chap. 3.

Freund, J. E., *Modern Elementary Statistics*, Chaps. 13, 14.

Goulden, C. H., *Methods of Statistical Analysis*, 2nd ed., Chaps. 6, 7.

Hoel, P. G., *Introduction to Mathematical Statistics*, 2nd ed., Chap. 7.

Hotelling, H., "New Light on the Correlation Coefficient and Its Transforms," *Journal of the Royal Statistical Society*, Series B, Vol. 15, No. 2, 1953.

Kendall, M. G., *The Advanced Theory of Statistics*, 3rd ed., Vol. I, Chaps. 14, 16.

Kendall, M. G., *Rank Correlation Methods*.

Lewis, E. E., *Methods of Statistical Analysis in Economics and Business*, Chap. 12.

Mather, K., *Statistical Analysis in Biology*, 2nd ed., Chap. 8.

Rider, P. R., *An Introduction to Modern Statistical Methods*, Chap. 4.

Riggleman, J. R. and Frisbee, I. N., *Business Statistics*, 3rd ed., Chap. 12.

Snedecor, G. W., *Statistical Methods*, 4th ed., Chaps. 6, 7.

Spurr, W. A., Kellogg, L. S. and Smith, J. H., *Business and Economic Statistics*, Chap. 17.

Tippett, L. H. C., *The Methods of Statistics*, 4th ed., Chaps. 8, 9.

Treloar, A. E., *Elements of Statistical Reasoning*, Chaps. 7, 8, 9.

Walker, H. M. and Lev., *Statistical Inference*, pp. 230-258, 278-287.

Waugh, A. E., *Elements of Statistical Method*, 3rd ed., Chaps. 11, 15.

Yule, G. U. and Kendall, M. G., *An Introduction to the Theory of Statistics*. 14th ed., Chaps. 9, 10, 11, 15.

The publishers and the dates of publication of the books named in chapter reference lists are given in the bibliography at the end of this volume.

CHAPTER **10**

.
.
.

The Analysis of Time Series: Secular Trends

The preceding sections have dealt with distributions of observations organized on the basis of frequency of occurrence. We have been concerned with patterns of variation, and with methods appropriate to inductive generalization and the testing of hypotheses when the variation present reflects the play of random factors. When data are organized in such frequency distributions the order, in time, of the various observations is neglected, as having no bearing on the problems at issue. Thus when a coin is tossed there is no reason for distinguishing the tenth throw from the second. We turn now to procedures employed when the chronological order in which observations are made is of the essence of the problems being studied—when our interest lies in variation over time. This is obviously the case in the study of biological growth; it is true for the physicist investigating variations in radioactivity over time. It is true, also, of many of the central problems faced in the social and economic sciences, and in business administration. Changes in birth rates and death rates, changes in national income, changes in prices and in the physical volume of production, variations in sales and in profits—in all these the time sequence is crucial.

Movements in Historical Variables

Time series, or historical variables as Schumpeter has called them, are subject to the play of a diversity of forces. Random factors are present, as with the frequency series discussed above,

FIG. 10.1. Construction Contracts in 37 States East of the Rocky Mountains, 1945-1954.*

*Source: F. W. Dodge Corporation.

but nonrandom factors are present too, and often dominate the behavior of the observations. The presence of nonrandom factors, indeed, gives rise to the special problems faced in the analysis of time series. Techniques suitable to the study of random variation are not appropriate in dealing with patterns of variation due to specific nonrandom factors.

A graphic representation of observations on a historical variable reveals, usually, a succession of discontinuous changes from month to month or year to year. If we are dealing, for example, with number of construction contracts awarded, by months, we have the record plotted in Fig. 10.1. The entry for any one month will be the resultant of many impinging factors—the plans of diverse private builders, the state of employment, construction programs of governmental units of all sorts, the time of year and the state of the weather, the supply of materials and the level of costs, the business situation, prevailing or impending strikes, the existence of peace or war, etc. In studying a historical series of this sort it is usually desirable to classify these diverse factors into categories that are significant for the purpose in hand and that correspond to realities in the field of study. Any such classification must be, in part at least, arbitrary. It will be affected by the preconceptions of the investigator, by the immediate objects of his study, and by the theoretical framework he has set up. Obviously, if the classification employed is to be useful these preconceptions and this framework must be in harmony with the processes to which the observations relate. Having set up such a classification the investigator seeks to decompose the observations into elements corresponding to the classes he has set up. The statistical procedures to be discussed in this and the two following chapters have as their central objective such "decomposition."

The forces affecting historical variables have been classified as nonrecurring or recurring; as evolutionary, periodic, or random. There has been introduced, also, the notion of structural change— a change, which may be sudden or progressive, in the relations among the elements of a system. Most commonly employed, and perhaps most generally useful in dealing with individual series, is a classification that distinguishes secular, seasonal, cyclical, and random components.

In speaking of the secular component, or the *secular trend*, of a historical variable we use the term secular in a sense relating to the ages, to long periods of time. Secular forces are those that determine the long-term movements of the series, movements that may reflect persistent growth, persistent decline, or successive stages of growth and decline in evolutionary, irreversible development. The concept of secular change entails notions of regularity, of essential continuity. Frequent and sudden changes either in absolute amounts or in rates of increase or decrease are inconsistent with the idea of secular trend. It is true that there may be changes in trend, changes due to the interjection of a new element or the withdrawal of an old one. But, essentially, the secular trend of a series of observations ordered in time is conceived of as a smooth, continuous process underlying the irregularities of month-to-month or year-to-year change that characterize most historical variables in the social and economic fields.

Seasonal variations are found in many historical series for which quarterly, monthly, or weekly values are obtainable. Railroad freight traffic, fire losses, the consumption of many commodities, department store sales, employment, and many other such variables are marked by seasonal swings repeated with minor variations (and sometimes with progressive changes) year after year. Such variations are definitely periodic in character, with a constant twelve-month period.

Less markedly periodic, but recurring, nevertheless, with considerable regularity are the *cyclical fluctuations* that are found in many economic and social series. Prices, wages, the volume of industrial production and of trade, marriage rates, trading on the Stock Exchange, and most series related to the activities of individual business enterprises are affected by the swings of business through alternating periods of expansion and contraction. The length of such periods may vary, but observable sequences of change during these cycles have in the past been sufficiently regular in pattern to render them capable of systematic study.

Entangled with these more or less irregular movements are the effects of accidental and irregular factors—the movements we think of as *random*. In time series analysis this category is usually a catch-all for the consequences of catastrophic events, such as earthquakes, wars, floods, and conflagrations, as well as for the effects of countless minor events equally fortuitous though less violent in their incidence. Such events influence the value of a variable at any stated date, modifying the effects of long-term movements and of seasonal and cyclical factors. The observed value at any time is the resultant of the play of all these forces.

The problem of decomposition. When an investigator analyzes a series in time he is usually interested in some one of these types of change. Is there a recurring seasonal pattern in the production of lumber? What is it? What is the pattern of change in the volume of industrial production during business cycles? What has been the character of development in the output of electric power over the last century? The investigator would like to dissociate the movements of immediate interest from all other movements that shape the observed behavior of the series in question. This is the task of decomposition. It will be noted that a fundamental problem is faced here: How are the constituent elements blended together to make up the historical series that is actually recorded? Are cyclical fluctuations superimposed upon an underlying trend that would be there if there were no cycles? Are seasonal fluctuations in turn superimposed upon a trend-cycle composite? Or are cycles superimposed upon a trend-seasonal composite? Are random factors added to the trend-cycle-seasonal composite? Reverting to secular movements: Is the trend a purely mental construct? Does growth come in fact by forward leaps and lesser retrogressions, rather than by smooth and continuous evolution? We shall have more to say about some of these questions at a later stage. At this point we may merely note that the questions raised are largely unanswerable. We don't know how the forces of historical change interact to yield the series we have observed. Whatever process of decomposition we may employ rests on certain assumptions about the manner in which the effects of different forces are combined. Some of these assumptions may be more tenable than others. But when we employ a given method we should be aware of the assumptions made.

Distinctive features of time series. Before discussing the details of analytical methods used in this field, we should note two facts that distinguish time-ordered observations of the kind we are here discussing from those we have dealt with in earlier chapters. The first is that the different observations making up a time series are not independent of one another. This is notably true of successive observations. The number of automobiles produced in February, 1955, is not independent of the number produced in January, 1955. This is in sharp contrast, of course, to the independence of out-

comes of successive tosses of a coin. Probability calculations that
rest on the assumption of independence are not applicable to the
closely related observations that make up historical series in the
economic and social sciences.

The other fact, also disturbing to one who searches for regularities, is that the variables studied in the social and economic
sciences are subject to change, over time, in their population or
"universe" characteristics. Business failures, for example, would
be materially affected by a change in the law relating to bankruptcies; the introduction of the Federal Reserve System in 1913
changed the whole character of banking in the United States. The
implications of this fact are significant. When we draw a sample
of black and white balls from an urn and on the basis of the sample
estimate the proportion of balls of the two colors in the population
we have sampled, we do so in the firm belief that the contents of
the urn will not be surreptitiously changed after we have sampled
it. If a counterpart of Maxwell's demon were to modify the
contents of the urn after we drew the sample, our estimate might
not be worth much. But something very like this occurs in the
world of human affairs. We study some aspect of group behavior—
social or economic—on the basis of observations necessarily local-
ized in time. We then apply to a subsequent period the conclusions
we have drawn from the sample observations. But in the meantime
social institutions may have changed, economic processes may have
been modified, the structure of laws within which men live may
have been altered. There is always a demon modifying the contents
of the urn from which social scientists and business men draw their
samples. The changes resulting may not be important for the
purpose a given investigator has in hand. Elements of continuity
are present, too. The past is never cut off from the present or the
future. But the possibility of significant change is always there,
and this means that projection into the future of inferences based
upon the study of past patterns, whether of trends, of cycles, or
of seasonal movements, is always subject to indefinable margins
of error.

The Preliminary Organization of Time Series

The data of time series usually require less preliminary organization than do statistical data that are to be reduced to the form
of a frequency distribution. The source, primary or secondary, from

which the figures are taken usually presents them in shape for analysis. Certain precautions should be observed, however.

The dates to which the figures apply should be clearly understood and definitely stated. Monthly data may be based upon a single daily figure (as are the price quotations entering into the BLS index of wholesale prices), they may be averages (such as average hourly earnings), or they may be totals for each month (as for figures on cotton consumption). They may be cumulative monthly figures, each item representing the total for the year to date, as in the case of certain coal production data. If average figures are given for a month or year it is important to know how the average has been secured.

Again, it is essential that in any time series there be strict comparability among data for different periods. Any attempt to analyze a series that is not homogeneous must be misleading and futile. Yet such series are not infrequently published. Commodity production or consumption figures published by trade associations and by governmental agencies are sometimes based upon returns from a varying number of reporting concerns. A series of price quotations for different dates may lack comparability because of changes in the unit or grade to which the quotations apply, or because quotations are drawn from different markets. Changes in census classifications may result in lack of comparability of census data. A change in a salesman's territory may alter his returns materially. It is stated that the character of the obligations represented by the United States Steel Corporation's figures for "unfilled orders" has varied from time to time. Records relating to the physical output of a given commodity in different periods may be rendered inaccurate by changes in quality or design. These are examples of faults that may be found in time series, rendering analysis futile. Strict testing is essential before a series be accepted as accurate and homogeneous.

Graphic representation. Normally the first step to be taken in visualizing a series in time and in preparing for further analysis consists of plotting the data. The trend and general characteristics of a series may be most readily apprehended through graphic representation. The data may be plotted on ordinary arithmetic or semilogarithmic paper. The advantages of the latter types for certain purposes have already been explained. The choice in a given case will depend upon the nature of the data and the object of the study. If interest lies in the absolute amount of fluctuations in sales, prices, pig iron production or whatever may be in process of analysis, or in the comparison of absolute differences between series, the ordinary rectilinear chart is to be employed. If percentage variations and the comparison of relative fluctuations are matters of interest, the semilogarithmic representation is preferable. In general, if one is accustomed to the interpretation of this latter type of chart, its use is advisable. A clearer, less-distorted presentation of relations and a more significant comparison of series are generally secured when economic data having time as one variable are plotted on paper with a logarithmic ruling on one axis.

For some purposes the process of studying series in time will have been completed when the data are thus plotted. The general trend may be roughly determined from the chart. The existence of seasonal and other periodic variations may be ascertained. Rough comparisons of trends and fluctuations may be made. All the knowledge thus secured, it should be noted, will be nonquantitative in character, and the comparisons will be tentative and approximative. Even so, such charts enable trends and relations to be much more clearly visualized than do the raw figures, and for some purposes the knowledge thus secured is sufficient, though it lacks precision and accuracy. For other purposes more exact measurement and more refined analysis are required. Certain appropriate methods may be described.

Moving Averages as Measures of Trend

As a first example of a historical variable we may consider the record of number of cars of revenue freight loaded on American railroads. In column (2) of Table 10-1 we have the weekly averages of carloadings, by years, from 1918 to 1953. Since the observations are recorded by years, the seasonal element does not enter in this case. The tabulated figures reflect the play of secular, cyclical, and random factors. Our first task is to seek to define the secular trend.

In Figure 10.2 the data of freight carloadings for the 36-year period have been plotted. Over these years carloadings have been subject to major variations, but a general declining trend is manifest. Several methods are available for arriving at approximations to this trend. By employing moving averages an attempt may be made to eliminate passing fluctuations and to arrive at values

TABLE 10-1

Cars of Revenue Freight Loaded for Class I Railroads
Weekly Averages, by Years, 1918-1953
(thousands of cars)

(1) Year	(2) Original data	(3) Three-year moving average	(4) Five-year moving average	(5) Seven-year moving average	(6) Nine-year moving average
1918	857.5				
1919	804.5	843.2			
1920	867.7	809.5	823.4		
1921	756.2	818.3	843.4	858.3	
1922	830.9	848.3	869.2	876.5	890.5
1923	957.9	907.4	892.7	907.5	905.5
1924	933.4	958.8	945.7	925.4	926.4
1925	985.1	979.9	978.1	959.1	942.8
1926	1021.1	999.7	984.9	985.5	956.9
1927	993.0	1002.1	1001.4	974.7	943.9
1928	992.1	1000.3	980.9	943.4	897.7
1929	1015.9	963.4	919.5	880.1	856.4
1930	882.3	870.9	829.3	814.5	812.9
1931	714.4	712.9	743.3	757.4	766.7
1932	541.9	606.1	658.7	702.2	733.5
1933	561.9	565.7	603.4	656.3	703.8
1934	593.2	587.0	599.4	633.7	656.0
1935	605.8	631.1	635.9	615.3	630.4
1936	694.4	674.9	640.7	631.1	628.7
1937	724.4	668.2	652.5	650.7	658.9
1938	585.7	654.1	671.2	682.1	688.0
1939	652.1	645.7	694.9	713.2	712.7
1940	699.2	721.5	714.8	730.6	738.2
1941	813.3	778.7	760.9	746.4	750.6
1942	823.6	817.7	797.4	777.9	758.4
1943	816.2	824.9	818.8	798.3	788.5
1944	834.8	819.0	815.1	820.7	807.3
1945	806.1	812.0	821.6	821.9	806.3
1946	795.0	819.0	822.6	802.9	799.1
1947	855.8	824.1	793.8	793.1	794.1
1948	821.5	789.3	782.2	785.1	784.6
1949	690.6	753.4	779.0	774.3	773.7
1950	748.1	739.2	753.9	766.0	
1951	778.8	752.5	736.9		
1952	730.5	748.6			
1953	736.6				

that define the influence of the steadily operating secular factor. If we assume that a definite functional relationship prevails (empirically at least) between the time factor and the other variable, an approximation to the trend may be secured by fitting an appropriate curve to the plotted data. Smoothing the data by

FIG. 10.2. Cars of Revenue Freight Loaded for Class I Railroads: Weekly Averages, by Years, 1918-1953, with Moving Averages (thousands of cars).

hand gives somewhat the same result, the curve being frankly approximative and empirical in character. In certain studies it has been found possible to use one statistical series as base or trend line for another series of homogeneous data.

When a trend is to be determined by the method of moving averages, the average value for a number of years (or months, or weeks) is secured, and this average is taken as the normal or trend value for the unit of time falling at the middle of the period covered in the calculation of the average. Table 10-1 shows the results secured when three-, five-, seven-, and nine-year moving averages are thus computed for freight carloadings for the period 1918-53.

The three-year moving average for 1946 is the average of 1945-6-7, the five-year figure for 1946 is the average of the years 1944-5-6-7-8. The other averages are computed in the same way. In each case the average is centered for the period included; that is, the average is taken to represent the trend value as of the middle of the given period. The employment of an odd number of years simplifies this centering process, though it is not essential that the number be odd. With an even number of years, the figure may be centered by taking a two-year moving average of the moving average first computed. The three- and nine-year moving averages for the entire period are plotted with the original data, in Fig. 10.2.

It is obvious that the effect of the averaging is to give a smoother curve, lessening the influence of the fluctuations that pull the annual figures away from the general trend. The longer the period included in securing each average, the smoother is the curve secured, though there are other factors to consider in deciding upon the length of the period. Certain of these factors may be noted.

Some characteristics of moving averages. Given cyclical fluctuations about a uniform level or about a line ascending with a uniform slope, the length of the cycle and the magnitude of the fluctuations being constant, a moving average having a period equal to the period of the cycle (or to a multiple of that period) will give a straight line, a perfect representation of the trend. Under the same conditions a moving average having a period greater or less than the period of the cycle will give, not a straight line, but a new cycle having the same period as the original, but with fluctuations of less magnitude. The minima and maxima of the cycles thus obtained will not necessarily coincide with the minima and maxima of the original cycles. In general, when such a new cycle is obtained the magnitude of the fluctuations will be less the longer the period on which the average is based.[1]

These propositions may be illustrated by the figures in Table 10-2, arbitrarily chosen. In the first example five figures have been selected which repeat themselves in sequence, fluctuating about a common level.

The moving averages in columns (2) and (3) represent the data with the cycles completely removed. When the period of the average is not equal to the period of the cycle, or to a multiple of that period, the cycle is not removed, as is apparent from the figures in columns (4) and (5).

The conclusions suggested above hold when the cyclical fluctuations take place about any straight line. In Table 10-3 the foregoing data have been employed but with a constant increment of 3. This is equivalent to superimposing the same cycles upon a line with a slope of + 3.

The trend values, with the effect of the cycles completely removed, are secured by taking moving averages equal in period to the cycle or to a multiple of that period. The cycle persists, with the same period but with diminished amplitude, when the average

---

[1] The decrease in the magnitude of the fluctuations is not regular, however, but cyclical.

TABLE 10–2

Illustrating the Application of Moving Averages

(1) Cyclical data	(2) Moving average of 5 items	(3) Moving average of 10 items (centered)	(4) Moving average of 3 items	(5) Moving average of 8 items (centered)
2				
6			$5\frac{1}{3}$	
8	$6\frac{1}{5}$		8	
10	$6\frac{1}{5}$		$7\frac{2}{3}$	
5	$6\frac{1}{5}$		$5\frac{2}{3}$	$6\frac{3}{8}$
2	$6\frac{1}{5}$	$6\frac{1}{5}$	$4\frac{1}{3}$	$6\frac{13}{16}$
6	$6\frac{1}{5}$	$6\frac{1}{5}$	$5\frac{1}{3}$	$6\frac{3}{8}$
8	$6\frac{1}{5}$	$6\frac{1}{5}$	8	$5\frac{3}{4}$
10	$6\frac{1}{5}$	$6\frac{1}{5}$	$7\frac{2}{3}$	$5\frac{11}{16}$
5	$6\frac{1}{5}$	$6\frac{1}{5}$	$5\frac{2}{3}$	$6\frac{3}{8}$
2	$6\frac{1}{5}$	$6\frac{1}{5}$	$4\frac{1}{3}$	$6\frac{13}{16}$
6	$6\frac{1}{5}$	$6\frac{1}{5}$	$5\frac{1}{3}$	$6\frac{3}{8}$
8	$6\frac{1}{5}$	$6\frac{1}{5}$	8	$5\frac{3}{4}$
10	$6\frac{1}{5}$	$6\frac{1}{5}$	$7\frac{2}{3}$	$5\frac{11}{16}$
5	$6\frac{1}{5}$	$6\frac{1}{5}$	$5\frac{2}{3}$	$6\frac{3}{8}$
2	$6\frac{1}{5}$		$4\frac{1}{3}$	$6\frac{13}{16}$
6	$6\frac{1}{5}$		$5\frac{1}{3}$	
8	$6\frac{1}{5}$		8	
10			$7\frac{2}{3}$	
5				

(The items in columns (3) and (5) have been centered by means of a moving average of 2 items.)

is based upon a period not equal to that of the cycle, as is clear from the figures in columns (4) and (5).

When these ideally simple conditions of constant period and amplitude do not exist, the moving average becomes more ambiguous and its interpretation less simple. If the period of the cycle varies, the selection of a period for the moving average is more difficult. In general, a period equal to or greater than the average length of the cycle is to be selected. An average having a shorter period will give a line that is marked by pronounced cycles, these cycles being reduced as the period covered in the calculation of the average increases.

When the amplitude of the cycle varies, the period being constant, a moving average with a period equal to the length of the cycle will give a line of trend marked by minor cycles. The amplitude of these secondary cycles will be a minimum when the period of the average is equal to the period of the cycle (or to a

TABLE 10–3

Illustrating the Application of Moving Averages to a Series with
Linear Trend

(1) Cyclical data	(2) Moving average of 5 items	(3) Moving average of 10 items (centered)	(4) Moving average of 3 items	(5) Moving average of 8 items (centered)
2				
9			$8\frac{1}{3}$	
14	$12\frac{1}{5}$		14	
19	$15\frac{1}{5}$		$16\frac{2}{3}$	
17	$18\frac{1}{5}$		$17\frac{2}{3}$	$18\frac{3}{8}$
17	$21\frac{1}{5}$	$21\frac{1}{5}$	$19\frac{1}{3}$	$21\frac{13}{16}$
24	$24\frac{1}{5}$	$24\frac{1}{5}$	$23\frac{1}{3}$	$24\frac{3}{8}$
29	$27\frac{1}{5}$	$27\frac{1}{5}$	29	$26\frac{3}{4}$
34	$30\frac{1}{5}$	$30\frac{1}{5}$	$31\frac{2}{3}$	$29\frac{11}{16}$
32	$33\frac{1}{5}$	$33\frac{1}{5}$	$32\frac{2}{3}$	$33\frac{3}{8}$
32	$36\frac{1}{5}$	$36\frac{1}{5}$	$34\frac{1}{3}$	$36\frac{13}{16}$
39	$39\frac{1}{5}$	$39\frac{1}{5}$	$38\frac{1}{3}$	$39\frac{3}{8}$
44	$42\frac{1}{5}$	$42\frac{1}{5}$	44	$41\frac{3}{4}$
49	$45\frac{1}{5}$	$45\frac{1}{5}$	$46\frac{2}{3}$	$44\frac{11}{16}$
47	$48\frac{1}{5}$	$48\frac{1}{5}$	$47\frac{2}{3}$	$48\frac{3}{8}$
47	$51\frac{1}{5}$		$49\frac{1}{3}$	$51\frac{13}{16}$
54	$54\frac{1}{5}$		$53\frac{1}{3}$	
59	$57\frac{1}{5}$		59	
64			$61\frac{2}{3}$	
62				

(The items in columns (3) and (5) have been centered by means of a moving average of 2 items.)

multiple of that period). When these last two irregularities are combined, and the data are characterized by cycles of varying amplitude and of varying length, the moving average giving the most effective representation of the trend is that which has a period equal to the average length of the cycle, or to a multiple of that length.

A new factor enters when the trend departs from linearity. If the underlying trend of a series is concave upward, a moving average will always exceed the actual trend value; if the reverse is true, and the trend is convex upward, a moving average will always be less than the actual trend value.

These conditions are depicted in the following examples. The figures in Table 10-4 give the values secured when a cycle of constant period and amplitude, as in column (3), is superimposed upon a line of trend that is concave upward, i.e., increasing at a

TABLE 10–4

Illustrating the Application of Moving Averages to a Nonlinear Series
(Increasing rate)

(1)	(2)	(3)	(4)	(5)	(6)
				Moving average	True trend
x	x^2	Cyclical data	Col. (2) plus col. (3)	of 5 items in col. (4)	values $(x^2 + 6.2)$
0	0	2	2		
1	1	6	7		
2	4	8	12	12.2	10.2
3	9	10	19	17.2	15.2
4	16	5	21	24.2	22.2
5	25	2	27	33.2	31.2
6	36	6	42	44.2	42.2
7	49	8	57	57.2	55.2
8	64	10	74	72.2	70.2
9	81	5	86	89.2	87.2
10	100	2	102	108.2	106.2
11	121	6	127	129.2	127.2
12	144	8	152	152.2	150.2
13	169	10	179	177.2	175.2
14	196	5	201	204.2	202.2
15	225	2	227	233.2	231.2
16	256	6	262	264.2	262.2
17	289	8	297	297.2	295.2
18	324	10	334		
19	361	5	366		

constantly increasing rate. If the moving average could completely eliminate the effects of the cycle, the values secured from the average would be equal to the average value of the five items in each cycle (6.2) plus the values of the function $y = x^2$, given in column (2).

The values of the moving average are, in this case, in excess of the true trend values, a form of distortion that will always occur with a series of this type.

In Table 10-5 are shown the results of superimposing the same cyclical values upon a line of trend that is convex upward, i.e., increasing at a constantly decreasing rate. In this case, a perfect method of eliminating the cycles would give results equal to the average value of the five items (6.2) plus the values of the function $y = \sqrt{x}$.

In this case the moving average values are consistently too low. The discrepancy is greatest for the lower values of x, as the decrease in the rate of growth is most marked for these values.

TABLE 10–5

Illustrating the Application of Moving Averages to a Nonlinear Series
(Decreasing rate)

(1)	(2)	(3)	(4)	(5)	(6)
					True trend
x	$\sqrt{x}$	Cyclical data	Col. (2) plus col. (3)	Moving average of 5 items	values $(\sqrt{x} + 6.2)$
0	0	2	2.00		
1	1.00	6	7.00		
2	1.41	8	9.41	7.428	7.61
3	1.73	10	11.73	7.876	7.93
4	2.00	5	7.00	8.166	8.20
5	2.24	2	4.24	8.414	8.44
6	2.45	6	8.45	8.634	8.65
7	2.65	8	10.65	8.834	8.85
8	2.83	10	12.83	9.018	9.03
9	3.00	5	8.00	9.192	9.20
10	3.16	2	5.16	9.354	9.36
11	3.32	6	9.32	9.510	9.52
12	3.46	8	11.46	9.658	9.66
13	3.61	10	13.61	9.800	9.81
14	3.74	5	8.74	9.936	9.94
15	3.87	2	5.87	10.068	10.07
16	4.00	6	10.00	10.194	10.20
17	4.12	8	12.12	10.318	10.32
18	4.24	10	14.24		
19	4.36	5	9.36		

Considerations previously reviewed have indicated that a moving average should, in general, be based upon a period at least
equal to the period of the cycle, and preferably equal to some
higher multiple of that period when the data are at all irregular.
The longer the period covered, the greater the stability of the
average. But when the underlying trend departs materially from
the linear form, following a curve bending upward or downward,
the error involved in the use of any moving average increases as
the period of the average increases. If a moving average is used in
such a case to measure the trend, the period of the average should
be the shortest which will serve to average out the cycles; equal,
that is, to the average length of one cycle.

In practice, however, these various conditions are found in
complicated combinations. The fact that cycles vary in amplitude
and length calls for a moving average based upon a fairly long
period. The fact that the trend of the data is usually nonlinear
calls for a short period average to lessen the upward or downward
distortion. A consideration of some importance in practical work

is that a moving average can never be brought up to date. The lag is less, of course, the shorter the period covered by the average. The selection of a period in a given case must rest upon a study of the actual data with these various considerations in mind.

It has been assumed in the preceding discussion that the purpose of the moving average is the representation of secular trend. The moving average may be used, also, in smoothing data for the purpose of eliminating random fluctuations. For this purpose a moving average based upon a period shorter than the average length of the cycle should be selected.

Appraisal of moving averages of varying periods. We return now to the data of freight carloadings. A study of the lines marked out by the different moving averages in Fig. 10.2 (p. 290) reveals clear differences between them. The three-year average follows the graph of the original data most closely, as would be expected. The nine-year average marks out the smoothest line of trend, but, on the other hand, departs most widely from the data. This is particularly noticeable from 1923 to 1930 and from 1931 to 1935. The sharp changes in the direction of movement of the original series that came after 1929 and after 1932 account for these departures.

In determining the relative merits of the different moving averages we are aided by the knowledge of the course of business during the period covered. The volume of freight carloadings is a sensitive index of general business conditions, responding immediately to changes in speculative and industrial activity. Major and minor business cycles are reflected in this series. Knowing the number of cycles through which business has passed during the period 1918-53, we may determine which of the moving averages serves best as a standard from which to measure cyclical deviations. In this case we are practically working backward from a known result, a method not always available.

If we take as a starting point in each cycle the year in which revival began, after recession, the following cycles in general business activity may be distinguished:[2]

1919—1921	1932—1938
1921—1924	1938—1946
1924—1927	1946—1949
1927—1932	1949—1954

---

[2] These dates are based upon the chronology of American business cycles developed by Arthur F. Burns and Wesley C. Mitchell. See Burns and Mitchell, Ref. 13, p. 78.

The cycles marked out by the three-year moving average are too numerous to enumerate. In fact, the deviations from this average are so greatly affected by minor short-term fluctuations that they usually give a poor representation of movements corresponding to cycles in the economy at large. Deviations from the five-, seven-, and nine-year averages mark out the following cycles:

Cycles of deviations from five-year moving averages	Cycles of deviations from seven-year moving averages	Cycles of deviations from nine-year moving averages
1921—1924	1921—1932*	1922—1932*
1924—1927	1932—1938	1932—1938
1927—1932	1938—1945	1938—1946
1932—1938	1945—1949	1946—
1938—1943		
1943—1946		
1946—1949		
1949—		

Differences between the series of cycles thus determined and the reference cycles distinguished by Burns and Mitchell reflect the characteristic features of moving averages. The seven- and nine-year averages fail to reveal short cycles. Neither of these series discloses the two short cycles (1921-24 and 1924-27) that occurred during the "twenties," and that are reflected in the carloadings series. Deviations from the five-year moving averages define these short cycles. On the other hand, this five-year series shows a deviation below the line of trend in 1943, and thus marks off two "cycles" during the one reference cycle of 1938-46 that is recognized in the Burns-Mitchell chronology.

If interest attaches to the shorter swings of business, to cycles with average durations of three to five years, a moving average of relatively short period should be used. A five-year average is appropriate. Averages of longer period define trend movements more faithfully, but may fail to reveal fluctuations properly classified as business cycles. We should refer, however, to recent attempts to establish the reality of long cycles, of nine, eleven, or as many as fifty years in average duration. In the study of such cycles moving averages of corresponding periods would be employed.

In general, the moving average has the prime advantage of flexibility. The representation of secular trend by mathematical

---

* The initial low of each of these cycles is, of course, not clearly marked by deviations beginning only in 1921 or 1922.

curves sometimes involves the breaking up of a period into two or three subdivisions, and the fitting of separate curves to each. This results from changing conditions and sharply changing rates of growth or decline. When such changes occur, the moving average has the merit of flexible adaptation to the new conditions and is often a more effective measure of secular trend than are more pretentious functions.

Simple and weighted moving averages, in varying combinations, have wide uses in the analysis of economic time series. An illuminating discussion of these uses, and of the procedures appropriate to different purposes, is to be found in *The Smoothing of Time Series*, by Frederick R. Macaulay.[3]

Representation of Secular Trends by Mathematical Curves

For many types of data the secular trend may be represented by a mathematical function rather than by a line based upon a moving average. Thus, if the growth (or decline) is by constant absolute increments (or decrements) a straight line will serve as an exact representation of the trend. Or the growth may be by constant percentages, as in the case of capital increase, when a principal sum increases in accordance with the compound interest law. An exponential curve defines such a trend. Where the secular course of a historical variable may be accurately described by a mathematical function, the tasks of analysis, interpretation, and projection may be facilitated by the use of such a function.

A mathematical representation of the trend of a social, economic, or business series is sometimes assumed to define an underlying "law" of development. This is an acceptable view, if we regard a "law" as no more than an observed regularity, and the mathematical expression as a convenient shorthand description of a piece of recorded history. It may be that in time somewhat more firmly based laws of change will be established in the social and economic sciences. Indeed, some students believe that certain mathematical functions do, in fact, define laws of growth that are something more than empirically observed regularities, but the evidence for this view is not yet convincing. For the present it is best to regard a secular trend, whether described by a frankly empirical moving average or by a mathematical function, as no

[3] Ref. 95.

more than an empirically established uniformity, subject to change without notice.

In the practical approach to a problem involving the determination of secular trend the first task is the selection of the appropriate type of curve. This is perhaps the most difficult part of the work; certainly it is the part in which the element of personal judgment enters most directly. For there is no objective rule to follow, no fixed standard by which the most appropriate curve may be selected. Something more will be said on this subject after the characteristics of the chief types of curves and the methods of fitting them have been described. For the present it may be assumed that a curve similar to one of the types described in Chapter 2, or to a related form, has been selected, and that we face the practical task of fitting it to the data.

The problem here is similar to that discussed in the preceding chapter, in considering correlation procedures. There we found that the method of least squares could be used in determining the most probable values of a and b in the equation to a straight line of regression. If the trend function desired in dealing with a given time series is linear, we must get most probable values for the same quantities in an equation of the form $y = a + bx$ (where x is time, and y is the historical variable in question). Customarily, the method of least squares is used in deriving such measures of trend, although the conditions on which that method logically rests are not realized in dealing with time series. For chronologically ordered observations are not independent of one another; deviations from the function to be fitted are likely to be due primarily to nonrandom forces. Thus if we use the method of least squares in fitting a mathematical curve to a series of observations ordered in time we do so on grounds of practicality and expediency. Its use on these terms is defensible, but the limitations attaching to this use of the least squares method reenforce the argument that mathematical trend lines should be viewed as empirically useful functions but not as representations of rationally based laws of historical change.

The least squares procedure in fitting a straight line calls, as we have seen, for the simultaneous solution of two normal equations (see Chapter 9). In handling historical variables the calculations may be simplified somewhat. When the x's are consecutive numbers, as they always are when an unbroken time series is plotted, the origin may be taken at the median value. When the number of observations is odd this will be the middle item, of course. The value of $\Sigma(x)$ will then be zero, and the normal equations become

$$\Sigma(y) = na$$
$$\Sigma(xy) = b\Sigma(x^2)$$

Thus if a time series extends, by years, from 1938 to 1954, the origin may be taken at 1946, the value of x corresponding to 1945 being -1, to 1947, $+1$, and so on. The solution for values of a and b is rendered much easier when the data may be disposed in this way. When there is an even number of years the same process is possible, time (the x-variable) being measured in units of one half year.

Again, when the values of x are consecutive positive numbers starting with one, the values of $\Sigma(x)$ and of $\Sigma(x^2)$ may be easily determined. The sum of the first n natural numbers is equal to $\dfrac{n(n+1)}{2}$. Thus the sum of the numbers from 1 to 5 is $\dfrac{5(5+1)}{2}$, or 15. This term may replace $\Sigma(x)$ in the normal equations. Similarly, the sum of the squares of the first n natural numbers is equal to $\dfrac{2n^3 + 3n^2 + n}{6}$. Thus the sum of the squares of the numbers from 1 to 5 is equal to $\dfrac{250 + 75 + 5}{6} = 55$. This expression may replace $\Sigma(x^2)$ in the normal equations, and we have

$$\Sigma(y) = na + b\left(\frac{n(n+1)}{2}\right). \tag{10.1}$$

$$\Sigma(xy) = a\left(\frac{n(n+1)}{2}\right) + b\left(\frac{2n^3 + 3n^2 + n}{6}\right).$$

It is sometimes easier to work from equations in this form than from those in the form first given. The data for time series may be handled in this way, the years being numbered consecutively, beginning with 1.

Examples of Linear Trends. Figures 10.3 and 10.4 show two historical series to each of which a straight line has been fitted to define secular trend. In Fig. 10.3 are plotted mean annual temper-

FIG. 10.3. Mean Annual Temperatures in New York City, 1871-1953, with Line Trend.

atures for New York City for the years 1871-1953. The equation to the trend line, fitted to the data for 1871-1949, is $y = 52.482 + 0.0346x$, where y is temperature in degrees Fahrenheit, and x is time measured in years from an origin at 1910.[4] This provides a good example of the use of a trend line. There has been, apparently, a slow rise in the mean temperature of New York over the last 80 years. The equation cited defines this rise in simple terms, indicating an average annual increase in temperature of 0.0346 degrees Fahrenheit. We may not say that this is a "law" in any fundamental sense. We know of no rational basis for the change, and we have no justification except that of past experience for projecting the observed movement into the future. Yet, as a summary statement of a segment of meteorological history, the equation has obvious utility. Not least, the clear definition of the historical movement suggests problems and stimulates inquiry as to the forces actually at work.

The graph in Fig. 10.4 shows employment in agriculture (family workers plus hired workers) over the years from 1935 to 1953. The procedure employed in fitting a straight line of trend may be illustrated with reference to this series. The observations are given in Table 10-6, together with the values required in the fitting process and the derived trend values. Only the entries in columns (2) to (5) are employed in the calculations.

---

[4] The temperature data are from *Local Climatological Summary, New York City, N Y.,* a publication of the Weather Bureau, U. S. Department of Commerce.

TABLE 10–6

Employment in Agriculture in the United States: Average Number of
Persons Employed, 1935-1953.*
Computation of values required in fitting line of trend.

(1)	(2)	(3) y Persons employed (thousands)	(4) xy	(5) x^2	(6) y_c Trend values (linear) of persons employed (thousands)
Year	x				
1935	1	12,733	12,733	1	12,269
1936	2	12,331	24,662	4	12,072
1937	3	11,978	35,934	9	11,875
1938	4	11,622	46,488	16	11,677
1939	5	11,338	56,690	25	11,480
1940	6	10,979	65,874	36	11,283
1941	7	10,669	74,683	49	11,086
1942	8	10,504	84,032	64	10,889
1943	9	10,446	94,014	81	10,692
1944	10	10,219	102,190	100	10,495
1945	11	10,000	110,000	121	10,298
1946	12	10,295	123,540	144	10,100
1947	13	10,382	134,966	169	9,903
1948	14	10,363	145,082	196	9,706
1949	15	9,964	149,460	225	9,509
1950	16	9,342	149,472	256	9,312
1951	17	8,985	152,745	289	9,115
1952	18	8,669	156,042	324	8,918
1953	19	8,580	163,020	361	8,721
Totals	190	199,399	1,881,627	2,470	

$$N = 19 \qquad \Sigma(y) = 199,399$$
$$\Sigma(x) = 190 \qquad \Sigma(xy) = 1,881,627$$
$$\Sigma(x^2) = 2,470$$

* Family workers plus hired workers.
  Source: *Farm Labor*, Agricultural Marketing Service, USDA, Jan. 13, 1954.

The equations to be solved in determining the required constants
(see p. 220 above) are of the form

$$\Sigma(y) = Na + b\Sigma(x)$$
$$\Sigma(xy) = a\Sigma(x) + b\Sigma(x^2)$$

Inserting the required values, which are of course derived from the
observations, we have

$$199,399 = 19a + 190b$$
$$1,881,627 = 190a + 2470b$$

from which

$$a = 12,465.965$$
$$b = -197.128$$

The equation to the line of best fit is therefore

$$y = 12,466.0 - 197.1x$$

with origin at 1934.

The trend values derived from this equation appear in column (6) of Table 10-6. From inspection of the graph in Fig. 10.4 we

FIG. 10.4. Average Number of Persons Employed in Agriculture in the United States, 1935-1953, with Line of Trend.

conclude that the fitted line provides a good representation of the trend of this series over the period covered. The decline in total agricultural employment has been persistent, broken only by a brief postwar advance. The movement away from agriculture has averaged 197,000 persons a year. The period covered is, of course, a fairly short one. In general our confidence in a fitted trend line as a representation of a secular movement is greater the longer the series of observations. In the present instance we have employed a period marked by fairly rapid mechanization in American agriculture, a fact that gives the trend line of employment a somewhat sounder base than it would have if there were no apparent explanation of the decline noted. (Of course, the decline in agricultural employment goes back beyond 1935, but the movement was accelerated in the middle and late 'thirties.)

Fitting a Polynomial. The discussion above has been confined to the case of linear trend. Such a function frequently defines secular movements accurately, but in many cases it fails to fit the data. This difficulty is sometimes overcome in practice by breaking a series into segments and fitting a separate line to the data for each of these periods. Where there is an actual break in the series, the period as a whole lacking homogeneity, this practice may be justified, but when the period is essentially homogeneous the whole concept of secular trend is violated by this process of subdividing and fitting separate lines. In many cases where a straight line will not fit, a polynomial may represent the trend accurately. The general process of fitting such a curve may be briefly described.

The generalized form of the equation of the type desired is $y = a + bx + cx^2 + dx^3 + \ldots$ For ordinary purposes such a curve should not be carried beyond the second or third power of x. If carried to the second power there are, of course, three unknowns, and three normal equations must be solved simultaneously in securing the required values.

The procedure is similar to that outlined for the linear case. Each observation equation is multiplied by the coefficient of the first unknown in that equation, and the resulting equations are totaled to give the first normal equation. The process is repeated for the two other unknowns, and the three normal equations thus obtained are solved for a, b, and c. The results are the most probable values of these three constants. The following are the general forms which the three normal equations take:

$$\Sigma(y) = na + b\Sigma(x) + c\Sigma(x^2)$$
$$\Sigma(xy) = a\Sigma(x) + b\Sigma(x^2) + c\Sigma(x^3) \qquad (10.2)$$
$$\Sigma(x^2y) = a\Sigma(x^2) + b\Sigma(x^3) + c\Sigma(x^4)$$

As an example of the process, the calculations involved in fitting a power curve of the second degree to the points 1, 2; 2, 6; 3, 7; 4, 8; 5, 10; 6, 11; 7, 11; 8, 10; 9, 9 may be outlined. It is of the greatest practical importance in curve fitting, as in all extensive calculations, that the work be laid out and carried on in a definite and systematic fashion, with each step definitely related to the preceding and succeeding operations. Checks should be introduced wherever possible, as mathematical errors creep into even the most careful work. A tabular arrangement is generally advisable, each operation being revealed and each set of results clearly presented. The data in the present problem may be arranged as in Table 10-7.

TABLE 10–7

Computation of Values Required in Fitting a Polynomial of the Second Degree

x	y	xy	x^2	x^2y	
1	2	2	1	2	$n = 9$
2	6	12	4	24	$\Sigma(x) = 45$
3	7	21	9	63	$\Sigma(x^2) = 285$
4	8	32	16	128	$\Sigma(x^3) = 2{,}025$
5	10	50	25	250	$\Sigma(x^4) = 15{,}333$
6	11	66	36	396	$\Sigma(y) = 74$
7	11	77	49	539	$\Sigma(xy) = 421$
8	10	80	64	640	$\Sigma(x^2y) = 2{,}771$
9	9	81	81	729	
45	74	421	285	2,771	

When the x's are consecutive integers beginning with 1, as in the present case, the values of $\Sigma(x)$, $\Sigma(x^2)$, $\Sigma(x^3)$, and $\Sigma(x^4)$ may be obtained by the use of formulas,[5] or from prepared tables.[6]

Substituting these values in the equations given above, the following normal equations are secured:

$$74 = 9a + 45b + 285c$$
$$421 = 45a + 285b + 2{,}025c$$
$$2{,}771 = 285a + 2{,}025b + 15{,}333c$$

[5] For convenience of reference we here give the formulas for the sums of the first four powers of the first n natural numbers (repeating two of these from an earlier page):

$$\Sigma n = \frac{n(n+1)}{2}$$
$$\Sigma(n^2) = \frac{(2n+1)}{3}\Sigma n$$
$$\Sigma(n^3) = (\Sigma n)^2$$
$$\Sigma(n^4) = \frac{3n^2 + 3n - 1}{5}\Sigma(n^2)$$

[6] See Table XXVIII, Pearson, *Tables for Statisticians and Biometricians*. Values to the sixth power for numbers from 1 to 50 are given in Appendix Table VII of the present volume.

When these equations are solved simultaneously the following values are secured for the three constants:

$$a = -.929$$

$$b = +3.523$$

$$c = -.267$$

The equation of the desired curve is

$$y = -.929 + 3.523x - .267x^2$$

This curve and the nine given points are plotted in Fig. 10.5.

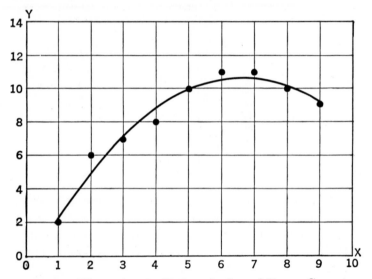

FIG. 10.5. Illustrating the Fitting of a Second Degree Curve to Nine Points.

If the values of x are consecutive, as in the present example, the work of computation is lightened if the mid-value is taken as origin. In this case $\Sigma(x)$ and $\Sigma(x^3)$ are equal to zero, and the normal equations become

$$\Sigma y = na + c\Sigma(x^2)$$

$$\Sigma(xy) = b\Sigma(x^2)$$

$$\Sigma(x^2y) = a\Sigma(x^2) + c\Sigma(x^4)$$

When a polynomial of the third degree, of the form $y = a + bx + cx^2 + dx^3$, is to be fitted to data, four constants must be determined, and four normal equations are necessary. These are of the following form:

$$\left.\begin{array}{l}\Sigma(y) = na + b\Sigma(x) + c\Sigma(x^2) + d\Sigma(x^3) \\ \Sigma(xy) = a\Sigma(x) + b\Sigma(x^2) + c\Sigma(x^3) + d\Sigma(x^4) \\ \Sigma(x^2y) = a\Sigma(x^2) + b\Sigma(x^3) + c\Sigma(x^4) + d\Sigma(x^5) \\ \Sigma(x^3y) = a\Sigma(x^3) + b\Sigma(x^4) + c\Sigma(x^5) + d\Sigma(x^6) \end{array}\right\} \quad (10.3)$$

The solution for four or more constants involves a considerable amount of arithmetical calculation, and there is some question as to the advisability of representing secular trend by equations of this type. With a sufficient number of constants a curve may be fitted that will follow every variation in the data, but such a curve could hardly be taken to represent the long-term trend.[7] Minor departures from a simple uniform trend, linear or otherwise, are to be expected with economic data, but, if a real trend exists, extreme departures from a fairly simple form are rare. If such departures are due to pronounced changes in conditions no single line of trend is likely to be satisfactory, and it is advisable to break the period into parts, with a separate line of trend for each part. "Empirical curves," says Steinmetz, "can be represented by a single equation only when the physical conditions remain constant within the range of the observations." Though this statement relates to the fitting of curves to data from the physical sciences, the general principle applies to economic data.

A Secular Trend of the Second Degree. The production and sales of electric power in recent decades are good examples of series following nonlinear trends. The sales of electric power to ultimate consumers, in the United States, for the years 1937-1953, are plotted in Fig. 10.6. The data, with computations needed for the fitting of a polynomial of the second degree, are presented in Table 10-8.

---

[7] The famous *razor*, or Law of Parcimony, of William of Occam, which specifies that in explaining things not known to exist the number of entities (here read "constants") should not be increased unnecessarily, has special pertinence to a problem of this sort.

Regarding the employment of potential series of the type indicated for representing empirical curves, Steinmetz states that their use is justified:

1. If the successive coefficients $a, b, c \ldots$ decrease in value so rapidly that within the range of observation the higher terms become rapidly smaller and appear as mere secondary terms.

2. If the successive coefficients follow a definite law, indicating a convergent series which represents some other function, as an exponential, trigonometric, etc.

3. If all the coefficients are very small, with the exception of a few of them, and only the latter ones thus need to be considered.

FIG. 10.6. Average Monthly Sales of Electric Power to Ultimate Consumers, 1937-1953, with Line of Trend.*

*Data from Edison Electric Institute.

TABLE 10–8

Sales of Electric Power to Ultimate Consumers, 1937-1953*
(Average monthly sales in billions of kilowatt-hours)
Computation of Values Required in Fitting Line of Trend

(1) Year	(2) x	(3) y (sales)	(4) xy	(5) x^2y
1937	− 8	8.3	− 66.4	531.2
1938	− 7	7.8	− 54.6	382.2
1939	− 6	8.8	− 52.8	316.8
1940	− 5	9.9	− 49.5	247.5
1941	− 4	11.7	− 46.8	187.2
1942	− 3	13.3	− 39.9	119.7
1943	− 2	15.5	− 31.0	62.0
1944	− 1	16.5	− 16.5	16.5
1945	0	16.1	0.0	0.0
1946	+ 1	15.9	+ 15.9	15.9
1947	+ 2	18.1	+ 36.2	72.4
1948	+ 3	20.1	+ 60.3	180.9
1949	+ 4	20.7	+ 82.8	331.2
1950	+ 5	23.4	+ 117.0	585.0
1951	+ 6	26.5	+ 159.0	954.0
1952	+ 7	28.6	+ 200.2	1401.4
1953	+ 8	31.9	+ 255.2	2041.6
		293.1	+ 569.1	7445.5

$$N = 17$$
$$\Sigma(x) = 0 \qquad \Sigma(x^4) = 17{,}544$$
$$\Sigma(x^2) = 408 \qquad \Sigma(y) = 293.1$$
$$\Sigma(x^3) = 0 \qquad \Sigma(xy) = 569.1$$
$$\Sigma(x^2y) = 7{,}445.5$$

* Compiled by the Edison Electric Institute.

In the fitting process the origin may be taken at the middle year, to facilitate the calculations. The sums of the second and fourth powers of x may be obtained from prepared tables, or from the formulas cited on p. 343. With the origin at the middle of the period the normal equations required for a fitting of the function $y = a + bx + cx^2$ (see formula 10.2 above) become

$$\Sigma(y) = Na + c\Sigma(x^2)$$
$$\Sigma(xy) = b\Sigma(x^2)$$
$$\Sigma(x^2y) = a\Sigma(x^2) + c\Sigma(x^4)$$

Inserting the appropriate values, we have

$$293.1 = 17a + 408c$$
$$569.1 = 408b$$
$$7,445.5 = 408a + 17,544c$$

Solving for the constants

$$a = 15.968$$
$$b = +1.395$$
$$c = +0.053$$

The required equation is

$$y = 15.968 + 1.395x + 0.053x^2$$

with origin at 1945. This equation is plotted in Fig. 10.6. The smooth growth of total sales of electric power was broken slightly by war and postwar adjustments, but the trend is reasonably well represented by the function employed.

The Use of Logarithms in Curve Fitting. The family of curves described above represents a simple and very useful type. Perhaps of even greater general utility, in the analysis of time series, are curves of a semilogarithmic type. The advantages of plotting many series of data on semilogarithmic or "ratio" paper were explained in an earlier section. A fundamental virtue of this type of plotting is that it presents a true picture of *relative* variations, of *ratios* between magnitudes. Relations of this type are ordinarily of primary interest in the analysis of economic data, and it is logical that determination of trends should proceed on the same basis.

In doing so, we can make use of a group of curves of the same general form as those already described, the one difference being that log y takes the place of y throughout. That is, the straight line form is log $y = a + bx$, while the general form for the polynomial series is log $y = a + bx + cx^2 + dx^3 + \ldots$. The curves secured may be constructed on arithmetic paper, plotting the natural x's and the logarithms of the y's, or natural values of both x's and y's may be plotted on semilogarithmic paper, the logarithmic scale extending along the y-axis. The latter is the simpler method.

To illustrate the procedure, the steps involved in fitting a curve of the type $\log y = a + bx$ will be shown. The trend of petroleum production in the United States from 1936 to 1953 is to be determined. The values needed in the normal equations are derived from Table 10-9. The equations to be solved are of the form

$$\Sigma(\log y) = Na + b\Sigma x$$
$$\Sigma(x \cdot \log y) = a\Sigma x + b\Sigma x^2$$

Substituting the given values we have

$$57.84863 = 18a + 171b$$
$$558.64891 = 171a + 2{,}109b$$

Solving for the constants

$$a = 3.03564$$
$$b = 0.01876$$

The equation to the desired curve is, therefore,

$$\log y = 3.03564 + 0.01876x$$

with origin at 1935.

In fitting this curve by the method of least squares, as is done above, we satisfy the condition that the sum of the squares of the *logarithmic* deviations shall be a minimum. That is, the deviations to which this condition relates are the differences between the logarithms of the observed values and the logarithms of the corresponding trend values. This curve, it should be noted, is not the same as that for which the sum of the squares of the arithmetic (natural) deviations is a minimum.

The substitution in the above equation of the value of x representing any given year will enable the logarithm of the trend or normal value to be calculated. Logarithms thus derived, and the corresponding natural numbers which are the trend values for the various years, are given in columns (6) and (7) of Table 10-9. The trend function is shown graphically in Fig. 10.7, with the original observations. The fit is good.

An equation of this type, defining a linear trend in the logarithms of the dependent variable, has certain distinctive advantages. The

TABLE 10–9

Petroleum Production in the United States, 1936-1953*
(in millions of barrels)
Computation of values required in fitting line of trend

(1) Year	(2) x	(3) y	(4) log y	(5) x log y	(6) log y_c (log of trend)	(7) y_c (computed trend value)
1936	1	1,099.7	3.04127	3.04127	3.05440	1,133.4
1937	2	1,279.2	3.10694	6.21388	3.07316	1,183.4
1938	3	1,214.4	3.08436	9.25308	3.09192	1,235.7
1939	4	1,265.0	3.10209	12.40836	3.11068	1,290.2
1940	5	1,353.2	3.13136	15.65680	3.12944	1,347.2
1941	6	1,402.2	3.14681	18.88086	3.14820	1,406.6
1942	7	1,386.6	3.14195	21.99365	3.16696	1,468.7
1943	8	1,505.6	3.17771	25.42168	3.18572	1,533.6
1944	9	1,677.8	3.22474	29.02266	3.20448	1,601.3
1945	10	1,711.1	3.23328	32.33280	3.22324	1,672.0
1946	11	1,733.4	3.23890	35.62790	3.24200	1,745.8
1947	12	1,857.0	3.26881	39.22572	3.26076	1,822.9
1948	13	2,020.2	3.30539	42.97007	3.27952	1,903.4
1949	14	1,841.9	3.26527	45.71378	3.29828	1,987.4
1950	15	1,973.6	3.29526	49.42890	3.31704	2,075.0
1951	16	2,247.7	3.35174	53.62784	3.33580	2,166.7
1952	17	2,290.0	3.35984	57.11728	3.35456	2,269.4
1953	18	2,360.0	3.37291	60.71238	3.37332	2,362.2
			57.84863	558.64891		

$$N = 18 \qquad\qquad \Sigma(\log y) = 57.84863$$
$$\Sigma(x) = 171 \qquad\qquad \Sigma(x \cdot \log y) = 558.64891$$
$$\Sigma(x^2) = 2,109$$

* Sources: Bureau of Mines; American Petroleum Institute.

FIG. 10.7. Production of Petroleum in the United States, 1936-1953, with Line Defining Average Rate of Growth.

reader will note that this is the logarithmic form of an equation to
a compound interest curve (an exponential curve). This equation
was given in Chapter 2 as

$$y = p(1 + r)^x \qquad (10.4)$$

or

$$\log y = \log p + x \log (1 + r)$$

In the example just given we have used the symbol a for $\log p$
and the symbol b for $\log (1 + r)$, but the equations are identical.

We may readily change to natural numbers the constants in the
equation defining the trend of petroleum production from 1936 to
1953. We have

$$\log y = 3.03564 + 0.01876x$$

where 3.03564 is $\log p$ and 0.01876 is $\log (1 + r)$. The natural
number corresponding to 3.03564 is 1,085.5. The natural number
corresponding to 0.01876 is 1.044. The trend of petroleum production in natural form is, therefore

$$y = 1085.5(1.044)^x$$

with origin at 1935. Subtracting 1 from the constant 1.044 we
secure 0.044, which is r, the rate of increase of a series growing in
accordance with the compound interest law. (If, on subtracting 1,
we have a negative value, the growth is negative, of course.) This
measure indicates that the production of crude petroleum increased
at an average rate of 4.4 percent a year between 1936 and 1953
(r being multiplied by 100 to place it on a percentage basis).

When the trend of a series in time may be described by a straight
line on ratio paper (and such functions are widely applicable) the
constant r is a highly useful measure. It defines the average annual
rate of growth or decline of the series. It is, of course, an abstract
measure and thus has the great merit of permitting comparison of
the trends of series relating to widely different original units. The
rate of growth of population, over a given period, may have been
1.4 percent per year; the production of gasoline may have increased
at a rate of 4.5 percent, the production of automobiles at 4.2
percent, the production of wheat at 1.1 percent, total national
income at 1.6 percent. The trends of these series are immediately
comparable, and conclusions concerning the direction and character

of a nation's development may be drawn. This measure provides a valuable device for the study of social and economic change.[8]

By the use of additional terms a function of the type just discussed may be modified when dealing with a series having a nonlinear trend on ratio paper. The addition of a third constant gives an equation of the type

$$\log y = a + bx + cx^2$$

This is, of course, the counterpart in logarithmic or ratio terms of a polynomial of the second degree in terms of natural numbers. Still further constants may be added—a process that is subject to the reservations already voiced concerning the addition of constants to such equations when natural numbers are employed.

Other Curve Types. The two families of curves described in the preceding sections meet most of the needs of the economic statistician. The trend in most time series may be described by polynomials fitted either to natural numbers or to the logarithms of the data (that is, to the logarithms of the y values; time, the x-variable, is treated in terms of natural numbers in fitting both the above types of curves). These classes constitute flexible and widely applicable curve forms.[9] Attention may be called to several other curve types which have been applied less extensively to time series, but with favorable results in particular cases.

Curves of the ordinary parabolic type ($y = ax^b$) are not generally applicable to economic data in the form of time series, as their use involves the treatment of the time variable as a geometric series. Such a curve, it will be recalled, becomes a straight line on double

[8] In any extensive application of this procedure time and labor may be saved by utilizing Glover's mean value table (cf. James W. Glover, *Tables of Applied Mathematics*, George Wahr, Ann Arbor, Michigan, 1923, 468ff.). By the use of this table the compound interest curve may be fitted directly to the natural numbers. All necessary computations are simply and quickly performed.

[9] There are available for fitting higher degree curves of the power series methods that lessen the labor involved, particularly if curves of different degree are to be fitted to the same data. These methods, which reduce the fitting process to a series of simple adding machine operations, are appropriate to extended research projects. Their use is not advisable, however, unless work involving a considerable number of routine operations is contemplated. It is desirable that the student master the basic least squares procedures outlined in the preceding pages, utilizing other methods only when extended computing tasks are undertaken.

For accounts of systematic methods of computing polynomial values and illustrations of the use of orthogonal polynomials see R. A. Fisher (Ref. 50), Fisher and Yates (Ref. 51, pp. 23-25 and Table XXIII for tables to be used in fitting), L. H. C. Tippett (Ref. 160), and M. G. Kendall (Ref. 78, Vol. II).

logarithmic paper. Yet if a curve of this form serves accurately to describe the trend of a given series, its use is justified, empirically.

Such curves may be fitted most readily by employing logarithms and using an equation of the linear type. The equation

$$y = ax^b$$

becomes, in logarithmic form,

$$\log y = \log a + b \log x$$

The equation to the simple exponential curve may be written

$$y = ar^x$$

(The r in this equation is the equivalent of $1 + r$, as given in earlier references.) This equation may be used to define the trend of a series increasing or decreasing in geometric progression. It has been observed that the trends of economic series frequently depart from such a geometric progression by constant magnitudes. By adding this magnitude, in a given case, to the original series (or subtracting it), a modified series with a clear exponential trend may be secured. The trend of the original series may be written

$$y = ar^x - K \tag{10.5}$$

where K is the constant magnitude by which the series departs from a geometric progression. A *modified exponential* curve of this type may give a highly satisfactory representation of trend, in certain cases. The method employed in fitting such a curve is discussed in Appendix D.

Some use has been made, in the interpretation of economic statistics, of the Gompertz curve, the equation to which was originally developed in the actuarial field. The equation is

$$y = ab^{c^x} \tag{10.6}$$

Its use in the analysis of economic statistics has been based upon the argument that there is a general law of growth characteristic of population increase, and that this same type of growth is found in industries in which volume of production is a direct function of the growth of population.

A somewhat similar curve of growth, the "logistic," has been employed by Verhulst, and by Raymond Pearl and Lowell J. Reed in forecasting population growth. This curve has been found to describe the trends of certain social and economic series. Examples

of the procedures employed in fitting Gompertz and logistic curves
are given in Appendix D.

Determination of monthly trend values. The procedures so far
described have dealt with annual measurements only. Having
fitted a line or curve to annual data it is frequently necessary to
effect a transition to monthly units. Problems involving such
monthly measurements are faced in the study of cyclical movements which are discussed in Chapter 12.

The constant a in the trend equation defines the trend value in
the year taken as origin. If the annual data employed in the fitting
processes are averages of 12 monthly values (e.g., the average price
of pig iron in a given year) the constant a measures the trend value
for a month centered at the middle of the year covered by the
annual figures. If the annual data are aggregates of 12 monthly
values (e.g., total production of pig iron in a given year) the
constant a must be divided by 12 to obtain the trend value for
the month centered at the middle of the year.

If the trend be linear, the constant b in the equation $y = a + bx$
defines the change due to trend over a 12-month period. In interpolating for monthly trend values, the increment (or decrement)
from month to month (e.g., from January to February of a given
year) is $\dfrac{b}{12}$, if the annual data employed in the fitting process are
averages of monthly values. The increment from month to month
is $\dfrac{b}{144}$ if the annual data are aggregates of monthly values.

The one further step needed is properly to center the monthly
trend values. These should, of course, be centered at points of
time corresponding to those to which the actual monthly data
relate. In averaging, or aggregating, monthly data relating to the
middle of each of the 12 months in a calendar year we secure a
figure centered at July 1. The month centered at the middle of
the year of origin thus centers at July 1. For comparison with
actual monthly data, we desire trend values centered at July 15,
August 15, etc. At the beginning, therefore, we must add to the
trend value for the month centered at the middle of the year of
origin $\left(\text{that is, to } a \text{ or to } \dfrac{a}{12}\right)$ one half of the month-to-month increment (or decrement) that we have obtained from b of the trend
equation. This procedure gives us the trend value for the month

centered at July 15. This value may be compared with the actual value recorded for that month. The addition to this of the month-to-month trend increment (or decrement) gives trend values for all following months; subtraction gives trend values for all preceding months.[10]

On the Selection of a Curve to Represent Trend

Various types of curves which may be fitted to represent the trend of economic data over a period of time have been described. But which of these many types is to be selected in a given case? Which will give the best standard of "normality" for each of the years covered? Several references to this problem have been made in the preceding sections, but no general principles have been laid down. And, in fact, no general principles can be evoked to answer this fundamental question. There is no absolute test of goodness of fit in such cases. It is largely a matter of personal judgment as to the type of curve which best represents the trend in a given instance, and experience must play a dominant part in such judgments. But certain general considerations are of assistance in selecting the appropriate type of curve.

1. The first step in the selection of a curve type is the plotting of the data. When this has been done, it is frequently possible by inspection to determine the appropriate form. The data may be plotted in four different combinations, of which the first two are of chief importance in dealing with economic material.

a. Natural x, natural y. (That is, plot the given figures on ordinary arithmetic paper.)

b. Natural x, log y. (Plot the x's on the natural scale, and plot the y's on the logarithmic scale; i.e., use semilogarithmic paper.)

c. Natural y, log x. (Plot on semilogarithmic paper, with the x-scale logarithmic.)

---

[10] If the original monthly data relate to the first or last of the month, rather than the middle, a similar correction is needed, but the monthly dates named in the text would be different, of course. If the trend equation is nonlinear, the process of interpolation must be correspondingly modified. For the simple exponential the rate of change from month to month is given by the twelfth root of the year-to-year rate. On general methods of interpolation see *The Calculus of Observations*, by Whittaker and Robinson (Ref. 190).

d. Log y, log x. (Plot on paper with logarithmic ruling on both scales.)

If in any of these cases a straight line trend is denoted, a type of equation which plots as a straight line under the given conditions (see Chapter 2) would be selected. If a linear equation is not appropriate some other simple type may be suggested by the plotted data. In studying such graphs for the purpose of selecting a curve to represent trend, one should be familiar with the curves representing all the simpler equations.

2. The appropriate curve may be determined by a study of the relations between the two variables, x and y. In the simpler cases the following relations hold:[11]

a. If, when the values of x are arranged in an arithmetic series, the corresponding values of y form a geometric series, the relation is of the exponential type, described by the equation

$$y = ab^x$$

b. If, when the values of x are arranged in a geometric series, the corresponding values of y form a geometric series, the relation is of the parabolic or hyperbolic type, described by the equation

$$y = ax^b$$

c. If, when the values of x are arranged in an arithmetic series, the first differences of the corresponding y's are constant, the relation is of the straight line type, described by the equation

$$y = a + bx$$

The differences between successive y values, when x's are arranged in an arithmetic series, are termed "first differences" or "first order differences" and are represented by the symbol Δy. The differences between successive first differences are called "second differences" and are represented by the symbol $\Delta^2 y$.

---

[11] It will be recalled that an arithmetic series changes by a constant absolute increment, while a geometric series changes by a constant percentage.

Differences of higher order are similarly derived. The following table illustrates the formation of differences:

x	y	Δy	$\Delta^2 y$	$\Delta^3 y$
1	11			
2	40	29	32	12
3	101	61	44	12
4	206	105	56	12
5	367	161	68	12
6	596	229	80	12
7	905	309	92	12
8	1,306	401	104	12
9	1,811	505	116	
10	2,432	621		

d. If, when the values of x are arranged in an arithmetic series, the nth differences of the corresponding y's are constant, the relation between the variables is described by a polynomial carried to the nth power of x; that is, by an equation of the type

$$y = a + bx + cx^2 + dx^3 + \ldots + qx^n.$$

Thus, in the example given above, in which the third differences are constant, the relation between x and y would be described by an equation of the form

$$y = a + bx + cx^2 + dx^3$$

When one is selecting a curve to use in the analysis of economic data, he will rarely, if ever, find these tests to be met perfectly. This would happen only when the curve chosen passed through all the plotted points. But data in a given case will generally approximate some one of the conditions described above, and the appropriate type of curve will be indicated.

3. If study of the original data does not render a definite decision possible, several types of curves may be fitted to the data and the decision made by comparing the results. If the equations to the curves being compared contain the same number of constants, a comparison of the root-mean-square deviations about the curves furnishes a valid test of the closeness of the fit within the limits of the data.

The root-mean-square deviation may be readily computed by making use of the following relationship

$$\Sigma(d^2) = \Sigma(y^2) - a\Sigma(y) - b\Sigma(xy) - c\Sigma(x^2y) - \dots \quad (10.7)$$

where $\Sigma(d^2)$ is the sum of the squares of the deviations about the line of trend. If the equations do not contain the same number of constants, a test of this sort is invalid and the comparison can only be made by inspection. Personal judgment as to the curve that represents the trend most accurately must be the basis of the decision in such cases.

It should be remembered that the closeness of fit within the limits of the data is not of itself a final criterion. An equation could be secured, having a number of constants equal to the number of points, which would give a curve passing through every point plotted, yet such a curve would not necessarily represent the trend. The concept of a *trend* is of a regular, smooth underlying movement, from which there are deviations, but which marks the long-term tendency of the series. In general, therefore, the curve should be of simple form, if it is to be consistent with the concept of secular trend. This does not mean, however, that a complex trend can be represented by a simple curve that fails to conform to the plotted data.

4. An important question to be answered before the form of curve can be selected relates to the limits within which the line of trend is to be used. If it is to be used only within the limits of the plotted data (i.e., for *interpolation*) one set of considerations governs the choice of a curve. If it is to be projected beyond the limits of the data and used as a basis for the determination of "normal"[12] levels during a subsequent period, other considerations enter. In the former case a reasonable fit to the data is the sole requirement; in the latter case it is necessary, in addition, that the trend of the projection be logical, and consistent with the past record.

---

[12] It is customary to think of the term "normal" as synonymous with "trend value," but we should not forget that "normal" is here used in a conveniently Pickwickian sense. Even in retrospect it is hard to say what was normal in the life of man; to say what will be normal in the future is doubly hazardous. In the *New Yorker's* words, "Normalcy, like love, is old yet ever new. It is the imponderable, haunting element in the statistical pudding. . . . Normalcy is a memory, a wisp, a piece of old lace, a crushed petal between the pages of a book."

The fact should be recognized that projection, or *extrapolation*, represents a guess, justified only on the assumption that a proper line of trend has been fitted and that the same conditions that affected the series in the past will prevail in the future. A change in conditions, the introduction of new elements, renders the projection invalid. When dealing with economic statistics, moreover, it is ordinarily impossible to tell, except in retrospect, when a change has taken place. Conclusions drawn from the projection of a line of trend are always subject to error, therefore. In practical statistical work such projections are made, and are justified on the ground that the most probable course in the future is that which prevailed in the past. Projections into the distant future are, of course, subject to wider margins of error than short-time projections. Lines of trend should be revised from time to time, therefore, as new data become available.

When a projection is to be made, a simple curve with few constants is to be preferred to a more complicated one. A polynomial of the third or fourth degree may give an excellent fit to the data in a given case, but the projection of such curves is inadvisable. It is well to remember, as Perrin has pointed out, that a curve suitable for interpolation may not be at all adapted to extrapolation.

The avoidance of distortion of trend lines by abnormal conditions in the terminal years of the period studied is particularly important when a trend is to be projected.

It seems to be true, in general, that simple curves fitted to the logarithms of the *y*'s give more reliable results when projected than do curves fitted to the natural numbers. In an interesting discussion of this point, Karl G. Karsten has argued that phenomena characterized by a uniform *rate of change* are more likely to maintain their trend than phenomena marked by a uniform *amount of change*. It is the semilogarithmic curves, of course, that best measure *rates* of change.

5. It is frequently true that no one curve will fit a given series during the entire period it is desired to study. This may be due to structural changes in the economy that alter the determinants of growth for the element in question. Thus the industrial revolution, which materially increased the productive powers of the people of Britain in the late eighteenth and nineteenth centuries, paved the way for a substantial advance in the rate of population growth in

the United Kingdom. Such structural changes affect many economic series. By breaking the entire period into sections, appropriate lines of trend may be fitted to the several periods thus marked off. This process may be carried to a quite illogical extreme, however. The concept of trend is of a gradual, long-term change, and the breaking up of a series in order to fit a number of trend lines is contrary to the whole conception. The assumption that a trend has been sharply broken may be justified on occasion, when a real change in underlying conditions is known to have occurred. But when trend breaks are introduced without such rational basis the significance of resulting trend values is of course reduced.

REFERENCES

Burns, A. F., *Production Trends in the United States Since* 1870.
Croxton, F. E. and Cowden, D. J., *Applied General Statistics*, Chaps. 15, 16.
Kendall, M. G., *The Advanced Theory of Statistics*, 3rd ed., Vol. II, pp. 363-387.
Koopmans, T., ed., *Statistical Inference in Dynamic Economic Models*, Chaps. 11, 12 (an econometric approach to the analysis of time series).
Kuznets, S., *Secular Movements in Production and Prices*.
Lewis, E. E., *Methods of Statistical Analysis in Economics and Business*, Chap. 10.
Macaulay, F. R., *The Smoothing of Time Series*.
Mills, F. C., *Economic Tendencies in the United States*.
Riggleman, J. R. and Frisbee, I. N., *Business Statistics*, 3rd ed., Chaps. 14, 15.
Sasuly, M., *Trend Analysis of Statistics: Theory and Technique*.
Schumpeter, J. A., *Business Cycles*, Chap. 5.
Spurr, W. A., Kellogg, L. S. and Smith, J. H., *Business and Economic Statistics*, Chap. 15.
Yule, G. U. and Kendall, M. G., *An Introduction to the Theory of Statistics*, 14th ed., Chap. 26.

The publishers and the dates of publication of the books named in chapter reference lists are given in the bibliography at the end of this volume.

CHAPTER 11

The Analysis of Time Series: Measurement of Seasonal Fluctuations

The measurement of secular trend is but one of the problems connected with the analysis of a series in time. Such series, it has been pointed out, are subject to periodic and semiperiodic fluctuations, seasonal and cyclical in character, and these fluctuations may be objects of major interest to the investigator. We deal in this chapter with the first of these classes of fluctuations.

The pervasiveness of seasonal movements. Seasonal changes in economic series are, of course, true periodicities. The swing of the earth around the sun brings in its wake a host of movements in weather and in harvests, in the flow of goods in domestic and international trade, in the needs and buying practices of consumers, and in the patterns of industrial production that are related to consumer demand, and ramifying consequences of all these.

A few examples will indicate the pervasiveness and amplitude of these movements.[1] Industrial production in the United States reaches a seasonal low in July, a peak in October, the range being from 94 to 103 (where 100 represents the average for the year). Metal mining rises from a low of 72 in January to a high of 121 in June; bituminous coal production is at a low of 75 in July, a peak of 109 in October-November. The production of food and beverages (manufactured products) reaches a low of 91 in February, a high

[1] These examples are based on seasonal indexes of the Board of Governors of the Federal Reserve System (see Chapter 14) and of the National Bureau of Economic Research. Such indexes are, of course, subject to change over time.

TABLE 11-1

Incurred Monthly Fire Losses in the United States 1936-1953*
(in thousands of dollars)

	January	February	March	April	May	June	July	August	September	October	November	December	Total
1936	27,730	30,910	29,177	25,786	21,479	20,407	22,357	21,714	20,413	20,439	22,808	30,133	293,353
1937	25,070	28,655	29,319	26,664	21,438	19,525	19,812	19,767	19,350	21,098	23,850	30,173	284,721
1938	27,676	26,473	29,051	25,616	22,917	19,474	20,435	20,821	23,372	24,798	28,659	32,758	302,050
1939	27,615	29,303	30,682	27,061	27,032	24,191	22,468	22,800	22,837	24,300	27,248	27,959	313,496
1940	36,261	34,410	29,789	26,657	23,446	19,506	20,323	20,722	21,198	22,091	23,449	28,617	306,469
1941	26,470	26,102	31,471	29,330	25,637	24,943	23,698	24,122	24,668	30,833	23,822	31,261	322,357
1942	35,565	30,819	30,505	27,960	23,233	22,410	21,000	19,680	20,443	22,621	24,144	36,469	314,849
1943	27,733	33,175	39,214	34,241	29,297	26,854	25,016	29,193	26,488	29,661	31,647	47,716	380,235
1944	38,572	38,280	39,084	34,746	32,815	30,555	32,706	30,618	31,448	32,173	33,847	48,694	423,538
1945	44,865	41,457	40,876	37,950	34,153	34,090	34,054	34,096	32,447	34,470	37,393	49,478	455,329
1946	49,808	51,759	53,252	52,153	46,094	44,240	40,998	40,019	40,256	40,108	44,706	58,094	561,487
1947	57,180	64,247	72,435	68,029	56,545	50,840	49,357	51,359	47,990	54,946	51,346	68,361	692,635
1948	63,010	71,521	74,236	63,751	59,256	54,706	50,955	49,543	49,945	51,845	52,949	69,397	711,114
1949	57,926	62,424	67,218	55,290	54,162	51,787	49,592	50,150	49,678	48,914	53,116	67,279	667,536
1950	58,823	58,340	72,468	61,605	58,765	57,116	52,980	49,878	45,922	49,953	55,790	66,820	688,460
1951	68,686	69,136	71,507	62,965	58,744	56,403	52,220	55,416	53,398	54,660	60,064	68,206	731,405
1952	74,155	69,925	72,254	67,380	62,354	58,585	61,675	56,462	58,949	63,958	65,129	74,127	784,953
1953	76,659	72,706	83,471	67,362	64,239	67,644	74,938	107,713	68,613	68,551	68,064	83,440	903,400

* Compiled by the National Board of Fire Underwriters.

of 114 in September. The consumption of cotton is at a low in July, a high in February, the seasonal amplitude being from 84 to 108. Portland cement production, on the other hand, is at a low of 76 in February, a high of 115 in October. Sales by mail order houses range from a low of 70 in February to a high of 145 in December. Consumer installment credit for purchases from department stores and mail order houses is at a seasonal low of 92 in August and September, a year-end peak of 110 in December, 111 in January. Freight ton-miles on railroads reach a low of 92 in February, a high of 112 in October. And the cold storage holdings of eggs rise from a seasonal low of 4 in February to a high of 192 in July! Some of these are, of course, extreme examples; there are stable series that are virtually unaffected by the march of the seasons. But many social activities and economic processes are affected. Our present concern is with these.

The study of weather and harvest rhythms and of their diverse economic effects can be a rewarding enterprise in its own right, and some few investigations have concentrated attention on them. In the main, however, statisticians seek to define seasonal patterns for the purpose of removing them. The Federal Reserve production index is "adjusted" in this fashion. In the traditional approach in time series analysis, trend and seasonal movements are eliminated in order that "cycles" may be defined. But whether the seasonal patterns are themselves of interest or are to be removed to further other purposes, the first step is to measure them with as much precision as possible.

An Example of the Use of Moving Averages

The figures in Table 11-1, which reflect the month-to-month variations in losses from fire and lightning in the United States, may be used to illustrate the measurement of seasonal fluctuations. The process of measurement begins with the computation of 12-month moving averages. Since the fluctuations to be defined take place within a constant period of 12 months, a moving average may be used with more confidence than when a rhythm of varying length is involved. However, the magnitude of the fluctuations (the *amplitude* of the seasonal swings) may vary somewhat from year to year; moreover, the individual observations to be averaged are affected by random and other nonseasonal factors. Accordingly, the line marked out by the moving averages will not be completely free of seasonal influences, and the deviations from it will not define pure seasonal fluctuations. We may meet these difficulties in part by averaging the ratios of the actual monthly items to the moving averages, by months, and basing indexes of seasonal variation upon these averages.

It is essential, of course, that the moving average, centered, fall at the same date as the original figure with which it is to be compared. This involves a second process of averaging. For example, the monthly totals of fire losses should be considered to be located at the middle of each month. The average of the 12 monthly items for 1936, when centered, falls on July 1. The average of the items from February, 1936, through January, 1937, centered, falls on August 1. To secure a figure comparable with the July 15 average, these two must be averaged. By this process of computing 2-month moving averages from the 12-month averages, comparability with the original figures may be secured. In the actual computations it is simpler to employ moving totals up to the point of final reduction to a properly centered 12-month moving average.

Ratios to Moving Averages. The procedure is illustrated in Table 11-2, which shows the calculations for 2 of the 18 years covered. The 12-month moving totals given in column (3) are centered by means of 2-month moving totals in column (4); dividing by 24, the moving averages given in column (5) are obtained. Expressing the original data in column (2) as ratios to the corresponding averages in column (5), we obtain the figures in column (6).

The derived percentages, showing the relation of actual fire losses, month by month, to the moving averages are given in Table 11-3, for the period 1936-53. These percentages, which are to provide the means by which we compute index numbers of seasonal variation, call for a brief discussion.

The base of each percentage, e.g., 24,335 for July 1936, is an average for 12 months. In the calculation of this average, it is assumed, recurring fluctuations with a period of exactly 12 months will be cancelled out. Thus the average is taken to be free of seasonal movements. The averages will, however, move with the long-term trend, if there is one. They will reflect periodic movements, such as business cycles, that run their courses in periods exceeding 12 months in length. Deviations from the moving

TABLE 11–2

Showing the Calculation of 12-Month Moving Averages of Monthly Fire
Losses and of the Ratios of Actual Fire Losses to Moving Averages
(Fire losses in thousands of dollars)

(1) Year and month	(2) Amount of loss	(3) 12-month moving total	(4) 2-month moving total of col. (3)	(5) Col. (4) ÷ 24	(6) Ratio of col. (2) to col. (5)
1936					
January	27,730				
February	30,910				
March	29,177				
April	25,786				
May	21,479				
June	20,407				
July	23,357	293,353	584,046	24,335	.9187
August	21,714	290,693	579,131	24,130	.8999
September	20,413	288,438	577,018	24,042	.8490
October	20,439	288,580	578,038	24,085	.8486
November	22,808	289,458	578,875	24,120	.9456
December	30,133	289,417	577,952	24,081	1.2513
1937					
January	25,070	288,535	574,525	23,938	1.0473
February	28,655	285,990	570,033	23,751	1.2065
March	29,319	284,043	567,023	23,626	1.2410
April	26,664	282,980	566,619	23,609	1.1294
May	21,438	283,639	568,320	23,680	.9053
June	19,525	284,681	569,402	23,725	.8230
July	19,812	284,721	572,048	23,835	.8312
August	19,767	287,327	572,472	23,853	.8287
September	19,350	285,145	570,022	23,751	.8147
October	21,098	284,877	568,706	23,696	.8904
November	23,850	283,829	569,137	23,714	1.0057
December	30,173	285,308	570,565	23,773	1.2692

Columns (3) to (6) must, of course, be blank for the first six months of 1936. Data
for the last six months of 1935 would be needed to compute moving totals for January-
June 1936. Entries for 1937 are complete, since 1938 data were available and have been
used. Table 11-2 is a portion of the work table covering the full eighteen years.

averages, deviations which make the percentages in Table 11-3
exceed or fall below 100, are taken to be due primarily to seasonal
movements. If the seasonal pattern were perfectly repetitive, and
if no other forces affected the percentages, the figures for any one
month, say December, would all be identical, and any one of them
could be taken as an index of December's seasonal movements. It
is clear that they are not identical. The December percentages
range from a low of 104.8 in 1939 to a high of 142.5 in 1943.
Various forces other than seasonal do in fact affect fire losses in
each month of the year. Random factors play an important role
in the incidence of fires; they may cause any month in a given

TABLE 11-3

Percentage Relations of Incurred Fire Losses to 12-Month Moving Averages, Centered, 1936-1953

	January	February	March	April	May	June	July	August	September	October	November	December
1936							91.9	90.0	84.9	84.9	94.6	125.1
1937	104.7	120.6	124.1	112.9	90.5	82.3	83.1	82.9	81.5	89.0	100.6	126.9
1938	116.3	110.9	120.6	105.0	92.6	77.7	81.2	82.3	91.8	96.9	111.0	125.0
1939	104.3	110.0	114.9	101.5	101.7	91.9	84.8	84.3	83.9	89.4	100.9	104.8
1940	137.4	131.3	114.3	102.9	91.4	76.5	80.9	85.0	87.9	91.0	95.8	115.4
1941	105.2	102.5	122.3	111.7	96.3	93.2	87.0	86.7	88.2	110.6	85.9	113.6
1942	130.3	114.1	114.5	107.0	90.1	86.1	81.0	76.6	78.2	84.5	88.5	131.6
1943	98.8	115.8	133.9	114.8	96.3	86.0	77.8	89.0	80.2	89.8	95.3	142.5
1944	113.6	111.5	112.9	99.5	93.4	86.7	92.0	85.2	87.0	88.5	92.6	132.5
1945	121.4	111.5	109.4	101.2	90.5	89.9	89.2	87.9	81.7	84.4	89.2	115.5
1946	114.3	117.4	119.2	115.3	100.7	95.3	87.0	83.5	81.7	79.1	86.3	110.6
1947	107.6	119.1	132.3	122.1	99.9	88.7	85.1	87.8	81.5	93.5	87.4	115.9
1948	106.4	120.8	125.4	107.7	100.2	92.4	86.3	84.7	86.4	90.7	93.6	123.4
1949	103.3	111.4	111.9	98.9	97.1	92.9	88.8	90.2	89.4	87.2	94.0	118.2
1950	102.7	101.6	126.6	107.8	102.6	99.5	91.6	85.1	77.8	84.6	94.4	113.1
1951	116.4	116.7	119.6	104.4	96.8	92.6	85.4	90.2	86.8	88.6	96.8	109.5
1952	118.1	110.6	113.8	105.1	96.4	89.9	94.1	85.9	88.9	95.8	97.4	110.1
1953	112.3	102.5	113.6	90.9	86.4	90.3						

year to be well below or well above the figure that might be expected on the basis of past experience. It is unlikely that the trend of fire losses is exactly reflected in the long-term movements of the 12-month moving averages; to the extent that the trend is not so defined, the monthly percentages of Table 11-3 will depart from 100. It is, similarly, unlikely that cyclical fluctuations in fire losses are fully embodied in the moving averages; the percentages of Table 11-3 will be affected by any discrepancy of this sort.

For these various reasons we find considerable variation among the percentages for each month of the year. The degree of variation is revealed in Fig. 11.1, a multiple frequency table showing the scatter of the percentages falling in each of the twelve months. There is, of course, an obvious escape from the difficulties presented by variation within a given month. We may average the 17 items for January, the 17 for February, etc. This procedure has an excellent rational justification. We may assume that the *seasonal force* is fairly constant in its influence upon fire losses in, say, the month of August. Losses in that month tend always to be low. But *random factors* will sometimes work to make the losses in a given month low, sometimes high. So, also, will *cyclical divergences* from 12-month moving averages, since the averages may be expected to be below the cyclical norm in some years, above in others. Trend divergences can conceivably offer greater difficulties; moving averages may consistently fall below or exceed trend values, if the true trends are nonlinear with persistent upward or downward curvature.[2] With this one exception, we should expect the effects of nonseasonal influences to be such as would be cancelled out, in the long run, by averaging the percentages for a given month. The persistent influence of the seasonal movement would be dominant, and would determine the location of the average for that month. The trend factor would be disturbing only if the series being studied were nonlinear, with considerable curvature.

That there is a seasonal pattern in fire losses is clearly shown by Fig. 11.1. Although there is considerable variation in some months, losses are persistently high from December to March, fall from March to August, remain low through the fall months, and rise again in December. The existence of such a pronounced pattern gives us confidence that the seasonal index numbers to be derived will be significant of real changes within the year.

[2] See pp. 293-5.

Relatives	Jan.	Feb.	Mar.	Apr.	May	June	July	Aug.	Sept.	Oct.	Nov.	Dec.
142 - 144.9												|
139 - 141.9												
136 - 138.9	|											
133 - 135.9			|									
130 - 132.9	|	|	|									||
127 - 129.9												
124 - 126.9			|||									|||
121 - 123.9	|		|	|								|
118 - 120.9	|	|||	|||									|
115 - 117.9	||	|||		|								|||
112 - 114.9	|||	|	卌|	||								||
109 - 111.9		卌|	||	|					|		|	|||
106 - 108.9	||			|||								
103 - 105.9	||||			|||								|
100 - 102.9	|	|||		|||	||||					||		
97 - 99.9	|			||	||	|				|		
94 - 96.9					||||	|	|			||	卌|	
91 - 93.9					|||	卌	|||		|	||	||	
88 - 90.9				|	|||	||||	||	||||	|||	卌|	||	
85 - 87.9				|		|||	卌	卌||	||||	|		|||
82 - 84.9					|	||	卌	||	||||			
79 - 81.9						|||		卌	|			
76 - 78.9					||	|	|	||				

FIG. 11.1. Frequency Distributions: Monthly Incurred Fire Losses Expressed as Relatives of Corresponding 12-Month Moving Averages.

Means and Medians of Ratios to Moving Averages. Various methods are employed in seeking to obtain a representative and accurate index figure for each month of the year. Of the conventional averages, the arithmetic mean and the median are appropriate. Averages of these types, for each of the 12 months, are given in Table 11-4, with corresponding adjusted measures. The

TABLE 11–4

Indexes of Seasonal Variation in Fire Losses. Arithmetic Means and Medians Computed from Ratios to 12-Month Moving Averages

(1) Month	(2) Arithmetic means	(3) Arithmetic means, adjusted	(4) Medians	(5) Medians adjusted
January	112.54	112.9	112.3	113.2
February	113.43	113.7	111.5	112.4
March	119.37	119.7	119.2	120.2
April	106.39	106.7	105.1	106.0
May	95.46	95.7	96.3	97.1
June	88.94	89.2	89.9	90.7
July	86.31	86.5	86.3	87.0
August	85.72	86.0	85.2	85.9
September	84.58	84.8	84.9	85.6
October	89.91	90.2	89.0	89.8
November	94.37	94.6	94.4	95.2
December	119.63	120.0	115.9	116.9
Average	99.72	100.0	99.17	100.0

adjustment is needed because the average of the 12 monthly means (or the 12 monthly medians) will seldom be exactly 100; there is rarely a complete cancelling out of the effects of nonseasonal forces. Thus for the arithmetic means in column (2) of Table 11-4 the average is 99.72. Since the monthly seasonal indexes are designed to show how a given annual total of fire losses would be divided among the 12 months, if seasonal forces alone were operative, the average of the 12 seasonal indexes should be exactly 100. The simple adjustment needed is made, in this case by multiplying each of the items in column (2) by the reciprocal of 99.72. The adjusted measures in column (3) will then average 100. (Two decimal places are used in the calculations, but the final indexes are carried to but one decimal place.) A similar adjustment is made for the medians of the original monthly percentages.

Both sets of adjusted indexes show a wide range of variation in fire losses, within the year. September falls to some 15 percent below the average monthly loss for the year; March and December mark seasonal peaks, from 17 to 20 percent above the yearly average. That this is a consistent pattern is clearly shown by the frequency distributions in Fig. 11.1.

The two sets of seasonal indexes agree very closely. The differences between them fall within a range of less than 2 percent, except for December, a month of considerable dispersion in fire losses. Each of the two types has its merits and demerits. The mean is affected by the values of all the measurements available for each month. It may, however, be unduly affected by exceptional cases. Thus a conflagration would swell fire losses in a given month to a quite unrepresentative figure. A seasonal index for that month might be misleading were the exceptional figure included in its calculation. The median, which avoids this danger, has its own drawbacks. It is subject to material changes in value by the addition or withdrawal of one or two entries, unless there is a definite concentration in the monthly distributions. Since the choice of an average is conditioned in part upon the character of the distribution of observations within given months, the tabular summary given in Fig. 11.1 can be made to serve as a very useful guide.

Positional Means. Use is often made of a third method of computing seasonal indexes, a method that combines many of the advantages of both mean and median. This involves the taking of an arithmetic mean of the central items in each monthly array of percentages. When there is an odd number of cases in each monthly distribution, this may be the mean of the three or five central observations; when the number is even, the middle four or six observations may be averaged. (The measures should be derived, of course, not from the frequency distributions, but from arrays of the original items.) Such a "positional average" is unaffected by extreme values, and is likely to be more stable than the median, i.e., less affected by the addition or removal of one or more items. In Table 11-5 are given indexes of seasonal variation in fire losses obtained by using such positional averages.

The indexes given in columns (3) and (5) of Table 11-5 trace out the same general pattern of seasonal variation that was defined by the indexes in Table 11-4. It is to be noted, however, that the indexes derived by averaging central items come between the extremes obtained from simple arithmetic means and medians for the month of December. The positional means have clear merit.

TABLE 11–5

Indexes of Seasonal Variation in Fire Losses
Positional Means based upon Ratios to Moving Averages

(1) Month	(2) Arithmetic mean of 3 central items	(3) Col. (2) adjusted	(4) Arithmetic mean of 5 central items	(5) Col. (4) adjusted
January	111.18	112.3	110.84	111.8
February	112.37	113.5	112.86	113.9
March	116.20	117.3	116.50	117.5
April	105.70	106.7	105.84	106.8
May	96.33	97.3	95.80	96.7
June	90.00	90.9	90.12	90.9
July	86.23	87.1	86.16	86.9
August	85.40	86.2	85.58	86.3
September	85.07	85.9	84.78	85.5
October	89.00	89.9	89.06	89.8
November	94.33	95.2	94.38	95.2
December	116.53	117.7	117.68	118.7
Average	99.03	100.0	99.13	100.0

In general, they are to be preferred to either the arithmetic mean or the median when the arrays of monthly relatives show any considerable degree of dispersion.

Other methods. The preceding example has illustrated the use of ratios to moving averages in defining patterns of seasonal variation. A somewhat similar method employs ratios to trend values. Such ratios are tabulated, for the different months of the year, in the manner shown in Fig. 11.1. Seasonal indexes are then obtained by averaging, exactly as in handling ratios to moving averages. The use of trend ratios is in general less satisfactory than the use of moving averages, and is not now generally employed. For the deviations from trend will reflect cyclical, random, and seasonal fluctuations, and the averaging of ratios to trend must be trusted to remove the full influence of cycles, as well as random effects. Since this removal can seldom if ever be achieved, the resulting indexes of seasonal variation are not too trustworthy. Still a third method of measuring seasonal movements rests on graphic procedures, utilizing the special advantages of ratio (or semilogarithmic) paper. The interested student will find an explanation of this method in Spurr, Kellogg, and Smith (Ref. 150).

We must note that not all series of observations recorded by months (or other subdivisions of the year) are marked by seasonal variation. In each case the investigator must assure himself that in making adjustments for seasonal movements he is correcting for truly repetitive fluctuations in the original series. The processes described in the preceding pages will almost always give monthly means of ratios to 12-month moving averages that vary, for the months of the year; the play of random factors will assure this. But the fact that the indexes thus obtained vary from month to month is no guaranty that a true seasonal pattern exists. Rational considerations, together with an orderly pattern of seasonal movements in such a presentation as that illustrated by the multiple frequency table in Fig. 11.1, will often be sufficient warrant for accepting a set of seasonal indexes as significant. (The observations should, of course, cover a number of years—eight to twelve may be thought of as a minimum, although working statisticians familiar with their materials sometimes base seasonal indexes on a record covering as few as five years.)

Changes in Seasonal Patterns

The basic seasonal impulses that are generated by the annually recurring rhythms of weather remain fairly constant over time, although there are slow secular changes in weather (see Fig. 10.3) and variations from year to year in the intensity of winter cold and summer heat. The derived patterns of economic behavior are by no means constant, however. Changes in seasonal patterns may be abrupt; they may be slow, but progressive in character; they may be gradual but irregular. Abrupt changes come, for example, when a national economy makes a swift transition from peace to war, or from war to peace. Evolutionary or secular changes in pattern may come with slow alterations in trade practices, in production procedures, or in consumption habits. The displacement of the open car by the closed car brought such a progressive modification in the seasonal pattern of automobile sales. The irregular changes may be due to a host of minor factors, or may be related to a definable cause. Thus the price of an agricultural product may follow one seasonal pattern in years of high production and quite a different pattern in years of low production. Shifts in the dates of annual automobile shows may affect the seasonal distribution of automobile sales. Patterns of retail sales in some fields vary with changes in the date of Easter. For these reasons the statisticians may never regard a seasonal pattern as fixed. Continuing checks are needed; these may lead to the use of new seasonal adjustments every five or ten years, or even more frequently. (Note, for example, the many shifts made between 1947 and 1952 in the seasonal adjustments in components of the Federal Reserve Index of Industrial Production.)[3]

When the change in a seasonal pattern is evolutionary, the progressive change in the index for each month may be measured separately. Thus when ratios to moving averages have been obtained, all the January items may be plotted chronologically, say from 1937 to 1953. If there is a progressive change in the January ratios, this movement may be defined by an appropriate line of trend. The trend value for January, 1937, is a first approximation to the January seasonal index for 1937; the trend value for January, 1938, provides a similar approximation to the seasonal index for January, 1938, and so on for January of each of the other years covered. All February ratios are treated in the same way, trend values for February of each year then providing first approximations to the February seasonal indexes. Similar procedures give corresponding measures for each of the other months of the year. The preliminary seasonal indexes for the 12 months of each year must then be adjusted to make their average equal to 100, just as was done with the preliminary indexes for fire losses cited above.

The key operation in this procedure is the determination of the trends of the ratios for the various months of the year. Careful study of the plotted figures for each month is, of course, a first step. The investigator may then decide to fit a mathematical function by least squares. A simple straight line is a useful form, if the secular movement for the given month is marked by regular increments or decrements in absolute terms. Alternately, a moving average of five or seven terms may be employed, or a free-hand curve may be drawn through the plotted points for a single month. Moving averages have been employed by the National Bureau of Economic Research in handling changing seasonals; the free-hand method has been extensively used by the Research Division of the Board of Governors of the Federal Reserve System in dealing with seasonal changes in elements of their production index.

Electronic Computations in Seasonal Analysis. A recent development in the work of the U. S. Bureau of the Census promises to extend and materially improve processes of seasonal analysis. A

---

[3] *Federal Reserve Bulletin*, September, 1953, pp. 54-5.

systematic procedure is now available for using Univac, one of the high-speed electronic computers, in the construction of seasonal indexes and in the testing of these indexes for significance. The operation is an adaptation of the ratio-to-moving-average method, using positional means, that was explained in the preceding pages. The derived measures are moving indexes—devised, that is, to take account, year by year, of true changes in seasonal patterns. The method is accurate, expeditious, and inexpensive in terms of machine time. Computations for a monthly series covering 10 years, with tests of the significance of the seasonal pattern and of the validity of the adjustments, can be completed in about one minute, at a cost of about two dollars.[4] Although the average investigator will not have such equipment at his disposal, its use in a central federal agency will mean that all basic economic and social series can be readily tested for seasonality, and adjusted, if adjustment is required.

REFERENCES

Burns, A. F. and Mitchell, W. C., *Measuring Business Cycles*, pp. 43-55.

Croxton, F. E. and Cowden, D. J., *Applied General Statistics*, Chaps. 17, 18.

Federal Reserve System, Board of Governors, *Federal Reserve Bulletin*, Dec. 1953, pp. 1260-1264.

Joy, A. and Thomas, W., "The Use of Moving Averages in the Measurement of Seasonal Variations," *Journal of the American Statistical Association*, Sept. 1928.

Kuznets, S., *Seasonal Variations in Industry and Trade*.

Lewis, E. E., *Methods of Statistical Analysis in Economics and Business*, Chap. 11.

Mendershausen, H., "Methods of Computing and Eliminating Changing Seasonal Fluctuations," *Econometrica*, July 1937.

Riggleman, J. R. and Frisbee, I. N., *Business Statistics*, 3rd ed., Chap. 16.

Shiskin, J., "A New Multiplicative Seasonal Index," *Journal of the American Statistical Association*, Dec., 1942.

Spurr, W. A., Kellogg, L. S. and Smith, J. H., *Business and Economic Statistics*, pp. 356-376.

Yule, G. U. and Kendall, M. G., *An Introduction to the Theory of Statistics*, 14th ed., Chap. 26.

The publishers and the dates of publication of the books named in chapter reference lists are given in the bibliography at the end of this volume.

[4] For an explanation of this innovation, with a full example of seasonal analysis by electronic means, see "Seasonal Computations on Univac," by Julius Shiskin, *The American Statistician*, February, 1955.

CHAPTER 12

.
.
.

The Analysis of Time Series: Cyclical Fluctuations

We deal in this chapter with the problems faced in identifying and measuring cyclical fluctuations in historical variables. Major interest in many economic and social studies is attached to these cyclical changes, and their measurement is regarded by many as the central task in time series analysis.

Our interest here is in cyclical fluctuations in individual time series. These are, obviously, not unrelated to cycles in the economy at large. Indeed, cyclical changes in the majority of economic series that reveal such movements conform with varying leads or lags and with varying amplitudes to broad cyclical swings in the general economy.[1] But every economic and social series has its own pattern of behavior over time. Our task is to identify cyclical patterns that are unique to individual series. The data thus provided may serve the needs of those who are concerned only with given series—with cyclical movements of interest rates, of wholesale prices, of automobile sales—or they may contribute to an understanding of the complex patterns of cycles in general business.

---

[1] In interpreting cyclical movements of individual series we should bear in mind the nature of cycles in the general economy. The characteristics of these general movements have been set forth by Burns and Mitchell: "Business cycles are a type of fluctuation found in the aggregate economic activity of nations that organize their work mainly in business enterprises; a cycle consists of expansions occurring at about the same time in many economic activities, followed by similarly general recessions, contractions, and revivals which merge into the expansion phase of the next cycle; this sequence of changes is recurrent but not periodic; in duration business cycles vary from more than one year to ten or twelve years; they are not divisible into shorter cycles of similar character with amplitudes approximating their own." (Burns and Mitchell, Ref. 13)

Residuals as "Cycles"

A method of cycle analysis long associated with the name of Warren Persons (Ref. 127) may be illustrated with reference to the data of pig iron production in the United States for the period 1926-1953. (Annual averages for this series, for the full period of 28 years, are given in Table 12-1. Monthly data for twelve selected years are cited in Table 12-2, column 2.) The essence of this procedure is the "elimination" of the trend and seasonal components of a given series in time; the residual movements are viewed as acceptable approximations to the cyclical component which is the object of interest. The residue will, of course, also contain

TABLE 12–1

Pig Iron Production in the United States, 1926-1953*
(Daily average, in thousands of gross tons)

(1) Year	(2) Actual output	(3) Estimate of normal output based on exponential trend
1926	107.0	65.4
1927	99.3	67.7
1928	103.3	70.2
1929	115.8	72.7
1930	86.1	75.4
1931	50.2	78.1
1932	23.8	80.9
1933	36.1	83.9
1934	43.6	86.9
1935	57.6	90.1
1936	83.6	93.4
1937	100.4	96.7
1938	51.4	100.3
1939	86.3	103.9
1940	114.5	107.7
1941	136.7	111.6
1942	146.3	115.6
1943	150.5	119.8
1944	151.1	124.2
1945	132.6	128.7
1946	110.8	133.3
1947	145.2	138.2
1948	148.1	143.2
1949	132.8	148.4
1950	160.0	153.8
1951	174.2	159.4
1952	151.6	165.2
1953	185.6	171.2

* Monthly data for this series, going back to 1877, will be found in *Historical Statistics of the United States*, 1877-1945, U. S. Bureau of the Census, 332-3.

elements reflecting the play of random factors. Account is taken of these (they may, indeed, be smoothed out to some extent) in interpreting the results of the analysis.

The first task is that of fitting an appropriate line of trend to the series that is to be analyzed. This, of course, is a crucial operation, since the assumptions that are made in the selection and fitting of a trend line will have great influence on the final measures that are taken to define patterns of cyclical behavior. We shall comment later on this matter. At this stage of the presentation we shall assume that a suitable function has been selected, for fitting to data covering an appropriate period of time. Although monthly data will be used in the analysis, it is usually desirable to fit a trend to annual data, with subsequent interpolation for monthly trend values.

Trend and seasonal components. In Fig. 12.1 we have plotted the annual pig iron production figures for the years 1926-1953, together with an exponential curve fitted to the data. The reader will note that the annual figures used are averages of daily output. The equation to the trend function (which is of the family $y = ar^x$,) is $y = 65.35537 (1.0363)^x$, with origin at 1926.[2] The value of r indicates that this series increased, during the 28 years here covered, at an annual average rate of 3.63 percent. As will be clear from the graph and from a comparison of the actual and trend values given

FIG. 12.1. Production of Pig Iron in the United States, 1926-1953, with Line of Trend (Daily Average).

---

[2] Such a function, as we have seen in Chapter 10, may be fitted by least squares, after putting the equation in the logarithmic form $\{\log y = \log a + (\log r)x\}$. We have here made use of Glover's Tables in the simplified procedure referred to in the footnote on p. 313 above.

in Table 12-1, the actual changes from year to year show wide departures from this average rate; the period covered was a disturbed one. But the underlying movement of pig iron production over these years conforms reasonably well to the indicated trend.

Examination of the monthly figures on the production of pig iron indicates that there was a fairly consistent seasonal pattern from 1926 to 1938 (earlier years are not here included), but no consistent pattern for the years since then. Accordingly, we shall make adjustments for seasonal movements for the earlier period only. (The seasonal indexes for this period are given in Table 12-2, below).

The Measurement of Cyclical Fluctuations. There remains the task of combining the measurements of secular trend and seasonal variation to secure measurements of cyclical changes in pig iron production. A suitable procedure is illustrated in Table 12-2. Since the process is the same from year to year (except for differences due to the application or nonapplication of a seasonal correction) the illustration is limited to 12 years, for 4 of which seasonal adjustments are made. In column (2) of Table 12-2 we have the actual output of pig iron by months. For the 4 years, 1935-38, a constant seasonal correction is made for each of the 12 months by dividing the actual output for that month by the seasonal index (in ratio form). Thus for January, 1935, the actual daily average output of 47.7 thousand tons becomes 48.2 after the seasonal adjustment. Since January is normally low, in seasonal terms (index = .99), the effect of the adjustment designed to eliminate the seasonal movement is of course to increase the output figure. For March, on the other hand, the seasonal index is high (1.11). Adjustment of the actual output of 57.1 thousands of tons for March, 1935, gives an adjusted figure of 51.4 thousand tons. The seasonally adjusted measures, represented by the symbol A_a, are given in column (4) of Part I of Table 12-2, for the period January 1935-December 1938. Part II of Table 12-2 covers the eight years 1946-53. For these years no seasonal adjustment is made. In subsequent operations we shall use the actual output in column (2) of this part of the table as equivalent to the seasonally adjusted output in Part I of the table.

The next step is to express the actual output (seasonally adjusted where necessary) as a deviation from trend. Monthly trend values, obtained by interpolation from annual trend values, are given in

TABLE 12–2 PART I

Illustrating the Analysis of a Series in Time: Pig Iron Production, 1935-38
(Daily average, in thousands of gross tons)

(1) Year and month	(2) Actual output	(3) Seasonal index (as ratio)	(4) Seasonally adjusted output (A/S)	(5) Trend value	(6) Deviation of seasonally adjusted output from trend	(7) "Cycles" in pig iron output
	A	S	A_a	T	$A_a - T$	$\dfrac{A_a - T}{T} \times 100$
1935						
January	47.7	.99	48.2	88.6	− 40.4	− 45.6
February	57.4	1.03	55.7	88.9	− 33.2	− 37.3
March	57.1	1.11	51.4	89.2	− 37.8	− 42.4
April	55.4	1.09	50.8	89.4	− 38.6	− 43.2
May	55.7	1.06	52.5	89.7	− 37.2	− 41.5
June	51.6	1.00	51.6	90.0	− 38.4	− 42.7
July	49.0	.93	52.7	90.2	− 37.5	− 41.6
August	56.8	.94	60.4	90.5	− 30.1	− 33.3
September	59.2	.94	63.0	90.8	− 27.8	− 30.6
October	63.8	.98	65.1	91.0	− 25.9	− 28.5
November	68.9	.98	70.3	91.3	− 21.0	− 23.0
December	68.0	.95	71.6	91.6	− 20.0	− 21.8
1936						
January	65.4	.99	66.1	91.8	− 25.7	− 28.0
February	62.9	1.03	61.1	92.1	− 31.0	− 33.7
March	65.8	1.11	59.3	92.4	− 33.1	− 35.8
April	80.1	1.09	73.5	92.7	− 19.2	− 20.7
May	85.4	1.06	80.6	92.9	− 12.3	− 13.2
June	86.2	1.00	86.2	93.2	− 7.0	− 7.5
July	83.7	.93	90.0	93.5	− 3.5	− 3.7
August	87.5	.94	93.1	93.8	− 0.7	− 0.7
September	91.0	.94	96.8	94.1	+ 2.7	+ 2.9
October	96.5	.98	98.5	94.3	+ 4.2	+ 4.5
November	98.2	.98	100.2	94.6	+ 5.6	+ 5.9
December	100.5	.95	105.8	94.9	+ 10.9	+ 11.5
1937						
January	103.6	.99	104.6	95.2	+ 9.4	+ 9.9
February	107.1	1.03	104.0	95.5	+ 8.5	+ 8.9
March	111.6	1.11	100.5	95.7	+ 4.8	+ 5.0
April	113.1	1.09	103.8	96.0	+ 7.8	+ 8.1
May	114.1	1.06	107.6	96.3	+ 11.3	+ 11.7
June	103.6	1.00	103.6	96.6	+ 7.0	+ 7.2
July	112.9	.93	121.4	96.9	+ 24.5	+ 25.3
August	116.3	.94	123.7	97.2	+ 26.5	+ 27.3
September	113.7	.94	121.0	97.5	+ 23.5	+ 24.1
October	93.3	.98	95.2	97.8	− 2.6	− 2.7
November	66.9	.98	68.3	98.0	− 29.7	− 30.3
December	48.1	.95	50.6	98.3	− 47.7	− 48.5

TABLE 12–2 PART I—Continued

Illustrating the Analysis of a Series in Time: Pig Iron Production, 1935-38

(1) Year and month	(2) Actual output	(3) Seasonal index (as ratio)	(4) Seasonally adjusted output (A/S)	(5) Trend value	(6) Deviation of seasonally adjusted output from trend	(7) "Cycles" in pig iron output
	A	S	A_a	T	$A_a - T$	$\dfrac{A_a-T}{T}\times 100$
1938						
January	46.1	.99	46.6	98.6	− 52.0	− 52.7
February	46.4	1.03	45.0	98.9	− 53.9	− 54.5
March	46.9	1.11	42.3	99.2	− 56.9	− 57.4
April	45.9	1.09	42.1	99.5	− 57.4	− 57.7
May	40.5	1.06	38.2	99.8	− 61.6	− 61.7
June	35.4	1.00	35.4	100.1	− 64.7	− 64.6
July	38.8	.93	41.7	100.4	− 58.7	− 58.5
August	48.2	.94	51.3	100.7	− 49.4	− 49.1
September	56.0	.94	59.6	101.0	− 41.4	− 41.0
October	66.2	.98	67.6	101.3	− 33.7	− 33.3
November	75.7	.98	77.2	101.6	− 24.4	− 24.0
December	71.3	.95	75.1	101.9	− 26.8	− 26.3

TABLE 12–2 PART II

Illustrating the Analysis of a Series in Time: Pig Iron Production, 1946-53
(Daily average, in thousands of gross tons)

(1) Year and month	(2) Actual output	(3) Trend value	(4) Deviation of actual output from trend	(5) "Cycles" in pig iron output
	A	T	$A - T$	$\dfrac{A-T}{T}\times 100$
1946				
January	76.2	131.2	− 55.0	− 41.9
February	36.6	131.6	− 95.0	− 72.2
March	127.4	132.0	− 4.6	− 3.6
April	107.6	132.4	− 24.8	− 18.7
May	70.4	132.8	− 62.4	− 47.0
June	109.6	133.2	− 23.6	− 17.7
July	135.5	133.6	+ 1.9	+ 1.4
August	141.1	134.0	+ 7.1	+ 5.3
September	139.5	134.4	+ 5.1	+ 3.8
October	138.7	134.8	+ 3.9	+ 2.9
November	132.0	135.2	− 3.2	− 2.4
December	115.0	135.6	− 20.6	− 15.2

TABLE 12-2 PART II—Continued

Illustrating the Analysis of a Series in Time: Pig Iron Production, 1946-53

(1) Year and month	(2) Actual output	(3) Trend value	(4) Deviation of actual output from trend	(5) "Cycles" in pig iron output
	A	T	$A - T$	$\dfrac{A - T}{T} \times 100$
1947				
January	146.5	136.0	+ 10.5	+ 7.7
February	145.1	136.4	+ 8.7	+ 6.4
March	147.5	136.8	+ 10.7	+ 7.8
April	143.7	137.2	+ 6.5	+ 4.7
May	146.4	137.6	+ 8.8	+ 6.4
June	143.2	138.0	+ 5.2	+ 3.8
July	132.1	138.4	− 6.3	− 4.6
August	141.6	138.8	+ 2.8	+ 2.0
September	142.9	139.3	+ 3.6	+ 2.6
October	155.6	139.7	+ 15.9	+ 11.4
November	149.3	140.1	+ 9.2	+ 6.6
December	149.1	140.5	+ 8.6	+ 6.1
1948				
January	147.7	140.9	+ 6.8	+ 4.8
February	147.2	141.3	+ 5.9	+ 4.2
March	144.6	141.8	+ 2.8	+ 2.0
April	114.3	142.2	− 27.9	− 19.6
May	146.2	142.6	+ 3.6	+ 2.5
June	148.5	143.0	+ 5.5	+ 3.8
July	141.1	143.5	− 2.4	− 1.7
August	151.4	143.9	+ 7.5	+ 5.2
September	155.0	144.3	+ 10.7	+ 7.4
October	159.0	144.7	+ 14.3	+ 9.9
November	160.7	145.2	+ 15.5	+ 10.7
December	161.2	145.6	+ 15.6	+ 10.7
1949				
January	164.9	146.0	+ 18.9	+ 12.9
February	166.5	146.5	+ 20.0	+ 13.7
March	167.6	146.9	+ 20.7	+ 14.1
April	164.6	147.3	+ 17.3	+ 11.7
May	158.9	147.8	+ 11.1	+ 7.5
June	143.4	148.2	− 4.8	− 3.2
July	120.2	148.7	− 28.5	− 19.2
August	128.9	149.1	− 20.2	− 13.5
September	129.5	149.5	− 20.0	− 13.4
October	17.6	150.0	−132.4	− 88.3
November	81.0	150.4	− 69.4	− 46.1
December	150.7	150.9	− 0.2	− 0.1
1950				
January	152.5	151.3	+ 1.2	+ 0.8
February	133.1	151.8	− 18.7	− 12.3
March	132.5	152.2	− 19.7	− 12.9
April	166.0	152.7	+ 13.3	+ 8.7
May	168.6	153.1	+ 15.5	+ 10.1
June	167.6	153.6	+ 14.0	+ 9.1
July	169.3	154.1	+ 15.2	+ 9.9
August	166.2	154.5	+ 11.7	+ 7.6
September	169.6	155.0	+ 14.6	+ 9.4
October	170.6	155.4	+ 15.2	+ 9.8
November	160.3	155.9	+ 4.4	+ 2.8
December	164.0	156.4	+ 7.6	+ 4.9

TABLE 12–2 PART II—Continued

Illustrating the Analysis of a Series in Time: Pig Iron Production, 1946-53

(1) Year and month	(2) Actual output A	(3) Trend value T	(4) Deviation of actual output from trend $A - T$	(5) "Cycles" in pig iron output $\dfrac{A - T}{T} \times 100$
1951				
January	169.7	156.8	+ 12.9	+ 8.2
February	165.0	157.3	+ 7.7	+ 4.9
March	173.3	157.8	+ 15.5	+ 9.8
April	175.2	158.2	+ 17.0	+ 10.7
May	177.8	158.7	+ 19.1	+ 12.0
June	177.9	159.2	+ 18.7	+ 11.7
July	174.8	159.6	+ 15.2	+ 9.5
August	174.6	160.1	+ 14.5	+ 9.1
September	175.3	160.6	+ 14.7	+ 9.2
October	178.5	161.1	+ 17.4	+ 10.8
November	175.9	161.6	+ 14.3	+ 8.8
December	172.2	162.0	+ 10.2	+ 6.3
1952				
January	174.0	162.5	+ 11.5	+ 7.1
February	178.1	163.0	+ 15.1	+ 9.3
March	181.5	163.5	+ 18.0	+ 11.0
April	155.5	164.0	− 8.5	− 5.2
May	158.2	164.5	− 6.3	− 3.8
June	31.8	165.0	−133.2	− 80.7
July	28.9	165.4	−136.5	− 82.5
August	167.9	165.9	+ 2.0	+ 1.2
September	183.5	166.4	+ 17.1	+ 10.3
October	187.6	166.9	+ 20.7	+ 12.4
November	185.3	167.4	+ 17.9	+ 10.7
December	187.5	167.9	+ 19.6	+ 11.7
1953				
January	189.1	168.4	+ 20.7	+ 12.3
February	187.6	168.9	+ 18.7	+ 11.1
March	192.3	169.4	+ 22.9	+ 13.5
April	185.4	169.9	+ 15.5	+ 9.1
May	189.7	170.4	+ 19.3	+ 11.3
June	189.7	170.9	+ 18.8	+ 11.0
July	187.7	171.4	+ 16.3	+ 9.5
August	186.4	172.0	+ 14.4	+ 8.4
September	184.6	172.5	+ 12.1	+ 7.0
October	187.2	173.0	+ 14.2	+ 8.2
November	180.4	173.5	+ 6.9	+ 4.0
December	166.5	174.0	− 7.5	− 4.3

column (5) of Part I of Table 12-2, in column (3) of Part II.
(Interpolation involves, in this case, the application of a month-
to-month rate of 1.00298, which is the twelfth root of the annual
rate of increase.) The deviations from trend, in absolute terms,
appear in column (6) of Part I of Table 12-2, in column (4) of
Part II. Finally, we obtain the desired measures by expressing the

deviations as percentages of the corresponding trend values (in column (7) of Part I and in column (5) of Part II of Table 12-2). These percentage deviations of seasonally adjusted data from trend (or of actual data from trend, when no seasonal adjustment is necessary) are taken to represent the combined influence of cyclical and accidental factors. (Use is sometimes made of a three- or five-month moving average, or of smoothing by hand, to reduce the effects of accidental factors.) These deviations are often spoken of as "cycles" in the series thus analyzed, but it is well to keep the term in quotation marks, for other than cyclical effects are always present in such measures.

The assumptions implicit in this method of breaking up a time series should be noted. In effect, we assume that the underlying trend gives a basic value, T, which would have been the actual value had there been no random, cyclical, or seasonal effects. The influences of random and cyclical forces are taken to be superimposed, additively, on these trend values, to give the actual values, A, if there is no seasonal pattern in the series in question, or the values A_a if seasonal forces are present. In this latter case, the seasonal factor is assumed to modify A_a for a given month by a constant percentage, plus or minus, to give the observed value for that month. Our process of analysis reverses this procedure, deriving A_a from A, and then measuring the deviation of A_a from an expected value given by the trend function. Other assumptions may be made concerning the manner in which the various forces interact, and these could lead to modifications of the analysis described above. But modification of this part of the procedure would not materially alter the final measurements.

The operations described above are shown graphically in Fig. 12.2. In the upper panel we have the actual monthly data for each of the two selected periods, together with the line of trend. (The trend line was determined, of course, with reference to data for the years 1926-1953; see Fig. 12.1.) The lower panel shows the final measures, the percentage deviations from trend given in the last column of Table 12-2.[3]

---

[3] It is sometimes desirable to reduce the percentage deviations from trend to a form permitting comparison with "cycles" in other time series. As derived, the percentage deviations from trend might have much greater amplitude for one series than for another; without a common denominator comparison would be difficult. The standard deviation can serve as such a common denominator. This is done by expressing the monthly deviations from trend for each series in units of the standard deviation of that series.

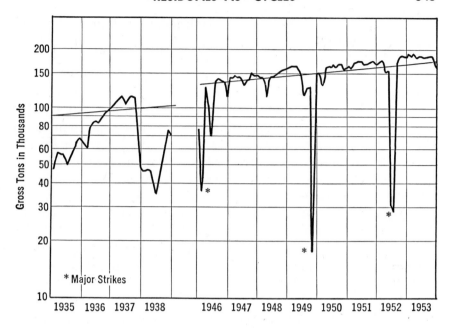

Panel A. Actual Output, with Line of Trend (Daily Average).

Panel B. "Cycles" in Pig Iron Output: Deviations from Trend (after Seasonal Correction, 1935-1938).

FIG. 12.2. Production of Pig Iron by Months, 1935-1938, 1946-1953.

The percentage deviations of pig iron production from trend define an apparent recovery from subnormal activity during 1935 and early 1936, a recovery that carried the series above the trend line in September, 1936. A peak was reached in August, 1937, when pig iron production was some 27 percent above trend. This was followed by a swift and severe recession, to a low in June, 1938 that was 65 percent below "normal." Thereafter a sharp advance began. The postwar record of pig iron output is broken by the effects of three brief but severe strikes that reduced production to very low levels in early 1946, in October, 1949, and in midsummer of 1952. Otherwise the story is one of fairly modest fluctuations about the high level of activity that was reached with recovery from the brief postwar recession of late 1945 and early 1946. Apart from the effects of strikes, which are here lumped with accidental factors, the only important period of subnormal activity came in 1949.

It is of some interest to compare this record with the movements of general business during the years in question. This is not to suggest that agreement with the broad swings of business is necessary to validate the observed "cycles" in pig iron production for, as we have noted, every series has its own distinctive pattern of behavior. But reference to the general pattern is always revealing, whether it shows similarities or differences. In this case there is fairly close agreement.[4] The year 1937 marked a peak in general business, the high point coming in May; 1938 brought a sharp drop to a low in May of that year, with recovery thereafter. The general record for the years 1946-53 was one of high activity, interrupted in 1949, and tapering off, as the pig iron series does, after mid-1953.

The reader will understand that the presentation of deviations from trend for selected periods covering only 12 years gives an incomplete picture of the behavior of pig iron production, on a monthly basis, between 1926 and 1953. This abbreviated record, in itself, provides a less than adequate basis for appraisal of the method. However, the evidence here given may be supplemented by reference to the discussion in Chapter 14 of a skillful use of this general method by the American Telephone and Telegraph Company, in constructing an index of industrial activity. Special

---

[4] See Table 12-3 below, for dates of cyclical turning points in general business.

attention is called to Fig. 14.2, showing fluctuations of industrial activity in terms of percentage deviations from a computed long-term trend.

Comment on Residuals as "Cycles." The entry in column (7) of Part I of Table 12-2 for March, 1937, indicates that in that month the actual output of pig iron, after seasonal adjustment, was 5 percent above "normal," as defined by the trend function employed in this example. This we have regarded as a measure of the cyclical component in the pig iron series, recognizing that it reflects also the influence of random factors. It is in order at this point to consider more carefully the nature of this and of similar residuals.

Each one of these derived measures is affected, of course, by the choice of a function to define secular trend, by the period employed in fitting a trend line, and by the method (e.g., least squares) used in fitting. It is affected by the choice of a period for the computation of seasonal indexes, by the method used in this computation, and by the investigator's decision to use constant or changing seasonal indexes. It is affected, finally, by the method employed in decomposing the original observation into trend, seasonal, and combined cyclical and random components (i.e., by the assumptions made concerning the way in which the underlying forces interact to yield the actually observed output). With these points in mind, and assuming for the moment that for pig iron production there is a true but to us unknown secular trend, and a true but unknown seasonal pattern, we may list the following as making up the content of such a residual as the one cited above, for March, 1937:

   a. A cyclical element;

   b. A random component—the resultant of the interplay of all forces other than secular, seasonal, and cyclical;

   c. An element representing any errors that may have been made in the definition of the trend;

   d. An element representing any errors that may have been made in the determination of the seasonal pattern for the year in question;

   e. An element representing any errors made in the decomposition of the original series.

The arbitrary factors contributing to elements (*c*) and (*d*) in this list have perhaps already been made clear. The choice of a trend function is in some degree arbitrary; a stated function will yield different trend values for a given month and year depending upon the length of the period to which it is fitted, and the choice of terminal years. Reference to Fig. 12.1 will show that a different fit would have been obtained, with the same function, had the initial year been 1932 instead of 1926.[5]

This means, obviously, that the residuals, and thus the derived "cycles" are similarly affected by the choice of a trend function and of the period used in establishing the fit. Indeed, an investigator will often make his decisions as to function and fitting methods with reference to the cycles that will be defined as a result of the fit. Equally arbitrary are many of the decisions leading to the application of seasonal corrections. Seasonals, indeed are particularly slippery, since seasonal patterns are for many series subject to change without notice. Since the magnitudes of elements (b), (c), and (d) can never be determined, there must always be some uncertainty in the interpretation of the "cycles" that constitute element (a) of the list.

More fundamental is the problem presented by element (e). The method described in this section represents what is in fact a mechanical breakdown of the actual observations. Back of it lies the assumption that the effects of the different forces playing on a series in time are mechanically combined—that a cyclical-random effect is superimposed upon a trend that is independent of the cyclical-random forces, and that a seasonal effect is added thereto.[6] It is not only possible but probable that change over time is not of this nature, that interdependent forces interact to produce an organic amalgam in social and economic development and in the growth or decline of individual series. To attempt mechanically to dissociate the elements of such an amalgam is to do violence to the data that define the results of these interacting forces.

---

[5] We may note that the present fit of the trend line makes 1927 a year of above-normal activity in pig iron production, whereas the National Bureau's chronology of cycles sets a cyclical trough at December of that year (see Table 12-3). That cycle was, however, a very mild one.

[6] If the seasonal adjustment is made by the addition or subtraction of an absolute amount for each month, this implies the independence of the seasonal factor, also. The use of a multiplicative relationship, as in the example above, introduces the assumption of a simple form of dependence, since the absolute size of the correction varies with the magnitude of the base to which it is applied.

There is ample evidence that the factors affecting series in time are in fact correlated. Willard Thorp (Ref. 157) has made the following illuminating observations on the relation of the structure of American business cycles to the trend of wholesale prices:

Period	Trend of wholesale price level	Years of prosperity per year of depression
1790–1815	Prices rising	2.6
1815–1849	Prices falling	0.8
1849–1865	Prices rising	2.9
1865–1896	Prices falling	0.9
1896–1920	Prices rising	3.1

A central aspect of the business cycle—the division of each cycle into phases of prosperity and depression—is fundamentally affected by the trend of the price level. A. F. Burns has remarked on the change in the cyclical pattern of railroad investment as the trend of railroad development was altered. When the pace of railroad growth was rapid, railroad investment tended to lead American recoveries by a substantial interval. As the pace declined, and the industry shifted from an active to a passive role in business cycles, these leads became shorter and finally disappeared. These examples of correlation between trends and cycles may be paralleled by illustrations of relations between seasonal and cyclical patterns. Thus the seasonal and cyclical factors are closely related. For example, the seasonal pattern of steel ingot production during a period of years prior to 1941 was quite different in phases of prosperity and depression. When the steel industry was operating at 95 percent of capacity, the range of steel ingot output, from the lowest month to the highest month of the year, was 11.50 percent of the average for the year; when operations were at 40 percent of capacity, the range from lowest month to highest month was 25.75 percent of the average for the year. The seasonal pattern was accentuated in periods of slack business.[7]

We are justified, therefore, in an attitude of caution toward the results of time series analysis. This is not at all to dismiss the procedures we have discussed, or to reject all derived measures. Trends are real, whether they represent net forward movements (or declines) in wave-like surges and retrogressions, or continuous underlying movements. Seasonal fluctuations are deeply imbedded

[7] Juliber, G. S., "Relation between Seasonal Amplitudes and the Level of Production", *Journal of the American Statistical Association*, Dec. 1941.

in all organic processes. Cycles are demonstrably present in many aspects of social and economic change. The analytical methods we have explained in this and the two preceding chapters represent a rather simple model which helps in the description and understanding of the complex processes of expansion and contraction, of growth and decline. Viewed as approximations, not as rigorously accurate measures, the results obtained by these methods can serve highly useful purposes, whether in research or in practical administration.

Measuring Business Cycles: the Method of the National Bureau of Economic Research

An alternative method of defining patterns of change in the movements of economic time series has been developed by the National Bureau of Economic Research. This method, which is set forth in detail in the monograph by Arthur F. Burns and Wesley C. Mitchell (Ref. 13), is aimed primarily at the study of cyclical fluctuations in time series; its proved fruitfulness makes it an instrument of general statistical interest.

With reference to individual time series the National Bureau procedure aims to answer two sets of questions:

(a) Is there in a given series a pattern of change that repeats itself (with more or less variation) in successive cycles in business at large? If so, what are its characteristics?

(b) Is there in a given series a wave movement peculiar to that series? If so, what are its characteristics?

The questions under (a) are concerned with the behavior of individual series during successive waves of expansion and contraction in the general economy; those under (b) relate to periodic or semi-periodic fluctuations in individual series, without reference to any broader framework. (In identifying these *specific cycles* there is a general reference to cycles in business at large, in that specific cycles must correspond in duration to the National Bureau's concept of business cycles. This means, roughly, a duration of over one year and not over ten or twelve years.) The object sought in answering the second set of questions is very close to the objective of the standard technique discussed in the first part of this chapter.

The questions under (a), however, point to a new and different goal. We shall deal first with these.

The Measurement of Reference Cycles; the Reference Framework. The first step in answering the questions under (a) above is the establishment of a reference framework that marks off the historical troughs and peaks in general business activity. This has been done for four countries—the United States, Great Britain, France, and Germany. The definition of these turning points in economic activity has called for extensive research on the qualitative and quantitative records of business in each of the countries covered. The annals of business, as recorded in contemporary newspapers, trade journals, and other records were exhaustively studied.[8] The provisional reference dates of troughs and peaks set on the basis of this study were checked against extensive compilations of statistical series, were modified, if necessary, and were rechecked as later data became available. The chronology of business cycles thus established for each country provides the reference frame for studying the cyclical behavior of individual time series. This chronology has been worked out on monthly, quarterly, and annual bases, for use with time series given in these time units. The monthly record is, of course, the most revealing, and lends itself to the most accurate analysis. Monthly and annual reference dates for the United States are given in Table 12-3, for the period 1854-1954.[9]

The chronology of business cycles is, of course, of great interest in itself. It indicates that 23 cycles ran their course in the United States between December 1854 and October 1949. The average duration of these reference cycles[10] was 49 months. Periods of expansion averaged 29 months in duration, or 59 percent of the full cycle; periods of contraction were shorter, averaging 20 months, or 41 percent of the full cycle. Individual cycles varied considerably from these averages. Thus in full cycle duration the measures range from 29 months (from a trough in April 1919 to a trough in September 1921) to 99 months (between low points in December

---

[8] See W. L. Thorp, Ref. 157.

[9] For quarterly reference dates for the United States see Burns and Mitchell (Ref. 13, p. 78).

[10] The interval of time falling between dates of successive troughs (alternatively, between successive peaks) is called a *reference cycle*. The term reference cycle is also used as a convenient expression for that portion of an individual time series, such as pig iron production, that falls between such dates.

1870 and March 1879).[11] But our concern at the moment is with the use of this framework in the description of the behavior of individual series.

The Description of Reference Cycle Patterns in Individual Series. Table 12-4 gives the monthly record of railroad freight, in ton-miles, from 1904 to 1953. The first step in analysis is the measurement and "elimination" of seasonal movements in the series, if such movements are present.

The pattern of seasonal variation in freight ton-miles has been subject to change over the 50 years here covered. Heavy traffic has always come in the fall months, with lighter traffic in the winter, but individual months have varied considerably. The seasonal indexes used by the National Bureau for the period 1946-53 are given in Table 12-5, and the method employed in correcting for seasonal variation is there illustrated.

[11] The chronology for Great Britain, which has been carried through 1938, shows cycles of somewhat greater average duration than those of the United States.

Reference Dates and Durations of Business Cycles in Great Britain, 1854-1938

Monthly reference dates		Duration in months			Calendar year reference dates	
Peak	Trough	Expan- sion*	Contrac- tion†	Full cycle	Peak	Trough
	Dec. 1854				1854	1855
Sep. 1857	Mar. 1858	33	6	39	1857	1858
Sep. 1860	Dec. 1862	30	27	57	1860	1862
Mar. 1866	Mar. 1868	39	24	63	1866	1868
Sep. 1872	Jun. 1879	54	81	135	1873	1879
Dec. 1882	Jun. 1886	42	42	84	1883	1886
Sep. 1890	Feb. 1895	51	53	104	1890	1894
Jun. 1900	Sep. 1901	64	15	79	1900	1901
Jun. 1903	Nov. 1904	21	17	38	1903	1904
Jun. 1907	Nov. 1908	31	17	48	1907	1908
Dec. 1912	Sep. 1914	49	21	70	1913	1914
Oct. 1918	Apr. 1919	49	6	55	1917	1919
Mar. 1920	Jun. 1921	11	15	26	1920	1921
Nov. 1924	Jul. 1926	41	20	61	1924	1926
Mar. 1927	Sep. 1928	8	18	26	1927	1928
Jul. 1929	Aug. 1932	10	37	47	1929	1932
Sep. 1937	Sep. 1938	61	12	73	1937	1938

* From trough on preceding line to peak.
† From peak to trough on same line.

TABLE 12–3

Reference Dates and Durations of Business Cycles in the United States, 1854-1954

Initial trough	Peak	Terminal trough	Ex-pansion	Con-traction	Full cycle	Trough	Peak	Trough
Dec. 1854	Jun. 1857	Dec. 1858	30	18	48	1855	1856	1858
Dec. 1858	Oct. 1860	Jun. 1861	22	8	30	1858	1860	1861
Jun. 1861	Apr. 1865	Dec. 1867	46	32	78	1861	1864	1867
Dec. 1867	Jun. 1869	Dec. 1870	18	18	36	1867	1869	1870
Dec. 1870	Oct. 1873	Mar. 1879	34	65	99	1870	1873	1878
Mar. 1879	Mar. 1882	May 1885	36	38	74	1878	1882	1885
May 1885	Mar. 1887	Apr. 1888	22	13	35	1885	1887	1888
Apr. 1888	July 1890	May 1891	27	10	37	1888	1890	1891
May 1891	Jan. 1893	Jun. 1894	20	17	37	1891	1892	1894
Jun. 1894	Dec. 1895	Jun. 1897	18	18	36	1894	1895	1896
Jun. 1897	Jun. 1899	Dec. 1900	24	18	42	1896	1899	1900
Dec. 1900	Sep. 1902	Aug. 1904	21	23	44	1900	1903	1904
Aug. 1904	May 1907	Jun. 1908	33	13	46	1904	1907	1908
Jun. 1908	Jan. 1910	Jan. 1912	19	24	43	1908	1910	1911
Jan. 1912	Jan. 1913	Dec. 1914	12	23	35	1911	1913	1914
Dec. 1914	Aug. 1918	Apr. 1919	44	8	52	1914	1918	1919
Apr. 1919	Jan. 1920	Sep. 1921	9	20	29	1919	1920	1921
Sep. 1921	May 1923	July 1924	20	14	34	1921	1923	1924
July 1924	Oct. 1926	Dec. 1927	27	14	41	1924	1926	1927
Dec. 1927	June 1929	Mar. 1933	18	45	63	1927	1929	1932
Mar. 1933	May 1937	May 1938	50	12	62	1932	1937	1938
May 1938	Feb. 1945	Oct. 1945	81	8	89	1938	1944	1946
Oct. 1945	Nov. 1948	Oct. 1949	37	11	48	1946	1948	1949
Oct. 1949	July 1953†	Aug. 1954†				1949	1953†	1954†

*The following revisions have recently been made in the monthly reference dates: July instead of September 1921; November instead of December 1927; June instead of May 1938.

† Preliminary. No measures of cyclical behavior have been based on the preliminary reference dates, which are subject to revision.

As we have seen on an earlier page, the seasonal adjustment involves merely the division of the original figure for a given month by the seasonal index for that month (with the decimal point shifted two places to the left). Thus for the adjusted figure for January 1948 we divide 51.266 by 0.95, getting 53.96. This seasonal correction, the Bureau is careful to say, is not expected to yield a series that would have been recorded in the absence of seasonal movements. No such decomposition of time series is believed to be possible. But nevertheless such adjustments, where appropriate, are believed to facilitate study and comparison of cyclical movements by giving the investigator measurements in which such movements are more clearly revealed than they are in the original series. The seasonally adjusted series is the subject of the subsequent analysis.

TABLE 12–4

Railroad Freight Ton-Miles, by Months, 1904-1954*

(in billions of ton-miles)

	1904	1905	1906	1907	1908	1909	1910	1911	1912	1913	1914	1915	1916	1917	1918	1919
January	14.55	15.69	18.55	19.89	18.03	18.69	20.58	21.17	21.33	26.43	23.93	21.76	28.87	31.51	28.78	31.00
February	14.80	15.24	19.08	20.19	17.71	18.62	21.33	20.81	22.53	26.88	23.12	22.53	29.87	31.76	29.91	28.75
March	14.92	15.66	18.68	20.03	17.38	18.97	21.90	20.49	23.19	25.52	23.61	22.88	30.74	30.01	34.18	26.54
April	14.80	16.38	17.87	20.55	17.23	19.10	22.13	20.66	22.10	24.22	23.48	22.90	29.44	31.06	36.71	27.89
May	14.84	16.53	17.93	21.36	17.02	19.00	21.79	21.16	22.01	25.27	22.17	23.26	27.43	34.95	36.43	30.16
June	14.85	16.70	18.49	21.37	16.98	19.24	21.71	21.16	22.56	25.65	22.33	23.62	26.49	36.40	35.34	
July	14.73	16.55	18.54	21.18	17.61	19.78	21.30	20.69	22.95	24.75	23.08	24.09	27.61	34.85	33.59	
August	14.84	16.65	18.68	21.12	18.02	20.22	21.08	20.82	23.08	24.80	23.10	24.00	28.66	32.29	33.45	
September	15.33	17.08	18.56	20.49	18.37	20.63	21.18	21.22	22.90	24.18	23.22	24.84	28.64	30.22	34.12	
October	15.45	17.20	18.57	20.12	18.73	20.91	20.89	21.16	23.48	24.26	23.13	26.44	28.40	30.01	32.41	
November	15.46	17.48	18.84	19.87	18.61	21.18	20.81	21.12	24.89	24.65	22.14	28.33	29.73	31.13	31.29	
December	15.85	17.89	19.15	18.80	18.72	20.72	21.10	21.33	25.84	24.52	21.68	29.64	30.60	30.84	31.41	

	1919	1920	1921	1921	1922	1923	1924	1925	1926	1927	1928	1929	1930	1931	1932
January		35.0	29.8		23.74	34.02	30.61	33.12	33.65	34.80	32.32	35.26	32.90	27.29	20.40
February		33.0	24.9		25.45	29.46	32.13	30.56	31.88	33.42	32.14	34.67	31.16	24.55	19.52
March	28.8	37.9	26.8		29.47	35.30	32.97	31.91	35.35	37.62	35.43	36.04	31.65	27.13	21.19
April	28.6	28.6	25.6		22.29	34.79	29.09	30.35	32.93	33.49	32.15	34.92	31.46	25.96	19.06
May	32.3	37.9	28.2		25.06	35.99	30.52	33.16	35.70	36.17	35.62	37.80	32.99	26.90	17.88
June	31.9	38.2	28.1		26.48	34.23	28.76	32.78	35.72	34.83	33.80	36.67	31.16	25.75	16.81
July	34.9	40.4	28.4		24.69	34.52	29.92	34.47	37.93	34.43	35.39	38.10	32.38	27.64	17.10
August	36.4	42.7	30.4	27.53	27.88	36.20	32.63	37.67	39.74	38.16	38.57	41.05	34.04	26.90	18.09
September	38.7	41.0	30.9	27.85	31.67	35.44	35.45	37.99	40.66	39.01	39.63	40.42	33.61	25.72	20.83
October	40.4	42.6	36.7	32.62	36.01	38.28	39.27	40.37	43.93	41.58	44.93	44.03	36.23	27.62	24.15
November	32.5	37.3		26.85	34.72	34.69	34.76	37.24	40.36	34.28	38.59	35.38	29.62	23.00	19.90
December	33.4	34.7		23.26	32.81	30.59	33.05	34.91	36.65	31.37	34.66	32.87	26.65	20.66	19.22

	1933	1934	1935	1936	1937	1938	1939	1940	1941	1942	1943	1944	1945	1946	1947	1948
January	18.01	21.53	22.40	25.04	29.86	23.81	25.56	29.68	32.94	42.96	55.13	60.49	56.81	48.23	53.29	51.27
February	17.31	20.92	21.81	26.31	29.05	21.07	23.11	27.16	31.19	40.81	54.42	59.31	55.42	45.08	48.49	50.20
March	17.37	24.94	24.59	25.30	33.41	23.59	26.03	28.20	37.24	48.25	61.23	62.66	64.38	52.39	56.15	49.83
April	17.79	21.09	21.32	25.22	29.46	20.69	21.66	27.43	28.96	49.99	59.04	60.29	61.37	37.41	50.70	46.48
May	19.81	22.69	22.08	26.91	30.99	21.50	23.29	30.31	39.72	54.29	62.15	64.10	64.18	39.46	56.13	56.40
June	21.54	22.68	23.13	26.23	29.15	21.81	25.88	30.12	40.68	53.85	57.96	61.71	62.53	49.78	53.42	54.92
July	24.10	21.86	20.83	28.31	30.60	23.82	27.26	31.17	42.85	56.96	63.74	62.54	60.68	51.92	51.03	52.73
August	24.14	22.81	23.38	29.17	30.75	25.24	28.73	33.50	45.49	58.63	65.10	64.45	56.79	55.84	58.01	56.31
September	23.83	23.36	25.42	30.21	31.98	26.72	33.36	34.19	44.31	58.16	62.54	61.15	52.66	52.92	56.11	55.42
October	24.18	24.26	28.50	34.08	33.72	30.03	37.29	36.02	47.73	62.16	65.22	63.84	49.78	57.39	61.06	59.06
November	21.75	21.70	25.12	31.12	26.88	26.27	32.55	33.14	42.63	56.98	59.86	59.38	49.77	51.93	56.16	53.27
December	19.95	20.98	23.71	31.03	24.82	25.60	28.69	32.28	41.31	55.04	60.61	57.18	46.29	49.57	54.13	49.40

	1949	1950	1951	1952	1953	1954
January	45.90	39.24	53.85	52.23	48.97	43.75
February	42.51	34.28	45.91	51.46	45.60	41.34
March	44.10	47.88	55.93	53.20	50.77	44.72
April	46.96	46.72	53.97	49.76	50.30	43.52
May	48.01	48.35	56.12	51.72	53.43	46.90
June	45.01	48.98	53.75	52.69	52.69	46.20
July	41.83	49.04	50.57	42.34	51.31	45.06
August	45.33	56.51	57.26	54.14	54.64	
September	41.81	54.94	55.23	55.70	51.94	
October	38.24	58.92	59.44	55.79	54.69	
November	43.33	52.19	54.31	54.35	47.91	
December	42.85	51.46	50.20	49.13	43.54	

* I am indebted to the National Bureau of Economic Research for this compilation, and for the measurements based on it.

The original records used by the National Bureau come from four sources: the Babson Statistical Organization (1866–1922); the American Railway Association (1907–14); the Bureau of Railway Economics and the Interstate Commerce Commission, 1916–24; the Interstate Commerce Commission, 1920–54. Nonrevenue freight is included in the second and third segments, not in the others; this difference does not materially affect the comparability of the segments. The overlaps in Table 12–4 are included for convenience in splicing the separate segments.

TABLE 12–5

Seasonal Correction of Freight Ton-Miles for 1948

	Freight ton-miles actual	Seasonal index	Freight ton-miles seasonally corrected
	(billions)		(billions)
January	51.266	95	53.96
February	50.204	88	57.05
March	49.830	104	47.91
April	46.476	96	48.41
May	56.396	103	54.75
June	54.918	100	54.92
July	52.735	95	55.51
August	56.308	107	52.62
September	55.425	104	53.29
October	59.064	112	52.74
November	53.269	101	52.74
December	49.400	96	51.46

We must next study the behavior of the given series in the framework provided by the dates of troughs and peaks set forth in Table 12-3. It is desirable to do this first graphically, by plotting the seasonally adjusted data (or unadjusted data, if there is no evidence of a seasonal pattern) in this reference frame. Figure 12.3 shows the results of this plotting, for the period 1933-1954. (The graphic record is extended to 1954, although no final reference date beyond the trough at October 1949 had been set when this was written.) The dates of reference troughs and peaks are marked by vertical lines, with phases of general business expansion shown

FIG. 12.3. Railroad Freight Ton-Miles in the United States, 1933-1954, with Phases of Reference Contraction and Expansion.

by white areas, phases of business contraction by shaded areas. (The asterisks in Fig. 12.3 mark troughs and peaks in cycles specific to freight ton-miles. These are discussed below.) This graphic portrayal indicates a fairly high degree of conformity of freight ton-miles to cycles in general business. There is, of course, a clearly evident rising trend in the volume of freight carried; this advance has come in successive waves that seem to agree, in general, in the timing of their troughs and peaks with the turning points in business activity in the economy at large. But something more precise than these general impressions is needed if we are to have objective measurements of the behavior of freight ton-miles in this reference framework.

Reference cycle relatives and stage averages. The vertical lines marking successive troughs in general business cut the freight ton-miles series into a number of segments. Each of these segments is spoken of as a "reference cycle" in freight ton-miles—a shorthand expression for "the record of freight ton-miles during a reference cycle." Each segment is a unit of experience in the total behavior of this series over the period covered. These units are to be individually described, in a manner that will permit combination of measures for separate units and comparisons among units.

For the description of a given reference cycle in freight ton-miles —say the cycle that extends from a trough at October 1945 to the next trough at October 1949—the monthly entries for that cycle are first averaged, to obtain the "cycle base." (In this averaging process a weight of one half is given to the observations falling at the initial trough and to those falling at the terminal trough. This is to avoid giving undue weight to troughs, as compared with peaks.) Freight ton-miles for the cycle specified had an average monthly value of 50.52 billions. The separate monthly figures for that cycle are then expressed as relatives of the cycle base. These "reference-cycle relatives" give a complete picture of the pattern of behavior of freight ton-miles during the time segment marked out by the reference cycle troughs at October 1945, and at October 1949. Since their average is 100 they conform to the concept of a cycle as a unit of experience. Because they are in abstract terms they may be compared with similar measures for other cycles. However, the picture they give is too detailed, and comparison of measures for different cycles would be difficult because the number of measures (i.e., monthly relatives) will vary with the durations of reference cycles. For purposes of study it is desirable that each reference-cycle pattern in a given time series be defined by a small number of measures that will summarize its essential features.

This end is achieved by breaking each reference cycle, regardless of duration, into nine stages, for each of which a "stage average" is computed. Stage I marks the initial trough of a given reference cycle; the measure defining the standing of the series at stage I is obtained by averaging reference-cycle relatives for three months centered on the trough. (Thus the measure for stage I in freight ton-miles in the reference cycle that extends from October 1945 to October 1949 is the average of reference-cycle relatives for the three-month period September 1945–November 1945. One month is borrowed from the previous cycle in this averaging process.) Stage V marks the reference-cycle peak; the measure for stage V is the average of reference-cycle relatives for three months centered on the peak. Stage IX marks the terminal trough; the measure for stage IX is the average of reference-cycle relatives for three months centered on the terminal trough. These three stage averages define certain important aspects of a reference-cycle pattern, since they mark the standing of the given series at three important turning points in general business activity. But what happens in the given series in the phase of general business expansion between stages I and V? And what happens during the general contraction between stages V and IX? These may be long phases, covering 50 to 60 months or more, and the investigator needs more details than the three averages cited will provide. Here an arbitrary judgment must be made, as to how much detail is wanted. For its own purposes the National Bureau decided to break the phase of expansion into three equal (or nearly equal) parts, and the phase of contraction into three corresponding parts. For each of these a stage average is constructed. In the expansion phase these are designated stages II, III, and IV; in the contraction phase VI, VII, and VIII.

The expansion phase, which is divided into thirds in these operations, is taken to begin with the month after the trough and to end with the month before the peak. If this time interval is exactly divisible by three there will, of course, be the same number of months in the three stages. If the division gives a remainder of one, this is assigned to the middle stage (III); if a remainder of two, one extra month is assigned to the first third (stage II) and one to the last third (stage IV). For each of these stages the standing of a series in a given reference cycle is measured by the average of the monthly figures falling in that stage. The procedure followed in breaking the contraction phase into thirds and deriving stage averages parallels that described for the phase of expansion.

The use of the method just described, when it is applied to the data of freight ton-miles for a single reference cycle, is illustrated in Table 12-6. The figure 50.52, the monthly average for the full reference cycle, is, of course, the *cycle base* on which the reference-cycle relatives are computed. The stage averages shown in the last column define the behavior of freight ton-miles during the first postwar reference cycle. The pattern marked out by these averages shows a net rise during the phase of reference expansion (between stages I and V) and a net decline during the reference contraction (between stages V and IX). However, there are timing disparities. The initial trough in freight ton-miles came after the trough in general business (i.e., it fell in stage II rather than in stage I), and the peak in freight ton-miles preceded the peak in general business (it came in stage III rather than in stage V).

When operations similar to those exemplified in Table 12-6 are performed for the 10 reference cycles preceding the one just discussed we have, for each of 11 cycles, the stage averages given on lines 1 to 11 of Table 12-7. The separate reference cycle patterns thus defined are shown in Fig. 12.4. For purposes of comparison

TABLE 12–6

Illustrating the Computation of Stage Averages in a Reference Cycle
Freight Ton-Miles, October 1945-October 1949
(Average monthly freight ton-miles: 50.52 billions)

Stage	Period covered	Number of months	Average monthly standing in cycle relatives
I	Sept. 45 – Nov. 45	3	99.5
II	Nov. 45 – Oct. 46	12	96.8
III	Nov. 46 – Oct. 47	12	106.3
IV	Nov. 47 – Oct. 48	12	105.9
V	Oct. 48 – Dec. 48	3	104.3
VI	Dec. 48 – Feb. 49	3	96.4
VII	Mar. 49 – June 49	4	92.6
VIII	July 49 – Sept. 49	3	81.6
IX	Sept. 49 – Nov. 49	3	77.1

TABLE 12-7

Reference-Cycle Patterns: Railroad Freight Ton-Miles, 1904-1949*

Dates of reference cycles			Cycle base	Averages of reference-cycle relatives at nine stages of the cycles								
				I	II	III	IV	V	VI	VII	VIII	IX
			Billions of ton-miles	Three months centered on initial trough	First third	Middle third	Last third	Three months centered on peak	First third	Middle third	Last third	Three months centered on terminal trough
Trough	Peak	Trough				Expansion			Contraction			
(1)			(2)	(3)	(4)	(5)	(6)	(7)	(8)	(9)	(10)	(11)
1 Aug04	May07	Jun08	18.10	82.7	87.9	98.6	106.2	116.6	116.3	106.1	95.8	95.1
2 Jun08	Jan10	Jan12	20.32	84.7	90.3	93.2	101.2	102.7	106.1	102.6	103.7	106.9
3 Jan12	Jan13	Dec14	23.76	91.5	94.5	96.2	102.2	111.1	106.5	100.9	95.7	92.0
4 Dec14	Aug18	Apr19	29.51	74.1	85.5	101.0	111.5	114.3	112.7	105.8	93.7	95.6
5 Apr19	Jan20	Sep21	33.60	93.0	95.1	102.0	101.0	112.9	111.4	105.9	82.3	86.7
6 Sep21	May23	Jul24	31.06	84.5	86.9	87.2	112.4	120.0	111.2	105.8	102.5	98.3
7 Jul24	Oct26	Dec27	35.36	86.3	93.7	98.8	104.1	106.2	105.8	102.1	99.9	96.5
8 Dec27	Jun29	Mar33	29.72	114.8	118.2	124.1	126.2	127.5	116.0	90.5	66.2	62.5
9 Mar33	May37	May38	25.17	73.8	88.2	91.2	116.3	127.3	119.4	106.0	93.9	90.9
10 May38	Feb45	Oct45	45.33	50.5	61.3	96.1	134.4	135.2	137.3	133.4	116.0	110.9
11 Oct45	Nov48	Oct49	50.52	99.5	96.8	106.3	105.9	104.3	96.4	92.6	81.6	77.1
Average 11 cycles 1904-1949				85.0	90.8	99.5	111.0	116.2	112.6	104.7	93.8	92.0
Average deviation				10.9	8.1	6.4	8.3	8.3	7.0	6.3	9.3	9.3

* In the standard notation of the National Bureau this is Table B1.

they are there plotted on a common axis marking the position of the peak, or stage V, entries.

This chart provides an illuminating portrayal of the patterns of behavior of freight ton-miles in successive reference cycles. In general, freight traffic shows a close correspondence with the major cyclical swings of business at large. There is in all cases a rise in freight volume from stage I to stage V, and in all cases but one a decline in volume from stage V to stage IX. It is clear, however, that the behavior of freight ton-miles during reference cycles shows no absolutely constant pattern. Neither troughs nor peaks in freight volume coincide at all turns with changes in the tide of general business activity. This particular series shows general conformity to the cycles in business at large, but with manifest variations from cycle to cycle.

These variations from cycle to cycle are not without interest, but at this stage of the analysis our concern is with the average behavior of freight ton-miles during cycles in general business. The

FIG. 12.4.
Patterns of
Successive
Reference Cycles
and Their Average
Pattern, Railroad
Freight Ton-
Miles, 1904-1949.

stage averages for separate cycles in Table 12-7 may be readily combined, since all are in abstract terms. A simple addition of the 11 entries for stage I, and division by 11, gives us 85.0 as the average standing of freight ton-miles at the initial trough of reference cycles; the average for stage II is 90.8; for stage III 99.5, etc. These stage averages are given at the bottom of Table 12-7; they define the average reference cycle pattern for freight ton-miles that is shown graphically as the bottom chart in Fig. 12.4. This average pattern, which is a synthesis of the 11 patterns for individual cycles, is free of the striking irregularities that appear in some of the separate patterns. The movement from trough to peak is quite regular; so is the decline from peak to terminal trough, except for a retardation of the drop between stages VIII and IX. The average behavior of freight ton-miles shows high conformity to the waves of expansion and contraction in general business.

We have noted that the variations of behavior from cycle to cycle, which are concealed in the averages, are of interest to the investigator. A simple measure—the average deviation among the items entering into each stage average—provides a useful indicator of the degree of variation at each stage of the reference cycle. These average deviations are given in Table 12-7, just below the stage averages. We may note that variation from cycle to cycle is greatest at stage I, that it is less at reference cycle peaks than at troughs, and that it is least at stages III and VII. To the student of business cycles this is a highly significant fact, indicating that the tides of freight traffic are most uniform, when we compare cycle with cycle, at the middle stages of general business expansion and of general business contraction.

Interstage rates of change. The National Bureau makes use of a number of derived measures descriptive of the behavior of individual series in the reference-cycle framework.[12] Among the most useful of these are measures of interstage changes, expressed as average monthly rates, in reference-cycle relatives. In deriving each measure of interstage rate of change, the absolute difference between standings in successive stages (as given in Table 12-7) is divided by the number of months between the middle of the first

---

[12] The reader will find full explanations of these measures and many examples of substantive results in *Measuring Business Cycles* by Burns and Mitchell (Ref. 13) and in *What Happens during Business Cycles* by W. C. Mitchell (Ref. 107).

of the two stages and the middle of the second. These rates, for freight ton-miles, are given in Table 12-8.

As is to be expected, there is considerable variation among the rates cited for any given interstage period. Thus the changes between stages IV and V ranged from + 6.0 per month in the 1919-21 reference cycle to − 0.2 per month in the 1945-49 cycle. By averaging the rates for each interstage period we may, in part, eliminate random irregularities. Two sets of derived averages are given at the bottom of Table 12-8. In computing the averages in the first set (unweighted) each measure of interstage change is given the same weight as all others, regardless of whether the interstage interval lasted ten months or three months. In computing those in the second set, the rate for a given interstage interval in a given reference cycle is weighted by the number of months in that interval. (The average number of months in each interval is shown in the table.) Each unweighted measure is

TABLE 12–8

Average Rates of Change per Month from Stage to Stage of
Reference Cycles, Railroad Freight Ton-Miles, 1904-1949*

			Rate of change per month in reference-cycle relatives from stage to stage of the cycles							
			I–II	II–III	III–IV	IV–V	V–VI	VI–VII	VII–VIII	VIII–IX
Dates of reference cycles			Expansion				Contraction			
			Trough to first third	First to middle third	Middle to last third	Last third to peak	Peak to first third	First to middle third	Middle to last third	Last third to trough
Trough	Peak (1)	Trough	third (2)	third (3)	third (4)	peak (5)	third (6)	third (7)	third (8)	(9)
1 Aug04	May07	Jun08	+ 0.9	+ 1.0	+ 0.7	+ 1.7	− 0.1	− 2.6	− 2.6	− 0.3
2 Jun08	Jan10	Jan12	+ 1.6	+ 0.5	+ 1.3	+ 0.4	+ 0.8	− 0.5	+ 0.1	+ 0.7
3 Jan12	Jan13	Dec14	+ 1.2	+ 0.5	+ 1.7	+ 3.6	− 1.2	− 0.7	− 0.7	− 0.9
4 Dec14	Aug18	Apr19	+ 1.5	+ 1.1	+ 0.7	+ 0.4	− 1.1	− 2.8	− 4.8	+ 1.3
5 Apr19	Jan20	Sep21	+ 1.0	+ 2.8	− 0.4	+ 6.0	− 0.4	− 0.8	− 3.6	+ 1.3
6 Sep21	May23	Jul24	+ 0.7	0	+ 3.9	+ 2.2	− 3.5	− 1.2	− 0.7	− 1.7
7 Jul24	Oct26	Dec27	+ 1.5	+ 0.6	+ 0.6	+ 0.4	− 0.2	− 0.8	− 0.5	− 1.4
8 Dec27	Jun29	Mar33	+ 1.0	+ 1.1	+ 0.4	+ 0.4	− 1.4	− 1.8	− 1.7	− 0.5
9 Mar33	May37	May38	+ 1.7	+ 0.2	+ 1.5	+ 1.3	− 3.2	− 3.8	− 3.5	− 1.2
10 May38	Feb45	Oct45	+ 0.8	+ 1.3	+ 1.4	+ 0.1	+ 1.4	− 1.6	− 7.0	− 3.4
11 Oct45	Nov48	Oct49	− 0.4	+ 0.8	0	− 0.2	− 4.0	− 1.1	− 3.1	− 2.2
Average 11 cycles 1904-1949			+ 1.0	+ 0.9	+ 1.1	+ 1.5	− 1.2	− 1.6	− 2.6	− 0.8
Average deviation			0.4	0.5	0.8	1.4	1.4	0.8	1.7	1.1
Average int. in mo.			5.7	10.2	10.2	5.7	3.2	5.5	5.5	3.2
Weighted average			+ 1.0	+ 0.9	+ 1.1	+ 0.9	− 1.1	− 1.4	− 2.0	− 0.5

* In the National Bureau's notation, this is Table B2.

accompanied by an average deviation indicative of the degree of uniformity, from cycle to cycle, in the rate of interstage movement.

The weighted averages show relative constancy in the monthly rates of increase in freight ton-miles during the four intervals that make up the phase of expansion. The contraction pattern is less uniform. Recession starts with a drop at the rate of 1.1 percent a month, with acceleration to rates of 1.4 percent and 2.0 percent a month between stages VI and VII and VII and VIII, respectively. The terminal period of contraction in general business, between stages VIII and IX, brings a sharp check to the rate of decline in freight ton-miles, which falls to 0.5 percent a month. (It is convenient to speak of these interstage rates in percentage terms. However, the reader must remember that we are dealing with reference-cycle relatives; the base of each set of relatives is the "cycle base"—the average standing of freight ton-miles in a given reference cycle).

Indexes of conformity to business cycles. We have noted the apparent close conformity of the movements of freight ton-miles to phases of expansion and contraction in general business activity, but this judgment has been based on rather loose impressions given by examination of the tables and charts so far presented. More precise and objective measures of conformity are required. The National Bureau constructs three indexes of conformity for each series—indexes measuring degree of conformity to expansions in general business, to contractions in general business, and to full cycles in general business. We shall briefly indicate the nature of these measures, without discussion of the details of calculation.

The National Bureau considers that a given series, such as pig iron production, conforms to reference expansion (i.e., moves in conformity with general business during a phase of cyclical expansion) when the average change per month in that series is positive between stage I and stage V of a given reference cycle.[13] When the average change per month between reference cycle stages I and V is negative, the series does not conform positively. There will be such an entry, plus or minus, for every stage of ref-

---

[13] The index of conformity to reference expansions could, of course, be derived from the signs of the absolute differences between reference cycle averages for stages I and V. If a given series increases between stages I and V of a given reference cycle, conformity is positive; if the series decreases, conformity is negative. In systematic work on many series it is convenient, however, to use the sign of the average change per month, which enters into related calculations noted below.

erence expansion covered by the historical record for the series in question. A credit of $+100$ is given for every positive entry, a debit of -100 for every negative entry. The algebraic sum of these credits and debits, divided by the number of reference expansions covered by the record, is the desired index. Thus for freight ton-miles there was perfect conformity during each of 11 reference expansions represented in Table 12-7. The index of conformity is given by $+1100 \div 11$, or $+100$.

The procedure is similar for reference contractions. Here a negative change between stage V and stage IX of a given reference contraction represents positive conformity, and yields a credit of $+100$ for the given series; a positive change between the same stages for a given cycle yields a debit of -100. For freight ton-miles during the 11 contractions represented in Table 12-7 we have 10 instances of positive conformity to reference contractions, and one instance (the contraction from January 1910 to January 1912) of a rise during a reference contraction. The sum of the 10 credits and 1 debit thus obtained is $+900$. Dividing by 11 we have $+82$ as the index of conformity to reference contractions.

It is obvious that these indexes of conformity may range from $+100$ to -100. The first of these figures represents perfect positive conformity. The second, we should note, does not indicate nonconformity; it represents inverse or negative conformity to expansions, or contractions, in general business. Thus for a series such as business failures, which generally declines during periods of expanding business, we should expect a negative index, but this would not denote failure to conform to the movements of business at large. True nonconformity, which would lead to a random assortment of credits and debits of $+100$ and -100 for successive phases of expansion (or contraction), would be represented by a conformity index of zero, or one close to zero.

The conformity indexes for the separate phases of expansion and contraction relate to consistency in *direction* of change. A somewhat different concept of conformity is needed for a full-cycle index. Conformity to the full reference cycle would of course be shown by a rise in the phase of reference expansion followed by a fall during reference contraction. But conformity would also be indicated by a rise during the expansion phase of general business, followed by a rise at a lower rate during the phase of contraction. This is the characteristic cyclical behavior of a series marked by a strong and persistent secular rise. Similarly, there would be full-cycle conformity in behavior marked by a decline in periods of expansion in general business, and by decline at an accelerated rate during contractions in general business. In each of these two cases the individual series shows a clear response to the cyclical movements of business at large, although the response takes the form of a *change in the rate* of advance or decline, rather than a change of direction.

The computation of an index of full-cycle conformity thus calls for the comparison of rates of change in two adjoining phases of expansion and contraction. If these rates define successive movements that accord with the shift from expansion to contraction in general business, there is positive full-cycle conformity; alternatively, if the successive movements of the individual series reverse the shifts through which general business is passing (as when a given series declines during a period of general expansion and then advances during the ensuing period of general contraction) there is negative conformity. Giving a series a credit of $+100$ for every instance of conformity, a debit of -100 for every instance of negative conformity, adding the debits and credits and dividing the algebraic sum by the number of entries, we have the desired index of full-cycle conformity. For freight ton-miles, as shown in Table 12-7, this index has a value of $+100$. Full-cycle conformity is positive and perfect.[14]

An indication of a few of the results obtained by the National Bureau in its use of conformity indexes will make clearer the

[14] In the actual calculation of the full-cycle index, use would be made of measurements of average change per month during reference expansion and reference contraction. Such measures of monthly change are not given in Table 12-7, but may be readily derived from the stage averages there recorded.

The reader will note that two indexes of full-cycle conformity may be constructed. One could be based on the conformity of a given series to the shift from expansion to contraction in general business. Here the cycle is thought of as running from trough to trough. This is the index explained in the text. Or we could base such a full-cycle index on the conformity of a given series to the shift from contraction to expansion. Here we regard the cycle as running from peak to peak. For freight ton-miles from 1904 to 1949 both full-cycle indexes are equal to $+100$, but this equality is not a necessary one. When the indexes differ they may be averaged to obtain a single full-cycle index.

I have here dealt with conformity within the rigid reference framework given by reference cycle stages I, V, and IX. For a limited number of series that show clear and persistent leads or lags in their relation to reference cycle turns, the National Bureau constructs additional sets of conformity indexes.

Indexes of conformity are explained in Mitchell (Ref. 107), Burns and Mitchell (Ref. 13) and in Mills, *Statistical Methods*, Third Edition, pp. 404-9.

usefulness of these measures. In Mitchell's final study, *What Happens during Business Cycles*, he summarizes conformity measures for the 794 monthly and quarterly series analyzed in the study of cyclical movements in the United States. This is not meant to be a sample completely representative of economic processes; there is unavoidable unevenness of coverage. However, the sample includes series representative of all major sectors of the economy and all phases of economic activity. When conformity indexes for these 794 series are arrayed in order of absolute magnitude (that is, without regard to sign), the following median values are obtained.

	Median
Indexes of conformity to reference expansion	67
" " " " reference contraction	60
" " " " full cycles	78

These indicate a high and significant degree of conformity of economic series to the cyclical fluctuations of business at large. The relative values of the median measures for expansion and contraction phases reflect the generally rising trend characteristic of the American economy over periods covered by these records.

Conformity varies, of course, from sector to sector of the economy. The measures in Table 12-9 reveal significant differences. Several economically important conclusions are suggested by this table. Production in agriculture shows the lowest degree of conformity; weather, rather than the state of business, determines output in many agricultural activities. Production in nonagricultural industries shows the highest conformity. Output is controllable at short notice in most of the activities falling in this class;

TABLE 12–9

Mean Conformity to Business Cycles
Prices and Production in Agricultural and Nonagricultural Industries*

	Prices		Production	
	No. of series	Average Numerical Value of Indexes of Conformity	No. of series	Average Numerical Value of Indexes of Conformity
Agricultural	51	51.6	47	41.8
Nonagricultural industries	96	64.2	141	84.2

* Adapted from *Measuring Business Cycles*, Ref. 13, p. 88, note.

production control is the preferred means of adaptation to changes in market conditions. The prices of nonagricultural products conform less closely to business cycles than does production. Typically, they are more resistant to declines, during business contractions, and are less responsive to the upward push of general expansion. This, of course, is familiar behavior in industries in which "administered prices" are the rule. Finally, we note that the prices of agricultural products are more responsive to cycles in general business activity than is agricultural production. Given a relatively nonconforming output, it is natural that prices should feel the impact of changes in demand.

Other measures given by Mitchell show a wide range of conformity among economic activities. Public construction contracts have an average full-cycle conformity of 32 (computed without regard to sign). For bond yields and other long-term interest rates the average is 66; for bank clearings 83; for private construction contracts 87; for payrolls in durable goods industries 100; and for hours of work per week 100. As presented in their full variety by Mitchell these indexes give a revealing picture of cycles in business, a picture marked by variation in the degree to which individual series participate in these general "cycles" and by diversity in the timing of their individual movements, but a picture, nevertheless, that discloses consistency of pattern and a significant degree of uniformity of movement.

The Description of Specific Cycles. In introducing the methods of the National Bureau we referred to two aspects of its work on cycles. We have studied the first of these—the analysis of the behavior of individual series in a framework set by cyclical turning points in business at large—and now turn to the second. Here we look for evidence of cyclical movements in individual series, and seek to define such movements in a given series, if they are present, in a framework set by the dates of troughs and peaks in that specific series. In place of a single, general framework, which the hypothesis of reference turning points involves, we shall have many frameworks, each defining turning points in cycles specific to a given time series. However, the study of these "specific cycles," as they are termed, is not completely divorced from the assumption that there is something like a common wave movement in general business activity. In searching for specific cycles in individual series the investigator looks for wave movements lasting from over one year to ten or twelve years—movements that correspond, in duration, to the National Bureau's working concept of business cycles. But apart from this general guidance in the selection of appropriate fluctuations the concept of general business cycles does not shape the analysis of specific cycles.

Basically, the method used in defining the characteristics of specific cycles parallels the method outlined for dealing with reference cycles. Monthly data, such as those for freight ton-miles (Table 12-4), are corrected for seasonal variation. The investigator then seeks to define the dates of cyclical troughs and peaks in the corrected series, seeking turning points that mark off cycles lasting more than one year but not more than ten or twelve years. Some subjective judgments must be made here, of course, although specific cyclical movements are clearly defined for many series. There are some series, of course, in which no evidence of cycles can be found. The prices of steel rails, for example, were constant and unchanging over many years in the early parts of this century. But in the Bureau's study of some 830 monthly and quarterly series there were only about 5 percent in which no specific cycles were discernible. Having identified successive troughs and peaks (these are marked by asterisks in Fig. 12.3), the investigator breaks the series into segments marked off by successive troughs. (For series such as bankruptcies, that move inversely to cyclical tides, specific cycle segments are taken from peak to peak.) The monthly observations within each of these segments are then averaged, and the monthly figures are expressed as relatives of the cycle average thus obtained. A nine-stage pattern, corresponding exactly to the nine-stage reference-cycle pattern, is then set up, and stage averages computed from the reference-cycle relatives. These stage averages define a "specific cycle pattern"—that is, the pattern of behavior of the given series within each of the specific cycle segments.

The results of this operation, as applied to monthly data for freight ton-miles between 1904 and 1949, are given in Table 12-10. The first specific cycle recorded for this series extended from a trough in January 1904, through a peak in June 1907, to a trough in June 1908. (The reader will note—see Table 12-7—that the last of these dates happens to coincide with the date of a reference cycle trough, but the other two dates do not coincide with the reference cycle turning points.) In this first specific cycle freight ton-miles rise from a stage I standing of 82.9 (in specific-cycle relatives) to a stage V peak of 120.6, and then fall to a stage IX trough of 97.4. In all, eleven specific cycles in freight ton-miles were identified in the 46 years here covered. Their patterns, as defined by the nine-stage averages, vary of course. To get away from these diversities we may average the measures for each stage, as we did for reference cycles, and thus get measures of the average behavior of the series in question during all the specific cycles observed. This average specific-cycle pattern is defined by the entries in the next to the last line of Table 12-10. It is shown graphically by the broken line plotted in Fig. 12.5. The vertical scale relating to this broken line is in specific cycle relatives, the horizontal scale in months. (The full horizontal distance from T to T—trough to trough—at the top of the diagram is proportionate to the average duration of specific cycles in freight ton-miles.) The average specific cycle pattern shows a fairly regular rise from initial trough to peak, a regular but smaller decline from peak to trough. (The difference between degrees of rise and fall reflects, of course, a secular growth in freight ton-miles over the period covered.) The graph indicates also that the phase of specific-cycle expansion (from T to P on the duration scale) was longer on the average than the phase of contraction. We shall refer to this point again.

The specific-cycle pattern for freight ton-miles, as plotted in Fig. 12.5, is an average of somewhat diverse movements. How much variation was there, from cycle to cycle, in the behavior of this series? This question is answered by the measures of average deviation given in the last line of Table 12-10. Each stage average, it will be seen, is accompanied by such a measure. There was greatest variation at the trough, when the ebb ceased and the flow began, least variation in the full flood of expansion (stages III and IV) and in midcontraction (stage VII). There was less variation at the peak than at the trough. These are significant facts to the student of cyclical movements.

The solid line in Fig. 12.5 traces the average reference cycle pattern in freight ton-miles, which was discussed in the preceding section. The relation between specific and reference cycles in the present instance is obviously close.

TABLE 12–10

Specific-Cycle Patterns: Railroad Freight Ton-Miles, 1904-1949*

Dates of specific cycles			Averages of specific-cycle relatives at nine stages of the cycles								
			I	II	III	IV	V	VI	VII	VIII	IX
			Three months centered on initial trough	Expansion First third	Middle third	Last third	Three months centered on peak	Contraction First third	Middle third	Last third	Three months centered terminal trough
Trough	Peak	Trough									
	(1)		(2)	(3)	(4)	(5)	(6)	(7)	(8)	(9)	(10)
1 Jan04	Jun07	Jun08	82.9	85.8	98.0	109.2	120.6	117.4	107.0	98.1	97.4
2 Jun08	Apr10	Mar11	85.5	91.5	95.8	104.6	109.1	107.4	104.4	104.6	102.7
3 Mar11	Feb13	Dec14	89.2	90.6	95.1	104.6	113.5	107.6	103.4	98.2	94.4
4 Dec14	Apr18	Mar19	74.0	84.1	99.1	107.9	121.0	118.8	111.0	102.8	93.8
5 Mar19	Feb20	Jul21	91.7	93.0	100.3	103.6	116.4	108.6	107.4	83.7	80.4
6 Jul21	Apr23	Jun24	80.2	85.0	86.6	107.1	120.9	116.0	105.1	108.0	100.1
7 Jun24	Jul26	Dec27	87.3	93.2	97.3	102.4	107.6	106.6	104.1	99.5	96.8
8 Dec27	Aug29	Jul32	109.1	112.4	118.4	120.3	121.0	109.8	91.8	69.2	54.7
9 Jul32	Apr37	May38	69.9	84.4	93.0	114.2	135.1	125.8	111.7	96.6	93.5
10 May38	Feb44	May46	50.3	59.6	82.9	127.9	139.4	133.6	134.2	108.5	95.2
11 May46	Dec47	Oct49	85.1	100.7	106.4	105.7	108.9	103.8	100.3	87.1	76.5
Average 11 cycles 1904–1949			82.3	89.1	97.5	109.8	119.4	114.1	107.3	96.0	89.6
Average deviation			10.0	8.5	6.3	6.0	7.6	7.4	6.4	8.8	10.4

* This is Table A4 in the notation of the National Bureau.

The attention of the reader is called to the diversity of information given in graphic form in this figure. We have noted the duration scale for specific cycles, from trough to trough, that is given at the top of the diagram. A parallel scale for reference cycles is at the bottom of the chart. The latter is proportionate in length, to the average duration of reference cycles. The shorter horizontal dotted line at the top, to the left, defines the average deviation of the duration measures for specific cycles, on the duration scale; the corresponding solid line at the bottom of the chart gives the same information for reference cycles in freight ton-miles. The perpendicular broken lines descending from the specific cycle duration scale at the top of Fig. 12.5 are proportionate in length to the average deviations of the measures defining the standings of freight ton-miles at stages I to IX of specific cycles; corresponding perpendicular solid lines at the bottom of the diagram measure the average deviations of freight ton-miles at successive stages of reference cycles. For specific cycles, the measures of average

FIG. 12.5. Patterns of Reference and Specific Cycles in Railroad Freight Ton-Miles in the United States, 1904-1949.

The nine black dots connected by lines of dashes in the specific cycle pattern and by solid lines in the reference cycle pattern mark the average standings of freight ton-miles in cycle relatives at the nine stages into which specific and reference cycles are divided.

Source: National Bureau of Economic Research.

deviations, like those for stage averages, are in specific-cycle relatives; for reference cycles they are in reference-cycle relatives. The arrows in the diagram mark time relations between specific-cycle and reference-cycle turning points. We comment on these below. The use of this standard form of graphic presentation, with a uniform set of scales, enables the user of these charts to grasp quickly the essential features of the cyclical behavior of any given series, and facilitates comparison of measures for different series.

In discussing reference-cycle patterns we have noted the utility of measures of rates of change between cycle stages. Similar rates may be computed for specific cycles. Averages of such rates are given in Table 12-11. Here as in the corresponding table for reference cycles (Table 12-8) we have rates of interstage change, per month, both weighted and unweighted. Each unweighted rate

TABLE 12-11

Average Rates of Change per Month from Stage to Stage of Specific Cycles, Railroad Freight Ton-Miles, 1904-1949*

	Rate of change per month in specific-cycle relatives from stage to stage of the cycles							
	I–II	II–III	III–IV	IV–V	V–VI	VI–VII	VII–VIII	VIII–IX
		Expansion					Contraction	
	Trough to first third	First to middle third	Middle to last third	Last third to peak	Peak to first third	First to middle third	Middle to last third	Last third to trough
(1)	(2)	(3)	(4)	(5)	(6)	(7)	(8)	(9)
Average 11 cycles 1904–1949	+ 1.3	+ 0.9	+ 1.1	+ 2.0	− 1.6	− 1.4	− 1.9	− 1.9
Average deviation	0.6	0.3	0.6	1.1	0.7	1.0	1.2	1.1
Average int. in mo.	5.6	10.2	10.2	5.6	3.3	5.8	5.8	3.3
Weighted average	+ 1.2	+ 0.8	+ 1.2	+ 1.7	− 1.6	− 1.2	− 1.9	− 1.9

* These are summary measures from Table A5, in the National Bureau's notation.

is the simple average of measures of monthly rates of change for a given interstage period during the 11 specific cycles covered by the present record. In getting the weighted average, each constituent measure is weighted by the number of months in the interstage interval to which it relates. Both weighted and unweighted rates indicate a rate of expansion in freight ton-miles that declines after stage II and accelerates thereafter; contraction is retarded slightly after stage VI, but reaches and maintains a high tempo between stages VII and IX.

Timing and duration of specific cycles. To the student of cyclical processes great interest attaches to *sequences of change* at the troughs and peaks of business cycles. Characteristically, business cycles are marked by a series of related movements in employment, production, wholesale and retail sales, inventories, prices, interest rates, and other series dealing with aspects of economic activity. The investigator seeks to define these sequences, and to discover regularities in them.

The National Bureau derives timing measures for individual series by comparing the dates of troughs and peaks of specific cycles with corresponding dates given by the reference-cycle framework. The method is illustrated by the entries in the first five columns of Table 12-12, relating to freight ton-miles. Columns (3) and (5) repeat the reference dates given in Table 12-7. In column (1) are the dates of troughs and peaks in the specific cycles marked out for this series. When the date of a turn in the specific cycle of a series precedes the corresponding reference date, the difference in months is termed a "lead," and is given a minus sign. When the specific-cycle turn follows the corresponding reference date, the difference in months is called a "lag," and is marked by a plus sign. Thus the first entry in column (2) of Table 12-12 is $+ 1$. This refers to the peak in freight ton-miles which came in June 1907, one month after the reference peak of May 1907. The zero entry in column (4) of the same line refers to the June 1908 trough in freight ton-miles, which coincided with the reference trough. The next trough in freight ton-miles came in March 1911, 10 months before the reference trough of January 1912; the entry in column (4) is $- 10$.

This brief statement describes the procedure appropriate to cases in which specific-cycle turns are clearly related to corresponding reference dates, with no complications arising from inverted patterns (characteristic of series that decline when general business is expanding, and vice versa), from the interjection of extra specific cycles, from "skipped" cycles (as when a stated series fails to reflect a given reference cycle), or from leads or lags long enough to raise doubts about the timing comparisons that should be made (e.g., is a specific-cycle peak that precedes a given reference peak by 12 months and lags 10 months behind the earlier reference peak to be identified with the earlier or later reference turn?). For the detailed application of the procedures the National Bureau employs in studying timing relations the student should consult the descriptions given in the Burns-Mitchell monograph.[15]

The averages and average deviations given in the last two lines of Table 12-12 are summary measures that define characteristic sequences. In deriving such averages the Bureau omits timing measures relating to ambiguous and nonconforming movements of individual series. Only timing measures that may be assumed to

[15] Ref. 13, pp. 116-23.

TABLE 12-12

Timing and Duration of Specific Cycles
Railroad Freight Ton-Miles, 1904-1949*

							Duration of cyclical movements				
	Dates of specific cycles		Lead (−) or lag (+) at				Specific cycles			Percent of duration of specific cycles	
			Reference peak		Reference trough						
Trough	Peak	Trough	No. of months	Reference date	No. of months	Reference date	Expansion mos.	Contraction mos.	Full cycle mos.	Expansion	Contraction
	(1)		(2)	(3)	(4)	(5)	(6)	(7)	(8)	(9)	(10)
1 Jan04	Jun07	Jun08	+ 1	5/07	0	6/08	41	12	53	77	23
2 Jun08	Apr10	Mar11	+ 3	1/10	−10	1/12	22	11	33	67	33
3 Mar11	Feb13	Dec14	+ 1	1/13	0	12/14	23	22	45	51	49
4 Dec14	Apr18	Mar19	− 4ª	8/18	− 1ª	4/19	40	11	51	78	22
5 Mar19	Aug20	Jan22	+ 7ª	1/20	+ 4ª	9/21	17ª	17ª	34ª	50ª	50ª
	Apr18	Mar19	− 4	8/18	− 1	4/19		11ª			
6 Mar19	Feb20	Jul21	+ 1	1/20	− 2ª	9/21	11	17	28	39	61
7 Jul21	Apr23	Jun24	− 1ª	5/23	− 1ª	7/24	21ª	14ª	35ª	60ª	40ª
		Jul21			− 2	9/21					
8 Jul21	Apr23	Jun24	− 1	5/23	− 1	7/24	21	14	35	60	40
9 Jun24	Jul26	Dec27	− 3	10/26	0	12/27	25	17	42	60	40
10 Dec27	Aug29	Jul32	+ 2	6/29	− 8	3/33	20	35	55	36	64
11 Jul32	Apr37	May38	− 1	5/37	0	5/38	57	13	70	81	19
12 May38	Feb44	May46	−12	2/45	+ 7	10/45	69	27	96	72	28
13 May46	Dec47	Oct49	−11	11/48	0	10/49	19	22	41	46	54
Average 11 cycles 1904-1949			− 2.2		− 1.4		31.6	18.3	49.9	61	39
Average deviation			3.9		2.9		14.6	6.0	13.7	13	13

ª Excluded from the averages.
* This is an extract from Table A1, in the notation of the National Bureau.

be connected with the revivals and recessions of general business are included. The timing averages for freight ton-miles indicate an average lead of 2.2 months in this series at reference peaks, an average lead of 1.4 months at troughs in general business.[16] In view of the size of the average deviations, these measures do not indicate significant departures, in time, from the turns in business activity at large. Although the sequences of change are clouded in

---

[16] The arrows in Fig. 12.5 indicate these average time sequences, when they appear to be regular. For freight ton-miles the arrow drawn from the trough of the average specific-cycle pattern to the trough of the average reference-cycle pattern points from left to right, indicating that in this series revival precedes the trough in general business by more than one month. The arrow from specific-cycle peak to reference-cycle peak points in the same direction, indicating a similar lead at the upper turning point of general business. (When a given series *lags* more than one month behind general business at trough or peak the arrow points to the left. When the average lead or lag is one month or less a vertical arrow is drawn to indicate rough coincidence of average turns.)

many cases, the Bureau's technique has enabled it to define major timing relations of clear economic significance. Thus Mitchell (Ref. 107, pp. 68-75) notes clear leads at reference troughs in new orders for durable goods, construction contracts, security issues, liabilities of commercial failures (an inverted series), stock market transactions and prices of securities, and other series. Many of the same series lead at reference peaks, with new orders for durable goods, construction contracts, series on bank investments and deposits, and stock exchange transactions and prices preceding the down turn in general business by one or two cyclical stages. But, of course, sequences at peaks by no means repeat the patterns of change at troughs.[17]

The specific cycles in any economic series vary in duration, and vary in the relative durations of the phases of expansion and contraction. These aspects of cyclical behavior, which are of obvious interest to the investigator, are defined in columns (6) to (10) of Table 12-12. The specific cycles in freight ton-miles ranged from 28 to 96 months in duration. The average duration was 49.9 months. Typically, the period of expansion constituted 61 percent of the duration of specific cycles in this series, while contraction made up 39 percent of the full-cycle duration. The measures of average deviation indicate the degree of consistency in these movements, from cycle to cycle.

Amplitudes of specific cycles. Are the cyclical fluctuations found in individual series wide or narrow? To answer this question the National Bureau constructs simple measures of amplitude. These are exemplified in Table 12-13. In the first specific cycle shown for freight ton-miles in this table, the expansion carried the series from a level of 82.9 at the trough centered at January 1904 to 120.6 at the peak centered at June 1907. These standings are given in specific-cycle relatives. The total rise of 37.7 points, given in column (5), is an index of the amplitude of cyclical expansion. From the June 1907 peak freight ton-miles fell to a low of 97.4 at the trough centered at June 1908. The decline of 23.2 points (see column (6)) is an index of the amplitude of cyclical fall. Each of these measures may be read as a percentage, the base of the percentages being the average monthly value of freight ton-miles

---

[17] G. H. Moore of the National Bureau staff has identified a number of sequences that he believes to be regular enough to warrant their use as indexes of turns in the state of general business. See *Statistical Indicators of Cyclical Revivals and Recessions* (Ref. 110).

TABLE 12-13

Amplitude of Specific Cycles, Railroad Freight Ton-Miles, 1904-1949*

						Amplitude of cyclical movements shown by specific-cycle relatives					
Dates of specific cycles			Standing			Total movement			Movement per month		
			At initial trough	At peak	At terminal trough	Rise	Fall	Rise and fall	Rise	Fall	Rise and fall
Trough	Peak	Trough									
	(1)		(2)	(3)	(4)	(5)	(6)	(7)	(8)	(9)	(10)
1 Jan04	Jun07	Jun08	82.9	120.6	97.4	+37.7	−23.2	60.9	+0.9	−1.9	1.1
2 Jun08	Apr10	Mar11	85.5	109.1	102.7	+23.6	− 6.4	30.0	+1.1	−0.6	0.9
3 Mar11	Feb13	Dec14	89.2	113.5	94.4	+24.3	−19.1	43.4	+1.1	−0.9	1.0
4 Dec14	Apr18	Mar19	74.0	121.0	93.8	+47.0	−27.2	74.2	+1.2	−2.5	1.5
5 Mar19	Feb20	Jul21	91.7	116.4	80.4	+24.7	−36.0	60.7	+2.2	−2.1	2.2
6 Jul21	Apr23	Jun24	80.2	120.9	100.1	+40.7	−20.8	61.5	+1.9	−1.5	1.8
7 Jun24	Jul26	Dec27	87.3	107.6	96.8	+20.3	−10.8	31.1	+0.8	−0.6	0.7
8 Dec27	Aug29	Jul32	109.1	121.0	54.7	+11.9	−66.3	78.2	+0.6	−1.9	1.4
9 Jul32	Apr37	May38	69.9	135.1	93.5	+65.2	−41.6	106.8	+1.1	−3.2	1.5
10 May38	Feb44	May46	50.3	139.4	95.2	+89.1	−44.2	133.3	+1.3	−1.6	1.4
11 May46	Dec47	Oct49	85.1	108.9	76.5	+23.8	−32.4	56.2	+1.3	−1.5	1.4
Average 11 cycles 1904–1949			82.3	119.4	89.6	+37.1	−29.8	66.9	+1.2	−1.7	1.4
Average deviation			10.0	7.6	10.4	17.1	13.0	22.7	0.3	0.6	0.3
Weighted average									+1.2	−1.6	1.3

* This is Table A2 in the notation of the National Bureau.

during the specific cycle that ran from January 1904 to June 1908. The entry in column (7), measuring full-cycle amplitude, is derived from the entries in columns (5) and (6). In general terms, the index of full-cycle amplitude is the change between stages I and V minus the change between stages V and IX, both changes being given appropriate signs. Thus for the first specific cycle shown in Table 12-13, we have

$$\text{Full-cycle amplitude} = + 37.7 - (- 23.2)$$
$$= 60.9$$

The averages at the foot of Table 12-13 indicate that freight ton-miles rise, on the average, 37.1 points during specific cycle expansions, decline 29.8 points, and have a full-cycle index of amplitude of 66.9. These are abstract measures which may be compared with similar measures for other series, and combined with them.

This same method may be employed in measuring the amplitudes of reference cycles in individual series. Averages measuring swings within the reference-cycle framework will be damped, of course, unless the timing of specific-cycle turns coincides throughout with the turns in general business. For this reason the ratio of the reference-cycle amplitude, for a given series, to its specific-cycle amplitude provides a rough but useful indication of the relation in time between specific cycles and cycles in general business. For freight ton-miles, as we have seen, the full-cycle amplitude of specific cycles is measured by an index of 66.9. The corresponding index for reference cycles is 55.3. (each of these measures is based upon records covering 11 cycles.) The ratio 55.3/66.9, or .83 is relatively high, since specific-cycle turns in freight ton-miles are related fairly closely to the troughs and peaks of the reference chronology.

Because phases of expansion and contraction, and full cycles, vary in duration, it is desirable to reduce the indexes of rise and fall, and of full-cycle amplitude, to monthly rates. These are given in columns (8) to (10) of Table 12-13. Here are measures of the rapidity of rise and of fall, and of full-cycle change, that are for many purposes more revealing than are the indexes of amplitude. It is interesting to note that the most rapid advance in freight ton-miles came in the period from March 1919 to February 1920, and that the most rapid decline came in the contraction between April 1937, and May 1938. The intensity of these movements would be lost sight of if one studied only the amplitude measures in columns (5) and (6). Weighted averages of the monthly rates (the weights being the number of months to which each of the individual entries relates) supplement the unweighted averages for the entries in columns (8) to (10).

Comment on the Method of the National Bureau. "When you cannot measure what you are speaking about, when you cannot express it in numbers," said Lord Kelvin, "your knowledge is of a meager and unsatisfactory kind." It is a great virtue of the National Bureau procedure that it has brought systematic and comprehensive measurement to the study of business cycles. The battery of measures we have discussed in the preceding pages gives our knowledge of the phenomena of business cycles new precision. Varied aspects of the cyclical behavior of individual economic series—duration, amplitude, timing, conformity to the cyclical swings of general business, and details of characteristic patterns of fluctuation—are defined by this technique. Most of the measures used are abstract numbers that may be compared with similar measures for other series and combined with such measures to permit study of average and aggregative cyclical behavior. These methods constitute a powerful, flexible tool, adapted to the systematic analysis of the complex combinations of regularities and variations that characterize business cycles.

Differences from the traditional approach to the study of cycles that was outlined in the early pages of this chapter are, of course, many. One point of resemblance is that in both methods an attempt is made to remove seasonal fluctuations. Both suffer from the difficulties faced in handling this slippery problem. But in the treatment of secular trends the two procedures are far apart. These are measured and "eliminated," in applying the older method. The National Bureau procedure serves, in effect, to remove intercycle trends, since both reference-cycle and specific-cycle characteristics are defined by relatives for which the mean value of the observations in each cycle is the base. However, the effects of intracycle trends are not removed. If a series is growing this will be manifest by an upward tilt in the average specific-cycle and reference-cycle patterns. The average standing at stage IX will exceed the average standing at stage I. (Differences between averages for other stages will, of course, be correspondingly affected by the secular lift.) The reverse will be true for a series marked by a secular decline. In thus retaining the secular changes that occur within the limits of each cycle the National Bureau staff believe that they are keeping closer to the reality of cycles than they would if intracycle trends should be removed. The business man making decisions about production and employment sees expansions followed by contractions. In appraising these he makes no sophisticated corrections for trend. A rapidly growing industry provides a stimulus to expansion that a declining industry does not; the secular lift that is the basis for this stimulus should not, in the judgment of the Bureau investigators, be eliminated from the cycle pattern. It is proper to add that the basic tables constructed by the National Bureau include one (not given here) containing detailed measures of secular changes between specific cycles. Thus, although no mathematical trend functions are fitted, secular movements are defined and relevant measures made available for study.

In using the method of the National Bureau the possibility of changes over time in the characteristics of reference and specific cycles must be recognized. An average pattern of cyclical fluctuations in pig iron production, based on data for 18 cycles occurring between 1879 and 1949, would have limited value as a piece of scientific evidence if the cyclical behavior of pig iron production had been significantly modified during this period. More generally, if the characteristics of business cycles at large had been substantially changed—in average duration, in the interrelated patterns of change that make up the broad swings of business activity, in causal relations among constituent elements—over the period covered by available business records, averages for the whole period and conclusions based on such averages would be suspect. If there are significant changes in cyclical patterns when a nation passes from peace to war or from war to peace similar reservations would be called for. The National Bureau has made various probability tests to determine whether such secular or structual changes as have occurred in the character of business cycles have been great enough to discredit the use of averages. The conclusion reached by Burns and Mitchell[18] is that such changes have not invalidated the measures of average behavior they have constructed. However, if there is reason to believe that measures for a single economic series, or for groups of such series, have been subject to secular or other changes, the averaging process may be adapted to this fact. War cycles may be omitted, if they are believed to be influenced by special forces. The record for a single series may be broken at a date believed to mark a structural change affecting cyclical behavior, and two sets of averages constructed; the hypothesis that there has been a significant change may then be tested. If such precautions are observed, the danger of combining heterogeneous materials in averages or aggregates may be avoided.

The use of a single cycle (reference or specific) as a unit of observation conforms to the view that the cycle is the unit of experience. This practice, which yields a diversity of measures of cyclical behavior, is a distinctive feature of the National Bureau procedure. It permits a variety of groupings and approaches adapted to the purposes of different investigators. Measures of many economic processes during a given reference cycle may be assembled for comparison and combination; measures descriptive of particular processes (e.g., production) in many reference cycles may be combined. In careless hands, however, a method that takes

[18] Ref. 13, pp. 412-13.

a single cycle as the unit of experience and observation could lead to faulty conclusions. It would be easy, and quite invalid, to assume that the events occurring between stages V and IX of each reference cycle could be completely explained by the events that took place between stages I and V. The economic process is a continuous one. Each cycle and each phase of each cycle is tied to earlier and later events. If we are seeking an explanation of what happened to the economy of the United States between the reference peak at June 1929 and the reference trough at March 1933 we should have to go much farther back in time than to the reference trough at December 1927. The experience we should have to include, if we were tracing the cumulation of events and stresses that led to the contraction of 1929-33, would cover a long stretch of time indeed. To include even the immediately pertinent events in this cumulative process we should have to go back to 1921 or to 1914. Chopping what is essentially a continuous process into segments, as is done in the National Bureau procedure, is a justifiable analytical device, but in the appraisal of evidence and the final formulation of conclusions these isolated portions must be seen as parts of an unbroken chain.

The National Bureau techniques constitute a flexible device for the organization and analysis of measures descriptive of cyclical behavior. The methods have been criticized as having no theoretical underpinning. They are not derived from a definite theoretical construct. This is true, although the methods do rest on certain broad conceptions of the nature of cyclical processes in a modern economy. This separation of techniques from a particular theory is, of course, deliberate. It reflects the view that in scientific research a theoretical construct should not dominate the data. It goes without saying that a research procedure should be adapted to the testing of hypotheses, for without such tests the cumulation of knowledge is impossible. The National Bureau procedure may be used in testing business cycle theories, although the difficulties in the way of conclusive tests are many, in a field in which numerous variables interact in changing combinations. The technique has a final advantage in the diversity of views it affords of cyclical processes, in both microscopic and macroscopic aspects. In revealing both diversity and elements of regularity in cyclical patterns the technique can be germinal of ideas, when used by an alert investigator—a point of merit in any research technique.

REFERENCES

Burns, A. F., "Frickey on the Decomposition of Time Series," *Review of Economic Statistics*, August 1944.

Burns, A. F. and Mitchell, W. C., *Measuring Business Cycles*, Chaps. 2-8.

Croxton, F. E. and Cowden, D. J., *Applied General Statistics*, Chap. 19.

Frickey, E., *Economic Fluctuations in the United States*.

Hald, A., *The Decomposition of a Series of Observations Composed of a Trend, a Periodic Movement, and a Stochastic Variable*.

Kendall, M. G., *The Advanced Theory of Statistics*, 3rd ed., Vol. II, Chap. 30.

Koopmans, T. C., "Measurement without Theory," (review of Burns and Mitchell, *Measuring Business Cycles*), *Review of Economic Statistics*, Aug. 1947.

Lewis, E. E., *Methods of Statistical Analysis in Economics and Business*, Chap. 11.

Mitchell, W. C., *What Happens During Business Cycles*, Chaps. 1-4, 6.

Persons, W., "Indices of Business Conditions," *Review of Economic Statistics*, Preliminary Vol. 1, 1919.

Riggleman, J. R. and Frisbee, I. N., *Business Statistics*, 3rd ed., Chap. 17.

Schumpeter, J. A., *Business Cycles*, Chap. 5.

Vining, R., "Methodological Issues in Quantitative Economics: Koopmans on the Choice of Variables to be Studied and on Methods of Measurement" (with Reply by Koopmans, and Rejoinder), *The Review of Economics and Statistics*, May 1949.

The publishers and the dates of publication of the books named in chapter reference lists are given in the bibliography at the end of this volume.

CHAPTER **13**

•
•
•

Index Numbers of Prices

The term "index number" has been applied to a number of somewhat similar devices employed in the analysis of statistical series. Index numbers have been most widely used in the study of price changes, but a brief consideration of certain other uses may make clear the essential characteristics of such measures. In its simplest form this name is used for a term in a time series expressed as a relative number. Thus the relative numbers given in columns (3) and (5) of Table 13-1 would be considered index numbers of this simple type.

TABLE 13–1

Examples of Time Series as Relatives (1950 = 100)

(1) Year	(2) U. S. production of crude petroleum (unit: 1,000,000 barrels of 42 gallons each)	(3) Petroleum production relative	(4) Wholesale price of No. 1 dark northern spring wheat Minneapolis Average of average monthly prices per bushel	(5) Wheat price relative
1950	1,974	100.0	$2.41	100.0
1951	2,248	113.9	2.52	104.6
1952	2,290	116.0	2.51	104.1
1953	2,360	119.6	2.53	105.0

The representation of the terms in a time series as relatives, with reference to a fixed base, makes possible a ready comparison of the values for different dates and enables one to follow the movements of the series much more easily than when the data are presented in their original form. Comparison of different series is also facilitated.

Though such relatives have been called index numbers it is better practice to reserve the term for figures that represent the combination of a number of series. The series to be combined may relate to prices, production, consumption, wages, volume of trade, or to any factor subject to temporal variation. (Index numbers have been used also in measuring such geographical differences as arise from variations in living costs from city to city or from country to country.) Quite complex problems may be involved in the construction of any one of these special forms of index numbers, but the essential aim in all cases is to secure a single, simple series that will define the net resultants of the changes occurring in the constituent elements. Our concern in the present chapter is with the procedures used in making index numbers of commodity prices.

Price Movements and Their Measurement: Preliminary Considerations

Price Changes. When price changes are surveyed in detail it is difficult to perceive order, or any definite trend. We find a multiplicity of conflicting movements. The price quotations in Table 13-2, taken at random, are roughly typical of what would be found were the entire field of prices canvassed in order to compare price movements from month to month. All 12 series listed advanced in price over the 15-year period covered by the record. Coffee, showing the greatest rise, was marked by a 12-fold increase in price, hides, at the bottom, by a gain of 13.5 percent. This was, of course, a period that included the inflationary movements of the war and postwar years. A similar period in peacetime would show much less pronounced changes, but the same absence of uniformity in price changes would be found. Each of the thousands of commodities traded in on the markets of any country, or of the world, moves in its own individual way, subject to a variety of influences. Yet it does not act in isolation. In its price movements it affects other commodities, and is affected by them. And, in addition to the forces peculiar to each commodity, there are general forces that act throughout the price system, influencing masses of commodities and services. It is the business of the maker of index numbers to bring order out of this multiplicity of price movements

TABLE 13-2

Commodity Prices at Wholesale*

Commodity	Unit	Price April 1939	Price April 1954	Relative price April 1954 (April 1939 = 100)
CATTLE—				
Fair to choice native steers, Chicago.....Dols. per 100 lbs.		10.55	23.75	225.1
COFFEE—				
Santos No. 4, New York..............Cents per lb......		7¼	89.50	1234.5
COPPER—Electrolytic, New York refinery.Cents per lb......		10.37½	29.87½	288.0
CORN—No. 2 yellow, Chicago..........Dols. per bu......		.48⅞	1.59¼	325.8
COTTON—Middling, ⅞″, New Orleans...Cents per lb......		8.43	32.70	387.9
HIDES—				
Green salted packers, No. 1, heavy native steers, Chicago.....................Cents per lb......		9¼	10½	113.5
HOGS—Good merchantable, pigs and rough stock excluded, Chicago.............Dols. per 100 lbs.		7.15	27.05	378.3
IRON and STEEL—				
Steel scrap, No. 1 heavy melting, Pittsburgh..............................Dols. per gross ton		15.50	28.50	183.9
PETROLEUM—Crude, at well Pennsylvania........................Dols. per bbl....		2.00	3.76	188.0
SUGAR—96° centrifugal, duty paid, N. Y.__Cents per lb......		2.92	6.20	212.3
WHEAT—				
No. 1 northern spring, Minneapolis......Dols. per bu......		.74⅜	2.33½	313.9
ZINC—Prime western, E. St. Louis......Cents per lb.,.....		4.50	10.25	227.8

* As compiled from trade sources by *The Guaranty Survey.*

by defining the broad movements that are the net resultant of the diverse forces impinging on prices.

The character of price changes in individual commodities, viewed collectively, is of concern to makers and users of index numbers, for it bears upon the methods that may be used in measuring price movements. In earlier pages of this book, dealing with methods of summarizing quantitative observations, we noted that an average is most meaningful when it represents a distinct central tendency in a mass of relatively homogeneous data. Moreover, the type of average to be employed may vary with the character of the distribution to be represented. We should first, then, determine what the raw materials of the problem are, and study the frequency distributions secured when these raw materials are organized.

Some of the specific purposes served by index numbers of prices are discussed in the following section. At the heart of each of these purposes is the comparison of price quotations for individual commodities at each of two dates. Each pair of quotations measures a change in the price of a single commodity, a change caused by the interplay of many forces. When a great many such price quotations are brought together we have a mass of data representing the interaction of a multitude of forces, some individual and specific in their incidence, some general, affecting the prices of large groups of commodities or of all commodities. What we seek to determine is the net price resultant of all these factors. We seek a measure of the composite effect of the numerous forces that are causing individual prices to rise or fall.

The unit with which we must deal is a single price variation. Whether the statistical methods with which we are familiar may be effectively employed in the organization and analysis of a number of such units depends on the behavior of such units in mass. The following examples illustrate the frequency distributions secured when these data are classified.

Frequency Distributions of Price Relatives. Each price variation is, of course, a ratio, the ratio of the price of a commodity at a given date to the price of the commodity at another date. The ratios may be reduced to a comparable basis by putting them all in the form of relatives, of the type illustrated in preceding examples. In constructing the frequency distribution shown in Table 13-3, the prices at wholesale in 1927 of 670 commodities were expressed as relatives, with the 1926 price as a base in each case.

The frequency polygon representing this distribution appears in Fig. 13.1. For purposes of comparison with similar distributions the figure shows the percentage distribution. The correspondence of this frequency distribution to the standard types portrayed in

FIG. 13.1. Frequency Polygon: Distribution of Relative Prices of 670 Commodities in 1927 (Average prices in 1926 = 100).

TABLE 13–3

Distribution of the Relative Prices of 670 Commodities in 1927*
(Average prices in 1926 = 100)

Relative prices	Midpoint m	No. of cases f	Percentage of total number of cases
52.5– 57.4	55	1	.1
57.5– 62.4	60	2	.3
62.5– 67.4	65	6	.9
67.5– 72.4	70	7	1.0
72.5– 77.4	75	8	1.2
77.5– 82.4	80	25	3.7
82.5– 87.4	85	50	7.5
87.5– 92.4	90	76	11.3
92.5– 97.4	95	136	20.3
97.5–102.4	100	196	29.3
102.5–107.4	105	83	12.4
107.5–112.4	110	26	3.9
112.5–117.4	115	16	2.4
117.5–122.4	120	14	2.1
122.5–127.4	125	12	1.8
127.5–132.4	130	2	.3
132.5–137.4	135	3	.5
137.5–142.4	140	5	.8
142.5–147.4	145	1	.1
147.5–152.4	150		
152.5–157.4	155	1	.1
		670	100.0

* The 670 commodities included were those employed by the U. S. Bureau of Labor Statistics in the construction of its index of wholesale prices. The original figures, and the relatives, appear in *Bulletin* 473, of that Bureau.

earlier sections is obvious. There is the same marked concentration about a central tendency, in this case a tendency of prices to remain stable, for 29 percent of all the cases showed a change not exceeding 2.5 percent from their prices in the base year. There is also, in this case, a fairly symmetrical distribution about this central tendency, though the range above the mode is slightly greater than the range below. Without at present considering the question as to which average might best be used to represent the central tendency in this distribution, it is apparent that the use of some average is quite legitimate.

The example just given has been based upon price variations from one year to the next, over a period during which the level of general prices declined slightly (4.6 percent). W. C. Mitchell gives a much more comprehensive illustration, based upon the distribution of 5,540 price variations from one year to the next over the period 1890-1913, which shows the same general grouping. The distribution secured by Mitchell is shown in Fig. 4.6 (page 80).

The inertia of prices is most conspicuous when year-to-year price changes are studied. It is therefore advisable to consider the character of price variations over a longer and more disturbed period, that we may learn whether the same type of distribution is obtained. Table 13-4 shows the distribution of 774 price variations,

TABLE 13–4

Distribution of Relative Prices of 774 Commodities in 1933
(Average prices in 1926 = 100)

Relative prices	Midpoint m	No. of cases f	Percentage of total number of cases
10– 14.9	12.5	3	.4
15– 19.9	17.5		
20– 24.9	22.5	1	.1
25– 29.9	27.5	7	.9
30– 34.9	32.5	13	1.7
35– 39.9	37.5	24	3.1
40– 44.9	42.5	28	3.6
45– 49.9	47.5	51	6.6
50– 54.9	52.5	49	6.3
55– 59.9	57.5	50	6.5
60– 64.9	62.5	62	8.0
65– 69.9	67.5	58	7.5
70– 74.9	72.5	93	12.0
75– 79.9	77.5	81	10.5
80– 84.9	82.5	62	8.0
85– 89.9	87.5	67	8.7
90– 94.9	92.5	40	5.2
95– 99.9	97.5	27	3.5
100–104.9	102.5	27	3.5
105–109.9	107.5	11	1.4
110–114.9	112.5	6	.8
115–119.9	117.5	8	1.0
120–124.9	122.5	1	.1
125–129.9	127.5	2	.3
155–159.9	157.5	1	.1
180–184.9	182.5	1	.1
190–194.9	192.5	1	.1
		774	100.0

prices in 1933 being expressed as relatives on a 1926 base. The general level of wholesale prices, it should be noted, declined some 33 percent from 1926 to 1933. The data in Table 13-4 are plotted

FIG. 13.2. Frequency Polygon: Distribution of Relative Prices of 774 Commodities in 1933 (Average prices in 1926 = 100).

in the form of a frequency polygon in Fig. 13.2, the percentage distribution being shown. It will be noted that the distribution is curtailed, the five upper classes being omitted.

The distributions depicted in Figs. 13.1 and 13.2 differ materially. The range of the variations is greater in the second case, a condition naturally to be expected because of the longer period covered. Secondly, a very much smaller percentage of cases is concentrated in the modal group, though there is still a pronounced central tendency. Both distributions, as plotted on the arithmetic scale, are fairly symmetrical, though a few extreme cases extend the actual upper limit of the second distribution. In Fig. 13.1 the concentration about the central tendency is much more marked, and the deviations of individual price ratios from the central tendency are smaller. This distribution resembles one that would be secured from highly accurate physical measurements, or the distribution of shots from a very accurate piece of artillery. The second curve corresponds to one representing less accurate physical measurements, or to the distribution of shots from an old or in-accurate field piece. The modal value occurs less frequently and the deviations from the central tendency are greater. It has been established that the longer the period covered in price comparisons such as those made above, the more pronounced is the tendency shown in Fig. 13.2. The value of the maximum ordinate falls and the range of the distribution increases. The curve becomes flatter and more extended as the time interval increases.

If we were to plot a frequency distribution of 1944 price relatives on 1926 as a base, or of 1954 relatives on the same base, we should expect to find an accentuation of the features we have noted in Fig. 13.2. The wartime distribution, particularly, would be marked by greater skewness than is evident in any of the price distributions referred to above. This point is to be emphasized. A price increase, expressed as a relative, has no upper limit. An increase of 100, 500, 1,000 percent or more is conceivable and possible. (The greatest price increase noted by the War Industries Board in its study of prices during the first world war was one of 4,981 percent, in the case of acetiphenetidin.) But 100 percent is the maximum decline possible, as that would mean that the price of a commodity had fallen to zero. Thus in a period of sharply rising prices positive skewness is characteristic of distributions of price relatives.

In the preceding pages we have briefly considered the character of the raw materials used in index number construction, and have remarked on the nature of the frequency distributions that are obtained when such materials are brought together in quantity. The data we have examined consist of individual price variations, expressed as ratios. When a number of these ratios are assembled a frequency distribution is secured which has points in common with distributions obtained from other collections of quantitative observations. A central tendency, which may legitimately be represented by an average, is apparent in the distribution of price variations. The central tendency is less marked, however, and the deviations from it are more pronounced, the longer the period covered in the price comparison, so that an average becomes less representative as this period increases. In addition, a tendency toward skewness has been noted, and this tendency, we have observed, could be quite pronounced in a period of rising prices. This skewness is due to the fact that we are dealing with ratios that have a definite lower limit and no upper limit.

Some Purposes Served by Index Numbers of Prices. On an earlier page we have said that in obtaining an average of price relatives we are seeking a measure of the composite effect, or net resultant, of the numerous forces that are causing the prices of individual commodities to rise or fall between two dates. A good measure of a clearly defined central tendency in a frequency distribution of price relatives may be taken to define such a net resultant. But this general statement of purpose does not go far enough. The price relatives of what commodities are to be included in such a frequency distribution? To answer this question we must face the question of purpose more directly.

The traditional purpose of the makers of index numbers has been to measure changes in the purchasing power of money. Carli in 1764, Jevons in 1863, Fisher in 1911 thought of their work in these terms. Back of this purpose lies the concept of an average defining a general price level. All commodities and services entering into exchange would be the components of such an average. The prices of all such commodities and services (or a sample fully representative of all) would make up the frequency distribution appropriate to this concept. It is now recognized that such a distribution, which would include commodities at all stages of production and distribution, services to producers and consumers, wages, salaries, rents, profits, taxes, etc., would be heterogeneous in the extreme. For the various elements of the general price system are subject to widely diverse forces. Accordingly, no omnibus measure of changes in prices, in the broadest meaning of that term, is now constructed. Indexes more restricted in scope are more useful to economists, to governmental administrators, and to business men.

The nearest approach to a general price index currently constructed is an index of commodity prices in wholesale markets. In the United States the wholesale price index of the Bureau of Labor Statistics, relating to "the first important commercial transaction for each commodity," is often thought of as measuring changes in the "level of prices," although it covers, in fact, only a portion of wholesale transactions and other markets not at all. But it comprehends a wide range of commodities, and is more inclusive as a measure of price movements than any other current index.[1]

We have referred to the diversity of movements found in the prices of economic goods of all sorts—commodities and services. This diversity is found whether we observe price changes within the year, during cycles of expansion and contraction in general

---

[1] Reference should be made, however, to the "implicit deflator" of Gross National Product (and to the separate elements of the general deflator) derived by the National Income Unit of the U. S. Department of Commerce in expressing Gross National Product in dollars of constant purchasing power. The "implicit deflator" which is available by years for the period since 1919, is, in effect, a very comprehensive price index, although affected by changes in the composition of the Gross Product as well as by price changes proper. A similar deflator for earlier years was constructed by Simon Kuznets in his measurement of national income.

business, or over longer periods. The student of business cycles and of economic growth knows that these diversities are not haphazard. There are patterns of price change, and in these patterns are found clues to the interacting forces of economic change. A central purpose of index number work today is the measurement of these differing group movements that lead to cyclical and secular changes in the structure of prices. Various classifications of prices are of interest to economists; still others are of concern to business and labor groups and to government officials. The prices of the factors of production (rent, wages and salaries, interest and profit rates), the prices of goods at wholesale and at retail, farm prices, tariff rates—these are among the major classes of contemporary concern. Within the broad category of wholesale prices the U. S. Bureau of Labor Statistics now constructs price index numbers for 15 major commodity groups and for 88 minor groups ranging from grains, milk, coal, and lumber to agricultural machinery, motor vehicles, and radios, television sets, and phonographs. The National Bureau of Economic Research has constructed indexes for raw and manufactured goods, durable and nondurable goods, producer goods and consumer goods, goods of agricultural and of nonagricultural origin, and for other classes of economic interest. Not all sectors of the price system are adequately covered, by any means, but the batteries of group index numbers currently available enable the student to trace shifting price relations in considerable detail.

Closely related to the general purpose just described is measurement of shifts in what may be called the "terms of exchange" of specified economic groups. This is a familiar concept in international trade. Britain's terms of exchange with the rest of the world, as defined by the changing ratio of export prices to import prices, are a matter of central concern to that trading country. The terms of exchange of United States farmers, as measured by the "parity ratio" (the ratio of the prices of farm products, at the farm, to prices paid by farmers for goods purchased), are the basis of federal aid to farmers, and an object of recurring political and economic controversy. Similar terms of exchange are measured by the ratio of wages to the prices paid by consumers, a ratio that affects bargaining over wages, and wage and price regulation in wartime. In increasing degree, special-purpose index numbers are being constructed to define the relations of prices received by specific economic groups to the prices they pay. For any group, or for any individual, this ratio defines a major factor in the economic welfare of that group, or individual. (It is not the only factor, of course. Favorable terms of exchange are of little comfort to a country that cannot sell its products, or to unemployed members of the labor force.)

Another important object in the making of index numbers is that of breaking a change in the aggregate value of a group of commodities into its basic price and quantity components. This purpose may be most readily illustrated with reference to a single commodity. Between 1940 and 1952 the value of raw cotton produced in the United States increased from $621,284,000 to $2,774,-230,000; the amount produced rose from 6,283,000,000 pounds to 7,519,000,000 pounds; the average farm price per pound increased from 9.89 cents to 36.90 cents. Reducing these several changes to relatives, we have

	1940	1952
Quantity of cotton produced, in lbs.	100.0	119.7
Average price of cotton, per lb.	100.0	373.1
Aggregate value of cotton produced	100.0	446.6

The relative numbers measuring the change in total value may be derived either from the aggregate value figures, or by multiplying the quantity relative by the relative measuring the change in unit price. The two processes give the same result. This is always the case when we work with relatives relating to prices, quantities, and values for single commodities. But identity of results is not necessarily found when we work with prices, quantities, and values for groups of commodities. The product of price and quantity indexes may in such cases differ materially from a measure of relative change in values derived directly from the aggregate value figures. When this object—that of breaking a value change (or a value ratio) into consistent price and quantity components—is regarded as of central importance by the maker of index numbers, the methods employed must be adapted to the purpose.

In this brief summary of purposes served by index numbers we have dealt primarily with index numbers of prices. Later we shall deal with problems faced in studying physical quantities. Differences of purpose in the construction of price indexes have some bearing on the choice of technical formulas, a more important bearing on the choice of commodities and determination of the number of commodities to be included in the sample. Technical methods employed are also affected by practical difficulties faced in obtaining data, by computational considerations, and by the time factor in publication of results. For these and other reasons varying methods have been advocated for the construction of index numbers. Differences among methods actually employed, however, are not great today. Although some conflicts of opinion remain, compulsions of practice and an approach to agreement on ends have reduced the differences that prevailed a generation ago.

The practical problems of index-number making in the price field include the choice of commodities (determination of the size and scope of the sample), the obtaining of quotations, and the selection of a method of combining price quotations that will yield a single satisfactory index figure. Our first concern will be the choice of a formula that may be employed in combining price quotations. Alternative possibilities may be illustrated most effectively by the application of a number of methods to the same data. Table 13-5 presents the raw material to which these various methods are to be applied—the average farm prices of twelve leading crops on December 1 of each year from 1929 to 1945. This period, which was marked by the wide price fluctuations brought on first by depression and then by war and inflation, provides a good vehicle for the desired comparisons.

Notation. The symbols to be employed in the computation of index numbers have the following meanings:

p_0': price of a given commodity at time "0" (the base period)

q_0': quantity of same commodity at time "0"

p_1': price of same commodity at time "1"

q_1': quantity of same commodity at time "1"

p_0'': price of second commodity at time "0"

q_0'': quantity of second commodity at time"0"

p_1'': price of second commodity at time "1"

q_1'': quantity of second commodity at time "1"

$\dfrac{p_1'}{p_0'}$: a price relative (relation of price of a given commodity at time "1" to price of same commodity at time "0"; such ratios are usually multiplied by 100 to give the customary relative numbers

$\dfrac{q_1'}{q_0'}$: a quantity relative

P_{01}: price index for time "1" on time "0" as base

P_{10}: price index for time "0" on time "1" as base

P'_{12}: price index obtained by a base-shifting procedure

Q_{01}: index of physical quantities (produced, exchanged, or consumed) in time "1" (or period "1") on time "0" as base

Q_{10}: index of physical quantities in time "0" on time "1" as base

V_{01}: ratio of aggregate values in time "1" to aggregate values in time "0"; an index of change in the aggregate values of commodities produced, exchanged, or consumed

L: the Laspeyres formula

P: the Paasche formula (P with no subscripts will be used as a symbol for the Paasche formula; not to be confused with P_{01}, P_{23}, etc. P with subscripts is used as a general symbol for a price index, the subscripts denoting the years compared.)

I: the ideal formula

E_1: a measure of formula error, as shown by the time reversal test

E_2: a measure of formula error, as shown by the factor reversal test

D: $L - P$; the difference between results given by the Laspeyres and Paasche formulas; an indication of degree of difference between two regimens

Simple Index Numbers of Prices

In his exhaustive analysis of methods of index number construction Irving Fisher (Ref. 46) distinguishes six fundamental types: the aggregative (or price aggregate), the arithmetic, harmonic, geometric, median, and mode. The latter has never been employed in a practical way, and may be omitted. The characteristics of the five remaining types may be brought out by considering each of them in its simplest form, before examining the more complicated combinations.

Aggregates of actual prices. In the construction of index numbers of the simple aggregative type, commodity prices pertaining to a given date are added; general price changes are measured by comparing the results thus secured for different dates. Using the above symbols

$$P_{01} = \frac{\Sigma p_1}{\Sigma p_0} \qquad (13.1)$$

TABLE 13–5

Average Farm Prices, on December 1, of 12 Leading Crops, 1929-1945*

Crop	Unit	1929	1930	1931	1932	1933	1934	1935	1936	1937	1938	1939	1940	1941	1942	1943	1944	1945
Corn	Bu.	.774	.655	.359	.192	.394	.805	.547	.951	.482	.415	.485	.556	.653	.780	1.080	1.060	1.100
Cotton	Lb.	.164	.095	.057	.057	.094	.124	.114	.122	.081	.087	.091	.094	.161	.194	.196	.208	.227
Hay	Ton (sh.)	12.19	12.62	9.03	6.65	8.10	13.72	7.22	10.90	8.76	6.81	7.61	7.39	9.07	10.15	14.85	16.05	15.15
Wheat	Bu.	1.035	.600	.443	.320	.678	.894	.882	1.104	.827	.528	.777	.720	.978	1.073	1.410	1.440	1.535
Oats	Bu.	.426	.315	.230	.134	.304	.525	.256	.463	.289	.234	.334	.320	.431	.458	.760	.678	.691
Potatoes, Wh.	Bu.	1.288	.890	.430	.353	.702	.457	.629	1.021	.521	.580	.700	.535	.800	1.100	1.340	1.465	1.340
Sugar	Lb.†	.038	.033	.032	.029	.032	.029	.031	.038	.032	.029	.030	.029	.035	.037	.037	.038	.038
Barley	Bu.	.544	.389	.353	.201	.407	.778	.376	.844	.507	.356	.430	.411	.546	.600	1.040	.971	1.065
Tobacco	Lb.	.183	.128	.082	.105	.130	.213	.184	.236	.204	.196	.154	.160	.264	.369	.405	.420	.426
Flaxseed	Bu.	2.843	1.398	1.999	.848	1.518	1.653	1.54	1.92	1.81	1.62	1.72	1.40	1.68	2.30	2.84	2.90	2.89
Rye	Bu.	.849	.384	.388	.223	.554	.732	.402	.857	.600	.322	.484	.420	.560	.533	1.045	1.070	1.465
Rice	Bu.	.995	.773	.561	.374	.779	.783	.739	.775	.706	.662	.742	.769	1.351	1.608	1.89	1.77	1.82

† The price of sugar given for each year is the wholesale price of the raw product (96° centrifugal) in the month of December at New York. No figure corresponding to the farm price could be secured for this commodity.

* Source: *Agricultural Statistics*, U. S. Department of Agriculture.

When such index numbers are constructed from the data of Table 13-5 the results in Table 13-6 are secured. The actual aggregates are given in column (2); to facilitate comparison the same figures are reduced to relatives, with the 1919 aggregate as base, in column (3).

TABLE 13–6

Index Numbers of Farm Crop Prices
(Aggregates of actual prices)

(1)	(2)	(3)
Year	Index (aggregate of actual prices)	Index, relative (1929 = 100)
1929	$21.329	100
1930	18.280	86
1931	13.964	65
1932	9.486	44
1933	13.692	64
1934	20.713	97
1935	12.920	61
1936	19.231	90
1937	14.819	69
1938	11.839	56
1939	13.557	64
1940	12.804	60
1941	16.529	77
1942	19.202	90
1943	26.883	126
1944	28.070	132
1945	27.747	130

The results secured by this method of constructing index numbers of prices will be compared shortly with results secured from the same data by other methods. The chief weakness of this type of index number is obvious. This is not an unweighted nor yet an equally weighted index. The influence of each commodity upon the result is dependent upon the price of the unit in which it happens to be traded. In the present index, hay, which is quoted by the ton, is given more weight than all the other 11 commodities combined, with flaxseed second in importance. The index secured by adding the quotations is weighted in an entirely illogical fashion and cannot be accepted as reflecting the course of farm crop prices.

Arithmetic averages of relative prices. Another method employed in the construction of index numbers involves the reduction of each quoted price to a relative, with reference to the price of the same commodity at a certain basic date, these relative figures then being averaged by any of the conventional methods. The example in Table 13-7 illustrates the first phase of this process, data for two years being utilized. The year 1929 is taken as base.

TABLE 13–7

Computation of Relative Prices for the Construction of Index Numbers

(1) Commodity	(2) Unit	(3) Price 1929	(4) Relative	(5) Price 1930	(6) Relative
Corn	Bu.	$ .774	100	$ .655	84.6
Cotton	Lb.	.164	100	.095	57.9
Hay	Ton (sh.)	12.19	100	12.62	103.5
Wheat	Bu.	1.035	100	.600	58.0
Oats	Bu.	.426	100	.315	73.9
Wh. Potatoes	Bu.	1.288	100	.890	69.1
Sugar	Lb.	.038	100	.033	86.8
Barley	Bu.	.544	100	.389	71.5
Tobacco	Lb.	.183	100	.128	69.9
Flaxseed	Bu.	2.843	100	1.398	49.2
Rye	Bu.	.849	100	.384	45.2
Rice	Bu.	.995	100	.773	77.7
			1200		847.3

From these figures the arithmetic averages of relative prices in these two years may be readily computed. The formula for any single relative is $\dfrac{p_1'}{p_0'}$. When there are N relatives the formula for the index number at time "1" is

$$P_{01} = \frac{\Sigma\left(\dfrac{p_1}{p_0}\right)}{N} \tag{13.2}$$

In the present case

$$\text{Index (1929)} = \frac{1{,}200}{12} = 100$$

$$\text{Index (1930)} = \frac{847.3}{12} = 70.6$$

Index numbers computed in this way for the years 1929 to 1945, inclusive, are shown in column (3) of Table 13-10.

This type of index number is usually termed an "unweighted" index of relative prices. It is weighted, however, just as are the types illustrated in the two examples preceding. The quantity employed as weight in each case is the amount of each commodity which would sell for $100 in the base year. In the preceding example the following quantities have been employed as weights:

Corn	129.2 bu.
Cotton	609.8 lbs.
Hay	8.20 tons
Wheat	96.6 bu.
Oats	234.7 bu.
Potatoes	77.6 bu.
Sugar	2,631.6 lbs.
Barley	183.8 bu.
Tobacco	546.4 lbs.
Flaxseed	35.2 bu.
Rye	117.8 bu.
Rice	100.5 bu.

What has been done, in effect, in the computation of the simple average of relative prices has been to determine the aggregate amount for which the above quantities would sell in each of the eleven years included. At 1929 prices each of the above quantities would sell for $100, the aggregate value being $1,200; at 1930 prices the aggregate value of the above quantities was $847.30. These aggregates, divided by 12, give the index numbers shown in column (3), Table 13-10: 100 for 1929, 71 (70.6) for 1930, etc. Thus the "unweighted average of relative prices" is in fact a weighted aggregate of actual prices. It is equally weighted in the sense that the value of the quantity of each commodity employed as weight was equal to $100 in the base year, 1929.

Medians of relative prices. The median rather than the arithmetic mean may be employed in securing the average of the relative prices for each year. When the relatives in column (6) of Table 13-7 are arranged in order of magnitude the following distribution is secured:

45.2	71.5
49.2	73.9
57.9	77.7
58.0	84.6
69.1	86.8
69.9	103.5

The median of these relatives, 70.7, is the index number for 1930. All the index numbers computed in this way from the medians of relative prices are presented in column (4), Table 13-10.

Geometric averages of relative prices. The geometric averages of the relative prices for the various years may now be computed and the results compared with those secured in the preceding examples. A single relative being represented by the symbol $\frac{p_1'}{p_0'}$, the formula for the geometric mean of N relatives is

$$M_g = \sqrt[N]{\frac{p_1'}{p_0'} \times \frac{p_1''}{p_0''} \times \frac{p_1'''}{p_0'''} \times \dots} \qquad (13.3)$$

A geometric mean is generally computed by the aid of logarithms; in this case

$$\text{Log } M_g = \frac{\log\left(\frac{p_1'}{p_0'}\right) + \log\left(\frac{p_1''}{p_0''}\right) + \log\left(\frac{p_1'''}{p_0'''}\right) + \dots}{N} \qquad (13.4)$$

The method of computation may be illustrated for the years 1929 and 1930 (see Table 13-8), the relative prices of the various

TABLE 13–8

Computation of Geometric Averages of Relative Prices

(1) Commodity	(2) Relative price, 1929	(3) Logarithm of figure in col. (2)	(4) Relative price, 1930	(5) Logarithm of figure in col. (4)
Corn	100	2.0	84.6	1.92737
Cotton	100	2.0	57.9	1.76268
Hay	100	2.0	103.5	2.01494
Wheat	100	2.0	58.0	1.76343
Oats	100	2.0	73.9	1.86864
Wh. Potatoes	100	2.0	69.1	1.83948
Sugar	100	2.0	86.8	1.93852
Barley	100	2.0	71.5	1.85431
Tobacco	100	2.0	69.9	1.84448
Flaxseed	100	2.0	49.2	1.69197
Rye	100	2.0	45.2	1.65514
Rice	100	2.0	77.7	1.89042
		24.0		22.05138

$$\text{Log } M_g \text{ (1929)} = \frac{24.0}{12} = 2$$

$$M_g = \text{antilogarithm of } 2 = 100$$

$$\text{Log } M_g \text{ (1930)} = \frac{22.05138}{12} = 1.83761$$

$$M_g = \text{antilogarithm of } 1.83761 = 68.8$$

commodities being repeated from Table 13-7. Averaging the logarithms, and obtaining the corresponding natural numbers, we have 100 as the geometric mean for 1929, 68.8 for 1930.

The results for all the years are summarized in column (5), Table 13-10.

Harmonic averages of relative prices. The characteristics of the harmonic average have been discussed in a preceding chapter. The reciprocal of the harmonic mean, it will be recalled, is the arithmetic mean of the reciprocals of the constituent measures. The constituent items, in the present case, are price relatives of the form $\frac{p_1'}{p_0'}$. The reciprocal of such a relative is $\frac{p_0'}{p_1'}$. The formula for the harmonic mean of N price relatives is, therefore,

$$\frac{1}{H} = \frac{\frac{p_0'}{p_1'} + \frac{p_0''}{p_1''} + \frac{p_0'''}{p_1'''} + \dots}{N} \tag{13.5}$$

or

$$H = \frac{N}{\Sigma\left(\frac{p_0}{p_1}\right)} \tag{13.6}$$

The method of computation is illustrated in Table 13-9.

The index numbers computed in this way for all the years included in the study are shown in column (6), Table 13-10.

In the construction of the five types of index numbers explained above no attempt has been made to use a logical weighting system. All are termed "unweighted" averages, a term which is quite misleading. The first index constructed, based on aggregates of actual prices, is a heavily weighted index number, though the weights are illogical. In the next four the quantities employed as weights are the amounts purchasable for $100 in 1929. The five results are brought together and compared in Table 13-10. In each case the index is given to the nearest whole number. These index numbers are plotted in Fig. 13.3.

Comparison of Simple Index Numbers: The Time Reversal Test. The four averages of relative prices agree much more closely with each other than with the index numbers based on aggregates. For reasons already suggested the latter is quite untrustworthy as a measure of price changes. Of the other index numbers, the arithmetic, geometric, and harmonic means show a consistent

TABLE 13–9

Computation of Harmonic Averages of Relative Prices

(1) Commodity	(2) Relative price, 1929	(3) Reciprocal of figure in col. (2)	(4) Relative price, 1930	(5) Reciprocal of figure in col. (4)
Corn	100	.01	84.6	.01182033
Cotton	100	.01	57.9	.01727116
Hay	100	.01	103.5	.00966184
Wheat	100	.01	58.0	.01724138
Oats	100	.01	73.9	.01353180
Wh. Potatoes	100	.01	69.1	.01447178
Sugar	100	.01	86.8	.01152074
Barley	100	.01	71.5	.01398601
Tobacco	100	.01	69.9	.01430615
Flaxseed	100	.01	49.2	.02032520
Rye	100	.01	45.2	.02212389
Rice	100	.01	77.7	.01287001
		.12		.17913029

$$H\ (1929) = \frac{12}{.12} = 100$$

$$H\ (1930) = \frac{12}{.17913029} = 67.0$$

relationship, a fact which follows from the nature of the averages employed. Except in the base year the geometric mean is always less than the arithmetic and the harmonic is always less than the geometric, the amount of difference increasing as the dispersion of prices becomes greater. The median, with only twelve items to be averaged, is somewhat unstable, and its relationship to the other averages is not always a consistent one.

How are we to choose among these varying results? No one of these "unweighted" index numbers is perfect, for weights which have crept in do not measure the relative importance of the various commodities included in the index numbers. But, neglecting for the moment the question of weights, is it possible to test the adequacy of the different methods of measuring changes in the prices as given?

For this purpose Irving Fisher has employed what he terms the "time reversal test." This is merely a test to determine whether a

TABLE 13–10

Index Numbers of Farm Crop Prices, 1929-1945 (1929 = 100)

(1)	(2)	(3)	(4)	(5)	(6)
Year	Aggregates of actual prices (as relatives)	Arithmetic averages of relative prices	Medians of relative prices	Geometric averages of relative prices	Harmonic averages of relative prices
1929	100	100	100	100	100
1930	86	71	71	69	67
1931	65	54	50	52	50
1932	44	39	33	37	35
1933	64	66	66	65	64
1934	97	91	86	86	80
1935	61	68	69	67	65
1936	90	101	100	98	96
1937	69	72	71	70	67
1938	56	60	55	58	57
1939	64	68	69	68	67
1940	60	66	71	64	63
1941	77	92	93	89	86
1942	90	109	102	104	100
1943	126	143	129	138	134
1944	132	143	134	139	136
1945	130	150	145	145	141

given method will work both ways in time, forward and backward. If from 1940 to 1941 sugar should increase from 3 to 4 cents a pound, the price in 1941 would be $133\frac{1}{3}$ percent of the price in 1940, and the price in 1940 would be 75 percent of the price in 1941. One figure is the reciprocal of the other; their product ($1.33\frac{1}{3}$ × 0.75) is unity. Similarly, if a given method of index number construction shows the general price level in one year to be $133\frac{1}{3}$ percent of the level in the preceding year, it should work correctly when reversed; it should show that the price level in the first year was 75 percent of the price level in the second year. When the data for any two years are treated by the same method, but with the bases reversed, the two index numbers secured should be reciprocals of each other. Their product should always be unity. That is, we should have the relation

$$P_{01} \cdot P_{10} = 1$$

where P_{01} is the index for time "1" on time "0" as base, and P_{10} is

FIG. 13.3. Comparison of Five Simple Index Numbers of Farm Crop Prices, 1929-1945 (1929 = 100).

the index for time "0" on time "1" as base. (In all such expressions as this, the decimal point in the customary price index is assumed to be shifted two places to the left; that is, we deal with ratios, not relatives.) If the product is not unity, there is said to be a *type bias* in the method.

For this error Mudgett (Ref. 113) has used the symbol E_1, where

$$E_1 = (P_{01} \cdot P_{10}) - 1 \qquad (13.7)$$

This will be equal to zero, of course, when the time reversal test is met.

This test may be applied to the methods employed above, using prices for 1929 and 1930. With 1929 as base the following results were obtained

Year	Aggregates of actual prices (as relatives)	Arithmetic averages of relative prices	Medians of relative prices	Geometric averages of relative prices	Harmonic averages of relative prices
1929	100.00	100.00	100.00	100.00	100.00
1930	85.71	70.61	70.73	68.80	66.99

and with 1930 as base:

Year	Aggregates of actual prices (as relatives)	Arithmetic averages of relative prices	Medians of relative prices	Geometric averages of relative prices	Harmonic averages of relative prices
1929	116.68	149.25	141.41	145.31	141.60
1930	100.00	100.00	100.00	100.00	100.00

When the index numbers for 1930 in the first table are multiplied by the corresponding index numbers for 1929 in the second table, we have the following values. (In securing these products the index numbers are put in the ratio, not in the percentage, form.)

Aggregates of actual prices	Arithmetic averages of relative prices	Medians of relative prices	Geometric averages of relative prices	Harmonic averages of relative prices
1.00	1.0539	1.00	1.00	0.9486

This time reversal test is met by three of the methods employed. It is not met by either the arithmetic or harmonic average. For the arithmetic average $E_1 = + 0.0539$; for the harmonic average $E_1 = - 0.0514$. The former has a distinct upward bias while the harmonic mean shows almost as large an error in the opposite direction. There is, thus, an inherent type bias in both these averages.

Weighted Index Numbers of Prices

Five simple index numbers of prices have been described in the preceding section. With the introduction of weighting the number of possible combinations is greatly increased, but only a few of these types need concern us here.

In the construction of an accurate measure of price changes logical weights must be employed, weights that truly reflect the relative importance of the commodities included. If the weighting problem is ignored haphazard and illogical weights will inevitably be present, whether recognized or not.

The data used in the preceding examples may be utilized to illustrate methods of weighting and to show the effects of varying weights upon index numbers. For present purposes we shall employ weights that define quantities of crops produced or, for certain index types, values of crops produced. The quantities produced during the period 1929-45 are given in Table 13-11.

TABLE 13–11

Annual Physical Production, 12 Crops, 1929-1945

Year	Corn (millions of bu.)	Cotton (millions of bales)*	Hay, tame (millions of short tons)	Wheat (millions of bu.)	Oats (millions of bu.)	White potatoes (millions of bu.)	Sugar† (millions of lbs.)	Barley (millions of bu.)	Tobacco (millions of lbs.)	Flaxseed (millions of bu.)	Rye (millions of bu.)	Rice (millions of bu.)
1929	2,516	14.83	76.02	824.2	1,113	333.4	6,590	280.6	1,533	15.9	35.41	39.53
1930	2,080	13.93	63.71	886.5	1,275	343.8	6,438	301.6	1,648	21.7	45.38	44.93
1931	2,576	17.10	66.99	941.5	1,124	384.3	6,679	200.3	1,565	11.8	32.78	44.61
1932	2,930	13.00	71.77	756.3	1,255	374.7	6,365	299.4	1,018	11.5	39.10	41.62
1933	2,398	13.05	66.30	555.2	736	343.2	6,218	152.8	1,372	6.9	20.57	37.65
1934	1,449	9.64	55.68	526.1	544	406.5	6,680	117.4	1,085	5.7	16.29	39.05
1935	2,299	10.64	78.46	628.2	1,210	378.9	6,641	288.7	1,302	14.9	56.94	39.45
1936	1,506	12.40	62.72	629.9	793	324.0	6,577	147.7	1,163	5.3	24.24	49.82
1937	2,643	18.95	73.27	873.9	1,177	376.4	5,996	221.9	1,569	7.1	48.86	53.42
1938	2,549	11.94	80.40	919.9	1,089	355.8	6,285	256.6	1,386	8.0	55.98	52.51
1939	2,581	11.82	76.38	741.2	958	342.4	7,078	278.2	1,881	19.6	38.56	54.06
1940	2,462	12.57	85.07	813.3	1,245	375.8	7,587	308.9	1,462	30.9	39.98	54.43
1941	2,676	10.74	82.74	943.1	1,181	355.6	6,569	362.1	1,262	32.3	45.36	51.32
1942	3,132	12.82	92.20	974.2	1,350	370.5	5,964	429.2	1,409	41.1	57.67	64.55
1943	3,034	11.43	87.24	841.0	1,138	465.0	6,809	324.2	1,406	51.9	30.45	64.84
1944	3,203	12.23	84.08	1,072.2	1,155	383.1	7,402	278.6	1,957	23.1	25.50	68.16
1945	3,018	9.02	91.57	1,123.1	1,548	425.1	5,319	264.0	1,998	36.7	26.35	70.16

† The figures for sugar represent the total supply available for consumption during twelve months beginning July 1 of the year indicated.
* Bales of 500 lbs., gross weight.

The Laspeyres Formula. The thoroughly illogical results obtained when actual prices, as quoted, are totaled to secure an index number have been pointed out. The same objection cannot be made when the prices are appropriately weighted before the aggregate is taken. If for weights we employ the quantities produced in the base year (at time "0") the formula for the weighted aggregate is

$$L = \frac{\Sigma p_1 q_0}{\Sigma p_0 q_0} \qquad (13.8)$$

This is, in effect, the method employed by the United States Bureau of Labor Statistics, for its index of wholesale prices, though the quantities come from a single year, 1947, while the base of the index is an average of three years, 1947-8-9. The formula for this type of weighted aggregative index is known as Laspeyres' formula, which we shall represent by the symbol L. The method is illustrated in Table 13-12.

TABLE 13–12

Computation of Weighted Aggregates of Actual Prices

(1)	(2)	(3)	(4) Weight (quantity produced 1929, in millions)	(5)	(6)	(7) Weight (quantity produced 1929, in millions)	(8)
Commodity	Unit	Price 1929		Price × weight	Price 1930		Price × weight
		p_0	q_0	$p_0 q_0$	p_1	q_0	$p_1 q_0$
Corn	Bu.	$ .774	2,516	1,947,384,000	.655	2,516	1,647,980,000
Cotton	Lb.	.164	7,089	1,162,596,000	.095	7,089	673,455,000
Hay	Ton(sh.)	12.19	76.02	926,683,800	12.62	76.02	959,372,400
Wheat	Bu.	1.035	824.2	853,047,000	.600	824.2	494,520,000
Oats	Bu.	.426	1,113	474,138,000	.315	1,113	350,595,000
Potatoes, Wh.	Bu.	1.288	333.4	429,419,200	.890	333.4	296,726,000
Sugar	Lb.	.038	6,590	250,420,000	.033	6,590	217,470,000
Barley	Bu.	.544	280.6	152,646,400	.389	280.6	109,153,400
Tobacco	Lb.	.183	1,533	280,539,000	.128	1,533	196,224,000
Flaxseed	Bu.	2.843	15.9	45,203,700	1.398	15.9	22,228,200
Rye	Bu.	.849	35.41	30,063,090	.384	35.41	13,597,440
Rice	Bu.	.995	39.53	39,332,350	.773	39.53	30,556,690
				6,591,472,540			5,011,878,130

The desired index numbers, in the form of relatives, may be computed from the aggregates secured by totaling columns (5) and (8) of Table 13-12. Either year may be taken as the base, and the price aggregate in the other year expressed as a relative of this base. With the 1929 aggregate as base, the index for 1930 is 76.0. Index numbers similarly computed for the other years are given in column (2), Table 13-15.

The Paasche Formula. Another type of weighted aggregate may be constructed, with weights taken not from the base period but from the later period in the given comparison. That is, we may employ q_1 (quantity at time "1") as weight in comparing prices at time "1" with prices at time "0", and employ q_2 (quantity at time "2") as weight in comparing prices at time "2" with prices at time "0." Algebraically, the formula for the index number at time "1" is

$$P = \frac{\Sigma p_1 q_1}{\Sigma p_0 q_1} \tag{13.9}$$

This is known as Paasche's formula. For it we shall use the symbol P. The process of computation is precisely the same as in the preceding example, except that the weights are changed with each successive year. The index numbers secured by this method are given in column (3), Table 13-15.

Averages of Relative Prices. The Laspeyres and Paasche formulas are weighted aggregates of actual prices. The weights employed are *quantities*: Prices multiplied by quantities give the two value aggregates from which each index number is derived. When we average price relatives of the form p_1/p_0, quantities will not serve as weights. The abstract relatives must be weighted by *values*, if the resulting products are to be comparable. For values are in a common dollar unit, while physical quantities may be expressed in a variety of units.

Note on weight bias. If we are comparing prices in years "0" and "1" we may weight each p_1/p_0 relative by the value of the given commodity in the base year, i.e., by $p_0 q_0$, or by the value of that commodity in the given year, i.e., by $p_1 q_1$. Before illustrating the procedure we should note the characteristics of these alternative weighting methods. Irving Fisher (Ref. 46), in an intensive study of weighting, has established that the general effect of weighting by base year values is to give an index number a *downward bias*, while the general effect of weighting by values from the second or given year is to give an index number an *upward bias*. These are not necessary effects, but they are effects usually present because of the patterns customarily found in the related movements of commodity prices and physical quantities.[2]

In the several examples next following we shall deal only with values of quantities produced in the base year, 1929, and in a single given year, 1930. These values are given in the third column of Table 13-13. For weighting purposes they are taken to the nearest million.

Arithmetic averages. In the computation of an index of this type, each relative is multiplied by the appropriate weight, and the sum of the products is divided by the sum of the weights. The process is illustrated in Table 13-13.

The index for 1930, it will be noted, is identical with that secured from the computations illustrated in Table 13-12. That index is a weighted aggregate of actual prices, the weights being the quantities

---

[2] The argument may be briefly summarized: If the price of commodity A rises from year "0" to year "1," the relative p'_1/p'_0 will be greater than 100. If the price of commodity B falls, its relative p''_1/p''_0 will be less than 100. If we assume for the moment that the q's of the two commodities remain unchanged (i.e., that $q_1 = q_0$ in each case) it is clear that base year weight $(p'_0 q'_0)$ for commodity A will be lower than given year weight $(p'_1 q'_1,)$ which by assumption equals $p'_1 q'_0$. This means that the price relative for commodity A, which is a high relative (since it exceeds 100), will be given less weight by a system of base year weighting than by a system of given year weighting. In the case of commodity B, for which the price fell, base year weight $(p''_0 q''_0)$ will be higher than given year weight $(p'' q'')$, which by assumption equals $p''_1 q''_0)$. But the price relative p''_1/p''_0 is a low relative, below 100. Base year weighting for this low relative means a higher weight than would given year weighting. Thus the effect of weighting by base-year values is to give a low weight to high relatives, a high weight to low relatives ("low weight" means, of course, lower than would result from given year weighting; "high weight" means higher than would result from given year weighting). In other words, the effects of price increases are underemphasized by base-year weighting, while the effects of price decreases are overemphasized. These two tendencies work in the same direction—toward a lower index than would be had with given year weighting. A similar argument leads to the conclusion that weighting by given year values tends to overemphasize price increases and to underemphasize price declines—both effects working toward a higher index than would be had with base-year weighting.

The conclusions stated rest on the assumption that physical quantities have not changed between year "0" and year "1." If the quantity movements have paralleled the price movements, the "biases" indicated are intensified. On the other hand, movements of quantities and prices in opposite directions over the period covered (negative correlation between quantity and price relatives) will tend to offset the indicated biases, and may, indeed, reverse them. The nature of the weight bias in a particular case will depend, therefore, on the actual behavior of the quantities and prices of commodities included in the index. Over short and medium periods, including business cycles, quantity and price movements are not, in general, inverse for commodities at large. (The inverse movements found in the representations of typical demand and supply curves relate, of course, to assumed static conditions.) Over longer periods, however, inverse movements may prevail. Thus for industrial commodities there was negative correlation between price and quantity movements between 1939 and 1947.

TABLE 13–13

Computation of Weighted Arithmetic Averages of Relative Prices

(1) Commodity	(2) Relative price 1929	(3) Weight	(4) Relative price × weight	(5) Relative price 1930	(6) Weight	(7) Relative price × weight
Corn	100	$1,947	$194,700	84.6	$1,947	$164,716.2
Cotton	100	1,163	116,300	57.9	1,163	67,337.7
Hay	100	927	92,700	103.5	927	95,944.5
Wheat	100	853	85,300	58.0	853	49,474.0
Oats	100	474	47,400	73.9	474	35,028.6
Potatoes	100	429	42,900	69.1	429	29,643.9
Sugar	100	250	25,000	86.8	250	21,700.0
Barley	100	153	15,300	71.5	153	10,939.5
Tobacco	100	281	28,100	66.9	281	19,641.9
Flaxseed	100	45	4,500	49.2	45	2,214.0
Rye	100	30	3,000	45.2	30	1,356.0
Rice	100	39	3,900	77.7	39	3,030.3
		6,591	659,100		6,591	501,026.6

$$\text{Weighted arithmetic mean (1929)} = \frac{\$659,100}{\$6,591} = 100$$

$$\text{Weighted arithmetic mean (1930)} = \frac{\$501,026.6}{\$6,591} = 76.0$$

(The weights employed are the values of the quantities produced in 1929, in millions)

produced in the base year. An arithmetic mean of relative prices, weighted by values in the base year, is always equal to a relative constructed from such an aggregate.[3]

Harmonic averages. A harmonic average of the relative prices in column (5) of Table 13-13, weighted by 1930 values, gives an index

---

[3] This may be readily demonstrated algebraically. The value of any commodity in the base year is $p_0 q_0$, while the price relative for a second year is $\frac{p_1}{p^0}$. The weighted mean

of such price relatives is equal to

$$\frac{\left(\frac{p_1'}{p_0'} \times p_0' q_0'\right) + \left(\frac{p_1''}{p_0''} \times p_0'' q_0''\right) + \left(\frac{p_1'''}{p_0'''} \times p_0''' q_0'''\right) + \cdots}{p_0' q_0' + p_0'' q_0'' + p_0''' q_0''' + \cdots}$$

which reduces to

$$\frac{\Sigma p_1 q_0}{\Sigma p_0 q_0}$$

a weighted aggregate of the type mentioned.

of 74.6 for 1930, on the 1929 base. This, it will be noted, is the same as the index yielded by the Paasche formula.[4] Similar measures for the other years covered are given in Table 13-15, column (3).

Geometric averages. The process of computing the weighted geometric mean is identical with that of computing the unweighted geometric mean, except that the logarithm of each relative is multiplied by the given weight and the sum of these weighted logarithms is divided by the sum of the weights, the result being the logarithm of the desired index. The method is illustrated in Table 13-14.

The index for 1930 on the 1929 base is 74.4. Measurements secured for all the years of the period covered are given in column (5), Table 13-15, together with the other weighted index numbers already explained.

How are we to judge of the relative merits of these three index numbers? We may, first, apply the time reversal test which was employed in comparing the five simple index numbers. This test is not met by any of the weighted types we have constructed. The geometric is equally at fault with the others. Though the simple geometric meets the test, the introduction of weighting imparts a bias to the result. Judged by that test alone none of the three is satisfactory. We may next try the second fundamental test that Fisher has developed, which is termed the "factor reversal test."

The Factor Reversal Test. The total value of a given commodity in a given year is, of course, the product of the quantity produced and the price per unit; algebraically, it is equal to $p'q'$. The ratio of the total value in one year to the total value in the preceding year is $\dfrac{p_1'q_1'}{p_0'q_0'}$. If, from one year to the next, both price and quantity should double, the price relative would be 200, the quantity relative 200, and the value relative 400. The total value in the second year would be four times the value in the first year. The value relative would be equal to the product of the price and

---

[4] By a process similar to that illustrated in the preceding footnote, the formula for a harmonic average of relative prices weighted by given year values may be reduced to the Paasche formula

$$\frac{\Sigma p_1 q_1}{\Sigma p_0 q_1}$$

TABLE 13–14

Computation of Weighted Geometric Average of Relative Prices, 1930
$(1929 = 100)$

Commodity	Relative price, 1930	Logarithm of relative price	Weight	Logarithm of relative price × weight
Corn	84.6	1.92737	1,947	3752.58939
Cotton	57.9	1.76268	1,163	2049.99684
Hay	103.5	2.01494	927	1867.84938
Wheat	58.0	1.76343	853	1504.20579
Oats	73.9	1.86864	474	885.73536
Potatoes, Wh.	69.1	1.83948	429	789.13692
Sugar	86.8	1.93852	250	484.63000
Barley	71.5	1.85431	153	283.70943
Tobacco	69.9	1.84448	281	518.29888
Flaxseed	49.2	1.69197	45	76.13865
Rye	45.2	1.65514	30	49.65420
Rice	77.7	1.89042	39	73.72638
			6,591	12,335.67122

$$\text{Log } M_g = \frac{\Sigma(\log p_1/p_0 \times p_0 q_0)}{\Sigma p_0 q_0}$$

$$= \frac{12,335.67122}{6591} = 1.871593$$

$$M_g = 74.4$$

quantity relatives, a relationship that is obvious in the case of a single commodity.

If, for a number of commodities, we use a given formula in constructing an index of the price change from one year to the next and an index of the quantity change from one year to the next, we should expect the product of the two indexes to be equal to the ratio of the total value of the commodities in the second year to their value in the first year. If the product is not equal to the value ratio there is, with reference to this test, an error in one or both of the index numbers.

As an illustration, we may apply the test to the formula for the first aggregative index constructed, based on the Laspeyres formula $\frac{\Sigma p_1 q_0}{\Sigma p_0 q_0}$. An index of quantities may be computed from this same formula, merely interchanging the q's and the p's; the formula becomes

$$Q_{01} = \frac{\Sigma q_1 p_0}{\Sigma q_0 p_0} \qquad (13.10)$$

The same price factor appears in numerator and denominator,

since we desire to measure only the effect of the quantity change. Substituting the given figures for the twelve farm crops we have, for 1930 on the 1929 base,

$$Q_{01} = \frac{\$6,287,520,870}{\$6,591,472,540} = 0.954$$

In percentage form the index of quantities produced in 1930 is 95.4, with 1929 as base. The corresponding price index, by the same formula, is 76.0. The product

$$P_{01} \cdot Q_{01} = 0.760 \times 0.954 = 0.7250$$

(In securing the product the index numbers are put in ratio, not in percentage form.) That is, if prices have decreased 24.0 percent, while quantities have decreased 4.6 percent, the total value should show a decrease of 27.5 percent.

For the value ratio, derived directly from the sums of the values of the individual commodities for 1929 and 1930, we have

$$V_{01} = \frac{\Sigma p_1 q_1}{\Sigma p_0 q_0} = \frac{\$4,690,816,010}{\$6,591,472,540} = 0.7116$$

As a measure of the magnitude of the error revealed by the factor reversal test we may use the formula proposed by Mudgett (Ref. 113)

$$E_2 = \frac{P_{01} \cdot Q_{01}}{V_{01}} - 1 \tag{13.11}$$

In the present case $E_2 = +0.0188$. The error is not great, but the formula definitely fails to meet the factor reversal test.

When this test is applied to the second aggregative index, that of Paasche, we secure the following values for 1930, with respect to 1929 as base:

$$P_{01} = \frac{\Sigma p_1 q_1}{\Sigma p_0 q_1} = \frac{\$4,690,816,010}{\$6,287,520,870} = 0.746$$

$$Q_{01} = \frac{\Sigma q_1 p_1}{\Sigma q_0 p_1} = \frac{\$4,690,816,010}{\$5,011,870,130} = 0.936$$

$$P_{01} \cdot Q_{01} = 0.746 \times 0.936 = 0.6983$$

In the computation of E_2 in this case we use, of course, the same V_{01} as in testing the Laspeyres index. For the Paasche formula $E_2 = -0.0187$. Here is an error of the same magnitude as for the Laspeyres index, but in the other direction.

The weighted geometric average also fails to meet this fundamental factor reversal test. With respect to both the geometric index and the aggregates we have, apparently, by the introduction of weights spoiled index numbers which in their simple form were unbiased. Yet weights we must have, if the index numbers are to represent the facts accurately. Neither a simple index nor a weighted form of a simple index will meet the two tests laid down as fundamental. Professor Fisher tested 46 such formulas, of which only 4 (the simple geometric, median, mode, and aggregative) met the time reversal test, and none met the factor reversing test. (The latter test, of course, is applicable only to weighted index numbers).

The "Ideal" Index. A way out of this difficulty is offered by the possibility of "rectifying" formulas in a crossing process, by averaging geometrically formulas that err in opposite directions. Professor Fisher has made exhaustive trials of all possible formulas by this process, finding 13 formulas in all which met both tests. Of these he has selected one as "ideal," from the viewpoint of both accuracy and simplicity of calculation. This ideal index is the geometric mean of the two aggregative types illustrated above. Its formula[5] is

$$I_{01} = \sqrt{\frac{\Sigma p_1 q_0}{\Sigma p_0 q_0} \times \frac{\Sigma p_1 q_1}{\Sigma p_0 q_1}} \qquad (13.12)$$

or, using the customary symbols for the Laspeyres and Paasche formulas,

$$I_{01} = \sqrt{L \cdot P} \qquad (13.13)$$

This index may be computed readily, in the present instance, from the results already obtained. Thus for 1930 we have

$$\text{Ideal index} = \sqrt{0.760 \times 0.746}$$
$$= 0.753$$

In the customary percentage form this is 75.3.

This index number meets both the time reversal and the factor

---

[5] The same formula was developed independently by Bowley, Pigou, Walsh, Young, and Fisher.

reversal test. For use in the first of these, when year "0" is 1929 and year "1" is 1930, we have from the ideal formula

$$P_{01} = 75.3$$

$$P_{10} = 132.8$$

Hence

$$E_1 = (0.753 \times 1.328) - 1 = 0$$

For the factor reversal test we need, in addition, a quantity index derived from the ideal formula. This is

$$Q_{01} = 94.5$$

From P_{01}, Q_{01}, and the previously derived V_{01} we have

$$E_2 = \frac{(0.753 \times 0.945)}{0.7116} - 1 = 0$$

It is a distinctive feature of the ideal index that it represents a blending of opposing biases. The base-year weighted arithmetic average of relatives (which is the mathematical equivalent of the Laspeyres index) has an upward type bias, a downward weight bias. The given-year weighted harmonic average (the mathematical equivalent of the Paasche index) has a downward type bias, an upward weight bias. The two formulas that embody the opposing type and weight biases are, in the ideal formula, crossed geometrically, i.e., by an averaging process that of itself has no bias. The result is the complete cancellation of biases of the kinds revealed by time reversal and factor reversal tests.

Comparison of weighted index numbers. The ideal index, the two weighted aggregates that enter into its construction, and the geometric mean weighted by values in the base year are given in Table 13-15 for the years 1929 to 1945. The index numbers are plotted in Fig. 13.4.

The wide discrepancies that were found between the various simple index numbers do not appear when the weighted indexes are compared. There are significant differences, but there is none of the erratic behavior of some of the simpler forms.

Of these four types the ideal index probably serves as the best measure of the average price change between 1929 and each of the given years. It is designed, it should be remembered, to measure the change between two stated times, and not for intermediate comparison. The value of the index for 1945, for instance, is

TABLE 13–15

Comparison of Weighted Index Numbers of Farm Crop Prices 1929-1945

(1)	(2)	(3)	(4)	(5)
	Aggregative (weighted by base year quantities)	Aggregative (weighted by given year quantities)	Ideal index Geometric mean of indices in cols.	Weighted geometric average of relatives (weighted by base year values)
Year	$\dfrac{\Sigma p_1 q_0}{\Sigma p_0 q_0}$	$\dfrac{\Sigma p_1 q_1}{\Sigma p_0 q_1}$	(2) and (3)	
1929	100.0	100.0	100.0	100.0
1930	76.0	74.6	75.3	74.4
1931	49.5	48.3	48.9	47.7
1932	35.9	34.9	35.4	34.0
1933	60.7	60.0	60.3	60.1
1934	94.7	90.3	92.5	91.1
1935	70.0	68.9	69.4	69.1
1936	103.0	100.3	101.6	100.9
1937	66.4	65.3	65.8	64.6
1938	56.5	56.1	56.3	55.5
1939	65.5	65.8	65.6	64.9
1940	66.4	66.3	66.3	65.5
1941	89.7	88.6	89.1	88.4
1942	105.7	104.0	104.8	103.7
1943	136.5	135.8	136.1	134.1
1944	138.2	139.1	138.6	136.6
1945	142.3	143.3	142.8	140.2

determined by the relation between prices and quantities in 1929 and 1945. There is double weighting and the weights vary from year to year. If 1945 is to be compared with 1939 a new index is needed, in which the prices and quantities for 1945 and 1939 alone are included. Direct comparison on the basis of the values for the ideal index given in Table 13-15 is liable to error, because of the weighting system employed.

The circular test. This last point calls for brief comment. If in the use of index numbers interest attaches not merely to a comparison of two years (i.e., to a binary comparison) but to the measurement of price changes over a period of years, it is frequently desirable to shift the base. Thus for any one of the index-number types given in Table 13-15 we might wish to change the base from 1929 to 1939. For many purposes 1939 is a more significant base of comparison for the war years and those following than is 1929. The question at once arises: Would the index derived by this shifting process for a given year, say 1945, on 1939 as base, be

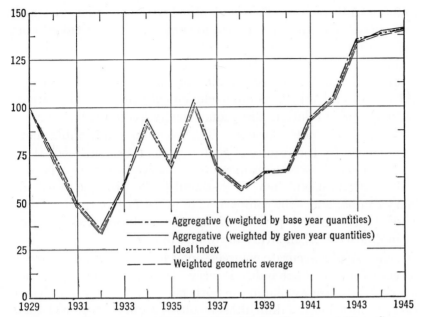

FIG. 13.4. Comparison of Three Weighted Index Numbers of Farm Crop Prices, 1929-1945 (1929 = 100).

equal to the index for 1945 on 1939 as base that would have been obtained had the 1945 index been computed, in the first instance, by the same formula, with 1939 as base? A test of this "shiftability" of base is called the circular test. To exemplify this test we may use the symbol P_{12} for a price index (for year "2" on year "1" as base) derived in the usual fashion for comparison of prices in two specified years, and the symbol P'_{12} for an index derived by a base-shifting procedure. Thus if the original base were year "0," a base-shifting procedure would give us

$$P'_{12} = \frac{P_{02}}{P_{01}} \qquad (13.14)$$

The circular test (which amounts, in fact, to a modification of the time reversal test) is met when $P'_{12} = P_{12}$.

The circular test is not met by the ideal index or by any of the weighted aggregatives with changing weights. The test, as applied to weighted index numbers, is met by an aggregative index with constant weights, and by the geometric mean with constant weights. Thus if we should shift the base from 1929 to 1939, for the indexes in column (5) of Table 13-15, the index for 1945 becomes

216.0 (i.e., 140.2/64.9). This is identical with the index we should have obtained from a geometric average of the individual commodity relatives for 1945, on 1939 as base, using 1929 values as weights. (The weights need not have been drawn from the base of the original index numbers, 1929. Any set of constant weights, used for P' and for P, would yield indexes meeting the circular test, when price relatives are geometrically averaged.)

Summary: alternative formulas. The selection of a formula should be influenced by the results of such tests as those outlined. It will also be affected by the purpose to be served, and by the data available. It is useful here to distinguish the problem faced in a binary comparison—the comparison of prices at two specified dates or for two specified periods—from the task of constructing a continuing series of monthly or annual indexes.

When a single, accurate comparison of just two periods is sought, the case for the ideal index is very strong, provided price and quantity data are available for both periods. This formula comes closest to meeting the difficulties resulting from economic changes. Since it meets the factor reversal test it has the special merit of giving consistent price and quantity indexes. By the use of this formula, that is, it is possible to break a value change into consistent price and quantity components—an objective given top priority by Mudgett (Ref. 113). The second choice would be a modification of the ideal formula recommended by Edgeworth and Marshall, and usually termed the Edgeworth formula. This is

$$\frac{\Sigma(q_0 + q_1)p_1}{\Sigma(q_0 + q_1)p_0} \tag{13.15}$$

It is a simple aggregative index, using as weights the sum of quantities for both base and given years. Thus it takes account of the regimens of both periods. It is a simple, readily constructed measure, giving a very close approximation to the result obtained from the ideal formula. Table 13-16 illustrates the method of computation. The other two formulas here suggested for binary comparisons are those of Laspeyres and Paasche. Either one involves use of weights from a single regimen. Whether these should be selected from the base period (Laspeyres) or taken from the given period (Paasche) will depend on the purpose to be served.

In the construction of a continuing series of index numbers, such as the Bureau of Labor Statistics' series measuring changes in

TABLE 13–16

Computation of Aggregative Index, Weighted by Combined Quantities

(1) Commodity	(2) Unit	(3) Price 1929	(4) Quantity 1929 + quantity 1930 (in millions)	(5) Price 1929 × sum of quantities col. (3) × col. (4)	(6) Price 1930	(7) Price 1930 × sum of quantities col. (6) × col. (4)
Corn	Bu.	$ .774	4,596	$ 3,557,304,000	$ .655	$ 3,010,380,000
Cotton	Lb.	.164	13,747	2,254,508,000	.095	1,305,965,000
Hay	Ton(sh.)	12.19	139.73	1,703,308,700	12.62	1,763,392,600
Wheat	Bu.	1.035	1,710.7	1,770,574,500	.600	1,026,420,000
Oats	Bu.	.426	2,388	1,017,288,000	.315	752,220,000
Potatoes (Wh)	Bu.	1.288	677.2	872,233,600	.890	602,708,000
Sugar	Lb.	.038	13,028	495,064,000	.033	429,924,000
Barley	Bu.	.544	582.2	316,716,800	.389	226,475,800
Tobacco	Lb.	.183	3,181	582,123,000	.128	407,168,000
Flaxseed	Bu.	2.843	37.6	106,896,800	1.398	52,564,800
Rye	Bu.	.849	80.79	68,590,710	.384	31,023,360
Rice	Bu.	.995	84.46	84,037,700	.773	65,287,580
				$12,828,645,810		$ 9,673,529,140

$$\frac{\Sigma(q_0 + q_1)p_1}{\Sigma(q_0 + q_1)p_0} = \frac{\$ 9,673,529,140}{\$12,828,645,810}$$

$$= 75.4 \text{ (index for 1930 on 1929 base, in percentage form)}$$

wholesale prices, the choice of formulas is more restricted. The Paasche, the ideal, and the Edgeworth-Marshall formulas are virtually ruled out, because "given-period" quantity data (i.e., data for the current month or year) are not available for the range of commodities represented by the price quotations used. The formula usually employed in such work is that of Laspeyres, in which base period weights are used, or a modification of Laspeyres employing fixed weights drawn from a year, or other period, other than the base period. The formula for this type of weighted aggregative may be written

$$\frac{\Sigma p_1 q_a}{\Sigma p_0 q_a} \qquad (13.16)$$

where the q_a's represent quantities for the year, or period, "a", which is not the base period. In making its current wholesale price index the Bureau of Labor Statistics uses weights for 1947 (a census year), while the base of the published indexes is the average of 1947, 1948, and 1949. The weighted aggregative represented by the formula cited above is the most generally useful type for a continuing series of index numbers.

A third and very satisfactory index type for a continuing series is the geometric mean of price relatives, weighted by constant-value weights which may or may not come from the base year. The general formula for the logarithm of such a weighted geometric mean is

$$\text{Log } M_g = \frac{\Sigma(\log p_1/p_0) \, p_a q_a}{\Sigma p_a q_a} \qquad (13.17)$$

where p_a and q_a represent the prices and quantities of individual commodities for either the base period or some other period. They must, of course, be constant. The geometric mean is a logical average, when ratios or relative prices are being combined. With fixed weights it is a flexible measure; the base may be shifted at will for it meets the circular test. It does not meet the time or factor reversal tests. If sampling error is a consideration, one must note that the geometric mean is more stable than the ideal, the Laspeyres, or the Paasche indexes. However, since samples of commodities to be used in the construction of index numbers are practically never "probability samples" (i.e., they are not selected by random sampling procedures[6]), this is not a controlling factor.

Changes in Regimen and the Comparison of Price Levels

In the opening pages of this chapter the fact was noted that the degree of dispersion found in frequency distributions of price relatives generally increases with the length of time covered in price comparisons. (Great economic disturbances such as those brought by war may, of course, cause wide dispersion over a short period.) Hence, on statistical grounds, there is justification for the conclusion that the accuracy of well-constructed price indexes is high for measurements extending over a short interval, and becomes progressively lower as the range of time comparison increases. This conclusion now calls for further consideration.

In Laspeyres' formula

$$L = \frac{\Sigma p_1 q_0}{\Sigma p_0 q_0}$$

the price factor alone varies, as between numerator and denominator. The weighting factor q_0 is assumed to relate to a system marked by complete constancy of consumption habits, living

[6] See Chapter 16.

standards, production coefficients, income distribution, and all other nonprice attributes of the economy. This environment, or milieu, for which Sir George Knibbs has used the term "regimen," is taken to be common to the two periods compared. Although the weights we employ may be merely quantities entering into trade, or quantities consumed, they have, in fact, much wider significance. They are assumed to define, directly or indirectly, all the attributes, other than price, of the economic system that prevails at a stated time. If these attributes are held constant as between the two periods compared, then we may expect to measure with accuracy the one factor that does change—the prices of economic goods. The condition we have here assumed is the orthodox one of *ceteris paribus*, the condition that factors other than the one subject to study remain unchanged.

In fact, of course, the regimen does not remain fixed. Changes in tastes and in consumption habits occur; changes in types of goods used as capital equipment take place; incomes shift, and the flow of goods is altered by changes in the distribution of buying power among consuming groups; the very price changes that we seek to measure bring alterations in the demand for given types of goods and in the quantities produced. Of no small moment in the total situation are the changes that occur in the quality of goods that continue to pass by the same trade names. The automobile of 1955 is the same commodity, by name, as the automobile of 1910, but to the average consumer the later model represents quite a different bundle of utilities. Similarly, steel, textiles, locomotives, even the staple articles of diet have undergone important quality changes. A comparison of price levels in 1910 and 1955 that depends for its accuracy on the assumption that all elements of economic life except prices have remained constant is suspect, indeed.

Our difficulties are not removed if we take as the standard of reference the regimen of the second of the two periods compared. This is done in Paasche's formula,

$$P = \frac{\Sigma p_1 q_1}{\Sigma p_0 q_1}$$

The system of consumption standards and all that goes with it may be of modern vintage in this case, but the differences between the regimens of the two periods compared is just as wide. We have not, in fact, held constant nonprice factors, and our measurement of price changes loses in accuracy, as a result.

The method exemplified by the ideal formula, that of employing weighting factors drawn from both periods, represents one attempt at the solution of this problem, but it is far from perfect. The use of quantities drawn from the two regimens does not create a common regimen, the indispensable condition of full accuracy in such comparisons.

The practical procedure in the face of this difficulty is to restrict our comparisons, if high accuracy is required, to periods not widely different in regimen. This will ordinarily mean periods not widely separated in time. Consumption habits, living standards, and technical production methods will be not widely dissimilar in two such periods, and hence the number of identical commodities common to the two periods will be large. Under these conditions considerable confidence may be placed in index numbers measuring average price changes. Comparison of price levels over longer periods may be desired, and may be justified, but the margin of error in the measurements may be expected to increase as the time span extends. Formal precision in weighting and in the selection of acceptable formulas will not provide an escape from the unavoidable difficulties arising out of alterations in the basic conditions of economic life. Real continuity of indexes covering a stretch of years is possible only on the basis of a persisting common regimen.

The regimen changes that come during a short period marked by transition from peace to war, or from war to peace, may be as great as those that come during long periods of peacetime existence, and the same difficulties are faced in measuring price-level changes. Thus all the reservations that attach to the comparison of price levels in years far apart in time attach to comparisons of peacetime and wartime price levels.

The fundamental consideration here is, of course, the magnitude of regimen differences between two stated periods. As an index of this magnitude Mudgett has proposed the quantity D, defined as

$$D = L - P \qquad (13.18)$$

That is, D is the difference between Laspeyres and Paasche indexes. If the regimen defined by the q_0's is very close to that defined by the q_1's, the two indexes will be close together; with widely different regimens the two will be far apart. There is no absolute criterion of "closeness," but the quantity D, considered with reference to the precision desired in a given comparison, gives a basis for accepting or rejecting a given measure. Thus for the Laspeyres and Paasche indexes of farm crop prices for 1945 (on the 1929 base) given in Table 13-15, we have

$$D = 142.3 - 143.3 = -1.0$$

This difference amounts to less than 1 percent. The error attributable to regimen change may be regarded as not serious if an error margin of 1 percent in the desired index is tolerable.

When a continuing series of monthly or annual index numbers is to be made, the problems posed by regimen changes are perplexing. They are, indeed, not open to any completely satisfactory solution. The procedure commonly employed in the face of these difficulties is to construct a series of indexes on a fixed base, with constant weights, but to change the weight base frequently. Thus it is the present intention of the Bureau of Labor Statistics to change the weight base of its wholesale price index every five years, with minor interim adjustments for individual commodities. This device, it is believed, will prevent the constant weights from becoming badly in error.

Chain indexes. The merits of an alternative method, involving the chaining of link relatives, has been very strongly urged by Bruce D. Mudgett (Ref. 113). Link relatives P_{01}, P_{12}, P_{23}, etc., are constructed for successive periods not far apart in time, say for successive years. The comparison of price levels by means of a link relating to two such periods, close together in time and with similar regimens, will be accurate if such an index as the ideal is used. The successive links are then chained, by multiplication, in deriving measures of price change between nonconsecutive periods. Thus we should have

$$P_{02} = P_{01} \cdot P_{12}$$
$$P_{03} = P_{01} \cdot P_{12} \cdot P_{23} = P_{02} \cdot P_{23}$$

Unfortunately there is no clear criterion for choosing between fixed-base and chain indexes. The two methods will give different results in a comparison of nonsuccessive periods; since neither may be accepted as accurate we may not say that the divergence is a measure of the "error" in either index. The fixed-base method clears the gap between year 0 and year n in one jump, assuming an unchanging regimen. The chain method takes account of the regimens of all intervening years. It is argued that we may more effectively bridge a gap between widely dissimilar regimens by this device, allowing our final results to be affected by all the shifts in consumer habits, production coefficients, income levels, income distribution, etc., that have occurred in the years between. But there is no test of the validity of this argument. It is perhaps safe to rest on the fact that there is no accurate method of comparing price levels in periods marked by widely different regimens. Margins of error will be wide, in such comparisons, whatever method of measurement be employed.

The detailed discussion of procedures in the preceding pages has clearly shown that there are some definitely faulty formulas, obviously unsuited for use in the construction of index numbers serving ordinary purposes. Among the better formulas there are some differences in respect of liability to bias and character of data needed, and some variations in sampling reliability. The maker of index numbers will have these in mind in choosing a formula to employ under given conditions. A more important factor in his choice, however, will be the purpose to be served by the index number, the question it is designed to answer. A weighted aggregate of actual prices answers one question definitively. It gives, without equivocation, the aggregate cost of a fixed bill of goods at one period, in relation to the cost of the same bill of goods at another. A geometric mean of relative prices answers another question. It measures with accuracy the average *ratio* of the prices of given commodities at one period to corresponding prices at another period. Some questions (for example, that answered by an unweighted arithmetic average of relative prices) have little if any economic significance. It is because one or two main questions have bulked large in economic discussion that emphasis has been placed upon the finding of a "best" type of index number. Yet the terms "best" and "ideal" are unfortunate, for they imply that some absolute standard exists, with reference to which all formulas may be tested. No such absolute criterion may be applied to the diversity of research problems that call for the construction of index numbers. On the basis of his knowledge of the characteristics of different formulas, the discriminating investigator will choose technical methods adapted to his data and appropriate to his purposes.

Other Problems in the Construction of Index Numbers of Commodity Prices

The preceding section has dealt with the technical problems connected with the averaging of a given set of data in order to secure an index number of price variations. Of equal importance with problems of averaging and weighting are practical questions connected with the gathering of basic data. Since it is impossible to cover the universe of price quotations during a given period, recourse must be had to the method of sampling. In seeking to obtain a representative sample, primary importance attaches to the number of commodities and the character of the commodities to be used in making a given index number.

Commodities to be included. Here again we are confronted with a relation that has already been mentioned, the relation between methods and uses. Decision as to the number of commodities and the kinds of commodities to be included in a given case must rest upon the purpose for which the index is to be constructed. In general, of course, a large sample is better than a small one. The frequency polygon based upon price relatives derived from a large sample will approach more closely to the curve that would represent the universe of price relatives than will that based upon a small sample. Thus, as a measure of general movements of wholesale prices, more confidence may be placed in the present Bureau of Labor Statistics index, which is based on some 2,000 commodity series, than on the Bureau's earlier index, which was based on about 900 price series. A large sample is particularly desirable when group index numbers are to be constructed for small subdivisions of the price universe. Yet index numbers based upon a small number of well-selected quotations must not be ruled out as without value. They can provide at modest expense good approximations to the results that large samples will give for the broad movements of prices. Moreover, for certain special purposes index numbers based upon a limited number of quotations may be preferable. This is particularly true when a "sensitive" index is desired, one that will serve as a forecaster of general price movements rather than as a precise measure of changes in the general price level. Of this type was the Harvard sensitive price index based upon quotations on 13 basic commodities (raw materials). The purposes of such an index are served by the selection of a

limited number of commodities the prices of which are subject to
extreme fluctuations, rather than by the inclusion of a great many
commodities. As a contemporary measure of the same sort we may
cite the Bureau of Labor Statistics daily index of spot market
prices that includes 22 series. Yet the uses to which an index of
this type may be put are limited. The "sluggishness" of the many-
commodities index number is a sluggishness which inheres in the
price system, and which must be reflected in a faithful index of
general prices.

The question of the number of commodities to be included
cannot be discussed apart from that of the character of these
commodities. The representative character of an index number
rests in part upon the number of price series included, but the
nature of these series is of even greater importance. For there are
highly significant differences in the behavior of the prices of
different commodity groups. These groups of prices, their inter-
relations, their behavior, their relation to the functioning of the
economic system and to the swings of prosperity and depression,
are matters of immediate and practical importance to economists
and business men.

Since an index number of wholesale prices must rest upon
sample quotations, the sample must be representative, must include commodities whose prices are typical of the various elements
in the price system. The division into elements for this purpose
may be based upon the character of the price changes peculiar to
the different groups. Of the groups thus distinguished, the most
obvious are those representing different industries. Textile prices
and steel prices, leather prices and the prices of chemicals are
subject to different influences. Trade depressions and revivals do
not affect all industries at the same time or in the same way, so
that an index of wholesale prices must include quotations from all
important industrial groups. If preponderant influence upon an
index is exerted by the prices of products of certain industries, the
index, by that much, loses its representative character.

But it is not sufficient that different industries be given appropriate representation in the sample. Differences in price behavior
are related to differences of origin (e.g., farm and nonfarm products), to differences of ultimate use (e.g., for capital equipment and
for human consumption), to differences in durability, and to
differences in the controllability of supply, particularly over short

periods. Producer goods differ in their price movements from consumer goods (the latter being goods—raw or fabricated—that are ready for use by final consumers). Fundamental, too are differences in price behavior that are related to differences in degree of fabrication. All these classifications (and others not mentioned) cut across one another, to reveal a universe of commodity prices that is highly heterogeneous in its patterns of price behavior. A thoroughly representative index of wholesale prices should be based, therefore, upon price quotations drawn from these various commodity groups, with weight given to each in proportion to the relative importance in trade of the commodities in each category. The coverage of an index serving a special purpose would, of course, be restricted to groups and to commodities specified with reference to the purpose to be served.

The comparison base. Continuing series of index numbers, of the type represented by the various national indexes of price and living cost monthly or annual measures, are generally published as relatives with reference to some selected year or combination of years as base. The present consensus of opinion is that such a base period should not be too remote in time. Because of regimen change, and of price dispersion that generally increases with time, the margins of error in price comparisons grow as the time period increases. A corollary to this conclusion is that bases should be frequently changed. To hold to a base some 40 years removed in time, as is done in the construction of prices received and paid by farmers (now on the 1910-14 base), intensifies the difficulties of accurate measurement. There is, of course, no stated period at the end of which a base should be changed. International and domestic developments affecting the economic regimen, the availability of new weights, and similar considerations will affect such decisions.

In the practical task of selecting a base period some attention is paid to the state of business during periods that might be chosen. If the base of comparison and the weight base should be a period marked by conditions widely different from those usually prevalent, the accuracy of comparisons with preceding or subsequent periods would be reduced. This is not to say that we should seek as base a period that is to be regarded as "normal." The essence of economic life in modern industrial economies is change. No period provides a standard of normality, with reference to which conditions in subsequent periods may be appraised. In selecting a base for a continuing series of indexes, the index-number maker looks for a period in which conditions are not exceptionally disturbed, but he does not consider that the base serves in any sense as a criterion of what is normal. This statement applies with particular force to relations among commodity prices. These are in constant flux—as they must be in a dynamic world.

A comment may be made on the desirability of standardizing base periods. Numerous index numbers, relating to diverse processes, are now elements of the economic intelligence system of the United States, and of the system of world intelligence that is being slowly developed. When these various indexes are constructed on varying bases they are much less useful than they might be. A definite forward step has been taken in the United States by the Office of Statistical Standards in recommending that the average of 1947, 1948, and 1949 be employed as a standard base period for index numbers constructed by governmental agencies. This is an important beginning in the task of developing a comprehensive battery of comparable measurements covering major economic processes in the United States.

In the preceding pages we have dealt with the general problems that arise in the making of index numbers. In referring to practice we have been concerned primarily with wholesale prices. We now turn briefly to the problems faced in two special fields.[7]

Index Numbers of Consumer Prices

In the literature of index numbers considerable attention is given to the measurement of changes in the cost of living. The term "cost of living" has been an ambiguous one, and remains ambiguous in much current usage. In its most precise sense it involves the determination of the changing money costs of commodity incomes that yield equal real incomes (i.e., satisfactions) at different times or in different places. The ratio of aggregate money costs, in two situations, of chosen combinations of consumer goods that yield identical aggregate satisfactions would be the desired index of

[7] We do not give here detailed descriptions of methods employed in the construction of particular index numbers. These may be had from the agencies concerned. In the United States the Bureau of Labor Statistics constructs index numbers of wholesale prices and of consumer prices. The Agricultural Marketing Service of the Department of Agriculture constructs index numbers of prices received and paid by farmers, the parity index, and the derived parity ratio. The United Nations' *Monthly Bulletin of Statistics* gives the names of agencies making the chief index numbers of other countries.

living costs in these two situations. (The composition of the market basket of consumer goods may vary, provided only that different combinations yield equivalent satisfactions.) The conditions necessary to perfect accuracy in measuring changes in living costs so defined (conditions that include identical and unchanging want structures, or taste patterns, among all the consumers to whom the measure is to apply) are extraordinarily difficult of attainment. No "true" index of living costs is currently constructed.[8] Contemporary measures that go by that name may be more appropriately regarded as index numbers of prices paid by consumers.

This change in title has, indeed, been made by the U. S. Bureau of Labor Statistics. The full and revealing title of its "Consumer Price Index" is "Index of Changes in Prices of Goods and Services Purchased by City Wage-Earner and Clerical-Worker Families to Maintain their Level of Living."

The customary problems of index-number making are faced in constructing the consumer price index. Price changes must relate to a stated regimen (or to an average of regimens). This regimen is usually defined by weights based upon the expenditures of a representative sample of consumers in a stated period. For the present United States index the weights were derived from a comprehensive survey of consumer expenditures for food, clothing, furniture, and all other goods and services. This survey, made in 1950, included samples of families from the 12 largest urban areas and from a considerable sample of other cities. The "index market basket" as thus established for 1950 was modified to take account of changes occurring between 1950 and fiscal 1951-52, the latter year being the weight base now employed.

The regimen that is assumed to be constant, therefore, is that of the fiscal year 1951-1952. However, the base of comparison is the average of the years 1947-1949. The published index defines the level of consumer prices in given months or years with reference to the average for 1947, 1948, and 1949 as 100. The regimen is represented by a sample of 296 commodities and services. This

[8] However, we must note that precision in the measurement of changes in consumer prices has been materially advanced by the explorations of relevant theory. For a lucid discussion of the principles involved see R. Frisch, "Some Basic Principles of Price of Living Measurements," *Econometrica*, Vol. 22, No. 4 (October 1954). The basic theory of cost of living indexes, with an appraisal of the pioneer work of Konus, and of later studies by Staehle, Frisch, Haberler, Wald, Hicks, Allen, and others, is clearly set forth by Ulmer (Ref. 164).

market basket of goods bought by consumers in 1951-52 is assumed to remain the same in quantity and quality. The specifications of individual items are spelled out with precision. Prices for these goods, collected in 46 cities, provide the basic materials for the current index.

The general division of weights in this Consumer Price Index is of interest as an indication of the character of consumer budgets in the United States in the middle of the twentieth century.

Category	Relative importance (percentage)
Food	30
Housing (incl. heat, light, etc.)	32
Apparel	10
Transportation	11
Medical care	5
Personal care	2
Reading and recreation	5
Other goods and services	5
All items	100

We should note that these weights represent national averages. In the detailed work use is made of a set of weights for each of the 46 cities included. The weights for a given city are based on consumer expenditures in that city and in similar cities which it may be taken to represent. In combining measures for separate cities, each city is given a weight proportionate to the wage-earner and clerical-worker population it represents. Worker population weights and family expenditure weights are thus combined in the derivation of the national indexes.

In the construction of the Consumer Price Index the first step is the calculation of an index for the current month (or year) on the preceding month (or year) as base. The formula employed, which utilizes weighted arithmetic averages of relative prices, is equivalent to a modified Laspeyres of the form

$$I_{(i-1)i} = \frac{\Sigma p_i q_a}{\Sigma p_{(i-1)} q_a}$$

where p_i is the price of a given commodity for the current month (or year), $p_{(i-1)}$ is the price of that commodity for the preceding month (or year), and q_a is a quantity weight based on 1951-52 family expenditure patterns. $I_{(i-1)i}$ is a symbol for the price index for period i on the preceding period, $i - 1$, as base. The second step is the shift to the fixed base 1947-49, which we designate period 0. For this operation we have

$$I_{0i} = I_{0(i-1)} \cdot I_{(i-1)i}$$

where I_{0i} is the desired index for period i on period 0 as base, and $I_{0(i-1)}$ is the index for period $i-1$ (the "preceding period") on the period 0 as base.

The practical difficulties faced in constructing wholesale price indexes are multiplied in the making of consumer price indexes. Regimen changes in a dynamic economy tend to make weight structures out-dated, if not obsolete. Variations in commodity standards, in business practice, and in local customs intensify the problem of obtaining accurate and representative price quotations on goods that may be regarded as unchanging in their specifications. To these working difficulties have now been added responsibilities for administering an instrument on which wage adjustments affecting millions of workers are currently based, and on which important national policy determinations are made. The burden on the Bureau of Labor Statistics is not a light one.

Farm Prices and the Parity Index

A distinctive and important set of special purpose index numbers has been developed in the field of agricultural economics. These measures are of particular interest because since 1933, when the Agricultural Adjustment Act was passed, they have served as instruments of national policy in agriculture. Their current construction and use are determined in part by Congressional action.

This set of indexes is designed to define variations in the terms of exchange of farm producers. They include an index of prices received by farmers for the goods they sell, indexes of prices paid by farmers for items used in family living and in production, and a *parity index* based upon the indexes of prices paid plus interest on indebtedness secured by farm mortgages, taxes on farm real estate, and wages paid to hired farm labor. From the index of prices received and the parity index is derived the *parity ratio*, which serves as a measure of changes in the average purchasing power of farm products.

The index of prices received by farmers is a monthly measure, based upon the prices of about 50 farm products. Prices quoted are those received at points of first sale—local markets or other centers to which farmers deliver their products. Average prices for all grades and qualities are used, without the specifications that define grades in wholesale trade proper. These farm prices, therefore, are not to be identified with the wholesale prices in the great exchanges or in large cities for goods of specified grades that enter into the measures of the Bureau of Labor Statistics. The index is of the weighted aggregative type, with minor modifications to permit changes in weights and in number of commodities included. Weights are based on average quantities marketed; for the current index weights are drawn from the period 1937-1941. The base of the index is the average of the five years January, 1910–December, 1914. Group index numbers are published for crops and for livestock and livestock products, and for 13 smaller subdivisions.

The other member of the exchange or parity ratio for farmers is the composite measure now termed the parity index. Of the three components of the parity index the most important (weight about 44 percent of the total in 1953) is the index of prices paid for items used in family living. This covers prices paid by farmers throughout the nation for consumers' goods. Precise specifications are not defined for these goods; the prices quoted are for the qualities being currently purchased by farmers. The number of price series included was 194 in 1953. Reports are made through mail questionnaires by several thousand retail merchants, both chain store and independent. Weights are based on estimates of the amounts of the various goods and services purchased by farm families. The formula, like that used for the index of prices received, is of the weighted aggregative type. The index base is January, 1910–December, 1914.

The second component of the parity index, with a weight of about 37 percent of the total in 1953, is the index of prices paid for commodities used in farm production. The price series included number 192 (of which 42 are duplicates of series used in the family living index). These series are for such items as feed, seed, livestock, motor vehicles and supplies, fertilizer, and farm machinery. Source of quotations, weight base, index base, and formula are the same as for the index for family living. Both indexes are supplemented by detailed subgroup measures.

With these two indexes of prices paid are combined measures of changes in interest rates, taxes, and wages paid by farmers, to yield the parity index defining changes in the total cost to farmers of the commodities and services they buy. These last three elements taken together accounted in 1953 for about 19 percent of the total parity index. For any month or year the ratio of the index of prices received by farmers to the parity index defines the parity ratio for that period. This ratio is a measure of shifts in the terms of exchange of farmers with the rest of the economy, with reference to the terms prevailing during a base period extending from January, 1910, to December, 1914.

These various measures are given in Table 13-17 for the base period and recent years. As has been indicated, the parity ratio may be thought of as a measure of the purchasing power of an average unit of farm products. In 1953 farmers were receiving, for such an average unit, 158 percent more in current dollars than they were in 1910-14; however, the measures defining changes in the average costs to farmers of goods and services purchased (column

TABLE 13-17

Prices Received and Paid by Farmers, the Parity Index and the Parity Ratio
Selected Years, 1910-1914 to 1954

(1)	(2)	(3)	(4)	(5)	(6)
				Parity index	
Year	Prices received by farmers	Prices paid for items used in		(prices paid, interest, taxes, and wage rates)	Parity ratio (2) ÷ (5)
		Family living	Production		
1910–1914	100	100	100	100	100
1939	95	120	121	123	77
1940	100	121	123	124	81
1941	123	130	130	133	92
1942	158	149	148	152	104
1943	192*	166	164	171	112
1944	196*	175	173	182	108
1945	206*	182	176	190	108
1946	234*	202	191	208	112
1947	275	237	224	240	115
1948	285	251	250	260	110
1949	249	243	238	251	99
1950	256	246	246	256	100
1951	302	268	273	282	107
1952	288	271	274	287	100
1953	258	270	253	279	92
1954	250	274	252	281	89

* Includes certain wartime subsidy payments to farmers.

5), indicate an advance of 179 percent in such costs. The index measuring changes in the real worth, or purchasing power, of an average unit of farm products had fallen from 100, in the base period, to 92 (the ratio of 258 to 279) in 1953—a decline of 8 percent from the "parity" level.

The parity index (column (5) of Table 13-17) is of key importance in the price support program for agricultural products. It is used not only in the derivation of the general parity ratio that has been cited. The parity price of a specific commodity for a given period is obtained by multiplying the base-period price of that commodity by the parity index for the period in question.[9] This parity price provides the basis on which price support levels are determined for that commodity.

The battery of measures relating to prices paid and prices received by farmers are revealing measures of economic change, notable as the products of the most comprehensive attempt ever made to define shifts in the buying and selling relations of a single major group of producers. In this brief summary we have traced certain of the distinctive features of these index numbers. We have noted that the prices received are not prices quoted in the great wholesale centers, but prices realized in first sales by producers. Since they are averages of qualities and grades, and not quotations on commodities of unvarying specifications, their movements may reflect shifts in the average quality of products marketed, as well as price changes proper. This last comment applies with special force to the index of prices paid by farmers. No fixed specifications are set forth here. The prices reported are those for qualities being currently purchased by farmers; if these qualities go up, the movement of the reported price will reflect the improvement in average quality of goods purchased. Thus the index of prices paid for family living, which is in a sense a "cost of living" index for farmers, differs from the consumer price index of the Bureau of Labor Statistics, which uses fixed specifications. The parity index and the consumer price index cover different universes, by different methods.

The period covered by farm price indexes exceeds 40 years—a long stretch of time, for accurate comparison in a dynamic economy. On technical and logical grounds the statistician could wish

---

[9] This statement refers to the so-called "old formula." A "new formula," providing for the use of a moving base period (the ten preceding years) has been written into law.

that a later base of comparison were employed (the 1910-14 base is set, of course, by law). However, the use for recent years of the 1937-41 weight-base (which is soon to be adjusted to take account of postwar patterns of living and production) serves, at least, to introduce comparatively modern weights, and thus sharpens the measures of recent shifts in the farmer's terms of exchange.

Price Index Numbers as Instruments of "Deflation"

Index numbers of prices are used frequently to reduce a monetary series to "real" terms. In one form, this is a process of deflating a series of values expressed in current dollars (or other monetary units). The purpose is to obtain an adjusted series that has been corrected for changes in the worth of the monetary unit. This adjusted series is said to be in "constant dollars," or in dollars of constant purchasing power. The rather loose terminology and practice in this field cover problems of three distinct, although related, types.

Measurement of Shifts in the Terms of Exchange. The measurement of these shifts, which have been spoken of earlier, is not usually thought of as involving deflation, but it is useful to view this as a phase of a broader procedure. In simple terms, we may consider the prices p_a and p_b of Commodities A and B in years 0 and 1:

		Price in	
		Year 0	Year 1
p_a	Actual	$1.00	$1.20
	Rel.	100	120
p_b	Actual	.50	.30
	Rel.	100	60
p_a/p_b		100	200

From the absolute price it is clear that in Year 0, 100 units of Commodity A would exchange for 200 units of Commodity B; in Year 1, 100 units of Commodity A would exchange for 400 units of Commodity B. The terms of exchange had moved in favor of the producers of Commodity A. The shift in these terms is defined by the ratio of the price relatives, which has advanced from 100 to 200.

In general terms we may think of such a relation as the ratio of average unit prices received to average unit prices paid—that is,

P_r/P_p. An increase in this ratio means improvement for the producers represented by P_r. If P_r should be the hourly wage rate for manufacturing workers and P_p the Consumer Price Index, the ratio becomes a measure of changes in "real" hourly wages. If P_r is an index of prices received by farmers and P_p an index of the prices of all goods and services bought by them, the ratio is a measure of the per-unit worth of farm products in terms of goods purchased by farmers—the familiar "parity ratio" previously discussed. If P_r is an index of export prices and P_p an index of prices of goods imported, the ratio P_r/P_p measures changes in the per-unit worth of exports in terms of goods imported. The comparison as thus expressed is always in unit terms (i.e., it measures shifts in purchasing power *per unit* of goods given in exchange). It has significance to the extent that the two index numbers accurately define prices of goods or services that are in fact exchanged. In an exchange system a ratio of this sort has significance, of course, for every individual and every group in the economy, and for every national economy that has dealings with other economies.

Measurement of Changes in Aggregate Purchasing Power. By a simple extension, the measurement of changes in purchasing power may be shifted from a unit to an aggregative basis. If instead of unit prices received we have a series of disposable value aggregates, the aggregate purchasing power of these totals may be derived by deflating the sums by appropriate index numbers of prices paid. If we represent by V_d a disposable value aggregate, by P_p an index of average unit prices paid by those who disburse V_d, and by Q_c the aggregate worth of V_d in terms of goods commanded, the process is given by

$$Q_c = \frac{V_d}{P_p}$$

Numerous examples of this kind of deflation could be cited. If we divide changes in the total wages received by manufacturing workers in given years by appropriate index numbers of consumer prices we have measures of changes in the aggregate real income of these workers. Changes in the real income of farmers may be similarly derived. The essence of this type of deflation is, of course, the division of the value aggregates, or of relatives based thereon, by a price index of the goods and services for which the sums are actually spent.

Conversion of Dollar Sums into Physical Volume Equivalents.
This is the most familiar form of deflation. We may have a series
of annual values of building construction and wish to estimate the
changes in the physical volume of building. Or we may have Gross
National Product for a series of years, in current dollars, and wish
to reduce these sums to terms of constant dollars. Here it is not
the "quantities commanded" by a series of value aggregates but
the physical volume equivalents of these value aggregates that we
wish to estimate. We should like to eliminate the effects of price
changes on these value aggregates, in order to reveal the undis-
torted quantity changes. The heart of this problem lies, again, in
the correct choice of the price index to be used as deflator.

If we are dealing with value aggregates for two years only,
(i.e., if a binary comparison is involved) the best solution of the
problem is given by the ideal index. As we have seen, this index
meets the factor reversal test, i.e., price, quantity, and value index
numbers are mutually consistent. What this means with reference
to the present problem is that when we divide a value index
$\left(\dfrac{\Sigma p_1 q_1}{\Sigma p_0 q_0} \right)$ by a price index constructed from the ideal formula
$\sqrt{ \dfrac{\Sigma p_1 q_0}{\Sigma p_0 q_0} \cdot \dfrac{\Sigma p_1 q_1}{\Sigma p_0 q_1} }$, we derive a quantity index constructed by the ideal
formula, $\sqrt{ \dfrac{\Sigma q_1 p_0}{\Sigma q_0 p_0} \cdot \dfrac{\Sigma q_1 p_1}{\Sigma q_0 p_1} }$. That is, the derived quantity index has
been weighted by prices representing the regimens of both base
and given years.

Deflation of a value index by a Laspeyres price index (i.e.,
division of $\dfrac{\Sigma p_1 q_1}{\Sigma p_0 q_0}$ by $\dfrac{\Sigma p_1 q_0}{\Sigma p_0 q_0}$) yields a quantity index with price
weights drawn from the second of the two years compared—i.e., a
quantity index constructed by Paasche's formula, $\dfrac{\Sigma q_1 p_1}{\Sigma q_0 p_1}$. Thus, in
effect, this type of deflation shifts the regimen, as we pass from
price to quantity comparisons, from the base year to the given year.
Similarly, deflation of a value index by a Paasche price index (i.e.,
division of $\dfrac{\Sigma p_1 q_1}{\Sigma p_0 q_0}$ by $\dfrac{\Sigma p_1 q_1}{\Sigma p_0 q_1}$) yields a quantity index with price
weights drawn from the base year—i.e., a quantity index con-
structed from Laspeyres' formula, $\dfrac{\Sigma q_1 p_0}{\Sigma q_0 p_0}$. If we are deflating a value

series covering a number of years, and wish to derive quantity indexes that are really weighted by constant base year prices, price indexes with quantity weights drawn from successive "given" years (i.e., Paasche indexes) should be the deflators.[10] This is not a practicable procedure. The usual process is to deflate by a Laspeyres price index, which has the effect indicated above, or by a modified Laspeyres, with q_a weights. The result is a somewhat hybrid type of quantity index, affected by the regimens of base year, given year, and the year a which is the weight base. We face here again, therefore, the difficulties that arise from regimen changes. If these are moderate, the particular manner in which the deflator is weighted does not greatly matter. If regimen changes have been great over the period covered, deflation is inevitably a less accurate process. In general, short-period comparisons of deflated value series will be more accurate than comparisons covering longer periods of time.

We must recognize, of course, that no factoring process of the sort described in the preceding paragraphs actually gives us measures of the quantity changes that would have occurred had there been no price movements. No algebraic manipulation can offset the results of the infinitely complex economic changes that occur over even the shortest period of time. But approximations serve useful purposes, and in such approximations mathematical consistency is desirable. More important than the choice of formula, in such deflation procedures, is the selection of appropriate price quotations in making the deflating index. The commodities and services represented should be those that enter into the value aggregate that is to be deflated. (Here, of course, the situation is quite different from that faced when we are concerned with purchasing power and seek to measure quantity commanded.) Deflation by inappropriate price indexes is one of the commonest sins of economic practice.

The most ambitious task of deflation economists have attempted has been that of reducing national income or national product

---

[10] We may express the conclusions of the preceding argument in a slightly different form. Price and quantity indexes that are mutually consistent, in that their product is equal to the value index, may be constructed by means of Laspeyres and Paasche formulas if the Laspeyres formula is used for one index and the Paasche formula for the other. Thus a base-year weighted Laspeyres price index multiplied by a given-year weighted Paasche quantity index will equal the true value index. The same would be true of a Paasche price index and a Laspeyres quantity index.

estimates, in current dollars, to terms of "constant" dollars. The usual procedure here is deflation in detail, rather than deflation of the grand totals by a single process of division. Deflation in detail involves the construction of deflators for separate components, each deflator being tailored to the task of correcting for price changes in a small segment of the total economy.[11]

An example of the process of deflation. The *Engineering News Record* compiles statistics on heavy engineering contracts awarded in the United States, by months and years. These cover large buildings (industrial, commercial, and public) and other heavy construction projects—highways, waterworks, bridges, etc. For the purpose of reducing the dollar totals for these projects to physical-volume equivalents, an index of building costs and an index of

TABLE 13–18

Actual and Deflated Values of Building Contracts Awarded, 1939-1953

(1) Year	(2) (3) Total value of building contracts awarded		(4) Index of building costs†	(5) Index of building volume (3) ÷ (4)
	Actual* (in millions of dollars)	Relative		
1939	1,264	100.0	100.0	100.0
1940	2,190	173.3	102.7	168.7
1941	3,768	298.1	107.1	278.3
1942	6,170	488.1	112.6	433.5
1943	1,817	143.7	115.9	124.0
1944	972	76.9	118.9	64.7
1945	1,485	117.5	121.1	97.0
1946	3,373	266.9	132.8	201.0
1947	3,375	267.0	158.5	168.5
1948	4,145	327.9	174.5	187.9
1949	5,092	402.8	178.2	226.0
1950	9,529	753.9	190.2	396.4
1951	9,457	748.2	202.9	368.8
1952	11,466	907.1	210.5	430.9
1953	9,911	784.1	218.2	359.3

* Contracts for large buildings only are here included. Value minima are given in the *Engineering News Record*. I am indebted to the *Engineering News Record* for the basic data.
† Components of the building cost index include structural steel shapes, Portland cement, lumber, and skilled labor, with appropriate weights.

[11] For details of the work done by the National Income Unit of the U. S. Department of Commerce in deflating Gross National Product see the latest National Income supplement to the *Survey of Current Business*.

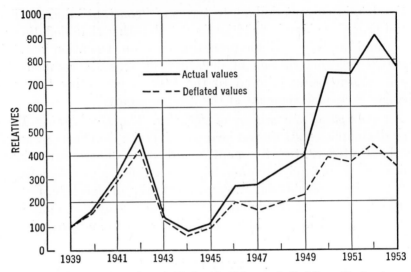

FIG. 13.5. Actual and Deflated Values of Building Contracts Awarded, 1939-1953 (1939 = 100).

construction costs (applicable to nonbuilding projects) have been developed. For the present example we give in Table 13-18 the total value of building contracts awarded in recent years, the index of building costs, and the deflated series that serves as an index of the physical volume of heavy building construction, of the types noted above. Actual and deflated values are shown graphically in Fig. 13.5. Over the 15-year period here covered building costs, as measured by the sample of commodities and services included in the cost index, more than doubled. The appropriate adjustments in obtaining the index of building volume substantially modify the record of contracts awarded, as first given in current dollars.

REFERENCES

Allen, R. G. D., *Statistics for Economists*, Chap. 6.

Croxton, F. E. and Cowden, D. J., *Applied General Statistics*, Chaps. 20, 21.

Fisher, Irving, *The Making of Index Numbers.*

Frisch, R., "Annual Survey of Economic Theory: The Problem of Index Numbers," *Econometrica*, Jan. 1936.

Frisch, R., "Some Basic Principles of Price of Living Measurements," *Econometrica*, Oct. 1954.

Konus, A. A., "The Problem of the True Index of the Cost of Living," *Econometrica*, Jan. 1939.

Lewis, E. E., *Methods of Statistical Analysis in Economics and Business*, Chaps. 8, 9.

Mills, F. C., *The Behavior of Prices*, pp. 219-251, 323-355.

Mitchell, W. C., "The Making and Using of Index Numbers," *Bulletin* 656, U. S. Bureau of Labor Statistics.

Mudgett, B. D., *Index Numbers*.

Riggleman, J. R. and Frisbee, I. N., *Business Statistics*, 3rd ed., Chap. 13.

Simpson, G. and Kafka, F., *Basic Statistics*, Chap. 9.

Staehle, H., "A Development of the Economic Theory of Price Index Numbers," *The Review of Economic Studies*, June 1935.

Stauber, B. R., Koffsky, N. M. and Randall, C. K., "The Revised Price Indexes," *Agricultural Economics Research*, April 1950.

Ulmer, M. J., *The Economic Theory of Cost of Living Index Numbers*.

U. S. Bureau of Labor Statistics, "The Consumer Price Index," *Bulletin* 1140, 1953.

U. S. Bureau of Labor Statistics, "A Description of the Revised Wholesale Price Index," *Monthly Labor Review*, Feb. 1952.

U. S. Bureau of Labor Statistics, "Techniques of Preparing Major BLS Statistical Series," *Bulletin 1168*, Dec. 1954, pp. 63-95.

Waugh, A. E., *Elements of Statistical Method*, 3rd ed., Chap. 14.

Yule, G. U. and Kendall, M. G., *An Introduction to the Theory of Statistics*, 14th ed., Chap. 25.

The publishers and the dates of publication of the books named in chapter reference lists are given in the bibliography at the end of this volume.

·
·
·

CHAPTER 14

Index Numbers of Production and Productivity

The era between the two world wars, and the decade after World War II, witnessed an extraordinary expansion and refinement of what may be called instruments of economic intelligence. This was notably true in the United States, but this country was by no means alone in this development. The first world war revealed great gaps in our knowledge of economic processes. The information then available on the volume and character of production, production capacity, the size and distribution of national income, the volume and sources of savings, the disposable income of consumers, stocks of goods and their location, and on many other aspects of economic life was of the most fragmentary sort. A striking improvement began with the end of the war. The needs of government, of business, of the banking system, and of other economic elements during the prosperous 'twenties, the depressed 'thirties, the war-torn 'forties, and the cycle-conscious 'fifties stimulated recurrent impressive advances on the statistical front. Among the great gains of these years was the development in this and other countries of comprehensive and accurate indexes of output.

Advances in the measurement of production took place on two fronts. The measurement of total national product and of national income was designed to provide global figures covering all economic activity. These measures in their early form were solely in terms of current monetary units—dollars, pounds, or other. They were, for this country, dollar measures of the performance of the national economy. Concurrently with estimates of national product and income there were developed in the United States a series of index numbers designed to measure in *physical* terms the volume of production in specified fields, and the volume of trade. Here the statistician worked from the beginning with physical units, and sought to construct index numbers free of distortion by the price changes that affect national income and product accounts. These two lines of progress have since merged, to some extent, with the development of methods of deflating national product and some of its elements, correcting, that is, for the effects of price changes. But despite improvement in deflating procedures, index numbers of physical output continue to play major roles as economic indicators in a number of specific fields, notably in measuring industrial production on a monthly or quarterly basis. Our present concern is with the methods employed in the construction of such measures.

Notation. In addition to symbols previously employed (such as Q, Q_{01}, for physical volume indexes, P, P_{01} for price indexes), certain new symbols are introduced in this chapter:

F: a measure of factor input in a productive process

E: all human effort entering into a productive process

M: a measure of man-hours of labor input

N: number of workers employed in the productive process

P_r: a productivity ratio, or productivity index, of the form $Q/F, Q/M$, or Q/N

R: an index of factor requirements per unit of output; F/Q, M/Q, or N/Q

Q/E: a productivity index in which human effort is the factor input

Q/M: a productivity index measuring output per man-hour of labor input

(Q/E and Q/M may be identical, although the latter expression is sometimes more restrictive)

M/Q: an index of man-hour labor requirements per unit of output

Lower case letters such as q, m, and r may be used to represent output, man-hours of labor input, and labor requirements per unit of output in individual plants or industries or for individual commodities.

The meaning of production indexes. In deriving an index of production for a given sector of an economy the task is that of combining, in some form, a number of measures of output. When such measures are in value terms, as they are when estimates of the national product are built up, the task of combination is simple. All are in dollar units. But when the basic observations are in quantum terms, i.e., in pounds, gallons, bushels, yards, etc., such simple aggregation is impossible. Some common factor must be introduced before a meaningful combination may be effected. The need to introduce some other factor that may serve as a common denominator means that a production index is not a simple aggregate of physical volume data—a significant fact for the understanding of these measures.

It would be gratifying to the economist if the common denominator could be provided by the concept of "utility." If each unit of the diverse products included in a "quantum basket" were the equivalent of a definite number of units of "utility," the same for all consumers, these utility units could be aggregated readily, and movements of the volume of production measured with precision. A Laspeyres index constructed on this basis would be of the form

$$Q_{01} = \frac{\Sigma q_1 u_0}{\Sigma q_0 u_0} \tag{14.1}$$

where u_0 represents the number of units of utility possessed by a physical unit of a given commodity in the base year. Unfortunately, this procedure is not open to us. "Utility" is an elusive quality of a consumer good. It varies from person to person and is inconstant even for a single consumer. We have no scales for converting physical units into utility equivalents. This means, among other things, that production indexes are not to be interpreted in welfare terms.

The denominators actually available for use in combining physical volume series are two in number—prices and labor time. If we multiply physical volume units by unit prices, we obtain dollar measures that may be combined in value aggregates and compared with similar aggregates for other periods. Alternatively, we may multiply physical volume units by the number of man-hours required for the production of each such unit. The product of each such operation is in man-hours; these man-hour measures may be combined in man-hour totals that may be compared with similar totals for other periods. When unit prices are used to provide the common value denominator, we are, in effect, defining the regimen of the period serving as weight base in terms of its price structure. When man-hours per unit are used to provide the common denominator, we are defining a regimen in terms of the unit labor requirements of the goods entering into the stream of production. In each case the institutions and circumstances of the time (i.e., of the time serving as weight base) place their impress on the production index.

We shall later consider means by which weights are selected and applied in the making of production indexes. The immediate purpose of the preceding discussion is to emphasize the fact that index numbers of physical output are not measures of purely physical change. We cannot abstract from the host of attendant circumstances that make up prevailing regimens. The significance of given output changes depends on the price structure or the structure of unit labor requirements, and each of these in turn reflects a complex economic regimen.

How then are we to regard index numbers of production? They are measures of the physical volume of work done in specified sectors of the economy, this work being measured in terms of quantum output but evaluated (or weighted) with reference to a given regimen, or to some combination of regimens. It is in the evaluation or weighting of the individual production series that we introduce the common denominator that permits aggregation.

It will be useful in the subsequent discussion to distinguish production indexes of four types. First we have *primary* measures, often called unadjusted index numbers. These parallel in construction and in meaning the index numbers of prices considered in the preceding chapter. Secondly, there are seasonally corrected monthly or quarterly measures. These are usually called *adjusted* indexes in the United States; the Statistical Office of the United Nations calls them secondary indexes. A third type, which may be called *trend-adjusted*, is modified by a correction for trend movements, as well as for seasonal fluctuations. As the name suggests, this type is used when the interest of the maker lies in cyclical movements of production or of trade volume. As a fourth type we may distinguish measures of physical output obtained by the deflation of output series originally expressed in value terms. These measures, to which we have referred on earlier pages, we may call *derived* indexes.

Primary Index Numbers of Production

The problems faced in constructing primary production index numbers are essentially the same as those that arise in the making of price indexes. A formula must be decided upon, weights chosen, the coverage of the sample determined, a weight base and a base of comparison selected. We deal briefly with each of these.

Choice of a Formula. For comparing the levels of production at two stated times (i.e., in a binary comparison), the chief formulas available are the Laspeyres, the Paasche, the ideal, the Edgeworth, and the modified Laspeyres (see Chapter 13). In constructing quantity indexes the p's and q's, as used in the price formulas are, of course, transposed. For the Laspeyres production index we have

$$Q_{01} = L = \frac{\Sigma q_1 p_0}{\Sigma q_0 p_0} \qquad (14.2)$$

The Paasche formula becomes

$$Q_{01} = P = \frac{\Sigma q_1 p_1}{\Sigma q_0 p_1} \qquad (14.3)$$

The other forms are correspondingly modified. This reversal of p's and q's means, as was pointed out above, that price weights are used to define a given regimen and to provide a common denominator. Thus the numerator of the Laspeyres formula (14.2) is the aggregate value of the physical amounts produced in time "1," when these physical amounts are multiplied by the unit prices prevailing in time "0." The denominator is the aggregate value of the physical amounts produced in time "0" when these physical amounts are multiplied by the unit prices prevailing in time "0." Numerator and denominator differ only because of *quantity* changes between the two periods.

The choice between formulas for such a binary comparison lies between those weighted with reference to the base-year regimen, to the given-year regimen, to a combination of the two, and to the regimen of a third, possibly intermediate, period. The ideal and the Edgeworth formulas, that combine base-year and given-year regimens, have strong claims, if the necessary data are to be had.

If the difference between base-year and given-year regimens, as measured by $E_2 = L - P$, is slight, choice between the Laspeyres, the Paasche, and one of the combined forms is a matter of convenience. If the regimen difference is great, the hazard of comparison is considerable regardless of formula used.

It is often deemed desirable that a production index and a corresponding price index be consistent in yielding a product equal to a true index of value. The Statistical Office of the United Nations emphasizes this as a general property that a quantity index should possess, and Mudgett regards it as a requirement of first importance. This requirement is met, of course, if the ideal formula is used. It can be met, also, by altering the weight base. Thus if we derive Q_{01} from the Laspeyres formula $\dfrac{\Sigma q_1 p_0}{\Sigma q_0 p_0}$ and P_{01} from the Paasche formula $\dfrac{\Sigma p_1 q_1}{\Sigma p_0 q_1}$, their product will be $\dfrac{\Sigma p_1 q_1}{\Sigma p_0 q_0}$, or V_{01}. The same product will be obtained from a Paasche quantity index and a Laspeyres price index. In practice this requirement is not easy to meet when the given period is a very recent month or year, because of data deficiencies.

A production index may be constructed by weighting quantity data by unit labor requirements, instead of by unit prices. The Laspeyres formula for such an index is

$$Q_{01} = \frac{\Sigma q_1 r_0}{\Sigma q_0 r_0} \qquad (14.4)$$

where the r_0 defines the man-hours of labor required, in the base period, to produce a unit of a given product. The numerator and denominator of the measure given above would be aggregates in man-hour terms; since the weighting factor, r_0, is fixed, the difference between numerator and denominator would be a measure of the change from time "0" to time "1" in physical quantities produced. There is much to be said on theoretical grounds for such a production index when the end purpose is the measurement of changes in productivity. However, our present information about unit labor requirements is so scanty that in practice little use can be made of this formula.

The preceding discussion has been concerned with binary comparisons involving production levels in only two periods. The choice of formulas and of weights is more restricted when the problem is that of constructing a series of index numbers designed to keep abreast of current changes. Here the choice really falls between the Laspeyres and a modified Laspeyres formula. The recommendation of the United Nations, which is seeking to standardize international practice, is that the base-weighted Laspeyres index be used for regular monthly or quarterly series of index numbers of industrial (i.e., nonagricultural) production. However, it is recognized that it may be necessary to use fixed weights from a year, or other period, different from the base of comparison of the published series. This alteration means that a modified Laspeyres index ($\Sigma q_1 p_a / \Sigma q_0 p_a$) would be used. This is the formula currently used by the Board of Governors of the Federal Reserve System. For the FRB index the base of comparison is 1947–49, the weight base 1947. Whatever the base of the fixed weights may be, the conclusion reached in discussing price index numbers holds here also: Fixed base weights should be modified frequently—say every five or at most every ten years in peace times—if the regimen reflected by the weights is not to become seriously out-dated.

Nature of the Quantities and Prices Entering Into a Production Index. The selection of suitable "production" series and weights is a problem of central concern in the making of output indexes. The object is to measure *work done* in each of many farms, mines, factories or industries, to the end that a general index of work done over a given time period may be constructed. Although farms are mentioned here, our chief concern in the present discussion is with nonagricultural production.

Four possible measures may be cited. We may use volume of output as a measure of work done; we may use deliveries; we may use the input of basic materials; or we may use the input of labor time. Each of these has its weaknesses. A count of the numbers of cars produced or of new houses finished in a given month would be unaffected by changes in the amount of work in progress. Moreover where repairs represent a considerable element of current work done, as they would in the construction field, this factor would be left out of a count of new products completed. A record of deliveries of finished products has these same defects and is subject, as well, to inaccuracies due to changes in the stocks of finished goods held by makers. If we measure work done in terms of input of basic materials (as in taking consumption of raw cotton as an index of total activity in the cotton textile industry) we are open to error if inventories of materials or of goods in process change materially. The accuracy of a record of materials input could also be affected by technical changes that modify the amount of material used per unit of final product, or by changes in the degree of fabrication of materials. The perhaps obvious procedure of measuring work done by a count of man-hours of labor input has the central weakness of ignoring changes in productivity. If the labor input measure is adjusted by a coefficient assumed to define current productivity changes, the danger of error arising out of faults in the coefficient is faced. Since productivity changes in given factories or industries are never constant over time, this error can be serious.

In general, production indexes are intended to define changes in quantum, or physical volume, output; hence the first of the four measures cited in the preceding paragraph is most relevant. We must sometimes use other records as approximations to output, but comprehensive counts of goods produced are the first objective in the making of these index numbers. Where variations in inventories (of basic materials, of goods in process, or of finished goods), or changes in technology or in degree of fabrication affect available records as indications of work done, correction should be made, if possible.

Since the primary index of production is intended to measure work done in comparable monthly, quarterly, or annual periods, correction should be made, also, for circumstances that are obviously distorting. Calendar irregularities that affect the number of working days per month are the most important of these mechanical difficulties. It is customary, for this reason, to reduce output records to production per working day or per working week (which is recommended as standard practice by the United Nations). The effects of public annual holidays, most of which are regular in their timing, are generally allowed for in a subsequent correction for seasonality, which is discussed below.

The p's that enter as weights in the aggregative forms of production index numbers are not, in all cases, the unit prices that are quoted in the markets. Where the commodity is a basic product such as iron ore (for which the quoted price covers all work that has been done on the unit offered for sale), the conventional price would be used. More frequently, the "work done" in a given factory or industry takes the form of fabricating raw or partially finished products. The price of the product of the factory or industry will include the price of materials used plus the value of the net product of the operations performed in the factory or industry. In such a case the p used as a weighting factor should be the value of the *net output* per unit of goods produced. If we are dealing with a manufacturing process what is wanted is the unit "price" of the services of fabrication performed in this operation. Such "prices" are, of course, not usually quoted. However, if the aggregate value of the net output is available, the maker of index numbers may use the value-weighted average of quantity relatives which is the equivalent of the weighted aggregative form. Thus instead of the Laspeyres index he would use the form

$$Q_{01} = \frac{\Sigma\left(\frac{q_1}{q_o} \times q_0 p_0\right)}{\Sigma q_0 p_0} \tag{14.5}$$

where $q_0 p_0$ is the aggregate value of the net output of a given product. Or, having the quantities in question, he may secure a "price" per unit of net output by deflating net output in a given period by the number of units produced in that period and then employ the usual aggregative formula.[1]

The familiar "value added" figure given in census records is usually a close approximation to the desired net output for a given industry. Since net output is usually wanted on a factor cost basis, however, certain adjustments may be required to exclude tax payments and costs of business services such as insurance and advertising, and to correct for changes over the census period in quantity of work in progress.

Coverage of Production Index Numbers. No new problems of method are faced in dealing with the scope and coverage of production indexes. There should, of course, be suitable representation of all sectors of the economy which the index purports to cover.

---

[1] In following either of these procedures we are assuming that input quantities (that is, the quantities of materials, fuel, and semifinished products utilized in production) vary proportionately with output quantities. If this is not the case a more accurate index of net output may be derived from the formula

$$\text{Net } Q_{01} = \frac{\Sigma q_1 p_0 - \Sigma q'_1 p'_0}{\Sigma q_0 p_0 - \Sigma q'_0 p'_0}$$

where p' and q' represent prices and quantities of inputs, and p and q represent prices and quantities of products of fabrication, that is, of outputs on a gross basis. On this point see Fabricant (ref. 39) and Geary (ref. 62).

Chief current use of the index number device is made in the field of industrial production. In the recommendations of the U. N. Statistical Office this is taken to comprehend the output of factories, workshops, mines, and handicraft establishments of all sizes, excluding only products of work in the home or farm. This means, in effect, that all nonagricultural production except home-made goods would be included. Very small establishments are excluded on practical grounds. The chief subdivisions of industrial production, as thus defined, are mining, manufacturing, construction, and electric and gas utilities. The Board of Governors of the Federal Reserve System accept this recommendation in principle, but for the present the FRB index is restricted to mining and manufacturing. (An annual physical volume index of agricultural production is constructed in the United States by the Bureau of Agricultural Economics.)

The selection of appropriate groups suitable for international comparisons as well as for domestic purposes has been made possible by the recent development of standard industrial classifications. There is now such an international classification;[2] there is also a widely used classification of the same sort for the United States, developed under the auspices of the Office of Statistical Standards of the Bureau of the Budget, and similar in general structure to the international standard.[3] Following this classification the Board of Governors of the Federal Reserve System constructs group index numbers for 21 manufacturing groups and for 5 mining groups, and for certain combinations of these industrial groups, by appropriate classification of basic monthly series. One classification distinguishes durable from nondurable manufactures. A separate output index, covering major durables weighted by gross values, is designed to measure changes in the supply of such durables entering final consumer markets. Such regroupings of basic industries and products yield index numbers especially adapted for use in the analysis of cyclical and other changes in economic processes.

As to the number of individual series to be included, the United Nations suggest 100 as the minimum, 500 as the maximum. The

[2] International Standard Industrial Classification of all Economic Activities, *Statistical Papers Series M*, No. 4, Statistical Office of the United Nations.

[3] *Standard Industrial Classification Manual*, Office of Statistical Standards, Bureau of the Budget.

index of industrial production constructed by the Board of Governors of the Federal Reserve System now includes 175 series.

Comparison Base and Weight Base. The same considerations that favor short-term comparisons in working with index numbers of prices support the case for similar limitations in using production indexes. Considerable regimen changes make fixed weights unrepresentative, and such regimen changes are the rule in a dynamic economy. In its recommendations concerning international practice the U. N. Statistical Office suggests a review and, if necessary, a reweighting of index numbers of industrial production every five years. Such reweighting should be based on censuses or extensive sample surveys of production. Such surveys of the structure of production, made at regular intervals, are essential to accuracy in the measurement of production changes. A corollary of these recommendations is that the comparison base should not be far removed in time. A change every five years, although perhaps desirable, is hardly to be expected in the practical work of index-making agencies. The Federal Reserve Board index is at present issued on the 1947-49 base, which is now standard for the United States. The weight base for this index is 1947.

Fixed weights are a practical necessity in the short-term comparisons for which monthly index numbers are primarily designed. However, such series of current index numbers may well be supplemented by index numbers constructed for the measurement of production changes over longer terms. Annual, biennial, or quinquennial censuses may provide comprehensive and accurate weights suitable for use in "crossed-weight" index numbers of the ideal or Edgeworth type (see Chapter 13). These index numbers may then be chained or combined in other ways to provide measurements covering fairly long periods of time. This has been done, in fact, for some years in the United States. The Bureau of the Census and the National Bureau of Economic Research have utilized census data as they became available, in the construction of bench-mark indexes to which current Federal Reserve index numbers have been adjusted. Comprehensive and independently constructed annual measures are currently used for the same purpose in reviewing and adjusting the Federal Reserve Index. Of course, the use of the bench-mark device for purposes of long-term comparison does not solve the fundamental problems raised by regimen changes. But the use of more comprehensive data, more satisfactory weights, and formulas that take some account of regimen shifts makes such index numbers more suitable for long-term comparisons than are the more restricted, fixed-weight monthly indexes.

Seasonally Adjusted Indexes

The volume of production in many industries is subject to seasonal variation. This is obviously the case in agriculture; similar but less extreme variations from month to month are found in metal mining, in coal production, in food and beverage manufacture, and in other manufacturing activities. These seasonal patterns in production are more marked and more regular than are seasonal patterns in commodity prices. For these reasons an adjustment not found desirable in constructing monthly price index numbers is common in the making of monthly production indexes. This adjustment is designed to eliminate movements that are purely seasonal in character, in order that month-to-month changes attributable to the play of other forces may be more clearly defined. Since the purely seasonal element in the total index of industrial production may account for a movement from the seasonal low to the seasonal high of as much as 10 percent, as it does in the Federal Reserve Index, the adjustment is not a minor one.

Actual production changes, including those due to the play of secular, cyclical, seasonal, and random factors are, of course, of central importance. These are measured by a primary, or seasonally unadjusted index. The seasonally adjusted index, where constructed, is a supplementary measure. There is need of both in following economic changes.

Standard methods of measuring seasonal patterns are employed in the construction of seasonally adjusted indexes. The Board of Governors of the Federal Reserve System uses, basically, 12-month moving averages (see Chapter 11). In applying the seasonal correction to a given series, the unadjusted measure for a stated month is divided by the seasonal index for that month, expressed as a ratio (i.e., as 1.10, if the seasonal index is 110). The original measure of production for a given month is thus reduced if the seasonal index for that month is above 1.00, raised if the seasonal index is below 1.00.

The seasonal adjustments may be applied directly to the many individual series entering into the production index, or they may be applied to unadjusted group indexes. The latter is now the procedure employed in making the Federal Reserve Index in the United States. Seasonal adjustments are made directly to each of 26 major group indexes. The seasonally adjusted total index is then obtained by combining the 26 seasonally adjusted group index numbers.[4] This procedure is designed to give flexibility to the seasonal adjustment program, so that revisions designed to allow for shifts in seasonal patterns may be readily made.

The amplitudes of seasonal movements in total industrial production in the United States and in certain of the major sectors of the American economy are indicated by the measures brought together in Table 14-1. These, be it noted, define the seasonal patterns prevailing in 1952. In the main, the patterns remain unchanged from year to year, but in certain industrial sectors shifts occur with some frequency.

TABLE 14–1

Seasonal Factors in Monthly Industrial Production Indexes, 1952
Board of Governors of the Federal Reserve System*

	Jan	Feb	Mar	Apr	May	June	July	Aug	Sept	Oct	Nov	Dec
Total Index	99	101	102	100	99	100	94	100	102	103	101	99
Primary Metals	102	104	105	104	102	101	91	95	98	101	100	97
Electrical Machinery	102	105	106	102	99	95	84	97	100	106	104	100
Transportation Equipment	97	102	105	104	101	103	97	99	99	100	97	96
Lumber and Products	90	96	101	105	102	107	94	105	106	105	99	90
Textile Mill Products	101	105	104	100	99	100	86	103	102	102	101	97
Rubber Products	101	104	104	102	99	101	88	96	101	106	102	96
Petroleum and Coal Products	101	100	99	97	98	100	100	102	101	101	101	100
Food and Beverage Manufactures	92	91	92	92	94	102	104	109	114	111	103	96
Bituminous Coal	105	100	100	100	95	98	75	100	104	109	109	105
Anthracite	100	100	92	96	102	106	79	96	105	121	110	93
Metal Mining	72	75	76	101	118	121	119	120	119	113	92	74

* From "Revised Federal Reserve Monthly Index of Industrial Production," *Federal Reserve Bulletin* December, 1953, pp. 54-5.

The abrupt seasonal drop in the total index in July, to a level 6 percent below the average for the year, is a striking example of a sharply changed seasonal pattern. In the unrevised Federal Reserve Index, for which prewar patterns provided most of the seasonal measures, the July seasonal index was 100. The general postwar adoption of industry-wide vacations accounts for the

[4] The seasonally adjusted Federal Reserve indexes of industrial production, as well as the primary or seasonally unadjusted indexes, are published currently in the monthly *Federal Reserve Bulletin.*

difference. This was a change that came suddenly, in contrast to the gradual shifts in seasonal patterns that reflect slowly changing social customs, technologies, and business policies.

An Index of Industrial Activity

In the analysis of time series we have seen that cyclical fluctuations are often the objects of primary interest. This is particularly true in the study of physical volume, for changes in the volume of production and trade are features of fundamental importance in business cycles. Methods have been explained, in the preceding chapters, by means of which we seek to measure the cyclical fluctuations in individual series (fluctuations inextricably entangled with accidental movements of major and minor degree). An obvious next step, in the study of general business conditions, is the construction of a comprehensive index of physical activity adjusted for trend as well as for seasonal movements.

Two somewhat different methods have been employed in making such index numbers. The first entails the fitting of an appropriate line of trend to each of the physical series entering into the general index, the expression of the actual observations as percentages of the corresponding trend values, the seasonal correction of these percentages, and the combination of such adjusted percentages in a general index. The resulting index is in relative terms, but the relatives refer to a hypothetical "normal," not to any fixed base in time. The alternative method calls, first, for the construction of a seasonally adjusted index, similar to that of the Board of Governors of the Federal Reserve System. The secular trend of this index, which will be a composite of the trends of the various constituent series, is determined in the usual way. The final trend-adjusted index is then obtained by expressing the actual monthly values of the general index as percentages of the corresponding trend values of the index.

This latter procedure is well exemplified in an "Index of Industrial Activity" constructed by the Chief Statistician's Division of the American Telephone and Telegraph Company.[5] The elements of this index are monthly data; seasonal corrections are therefore necessary. When these corrections have been made a

[5] This index has been constructed for the use of the staffs of the Bell system companies, and is not available for distribution. It is published here by courtesy of the American Telephone and Telegraph Company.

FIG. 14.1. The Growth of Industrial Activity in the United States, 1899-1954,*
1939 = 100.

*Source: American Telephone and Telegraph Company.

general index measuring long-term growth and cyclical-accidental
fluctuations, in combination, is constructed by averaging 25 series,
with appropriate weights.[6] In this form the index, which is not as
yet trend-adjusted, defines the growth of industrial activity in
the United States. It reflects secular factors as well as cyclical-
accidental fluctuations.

This index of growth is shown in Fig. 14.1, for the period
1899-1954. The trend there shown is a modification of an exponential curve fitted to measures of industrial activity per capita of
the population; the modification (by a population index) is designed
to provide a trend line reflecting both the growth of population
and the increase in activity per capita. It will be clear from the
list of series included that this is not an index of production. The
varied series included, among which there are five employment

[6] The following series have been used for the period from 1939 to date:

Metals (weight 30 percent): steel production; copper consumption; lead consumption;
zinc shipments; aluminum, shipments of fabricated products

Textiles (weight 15 percent): cotton consumption; wool consumption; rayon and
acetate production; hosiery shipments

Paper and printing (weight 10 percent): paper production; printing paper production;
newsprint consumption

Lumber production (weight 5 percent)

Food (weight 10 percent): slaughter of cattle; slaughter of hogs; wheat grindings;
corn grindings; malt liquor production

Man-hours in four manufacturing industries (weight 15 percent): chemicals and
allied products; stone, clay, and glass products; petroleum and coal products;
rubber products

Industrial power and man-hours (weight 15 percent): kilowatt hour sales to large
commercial and industrial users; electricity generated by industrial plants;
man-hours in manufacturing industries

TABLE 14–2

Industrial Activity as Related to Long-Term Growth, 1937-1954
Percentage Deviations from Trend

	1937	1938	1939	1940	1941	1942	1943	1944	1945
Jan.	+ 0.6	−38.4	−19.8	− 3.6	+ 9.4	+22.2	+29.9	+31.4	+27.0
Feb.	+ 2.5	−36.7	−18.8	− 8.6	+11.7	+22.4	+30.8	+31.9	+27.5
Mar.	+ 4.5	−36.1	−17.4	−12.6	+14.5	+22.8	+31.1	+31.4	+27.5
Apr.	+ 4.8	−37.0	−19.0	−13.6	+16.7	+23.7	+31.4	+31.4	+26.3
May	+ 5.1	−37.5	−19.6	− 9.9	+19.5	+23.2	+31.7	+29.4	+24.5
Jun.	+ 0.5	−37.6	−17.7	− 5.0	+21.0	+22.7	+31.4	+28.1	+23.1
Jul.	− 0.6	−32.4	−16.9	− 3.2	+21.2	+25.0	+32.2	+28.3	+20.1
Aug.	− 3.4	−28.2	−14.7	− 2.4	+21.1	+25.1	+32.5	+28.3	+12.4
Sep.	− 7.9	−25.8	− 9.6	− 0.4	+19.9	+25.7	+33.8	+27.9	+ 7.1
Oct.	−20.5	−24.2	− 3.2	+ 1.5	+19.3	+27.6	+33.9	+27.5	+ 3.9
Nov.	−33.0	−19.1	− 0.7	+ 3.8	+20.4	+28.3	+33.5	+27.8	+ 5.5
Dec.	−39.5	−20.2	− 1.2	+ 7.2	+21.5	+29.0	+30.5	+28.5	+ 7.2
Avg.	− 7.2	−31.1	−13.2	− 3.9	+18.0	+24.8	+31.9	+29.3	+17.7

	1946	1947	1948	1949	1950	1951	1952	1953	1954
Jan.	+ 0.6	+17.8	+17.7	+12.8	+ 8.5	+17.6	+11.9	+15.7	+ 3.7
Feb.	− 9.8	+18.4	+17.0	+11.1	+ 7.8	+17.3	+13.7	+17.7	+ 3.5
Mar.	+ 2.1	+17.3	+15.7	+ 8.4	+ 7.4	+17.3	+13.5	+19.9	+ 2.5
Apr.	+ 7.6	+17.2	+13.5	+ 5.1	+12.7	+20.4	+ 9.7	+19.4	+ 2.4
May	+ 1.2	+17.0	+15.7	+ 2.4	+14.9	+20.2	+ 7.2	+20.3	+ 2.9
Jun.	+ 4.8	+16.0	+17.6	− 0.3	+15.8	+20.1	− 7.8	+19.9	+ 4.3
Jul.	+11.6	+15.1	+17.9	− 1.3	+17.7	+18.3	−16.4	+18.6	+ 2.1
Aug.	+15.9	+14.9	+17.3	+ 0.5	+18.8	+16.0	+ 3.6	+16.6	− 0.3
Sep.	+15.6	+15.6	+16.6	+ 3.9	+18.3	+14.7	+14.1	+13.6	− 0.2
Oct.	+15.8	+17.7	+16.5	−12.0	+19.0	+12.0	+14.7	+11.5	+ 2.6
Nov.	+17.1	+19.1	+15.4	−10.4	+17.5	+12.6	+16.6	+10.0	+ 5.8
Dec.	+15.4	+18.0	+14.6	+ 3.5	+18.1	+12.2	+15.7	+ 5.3	+ 6.4
Avg.	+ 8.2	+17.0	+16.3	+ 2.0	+14.7	+16.6	+ 8.0	+15.7	+ 3.0

series, are taken to be indicators of "activity," not of physical output.

When each monthly value of the index is expressed as a percentage deviation from trend we have an index of industrial activity as related to long-term growth. Measures in this form are given in Table 14-2, for the period 1937-1954. (This is, of course, only a portion of the period for which the trend line was fitted). The deviations are graphically portrayed in Fig. 14.2. The cyclical-accidental fluctuations in industrial activity in the United States, as represented by the 25 series employed, are traced by the movements of this index.

FIG. 14.2. Industrial Activity as Related to Long-Term Growth, 1937-1954 (percentage deviations).*

*Source: American Telephone and Telegraph Company.

The Measurement of Productivity Changes

Changes in productivity, that is, in the effectiveness with which productive factors are applied in the making of economic goods, have contributed mightily to advances in living standards in the United States. But it is not alone as a key element in the long-term growth of a single economy that productivity is studied today. The advancement of productivity among all western nations and in economically underdeveloped regions is sought through the interchange of technicians and of technical information. Productivity has become a central issue in industrial bargaining. The "improvement factor" that is embodied in a number of wage contracts rests upon past and expected productivity gains. For these and other reasons the measurement and interpretation of productivity changes are among the important tasks now falling to the statistician.

The Productivity Ratio. Customary measures of productivity take the form of a ratio in which quantity produced, Q, is set against input of production factors, which we may represent by F. In this form we may call the ratio an index of *productivity* and use for it the symbol P_r. Thus $P_r = Q/F$. Changes in this index define changes in average output per unit of factor input. Inversely, the ratio may be put in the form F/Q which defines factor input per unit of output. We may think of the latter ratio as an index of factor *requirements* per unit of goods produced, and use for it the symbol R. The meaning of either index will depend, obviously, on what is included in the output measure, Q, and in the input measure, F. We have already considered the nature of production indexes. As to the factor input measure, many alternatives are open. F might be a composite measure of all productive factors—natural resources, capital, labor, and enterprise—or a composite of some of these factors. Or F might be any one factor, or an element of some one factor. Thus we might measure agricultural production per acre of land, or industrial production per dollar of capital invested, per manufacturing establishment, or per horse-power of energy. We might measure output in any economic sector per man employed or per man-hour of work done. In this latter case, we might restrict the employment measure to individuals directly engaged in the productive process, or we might enlarge it to include all forms of human effort, supervisory and managerial as well as direct, that enter into a given process of production. Perhaps the most meaningful general form of productivity index would be Q/E, where Q is the output and E represents all human effort entering into the productive process. This form appears commonly as Q/M, where M stands for man-hours of work, the scope of the man-hours measure depending on the purpose of the investigator and the availability of data.

We should emphasize at this point that such measures of productivity carry no causal imputation. If we say that so many bushels of wheat are produced per acre of land, we do not mean that only the services of land enter into the productive process, nor that the land factor is responsible for any gains recorded. Similarly, a measure that sets output against volume of invested capital is not to be taken to mean that the capital factor is responsible for the changes that may occur in the ratio. Again, if an advance is shown by a productivity ratio that sets output against man-hours of work done, this is not to be taken to mean that the gain is to be attributed to the labor factor in production. In all cases the actual factor input is a composite of all agents of production. The human factor uses power, capital equipment, and organizational devices of various sorts in exploiting natural resources to produce economic goods. It is convenient, and meaningful, to measure changes in output with reference to changes in some one component of the factor composite, but it would be a great mistake to assume that this factor operates alone in bringing about a gain or loss. In general, as has been suggested, it is most useful to measure output with reference to the input of human effort. This we shall do in the following discussion. But we must recognize that the effectiveness of this effort varies not alone with the intensity and skill of the human factor, but also with the number and quality of the tools employed, the amount of power utilized, the nature of the productive organization, and other features of the productive process.

It will be useful to distinguish two different methods of obtaining a general index of the effectiveness of productive effort, whether it be of the form Q/M or M/Q. In using one method we work from measures of productivity, or of unit labor requirements, in the factories or industries that are the basic units of study. In the other case we derive productivity indexes from comprehensive measures of output and of labor input covering many commodities or industries. We shall call the first type *directly defined* measures, and the other type *derived* measures.

The Direct Construction of Index Numbers of Unit Labor Requirements. In employing this procedure the statistician works with basic measures of output and of effort input for the individual commodities, establishments, or industries that are to enter into the index. Having the output, q, and the corresponding man-hours of work done, m, for each commodity or industry, he may determine r, the labor requirement per unit of output. This is given, of course, by $r = m/q$. It is essential that m and q be exactly comparable, that is, that q be the product of the effort represented by m. The chief danger of error here is that q may be a gross measure, such as the number of automobiles produced by a given factory, while m is a net measure covering only the final operations in the productive process. The measure m, that is, would not cover the production of the materials and parts embodied in the cars but only the final fabrication. Other possible sources of error, such as failure to allow for changes in work in process, in inventories, etc., have been noted in earlier pages. But when m and q are directly comparable, these and the derived r's provide the statistician with basic materials for the accurate measurement of productivity changes.

The measure of unit labor requirements, r, may be thought of as corresponding to a unit price. In these terms, the formulas available for the construction of index numbers of unit labor requirements (which are reciprocals of productivity measures) correspond to those available for the making of price indexes. If we are to use Laspeyres index, we have

$$R_{01} = \frac{\Sigma r_1 q_0}{\Sigma r_0 q_0} \tag{14.6}$$

This is a measure of unit labor requirements in time "1" on time "0" as base, the weighting factors being the base period q's. Thus the relative importance of r for each commodity is proportionate to the number of physical units of that commodity produced in the base year. The regimen assumed to be constant is that of the base year, and this regimen is defined by the quantities of the several commodities produced in that year. If we should weight the r's with given year quantities, we should have the Paasche index

$$R_{01} = \frac{\Sigma r_1 q_1}{\Sigma r_0 q_1} \tag{14.7}$$

The geometric mean of the Laspeyres and Paasche indexes would be the ideal index of unit labor requirements. In all these we are paralleling the measurement of price changes, for unit prices and unit labor requirements are similar measures.

This parallelism extends to the testing of related indexes for mutual consistency. For prices, quantities, and values there is mutual consistency (i.e., the factor reversal test is met) when $PQ = V$, the capital letters standing for the respective index numbers. If we use the symbol M for total man-hours, R for an index of unit labor requirements, and Q for a physical volume index, there is mutual consistency when $RQ = M$. For an individual commodity the relationship $rq = m$ necessarily holds. But the algebraic identity will hold only for an index number formula that meets the factor reversal test. This is true of Fisher's ideal formula, when used in the construction of index numbers of physical output and of unit labor requirements. If we vary the formula, we may derive mutually consistent measures by constructing a Laspeyres index of production and a Paasche index of labor requirements.[7]
That is

$$\frac{\Sigma q_1 r_0}{\Sigma q_0 r_0} \times \frac{\Sigma q_1 r_1}{\Sigma q_1 r_0} = \frac{\Sigma q_1 r_1}{\Sigma q_0 r_0} \tag{14.8}$$

The product of the production index and the labor requirements

[7] See pp. 437-8 above.

index is a measure of the change in total man-hours of work done. This relationship has a bearing on the problem we face when we derive indexes of productivity, or of unit labor requirements, from indexes of total man-hours and of production.

Derived Index Numbers of Labor Requirements and of Productivity. For an individual commodity $r = m/q$. If the same relationship holds among index numbers relating to many commodities we should have $R = M/Q$. A measure of changes in M is given, of course, by $\Sigma q_1 r_1 / \Sigma q_0 r_0$, the total man-hours of the given year divided by the total man-hours of the base year. If we wish to derive an index R from M/Q, we shall have mutually consistent and compatible measures if we employ an index of production in which the q's are weighted by r's. Thus

$$R = M/Q = \frac{\Sigma q_1 r_1}{\Sigma q_0 r_0} \div \frac{\Sigma q_1 r_0}{\Sigma q_0 r_0} = \frac{\Sigma q_1 r_1}{\Sigma q_1 r_0} \tag{14.9}$$

This is an index of unit labor requirements, in which the r's are weighted by given year q's.

This process is logically and algebraically satisfactory. The elements of M are of the same order as the elements of Q. The practical difficulty in this procedure has been noted in discussing production indexes. We do not usually have the r's that are employed in constructing the production index. Customarily, in making physical volume indexes, price weights are employed. Using such an index, say of the Laspeyres type, the process of deriving R from M and Q is described by

$$R = M/Q = \frac{\Sigma q_1 r_1}{\Sigma q_0 r_0} \div \frac{\Sigma q_1 p_0}{\Sigma q_0 p_0} \tag{14.10}$$

It is clear that incommensurable quantities are involved in this derivation. A pure man-hours measure is divided by a price-weighted quantity index. A pecuniary factor has been introduced into the derived index of unit labor requirements.

Although the process just described is disturbing to a purist, it is not entirely without merit. Representation of a given regimen by unit prices, rather than by unit labor requirements, is appropriate for many purposes in dealing with a money economy. When we shift labor from sectors of low value-productivity to sectors of higher value-productivity there is a gain that may properly be included in productivity measures. Accordingly, it is not alone considerations of expediency that lead to the general use of value- or price-weighted production index numbers in deriving measures of unit labor requirements, or of productivity.

It is true today that all comprehensive index numbers of labor requirements and productivity are *derived* measures of the form $P_r = Q/M$ or $R = M/Q$. They are usually obtained by dividing price-weighted index numbers of physical output by measures of changes in the total man-hours of work entering into the given volume of production. (Some indexes define changes in output per man employed, rather than per man-hour of work done. That is, we have $P_r = Q/N$, where N is the number employed.) The prime requirement here is that the components Q and M be truly comparable. The "intrusion of the pecuniary factor" we may accept, and indeed welcome for many purposes, but we may not tolerate material differences in the coverage of the indexes of production and of man-hours.[8]

We should recognize that such derived measures, covering a period of years, are seldom open to unambiguous interpretation, for they are affected by many variables. The quality of goods entering into Q (or more broadly, the product designs of such goods) will vary; the composition of the total Q will certainly change, in respect of kinds of goods included and of the relative shares coming from different manufacturing plants. Changes will occur in the composition of labor input, and in the complex of instruments and organizations used in the productive process. The interaction of these many variables will lead to the net result defined by a productivity index for a given year.

Some Current Measures of Productivity Changes

Current productivity indexes in the United States range from global measures, covering the economy, to measures defining changes in individual plants, or even divisions of a plant. Most of them relate changes in physical output to changes in the input of human effort, measured in man-hours or in man-years, although some efforts have been made to relate productive output to capital

---

[8] Adjustments to correct for inequalities in the coverage of available measures of output and of labor input, which have been made by the National Bureau of Economic Research and by other agencies, are sometimes warranted, although subject to error. For a critical appraisal of such adjustments see Siegel, Ref. 142.

input and to power input. The indexes of broad scope, covering major industries or the economy, are all of the derived type, being subject therefore to the limitations we have just noted. Many of narrower coverage, however, are now built up from careful records of production and man-hour input obtained from individual plants. These, though of limited scope, promise to be of greater analytical value in studies of factors making for productivity gains.

The measures given in Table 14-3 exemplify the global approach. In column (3) are indexes of the real gross national product, by decades, from the late nineteenth century to the middle of the present century. (These are derived from estimates of the gross national product, corrected for price changes.) The indexes of corresponding labor input in column (4) come from estimates of the total employed labor force, by decades, with an adjustment to take account of changes in the length of the average work week. Derived indexes of output per man-hour are given in column (5). The record is one of unbroken advance, but the gains were uneven. The greatest relative increase in output per man-hour came in the decade of the 'twenties—a period of extraordinary advance. The smallest relative gains were made during the decade that spanned the first world war, and in the depressed 'thirties.

TABLE 14–3

Real Gross National Product, Labor Input, and Productivity, United States, by Decades, 1891-1950*

(1)	(2)	(3)	(4)	(5)
	Gross national product		Total man-	Output
	(*billions*		hours of	per
	of 1929		labor input	man-hour
Decade	*dollars*)	(*relative*)	(*relative*)	(*relative*)
1891-1900	294	100.0	100.0	100.0
1901-1910	455	154.8	126.1	122.8
1911-1920	603	205.1	140.5	146.0
1921-1930	838	285.0	145.1	196.4
1931-1940	843	286.7	122.8	233.5
1941-1950	1,493	507.8	180.5	281.3

* From Mills, ref. 103.

Such comprehensive estimates are useful as broad indications of changes in the effectiveness with which productive resources are utilized. By themselves, however, they throw little light on the causal forces behind observed movements of productivity indexes.

For analytical purposes we need intensive field studies, made under controlled conditions, with product design specified, so that the final indexes will measure, essentially, changes in productive efficiency in individual plants. Indexes based on such field studies are given in Table 14-4.

TABLE 14-4

Indexes of Man-hours per Unit of Output, 1939-1950*
Specific Industrial Products

(1)	(2)	(3)	(4)	(5)
	Track-laying tractor	Selected types of machine tools		
Year		Direct factory labor†	Indirect factory labor‡	Total factory labor
	Total factory labor			
1939	100	100	100	100
1940	99	93	87	90
1941	91	90	89	90
1942	91	86	94	91
1943	95	82	100	92
1944	99	88	115	102
1945	101	89	116	103
1946	105	95	119	108
1947	99	96	122	111
1948	99	98	121	112
1949	97	94	120	108
1950	91	91	115	105

(Man-hours per unit)

* These indexes (which are here rounded off to the nearest unit) have been constructed by the U. S. Bureau of Labor Statistics. (See Bureau of Labor Statistics, refs. 174 and 177.) For a general statement of the work of the Bureau, covering both secondary source data and field-collected data, see Ref. 173.
† Direct hours of labor input include the work of wage earners engaged directly on production operations, primarily machine operators and assembly workers.
‡ Indirect hours represent functions of time-keeping, shipping and receiving materials, handling, production scheduling, machine set-up, inspection, maintenance, engineering of tools, dies, and gauges, and plant supervision. Where possible, the Bureau excluded from both direct and indirect hours the functions of general accounting, purchasing, personnel relations, welfare services, and developmental engineering. The sum of direct and indirect hours constitutes total factory labor.

The indexes of labor requirements given in column (2) of Table 14-4 relate to three precisely specified types of track-laying tractors. The general record is one of declining unit labor requirements (increasing productivity) in the early years of the war period, followed by rising labor requirements to 1946 and a renewed decline between 1946 and 1950. The information the Bureau compiles concerning conditions in the individual plants from which these records were obtained makes it possible to define with some precision the factors responsible for these changes.

The labor requirement indexes for selected machine tools given in columns (3), (4), and (5) are broader in coverage, since they include types that make up about three quarters of the output, in value terms, of the machine tools industry. (In combining indexes of unit labor requirements for different products, value weights are used.) Here total factory labor is broken into two components— direct and indirect labor. The interesting feature of this record is the sharp divergence of trends in unit labor requirements for direct and indirect labor. A substantial reduction, per unit of product, in the amount of direct labor used in producing machine tools has been paralleled by a material increase in indirect labor. This represents, of course, a major change in factory organization. The net result for the period as a whole was an advance in unit labor requirements, when account is taken of all factory labor. The movement was downward, however, for the last two years covered.

Standing between global estimates of productivity movements in the whole economy and measures based on intensive establishment studies are the indexes given in Table 14-5. These are estimates of productivity changes in four major sectors of the economy. Being based on secondary sources, not on records for individual plants, they suffer from some of the defects noted in discussing economy-wide indexes. However, care has been taken to ensure the reasonable comparability of output and input measures. Although significance should not be attached to minor year-to-year movements of these indexes, they do define with acceptable accuracy broad movements of productivity in the several sectors covered.

The most striking gain in productivity in recent years has been scored in the generation of electric power. Technological advances have here been great. Output per man-hour rose sharply on steam railroads with the increase in volume of traffic that came in the war years, and these gains have been held and in recent years extended. Agriculture, a laggard industry for many generations, opened a new era in the mid-'thirties, as the mechanization movement spread. Recent years have shown continued advance. Productivity gains in mining have been relatively low. Such evidence as we have on productivity in manufacturing industries indicates a gain, since 1939, that exceeds the increase recorded for

TABLE 14-5

Indexes of Productivity in Selected Sectors of the U. S. Economy,
1939-1952*

| Year | Output per man-hour | | | |
	Agriculture	Mining	Steam railroads†	Electric light and power
1939	100	100	100	100
1940	105	102	105	109
1941	110	104	116	123
1942	119	104	140	146
1943	117	102	151	183
1944	121	105	148	191
1945	127	106	140	183
1946	134	107	129	161
1947	133	111	135	167
1948	147	111	133	171
1949	146	109	132	
1950	153	117	150	
1951	151		159	
1952	162		160	

* Sources:
    Index of farm output: U. S. Bureau of Agricultural Economics
    Other indexes: U. S. Bureau of Labor Statistics
† Revenue traffic per man-hour on Class I railroads.

mining, but falls short of the gains cited for the industries listed in Table 14-5.[9]

The accurate measurement of productivity movements is one of the challenging tasks facing statisticians today. It is obvious that we are dealing here with a major dynamic factor in economic life, one that plays a central role in economic growth. Yet only a beginning has been made in the art of measuring such changes. Global indexes, which are almost inevitably rough and inaccurate, are easily constructed. Such measures will continue to be useful, but progress lies in the direction of intensive measurement, for specific products and individual plants and industries. Building

[9] No general index of productivity in manufacturing is available for the period since 1939, although *Bulletin 1046* of the Bureau of Labor Statistics gives indexes for selected manufacturing industries. A period prior to 1939 is covered by Fabricant's index (Ref. 38). One may approximate changes in man-hour output in manufacturing by using the Federal Reserve index of manufacturing production as an output measure, and estimating labor input from Bureau of Labor Statistics' records of manufacturing employment and average length of work week. But these output and input figures are not really comparable; the resulting indexes are of dubious value. The Bureau of Labor Statistics is at present preparing to publish a continuing series of productivity indexes for manufacturing as a whole.

from these we may hope to obtain fuller understanding of the factors that contribute to productivity gains, as well as greater accuracy in defining changes in productive efficiency.

REFERENCES

Anglo-American Council on Productivity, *Final Report*, 1952.

Barger, H., and Schurr, S. H., *The Mining Industries: A Study of Output, Employment and Productivity*.

Barger, H., *The Transportation Industries*, 1889-1946: *A Study of Output, Employment and Productivity*.

Carter, C. F., Reddaway, W. B. and Stone, R., *The Measurement of Production Movements*.

Fabricant, S., *Employment in Manufacturing*, 1899-1939.

Fabricant, S., *The Output of Manufacturing Industries*, 1890-1937.

Federal Reserve System, Board of Governors, "The Revised Federal Reserve Index of Industrial Production," *Federal Reserve Bulletin*, Dec. 1953.

Geary, R. C., "The Concept of the Net Volume of Output with Special Reference to Irish Data," *Journal of the Royal Statistical Society*, Vol. 107, 1944.

Gould, J. M., *Output and Productivity in the Electric and Gas Utilities*.

International Labor Office, "Methods of Labor Productivity Statistics," *Studies and Reports, New Series*, No. 18, Geneva, 1951.

Mills, F. C., "Productivity and Economic Progress," *Occasional Paper 38*, National Bureau of Economic Research, 1952.

Siegel, I., *Concepts and Measurement of Production and Productivity*.

United Nations, Economic Commission for Europe, *Economic Survey of Europe Since the War*, pp. 317-335 (on sources and methods, index numbers of industrial production).

United Nations Statistical Office, "Index Numbers of Industrial Production," *Studies in Methods*, No. 1, 1950.

U. S. Bureau of Labor Statistics, "The Productivity Measurement Program of the Bureau of Labor Statistics," 1950.

U. S. Bureau of Labor Statistics, "Productivity Trends in Selected Industries Through 1950," *Bulletin* 1046, Oct. 1951.

U. S. Bureau of Labor Statistics, *Technical Note on the Measurement of Trends in Output per Man-Hour*, April 1954.

The publishers and the dates of publication of the books named in chapter reference lists are given in the bibliography at the end of this volume.

.
.
.

CHAPTER 15

Generalizing from Small Samples:
the *t* - Distribution

In employing the various methods of inference discussed in chapters 7 and 8, and in subsequent pages, we have benefited from the fortunate circumstance that the sampling distributions of many statistics tend toward normality as n increases. This condition of asymptotic normality makes it possible to test for significance many measurements derived from large samples without special attention to the exact form of the sampling distributions in question, or to the form of the parent populations from which the samples were drawn. But when samples are small, procedures valid for large samples may be very crude and inaccurate. If one must make a decision on a sample including only 6 or 8 observations it is of little help to know that a statistic derived from a sample of 1,000 observations would be a normally distributed variable. If rational action is to be taken in such a case we need more exact knowledge of distributions of sample characteristics, for samples drawn from specified parent populations. Pioneer work in this field has been done by "Student" (W. S. Gosset), R. A. Fisher, and others, but our knowledge of exact sampling distributions is still limited in scope. Within certain not unimportant areas, however, we can generalize from small samples with a fair measure of confidence. At this point we shall discuss one such sampling distribution, the first to be accurately defined, and shall exemplify some of its uses.

We have made use in earlier pages of the fundamental fact that the deviation of a sample mean from the mean of a parent population, when this deviation is expressed in units of the standard error of the sample mean, gives a quantity T which may be interpreted as a normal deviate. That is

$$T = \frac{\overline{X} - \mu}{\sigma_m} \qquad (15.1)$$

T may be taken to be a normal deviate for large samples even when we have to approximate σ_m with s_m, the latter being an estimate of the standard error of the mean based on the information provided by the sample alone. The formula for T, thus derived, is

$$T = \frac{\overline{X} - \mu}{s/\sqrt{N-1}} \qquad (15.2)$$

where s is the standard deviation of the sample. T may be regarded as a ratio—the ratio of a normally distributed variate, $\overline{X} - \mu$, to its estimated standard error, $s/\sqrt{N-1}$. If in place of s we should use s' ($= \sqrt{\Sigma d^2/N - 1}$), we should have

$$T = \frac{\overline{X} - \mu}{s'/\sqrt{N}}$$

When N is as large as 30 the error involved in interpreting T as a normal deviate is not appreciable, except for extreme deviations; if N is as large as 100 the error is very small indeed. But when N is small the expression given above for T does not yield a normal deviate. A consistent bias is introduced, one that leads to a persistent and, for very small samples, a very considerable departure from normality. For such small samples a method appropriate to large samples breaks down badly. Asymptotic normality then becomes a very weak reed on which to lean.

The Work of "Student"

In the first decade of this century W. S. Gosset, who wrote under the pseudonym "Student," became aware of the deficiencies of the conventional ratio (which we have termed T above), when it was applied to small sample results. His studies indicated that the difficulty lay in unsuspected aberrations of s, the standard deviation derived from the sample. The distribution of s for small samples, he discovered, departs systematically from the normal form. This leads to inaccuracy in the estimation of σ, and hence to faulty estimates of the standard error of the mean when the procedure appropriate to large samples is applied to small samples. Student was able to define the sampling distribution of s^2. He then investigated the distribution of the ratio $(\overline{X} - \mu)/s$, a quantity which has been termed z; in establishing its exact distribution Student made one of the great forward steps in sampling theory. (See Student, Ref. 153, 1908). Seventeen years later R. A. Fisher provided a more rigorous theoretical foundation for Student's ratio, and at the same time put the ratio in the form in which it is now generally employed. This is

$$t = \frac{\overline{X} - \mu}{s/\sqrt{N-1}} \tag{15.3}$$

where $\overline{X}$ is the mean of a sample, μ is the mean of the parent population from which the sample has been drawn, s is the standard deviation of the sample (derived[1] from $\sqrt{\Sigma d^2/N}$) and N is the number of observations in the sample. (The distinctive feature of the formula for t, as will be brought out later, is that the s in the denominator is the sample s, used as such and not as an estimate of the population σ. The standard deviation of the population does not enter into the determination of t.) The quantity t, it is obvious, equals $z\sqrt{N-1}$, where z is Student's original ratio $(\overline{X} - \mu)/s$. The sampling distribution of t (which is sometimes spoken of as Student's t, sometimes as Fisher's t) is one of the fundamental instruments of sampling today. In considering this distribution and its uses we may first give attention to the nature of the bias that is present in s when samples are small.

The essential feature of the sampling distribution of s is effectively revealed by the results of an interesting experiment conducted by W. A. Shewhart.[2] Shewhart drew 1,000 samples, each consisting of four observations, from a normally distributed parent population with a known standard deviation, equal to unity. The standard deviation, s, of each sample was computed, with 4 as the divisor of Σd^2. The distribution of these 1,000 values of s is represented by the dots in Fig. 15.1.[3] (The line running through the dots defines the theoretical distribution of the s's to be expected, with samples of 4, on the basis of Student's theory. There is a notably close agreement between the theoretical and observed distributions.) Traditional sampling concepts would lead us to expect a normal distribution of s's, centered at 1, the value of σ in the parent population. Instead, the distribution is definitely skew, with

---

[1] If instead of s we have s', derived from $\sqrt{\Sigma d^2/N-1}$, t would be given by $\dfrac{\overline{X} - \mu}{s'/\sqrt{N}}$.

[2] W. A. Shewhart, Ref. 140, 163-173, 185-6.

[3] The figure is here reproduced with the permission of Dr. Shewhart and his publishers.

FIG. 15.1. Distribution of Standard Deviations in Samples of Four Drawn from a Normal Universe.

the measurements clustering about a central tendency well below unity. The mode of the 1,000 values of s here represented is, in fact, 0.717 and the arithmetic mean is 0.801. There is a clear tendency for these s's, based on samples of 4, to understate the true value. As estimates of σ they are clearly biased.[4]

[4] The degree of error involved in using s as an approximation to σ, for small samples, is indicated by the following figures, taken from W. A. Shewhart (*loc. cit.*, 185). They define the relation between the modal s, for samples of size N drawn from a population of which the standard deviation is known, and the true σ of that population.

Size of sample N	Modal s as a decimal fraction of true σ
3	.577
4	.707
5	.775
6	.817
7	.845
8	.866
9	.882
10	.894
15	.931
20	.949
25	.959
30	.966
50	.980
100	.990

The fractions given above define relations that are to be expected on the basis of error theory, as modified by Student to take account of conditions affecting small samples. The modal value of the 1,000 standard deviations obtained by Shewhart in his empirical test of this theory was, as we have seen, .717 of the standard deviation of the universe. This result is very close indeed to the expected value of .707, for samples in which $N = 4$.

The Distribution of *t*. The nature of *t* and the form of its distribution call for brief comment. The numerator of the ratio

$$\frac{\overline{X} - \mu}{s/\sqrt{N - 1}} \qquad (15.4)$$

which defines *t* is a normally distributed variable with mean zero; the denominator is the square root of an independently distributed estimate of the variance of that variable. (We speak of the denominator as the square root of the variance of the variable in question, not as the standard error of that variable. The term "standard error" would suggest that the ratio is to be interpreted as a normal deviate. This is not so, as has been noted, when N is small.) Attention is called to the phrase "independently distributed." This means that the distributions of the variables in numerator and denominator of expression (15.4) are independent of one another. This is an essential condition. Only when $\overline{X}$ and s^2 are independent variables is the ratio given by formula (15.4) distributed in the form defined by Student and Fisher. *This condition holds only for samples drawn from a normal parent population.* In a single sample thus drawn, $\overline{X}$ may be small (i.e., well below μ in value) and s^2 large (i.e., well above σ^2 in value); in another sample $\overline{X}$ may be large and s^2 small; in a third sample both may be small, or both large. The sampling distribution of *t* is restricted, in its fully accurate applications, to samples from normal parent distributions.

We have noted above that no population parameter is involved in the derivation of the *t* ratio. In the computation of *T*, for testing the deviation of a sample mean from an assumed population mean (formula 15.1), we use σ; when we do not know σ we use s', a quantity derived from the sample but used as an approximation to σ. But in the computation of *t*, only the sample mean and the standard deviation of the sample (and, of course, N) are employed. Herein lies its great value. *The theoretical distribution of t relates to a quantity derivable from observations.*

The distribution of *t* may be defined by the equation

$$y = \frac{y_0}{\left(1 + \dfrac{t^2}{n}\right)^{\left(\frac{n+1}{2}\right)}} \qquad (15.5)$$

In this expression y is an ordinate at a stated distance t from an origin at zero on the t-scale; y_0 is the maximum ordinate at $t = 0$;

n is the number of degrees of freedom of t. This will be $N - 1$ in a problem of the type here discussed; in other cases more than one degree of freedom may be lost. It will be clear that from the maximum ordinate at zero on the t-scale the t-curve falls away symmetrically for plus and minus values of t. For very small values of n the curve is flat-topped, with a larger proportion of the area in the tails than is found in a corresponding normal distribution. Since areas under the curve are to be interpreted as relative frequencies, or probabilities, this fact means that large deviations from the mean are more probable for the t-distribution than for the normal distribution. As n gets larger, the t-distribution approaches the normal form. With n as large as 30, as we have noted, the difference is small. Relations between t-distributions and the normal form are shown in Fig. 15.2, in which are plotted t-curves for $n = 2$ and $n = 25$, together with a normal frequency curve.

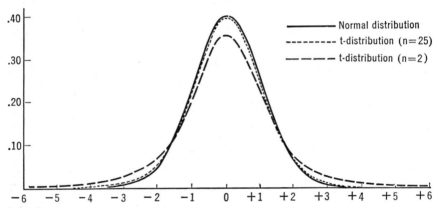

FIG. 15.2. Frequency Curves of the Normal Distribution and of t-Distributions for $n = 2$ and $n = 25$.

Tabulations of the t-distribution greatly facilitate the use of this measure in practice. Extracts from two such tabulations are given in Table 15-1. The entries in Part A of that table define the percentile values of t for varying values of n. As has been indicated above, the form of the distribution varies as n changes. There is a specific distribution of t for every value of n.

We may briefly explain the entries in Part A of Table 15-1. If we had a graph of the t-distribution for $n = 10$, an ordinate erected on the horizontal scale (the t-scale) at a point 2.764 units to the left of the mean would cut off a tail that included 0.01 of the total area under the curve. As for the normal distribution, such a proportion is to be read as a probability. There is only 1 chance out of 100 that a random drawing from such a distribution would give a measure falling in this tail of the distribution. The figure cited, 2.764, which is the first percentile value of t for a distribution with 10 degrees of freedom, is found in the column headed $t_{.01}$ (the subscript to t defines the percentile) in the line for which $n = 10$. Since the distribution is symmetrical, the 99th percentile value of t ($t_{.99}$) is also 2.764, but this represents a point to the right of the mean. (Deviations to the left of the mean, corresponding to percentiles below 0.50, are, of course, negative; those corresponding to percentiles above 0.50 are positive. These signs are not given in the table, but will be understood.)[5]

Since the form of the *t*-distribution varies with n, the percentile values of t in a given column of Part A of Table 15-1 change from line to line. Thus, at the 99th percentile, t is 31.821 when n is 1; it is 6.965 when n is 2, drops to 2.457 when n is 30, and to 2.326 when n is infinitely large. These reductions mean, of course, that large deviations become less and less likely, as n increases.

The entries in Part B of Table 15-1 are those given in most presentations of the *t*-distribution. These are the measures that would be used in a two-tailed test, the kind usually made in employing the *t*-distribution. In making such a test we are asking: What is the probability of a given deviation (or one that is greater) *above or below* the mean of the *t*-distribution? This question could, if desired, be answered with reference to Part A of Table 15-1. For example, with a sample for which $n = 10$, the chance of a deviation of 3.169 (or more) *below* the mean is 0.005 (see column for $t_{.005}$ in Part A); the chance of a deviation of 3.169 (or more) *above* the mean is 0.005 (see column headed $t_{.995}$ of Part A.) The sum of these probabilities, or 0.01, measures the probability of a deviation of 3.169, or more, in either direction. But we may obtain this combined probability more directly from the entries in Part B of Table 15-1. In the column headed 0.01 in the line for $n = 10$, we

[5] In using subscripts for percentiles, with the meaning indicated in the text, I am employing a notational scheme introduced by Dixon and Massey (Ref. 32) and followed by Walker and Lev (Ref. 186). This scheme differs from current practice (which is exemplified in Part B of Table 15-1) but is to be preferred as a simpler and more; straightforward representation of the *t*-distribution. Strictly speaking, only the columns in Table 15-1 that give .01, .05, .95, and .99 values of t define percentiles however, the fractional percentile values given, for $t_{.005}$ etc., are of special interest, as will appear.

TABLE 15-1

Part A: Distribution of t: Percentile Values

n	$t_{.005}$	$t_{.01}$	$t_{.025}$	$t_{.05}$	$t_{.95}$	$t_{.975}$	$t_{.99}$	$t_{.995}$
1	63.657	31.821	12.706	6.314	6.314	12.706	31.821	63.657
2	9.925	6.965	4.303	2.920	2.920	4.303	6.965	9.925
3	5.841	4.541	3.182	2.353	2.353	3.182	4.541	5.841
4	4.604	3.747	2.776	2.132	2.132	2.776	3.747	4.604
5	4.032	3.365	2.571	2.015	2.015	2.571	3.365	4.032
6	3.707	3.143	2.447	1.943	1.943	2.447	3.143	3.707
7	3.499	2.998	2.365	1.895	1.895	2.365	2.998	3.499
8	3.355	2.896	2.306	1.860	1.860	2.306	2.896	3.355
9	3.250	2.821	2.262	1.833	1.833	2.262	2.821	3.250
10	3.169	2.764	2.228	1.812	1.812	2.228	2.764	3.169
20	2.845	2.528	2.086	1.725	1.725	2.086	2.528	2.845
30	2.750	2.457	2.042	1.697	1.697	2.042	2.457	2.750
∞	2.576	2.326	1.960	1.645	1.645	1.960	2.326	2.576

Part B: Values of t Corresponding to Stated Probabilities in Two-Tailed Test

n	\multicolumn{8}{c}{Probability}
	0.80	0.50	0.40	0.20	0.10	0.05	0.02	0.01
1	.325	1.000	1.376	3.078	6.314	12.706	31.821	63.657
2	.289	.816	1.061	1.886	2.920	4.303	6.965	9.925
3	.277	.765	.978	1.638	2.353	3.182	4.541	5.841
4	.271	.741	.941	1.533	2.132	2.776	3.747	4.604
5	.267	.727	.920	1.476	2.015	2.571	3.365	4.032
6	.265	.718	.906	1.440	1.943	2.447	3.143	3.707
7	.263	.711	.896	1.415	1.895	2.365	2.998	3.499
8	.262	.706	.889	1.397	1.860	2.306	2.896	3.355
9	.261	.703	.883	1.383	1.833	2.262	2.821	3.250
10	.260	.700	.879	1.372	1.812	2.228	2.764	3.169
20	.257	.687	.860	1.325	1.725	2.086	2.528	2.845
30	.256	.683	.854	1.310	1.697	2.042	2.457	2.750
∞	.253	.674	.842	1.282	1.645	1.960	2.326	2.576

The entries in Part B are extracts from a more detailed table (Table IV) in R. A. Fisher's *Statistical Methods for Research Workers*, Edinburgh, Oliver and Boyd. The table is printed here through the courtesy of Dr. Fisher and his publishers. (See also Fisher and Yates, *Statistical Tables*, Ref. 51.

find 3.169, the deviation that will be reached or exceeded 1 time in 100. The entries in Part B all refer to absolute deviations, i.e., without regard to sign. They are thus directly adapted for use in applying a two-tailed test, whereas the entries in Part A are adapted to a one-tailed test.

It will be noted that the several entries in Part B of Table 15-1 in the column for which the probability is 0.01 are the same as the corresponding entries in Part A in the columns headed $t_{.005}$ and $t_{.995}$; that the entries in Part B in the column for which the probability is 0.05 are the same as the corresponding entries in Part A in the columns headed $t_{.025}$ and $t_{.975}$. The reason for the identities has been indicated: the probability of a stated absolute deviation, as given in Part B, is the sum of the probabilities corresponding to the same deviation, plus and minus, as given in Part A.

The table of areas under the normal curve is usually given in a form comparable to that used in Part B of Table 15-1. In the last line (for which the entry in the n column is ∞) we have the familiar values of T (a normal deviate) corresponding to probabilities of 0.01, 0.05, etc. Thus for a probability of 0.01 the corresponding normal deviate is 2.57582. These entries in the last line of Part B of Table 15-1 are the limiting values of t, the values which t approaches, for stated probabilities, as n increases. For an n infinitely large, t and T coincide. Even for n as large as 30 the approach to the normal values is fairly close. Which means, of course, that we need resort to the t-distribution only when dealing with small samples.

Some Uses of the t-Distribution

Significance of a Mean. In determining whether the mean of a sample drawn from a normal population deviates significantly from a stated value (the hypothetical value of the population mean), we compute t from the ratio previously given:

$$t = \frac{\overline{X} - \mu}{s/\sqrt{N - 1}}$$

In interpreting t when the arithmetic mean of a sample is being tested for significance, $n = N - 1$.

A study of interest rates paid on business loans by various classes of borrowers[6] revealed that large borrowers (i.e., those

---

[6] The study, made by the Board of Governors of the Federal Reserve System, related to loans outstanding in November, 1946. See Youngdahl, Ref. 198. The rates given for individual groups in this example are weighted averages of the rates paid by individual borrowers, weights being the dollar volume of loans outstanding at each rate. In combining rates for retail trade groups in the present example, to get an average for all retail trade, no weights were used.

with assets of $5,000,000 or more) in five retail trade groups paid the following average rates:

Retail trade	Average interest rate on business loans Percent
Food, liquor, tobacco, and drugs	1.8
Apparel, dry goods, and dept. stores	1.9
Home furnishings, metal products, and building materials	2.0
Automobiles, parts, and filling stations	1.7
All other	2.2

The arithmetic average of these five group rates is 1.92 percent; the standard deviation s (derived with N as the divisor of the sum of squared deviations) is 0.172. Our problem is to determine whether the mean rate paid by these groups of large retail merchants differs significantly from the mean rate paid by all business borrowers in the United States. We shall here use 2.9 percent, the weighted mean of the average rates paid by 100 groups of business borrowers, as the population mean. It is appropriate to use a significance level of 0.01 in testing the null hypothesis in this case. For t we have

$$t = \frac{\overline{X} - \mu}{s/\sqrt{N-1}} = \frac{1.92 - 2.9}{0.172/\sqrt{5-1}} = \frac{-0.98}{0.086}$$
$$= -11.4$$

This test of significance should be a two-tailed test, since we are concerned with the probability of a deviation as great as 0.98 above or below the population mean. From Part B of Table 15-1 (or from Appendix Table III), we find that for $n = 4$, the value of t corresponding to a probability of 0.01 is 4.604. The observed value of t is far greater than this. On the level of significance here employed, we should reject the null hypothesis. The interest rates paid by large retail borrowers are significantly lower than those paid by business borrowers as a whole.

Setting Confidence Limits. The examples just cited have involved tests of hypotheses using small sample results. We revert briefly to *estimation*, with reference to the special problems that are faced when estimates of population parameters are based on small samples. The procedure employed is similar to that outlined in Chapter 7, for large samples, but use is made of the t-distribution rather than the normal distribution in setting limits corresponding to a chosen confidence level.

We have the following observations on the yield of alfalfa, in tons per acre, on four plots each of which received 18 inches of irrigation water during the growing season.[7]

$$5.69;\ 6.46;\ 7.02;\ 8.02$$

We are required to set confidence limits for the mean of the population from which this sample comes. For the sample we have

$$\overline{X} = 6.7975$$

$$s = \sqrt{\frac{\Sigma d^2}{N}} = 0.849$$

Consider the relation

$$t = \frac{\overline{X} - \mu}{s/\sqrt{N-1}}$$

We have the values of s and N, hence the degrees of freedom $n\ (=N-1)$. Let us say that the confidence level for the estimate is to be 0.95. Knowing P and n we may readily determine from the t-table the appropriate value of t. For a P of 0.05 and an n of 3, $t = 3.182$. The unknown quantity in the above equation is the numerator of the right-hand term, the range $\overline{X} - \mu$. We wish to set limits on either side of $\overline{X}$ within which we may, with the stated degrees of confidence, expect μ to fall. The desired range may be written (from the equation nine lines above)

$$\overline{X} - \mu = t \times s/\sqrt{N-1} \qquad (15.6)$$

$$= 3.182 \times (0.849/\sqrt{3})$$

$$= 1.5592$$

The desired limits of the confidence interval are thus 6.7975 ± 1.5592. Rounding off the fractions we may write this: 6.80 ± 1.56. We may say, with confidence measured by a probability of 0.95, that the mean of the population from which the sample comes falls between 5.24 tons and 8.36 tons.

We may take opportunity at this point to give an example of estimation from small samples that will serve, at once, to demonstrate modern procedures in interval-estimation and to illustrate the use of the t-distribution in such estimation. The data employed are from W. A. Shewhart (Ref. 140) and the graphic illustration

[7] Beckett and Robertson, Ref. 10.

given is taken, with permission, from the same author (Ref. 141, p. 59). Shewhart set up a normal universe with mean zero. From this universe he drew 100 samples, with four observations in each sample; for each sample he computed $\overline{X}$ and s (the latter derived with 4 as the divisor of Σd^2). On these two statistics for each sample he then based a statement setting confidence limits corresponding to a confidence level of 0.50. That is, each statement belonged to a family of statements of which, in the long run, one half would be expected to be true and one half false. The 100 samples thus provided bases for 100 estimates of confidence intervals.

The two following hypothetical sets of drawings will illustrate the procedure:

| Sample A | $+ 0.5, - 0.3, - 0.6, + 0.8$ |
| Sample B | $- 2.1, + 0.5, - 2.6, - 0.2$ |

In the first sample the mean $\overline{X} = + 0.10$, $s = 0.570$. For a P of 0.50 and an n of 3, $t = 0.765$. Following the method employed in the preceding example, we compute

$$t \times s/\sqrt{N - 1} = 0.765 \times 0.570/\sqrt{1.732} = 0.25$$

Limits of the 0.50 confidence interval for an estimate of the population mean, based on this sample, are $- 0.15$ and $+ 0.35$. (These, of course, are derived from $+ 0.10 - 0.25$ and $+ 0.10 + 0.25$). The second sample, of which the mean is $- 1.0$ and s is 1.366, provides the basis of a similar estimate. By an identical procedure we set 0.50 confidence limits at $- 1.60$ and $- 0.40$.

The evidence of the first sample warrants the statement, "The mean of the parent population lies between $- 0.15$ and $+ 0.35$." The evidence of the second sample warrants the statement, "The mean of the parent population lies between $- 1.60$ and $- 0.40$." Since Shewhart's illustration was experimental, we know the parent mean. It is zero. Thus the first statement is true, the second is false. Shewhart's data provided him with bases for 100 such statements. The range and location of each of the 100 confidence intervals thus set up are shown in the left-hand panel of Fig. 15.3, which is reproduced from Shewhart's *Statistical Method from the Viewpoint of Quality Control.*

This figure is an illuminating representation of statistical inference. The heavy horizontal bar is drawn at zero on the vertical scale, that is, at the value of the population mean. Each

FIG. 15.3. Showing Confidence Intervals Based upon Samples Drawn from a Normal Universe with Mean Zero and Standard Deviation Unity.*

* Reproduced with permission from W. A. Shewhart, *Statistical Method from the Viewpoint of Quality Control*, Washington, D. C., The Graduate School, U. S. Department of Agriculture, 1939.

vertical line depicts a confidence interval based on one of the 100 samples. The center of each vertical line is located at the value of a sample mean. The range of the corresponding confidence interval above and below that sample mean is determined by an operation similar to that represented by formula (15.6) above.[8] The vertical lines differ greatly, it is clear, in the location of their midpoints, and in their range. If a sample mean fell close to the true mean of the population the center of the corresponding bar would be close to the heavy central bar; if not, the center of the line would be far from the central bar. If the sample s were small the range of the corresponding vertical line would be narrow; if the sample s were large, the length of the corresponding vertical line would be great. In the diverse locations and varied lengths

---

[8] For the entries in this panel the range of each confidence interval is given by $\bar{X} \pm 0.4417s$, where s is the sample standard deviation. The coefficient 0.4417 is derived from $t/\sqrt{N-1}$ (i.e., from $0.765/1.732$.) For present purposes it is convenient to divide by 1.732, the first term of the right-hand member of formula (15.6) instead of the first factor in the second term. That is, we divide t, instead of s, by $\sqrt{N-1}$, since s varies from sample to sample, while the other quantities do not. We may note that $t/\sqrt{N-1}$ is Student's original z (see p. 471).

of these vertical lines we have a vivid picture of the play of chance in shaping the results of sampling operations.

Yet, despite the diversity of sample results, a soundly based procedure makes rational estimation possible. According to sample theory approximately half of the confidence intervals set up by Shewhart should include the population mean (his confidence level was 0.50). If a given vertical line in Fig. 15.3 cuts across the heavy central line this means, of course, that the confidence interval in question does in fact include the population mean. It is of interest to note that 51 of the 100 confidence intervals represented on the diagram do in fact include the parent mean; 49 do not. The agreement with expected results is very close indeed.

The fact that small sample theory makes rational estimation possible when we have but a few observations does not, of course, remove the uncertainties from sampling procedures. Nor does it mean that small samples are as good as large ones. Apart from the consideration that the use of the t-distribution is fully accurate only with samples drawn from normal universes, the investigator who works with very small samples must know that his estimates will vary widely from sample to sample. Moreover, he must content himself with relatively wide confidence intervals. Precision of statement is less, of course, the wider the intervals employed. Large samples are more stable than small ones (in the sense that the means of large samples will be clustered much more closely about the population mean), and they permit more precision in inferences based on them.

These attributes of large samples, and their great superiority to small samples, are well illustrated by the right-hand panel of Fig. 15.3. This presents confidence intervals relating to the same parent population as does the left-hand panel. Here, however, each vertical line defines the limit of a confidence interval (at confidence level 0.50) designed to include the population mean, but based upon a sample of 100 observations.[9] The vertical scale is the same as for the left-hand panel, so the results may be compared. The centers of the vertical lines in the right-hand panel (these centers are located, as we have noted, at the sample means) are much more closely concentrated about the population mean. More striking, however, is the fact that the ranges of the confidence

---

[9] The range of each confidence interval in this case is given by $\overline{X} \pm 0.0769s$ (the value 0.0769 being derived from $t/\sqrt{N-1}$, or $0.765/\sqrt{99}$).

intervals based on samples of 100 are much smaller. Each inference drawn from large sample results is far more precise, in the limits it sets up, than is an inference based on a much smaller sample. (Of the 40 confidence intervals based on large samples, we may note, 45 percent include the population mean, while 55 percent do not. These percentages stand reasonably close to the long-run expectation of 50 percent right and 50 percent wrong.) The meaning of this is obvious, of course. Inferences based on small samples are inherently less reliable than inferences based on large samples. However, when we must infer from small samples, under the conditions set forth, we can have a trustworthy procedure.

Significance of a Difference between Two Means. The method we have employed above for testing the significance of the mean of a sample from a normal universe may be applied in determining whether the means of two samples differ significantly. This very important extension of Student's procedure, which is due to R. A. Fisher, is applicable in testing the hypothesis that the two samples whose means are compared are from the same normal parent population. Here, as in the previous example, Student's distribution gives us an unbiased test.

In form, this test follows that discussed above in dealing with the same problem for large samples. On the assumption that the samples are from the same population it is appropriate to pool the sums of the squared deviations from the respective means of the two samples in deriving a single s', which is our best estimate of the standard deviation of the population. Thus we have

$$s' = \sqrt{\frac{\Sigma d_1^2 + \Sigma d_2^2}{N_1 + N_2 - 2}} \tag{15.7}$$

Having this estimate s', we compute the standard error of the difference between means from the customary formula

$$s_{\bar{x}_1 - \bar{x}_2} = \sqrt{\frac{s'^2}{N_1} + \frac{s'^2}{N_2}} \tag{15.8}$$

$$= s'\sqrt{\frac{N_1 + N_2}{N_1 N_2}} \tag{15.9}$$

The ratio of $\bar{X}_1 - \bar{X}_2$ to $s'\sqrt{(N_1 + N_2)/N_1 N_2}$ is distributed in the t-distribution. That is

$$t = \frac{\bar{X}_1 - \bar{X}_2}{s'\sqrt{\frac{N_1 + N_2}{N_1 N_2}}} = \frac{\bar{X}_1 - \bar{X}_2}{s'}\sqrt{\frac{N_1 N_2}{N_1 + N_2}} \tag{15.10}$$

The quantity t, in this case, is to be interpreted with n, the degrees of freedom, equal to $N_1 + N_2 - 2$. (We may think of one degree of freedom being lost in the calculation of each of the two components of s', in formula (15.7) above.)

We may illustrate the application of a test of this sort by comparing a sample of six small cities with a sample of five large cities, in respect of average family expenditures on current consumption (Table 15-2). The unit observation for present purposes is

TABLE 15–2

Average Family Expenditures on Current Consumption in Samples of Small and Large Cities*

Small Cities	Average family expenditures on consumption	Large Cities	Average family expenditures on consumption
Grand Junction, Colo.	$3,538	Providence, R. I.	$3,916
Madill, Okla.	3,190	Milwaukee, Wis.	4,331
Camden, Ark.	3,094	Youngstown, Ohio	4,166
Garrett, Ind.	3,699	Kansas City, Mo.	3,989
Pulaski, Va.	3,326	Cincinnati, Ohio	4,186
Dalhart, Texas	3,548		
Average	3,399.17		4,117.60

* The data are from U. S. Bureau of Labor Statistics Bulletin 1097 (revised June, 1953), *Family Income, Expenditures and Savings in 1950*. In the present illustration cities with population of 2,500 to 30,500 are classed as small; those with population of 240,000 to 1,000,000 as large. Cities and metropolitan areas with populations of 1,000,000 and over are not included.

a city average of consumption expenditures by a sample of individual families resident in that city. (The number of families in such a sample ranged from 65 in small cities to 250 in the group of large cities.)

The figures cited in Table 15-2 indicate that family expenditures on current consumption are less in small cities than they are in large cities, but an objective test is needed. Again we shall use a significance level of 0.01. For the computation of s' (using the relations shown in formula 15.7) we have

$$s' = \sqrt{\frac{273,557 + 109,741}{11 - 2}} = 206.4$$

For t (from formula 15.10)

$$t = \frac{4{,}117.60 - 3{,}399.17}{206.4}\sqrt{\frac{30}{11}}$$

$$= 5.75$$

Consulting the t-table (Part B of Table 15-1, or Appendix Table III) we find that for $n = 9$ the value of t corresponding to a probability of 0.01 is 3.250. The present value is clearly significant. The two samples of cities could not have come from one homogeneous parent population. Average family expenditures for purposes of current consumption appear to be clearly higher in large cities than in small cities.

The hypothesis here tested is that two samples, the means of which are compared, come from the same normal universe. The direct test is applied to the difference between means, but since the sample s's enter into the calculations their values obviously affect the outcome. It is possible that a significant value of t might appear in a test of this sort because samples were drawn from populations with different standard deviations, rather than different means. This would lead, properly, to the rejection of the hypothesis, although the factor responsible for the rejection would not be a difference in means. But this possibility, as Fisher suggests, is not great. If there is reason to believe that the sample standard deviations differ significantly, their difference may be tested.

Significance of a Coefficient of Correlation. For a test of the null hypothesis, when N is small, a quantity following the familiar t-distribution may be derived from the relation

$$t = \frac{r\sqrt{N-2}}{\sqrt{1-r^2}} \tag{15.11}$$

This is equivalent, of course, to dividing the quantity $r - 0$ (i.e., the deviation of the given r from the hypothetical value of zero) by $\sqrt{1-r^2}/\sqrt{N-2}$. In consulting the t-table for the interpretation of the values thus obtained, n, the number of degrees of freedom, is taken as equal to $N - 2$. (The value of r which is tested here should be obtained without the use of Sheppard's correction.)

As an illustration, we may test the results obtained from a study of the relation between the production and the price of cotton in

the United States, covering 35 observations. The value of r is
$- 0.65$. We have

$$t = \frac{- 0.65\sqrt{35 - 2}}{\sqrt{1 - (-0.65)^2}} = - 4.91$$

In consulting the t-table we find that for $n = 33$ the value of t
corresponding to a probability of 1 percent is approximately 2.73.
If the true value of t were zero, a value as great as 2.73 or greater
would occur only 1 time out of 100, as a result of chance fluctuations
of sampling. The present value of t is substantially greater than
2.73. It is highly improbable that it reflects a chance drawing from
a population in which the true value of r is zero. There appears to
be a significant negative correlation between the production and
the price of cotton.

REFERENCES

Dixon, W. J. and Massey, F. J. Jr., *Introduction to Statistical Analysis*,
Chap. 9.
Fisher, Sir Ronald (R. A.), *Statistical Methods for Research Workers*, 11th
ed., Chap. 5.
Freeman, H. A., *Industrial Statistics*, Chap. 1.
Kendall, M. G., *The Advanced Theory of Statistics*, 3rd ed., Vol. II, pp.
96-106.
Mather, K., *Statistical Analysis in Biology*, 2nd ed., Chaps. 4, 5.
Shewhart, W. A., *Economic Control of Quality of Manufactured Product*,
Chap. 14.
Shewhart, W. A., *Statistical Method from the Viewpoint of Quality Control*,
pp. 56-63.
"Student, The Probable Error of a Mean" *Biometrika*, Vol. 6, 1908.
Tippett, L. H. C., *The Methods of Statistics*, Chap. 5.
Tippett, L. H. C., *Technological Applications of Statistics*, Chaps. 8, 9.
Walker, H. M. and Lev, J., *Statistical Inference*, pp. 135-40 and Chap. 7.
Yule, G. U. and Kendall, M. G., *An Introduction to the Theory of Statistics*,
14th ed., Chap. 21.

The publishers and the dates of publication of the books named in chapter reference lists are given in the bibliography at the end of this volume.

CHAPTER 16
· · ·

Sampling and Sample Surveys

The preceding pages have dealt with a variety of techniques that may be applied in the description and analysis of observations, and in generalizing from a set of observations. Our concern in the present chapter is with some of the problems that are faced in gathering statistical data. We have spoken of the great advances made in recent decades in the quantity and scope of the observations available to social scientists, businessmen, and public administrators. This expansion has given the social sciences a sounder empirical foundation, and has provided better bases for informed decisions in the making of business and public policies. But our concern with data is not alone with the number of social, economic, and business measurements published monthly or annually. The fruitfulness of the whole process of statistical analysis and inference rests upon the accuracy of the observations employed, and upon the suitability of these observations for the purposes they serve.

On Varieties of Statistical Data

In earlier discussions of the treatment of statistical observations we have emphasized that data should be obtained by methods of random sampling, if inferences with definable margins of error are to be made from them. Nonrandom observations have their place and value—and their value in research and decision-making may be great—but for purposes of statistical generalization and the testing of hypotheses, when conclusions are meant to hold with stated degrees of probability, random data are requisite.

In this respect great gains have been made in recent years. Truly random samples of social, economic, or business data were rarities a quarter of a century ago. The data gathered in these fields by public and private agencies were almost all obtained by what would today be regarded as unplanned procedures. What was readily available was picked up, sometimes without much reference to accuracy, often without adequate regard to its appropriateness for specific purposes. Such a method gives not a sample, but what Hauser and Deming have called a "chunk"—a convenient slice of population selected on grounds of ready availability. But the advances of recent years have strengthened statistics on this front. Techniques of data-gathering have been improved; casual collection of statistics is being replaced by well-designed procedures focused on specified objectives. The essential feature of all such designs is the emphasis on randomness.

This is not to say that random methods are today generally employed in the gathering of economic and social data. They are not, and in the nature of things cannot be. Many of the quantitative observations used by social scientists and administrators will remain nonrandom. But in major sectors of social and economic life carefully designed random samples are now currently drawn. Population surveys provide information on the size of the labor force and on its division between employed and unemployed; studies of consumer finances throw light on consumer behavior in spending and saving; samples of family budgets furnish weights for the consumer price index; the profits of corporations are currently reported on the basis of sample data; the distribution of income, by size, among income recipients is estimated from samples of income tax returns to federal and state authorities; market surveys are used by business research units in appraising markets and studying consumer attitudes. These, and many other sample surveys of limited as well as of wide scope, provide aids to rational judgment on current issues. Beyond this, they can be of great value in the development of all the social sciences.

In discussing the theory of sampling distributions and sampling errors the statistician lays down the conventional conditions that the probability of selection be definable for each element of the population sampled, and that the events (the draws) be independent. These conditions are usually illustrated by the drawing of cards from a pack or of balls from an urn. Since the requisite conditions are not hard to realize under the controlled circumstances of laboratory operation, teacher and student may give too little attention to the task of achieving these conditions, or an adequate approximation to them, in the complexities of actual field work. This task is far from simple. A sample haphazardly drawn is not a random sample. Close thought and careful design must precede the field work of drawing truly random samples, and scrupulous attention to detail is needed in the execution of the survey plan. Recent gains in the gathering of random data are not due, primarily, to the fact that sample surveys are more numerous and broader in scope. The significant advances have been gains in technique. It is not too much to say that a whole new art of survey design and field sampling has been developed within the last several decades. The art is not a finished one as yet, but its present contributions are great, and its potential contributions far greater.

The primary aim of this modern art is to obtain a *probability* sample. A probability sample is one for which the inclusion or exclusion of any individual element of the population depends on the application of probability methods, not on personal judgment, and which is so designed and drawn that the probability of inclusion of any individual element is known. Randomness in drawing is an essential feature of such a sample. Measures of precision, of sampling error, can be obtained for the results yielded by probability samples. As against probability samples we set a variety of other sample types, variously termed judgment samples, purposive samples, quota samples (in their usual form), etc. These differ widely in character, but they have one distinguishing feature: personal judgment rather than a random procedure determines the composition of what is to be taken as a representative sample. This judgment may affect the choice of individual elements; it may define specific attributes that are imposed purposively on the sample. All such samples are nonrandom, in one respect or more. This being so, no objective measure of precision may be attached to the results they yield.

Some Terms and Definitions. Sample surveys are concerned with the attributes of certain entities such as human beings, families, residential structures, business enterprises, or farms. The attributes that are the object of study are termed *characteristics*; the units possessing them are called *elementary units*. We may be concerned with *measurable* characteristics of such units (in which

case we work with one or more of a series of variates, designated
X, Y, etc.), or with the number or proportion of such units marked
by the presence or absence of some *qualitative* characteristic. Thus
if we are dealing with the incomes of individual income recipients
in the United States we are working, of course, with a measurable
characteristic; if with their status as married or unmarried, we are
studying a qualitative characteristic. The aggregate of elementary
units to which the conclusions of the study will apply is the
population. Field surveys deal with finite populations, in contrast
to the infinite populations usually assumed in formulations of
theories of statistical inference. (Some of the modifications called
for, when such theories are applied to finite populations, will be
noted.) The units that form the basis of the sampling process are
called *sampling units*. The sampling unit may be an elementary
unit, or it may be a group or cluster of such elementary units.
Thus the sampling unit might be a city block, although the
elementary units with which the investigator is ultimately concerned might be human individuals or residential structures. The
sample is the aggregate of sampling units actually chosen in
obtaining a representative subset from which inferences concerning the population may be drawn. From the sample we get objective
estimates of population means, totals, or proportions, and information needed in estimating the precision of such estimates. The
sampling plan is the blue print of steps to be taken in obtaining a
sample from a designated population. Finally, we note the need of
a basic survey instrument termed the *frame*—a list, or map, or
directory defining all the sampling units in the universe to be
covered by the survey. This frame may be constructed for the
purpose of the particular survey or, as is more usual, may consist
of previously available descriptions of the population in question.

Notation. The system of notation used in sample surveys is not
completely standardized, but substantial progress is being made in
that direction.[1] To accord with what is coming to be conventional
procedure, I shall in this chapter modify somewhat the notations
used in earlier chapters. A chief feature of sampling survey notation

---

[1] An approach to standard international practice in sampling survey terminology is
set forth in a United Nations document, "The Preparation of Sampling Survey
Reports," *Statistical Papers*, Series C, No. 1 (revised), Statistical Office of the United
Nations, February, 1950.

is the use of capital letters for the number of units, or the attributes of units, in the finite population being sampled, and of lower case letters for corresponding features of samples. Thus X is a general symbol for a variate defining a measurable characteristic of a unit of the population; X_i represents a particular value of that variate (i.e., a single observation). The symbols x and x_i have corresponding meanings for units of a sample. When population and sample are broken into classes, or strata, the subscript h is added, as in X_h, X_{hi}, x_h, x_{hi} to provide similar general symbols for the attributes of units falling in a class, or stratum. Some elements of the notation to be employed are outlined below.

| Quantity or element | Symbol | | | |
| | Population | | Sample | |
	Total	A stratum	Total	A stratum
Number of units*	N	N_h	n	n_h
Mean value of a measured characteristic	$\overline{X}$	$\overline{X}_h$	$\bar{x}$	$\bar{x}_h$
Total value of a measured characteristic	X_t	X_{ht}	x_t	x_{ht}
Variance of a measured characteristic	S^2	S_h^2	s^2	s_h^2
Number of units possessing a given qualitative characteristic	U	U_h	u	u_h
Proportion of units possessing a given qualitative characteristic	$P\,(=U/N)$	P_h	$p\,(=u/n)$	p_h
Proportion of units not possessing the stated characteristic	$Q\,(=1-P)$	Q_h	$q\,(=1-p)$	q_h
Coefficient of variation of variate X	V		v	
Relative variance, or rel-variance, of variate X	V^2		v^2	

Specific strata will be designated by $h_1, h_2, h_3 \ldots$, and symbols relating to such strata will bear corresponding subscripts (e.g., $n_{h_1}, n_{h_2}, n_{h_3} \ldots$).

Symbol	Quantity or element represented

$\overline{X}'$: an estimate of $\overline{X}$ (the sample value $\bar{x}$ is also used for such an estimate)

X_t': an estimate of X_t

U': an estimate of U

* Attention is drawn specifically to the only point of difference that might lead to uncertainty in this notation: the use of n in this chapter for the number of observations in a sample. Elsewhere in the book, and in the appended tables, n is used for degrees of freedom.

P': an estimate of P (the sample value p is also used for such an estimate)

$f\ (=n/N)$: sampling fraction; the proportion of the finite population included in the sample

$f_h\ (=n_h/N_h)$: sampling fraction of a stratum

$g\ (=1/f = N/n)$: expansion factor; the factor by which a sample total is raised to give a population total

$1 - f\ \{ = (N - n)/N \}$: the finite multiplier; the proportion of the population not included in the sample; a factor that affects the precision of sample estimates

$s_{X't}^2$: the variance of an estimate of a total

s_p^2: the variance of an estimate of a proportion

$v_{\bar{x}}^2$: the relative variance (square of the co-efficient of variation) of an estimate of a mean

$v_{X't}^2$: the relative variance of an estimate of a total

v_p^2: the relative variance of an estimate of a proportion

k: the multiplier of the coefficient of variation in specifying the precision to be sought in a sampling operation

D: a difference in relative terms between an estimated population mean and the true population mean

In interpreting and using formulas involving standard deviations or variances of original units, we shall assume throughout that these are derived with degrees of freedom equal to the number of units less 1 (equal, e.g., to $N - 1$, or $n - 1$).

Simple Random Sampling

Sample survey techniques employed today include a diversity of methods for obtaining representative samples. Of the methods that yield probability samples, *simple random sampling* is the simplest, and the one that is basic to all others. Modifications of this fundamental method are more frequently employed in actual field work, but all these modifications involve the principles represented in the basic procedure.

We have noted that, in simple sampling, a drawing from a population is random when the choice of an element is made in such a way that every element in the population has the same chance of being chosen. The same rule holds when a simple sample of stated size is to be randomly chosen. The drawing of a sample of n elements from a population is random when the sample is so selected that every possible set of n elements has the same chance of being drawn. With N of fairly large size, the number of such possible sets is of course very great. This number is given by the expression $\dfrac{N!}{n!\,(N-n)!}$. [Factorial N (i.e., $N!$) is the product of the integers from 1 to N.] Thus (to illustrate with unrealistically small numbers) for samples of 2 drawn from a population of 5, this becomes $\dfrac{5!}{2!\,(5-2)!}$, or 10. (Five individuals, a, b, c, d, e, can be combined in 10 different ways into samples of 2 each.) Of course, it is unnecessary in a specific case to compute the number of possible sets of stated size that might be drawn from a given population, but the process of sample selection should be such that the probability of selection is the same for every such set. When this condition is met, with equal probabilities for the selection of elements in a given set, we have a simple random sample.

The heart of any sampling process is in the means by which randomness is achieved in drawing the individual elements of a single sample, and in ensuring that all possible samples have the same chance of being selected. If we are to draw from a population containing N elementary units, the elementary unit being also the sampling unit in this case, it is necessary that each of the N units be individually numbered or otherwise distinctively designated. If the N numbers could be copied on individual cards, chips, or balls that are uniform in size and weight, if these cards, chips, or balls were then thoroughly mixed in an urn or bowl, and if n numbers were drawn at random from the vessel, the n units corresponding to these n numbers would be a simple random sample. (For true equality and independence of probabilities in the selection of a simple random sample, numbers drawn should be replaced before

the next draw. This is not usually done, since it is seldom desirable
to count one individual more than once. This minor departure from
the strict requirements of simple sampling is of no consequence
with N as large as it ordinarily is in field surveys.) There are some
difficulties in this procedure. Mixing to obtain randomness in the
urn is not as simple as it may appear to be. Cards may stick
together, or may stick to the sides or bottom, so that the probability
of being drawn is not the same for all the cards in the urn. Moreover, if N is large, the task becomes physically complicated. For
any considerable undertaking, and even for small ones, better
methods of ensuring randomness are available.

Use of a table of random numbers. If the N elements of a total
population are numbered serially from 1 to N, a random sample
may be most readily and most reliably drawn by using prepared
tables of random numbers. Such tables enable an investigator to
select n numbers at random from the full list of serial numbers
from 1 to N. Table 16-1, which is an extract from a larger table
constructed by the Interstate Commerce Commission, will exemplify such an arrangement and its uses. The digits in each column
of Table 16-1 are in random order; so are the digits in each row.
Since the arrangement is random in all directions, it makes no
difference where one begins in his selection of random numbers
from such a table. The column arrangement is usually found most
convenient for reference, the number of columns used depending
on the size of N.

Let us assume that an investigator wishes to select a random
sample of 10 from a population of 900 units. The units in the
population have been numbered from 1 to 900. Any convenient
order of arrangement may be used in this numbering. The digits
in three columns will be used, since N runs to 900. Any three
columns may be employed, and the start may be made at any
point in the table, but decisions on these matters should be made
before turning to the table. (This is to avoid any possibility that
the choice of a starting point might be nonrandom, as it could be
if the decision on where to start were made after examination of
the table to be used.) In the present instance the investigator
decides to use the last three columns of the set of five columns
making up group (3), as numbered on the horizontal axis of Table
16-1, and to start at the seventh line. The entry on the seventh

TABLE 16–1
Random Numbers*

Line	(1)	(2)	(3)	(4)	(5)	(6)	(7)	(8)
1	78994	36244	02673	25475	84953	61793	50243	63423
2	04909	58485	70686	93930	34880	73059	06823	80257
3	46582	73570	33004	51795	86477	46736	60460	70345
4	29242	89792	88634	60285	07190	07795	27011	85941
5	68104	81339	97090	20601	78940	20228	22803	96070
6	17156	02182	82504	19880	93747	80910	78260	25136
7	50711	94789	07171	02103	99057	98775	37997	18325
8	39449	52409	75095	77720	39729	03205	09313	43545
9	75629	82729	76916	72657	58992	32756	01154	84890
10	01020	55151	36132	51971	32155	60735	64867	35424
11	08337	89989	24260	08618	66798	25889	52860	57375
12	76829	47229	19706	30094	69430	92399	98749	22081
13	39708	30641	21267	56501	95182	72442	21445	17276
14	89836	55817	56747	75195	06818	83043	47403	58266
15	25903	61370	66081	54076	67442	52964	23823	02718
16	71345	03422	01015	68025	19703	77313	04555	83425
17	61454	92263	14647	08473	34124	10740	40839	05620
18	80376	08909	30470	40200	46558	61742	11643	92121
19	45144	54373	05505	90074	24783	86299	20900	15144
20	12191	88527	58852	51175	11534	87218	04876	85584
21	62936	59120	73957	35969	21598	47287	39394	08778
22	31588	96798	43668	12611	01714	77266	55079	24690
23	20787	96048	84726	17512	39450	43618	30629	24356
24	45603	00745	84635	43079	52724	14262	05750	89373
25	31606	64782	34027	56734	09365	20008	93559	78384
26	10452	33074	76718	99556	16026	00013	78411	95107
27	37016	64633	67301	50949	91298	74968	73631	57397
28	66725	97865	25409	37498	00816	99262	14471	10232
29	07380	74438	82120	17890	40963	55757	13492	68294
30	71621	57688	58256	47702	74724	89419	08025	68519
31	03466	13263	23917	20417	11315	52805	33072	07723
32	12692	32931	97387	34822	53775	91674	76549	37635
33	52192	30941	44998	17833	94563	23062	95725	38463
34	56691	72529	66063	73570	86860	68125	40436	31303
35	74952	43041	58869	15677	78598	43520	97521	83248
36	18752	43693	32867	53017	22661	39610	03796	02622
37	61691	04944	43111	28325	82319	65589	66048	98498
38	49197	63948	38947	60207	70667	39843	60607	15328
39	19436	87291	71684	74859	76501	93456	95714	92518
40	39143	64893	14606	13543	09621	68301	69817	52140
41	82244	67549	76491	09761	74494	91307	64222	66592
42	55847	56155	42878	23708	97999	40131	52360	90390
43	94095	95970	07826	25991	37584	56966	68623	83454
44	11751	69469	25521	44097	07511	88976	30122	67542
45	69902	08995	27821	11758	64989	61902	32121	28165
46	21850	25352	25556	92161	23592	43294	10479	37879
47	75850	46992	25165	55906	62339	88958	91717	15756
48	29648	22086	42581	85677	20251	39641	65786	80689
49	82740	28443	42734	25518	82827	35825	90288	32911
50	36842	42092	52075	83926	42875	71500	69216	01350

* A portion of page 5 of *Table of 105,000 Random Decimal Digits* constructed by H. Burke Horton and R. Tynes Smith III, for the Bureau of Transport Economics and Statistics, Interstate Commerce Commission. These numbers are reproduced here with the permission of W. H. S. Stevens, Director of that Bureau.

line in these three columns is made up of three digits 1 7 1. The element numbered 171 is included in the sample. Next in order are the digits 0 9 5; unit number 95 is included. The next entry is 916; since this is larger than N, this number is ignored; there is no element of the population so numbered. Continuing in this fashion the investigator selects the following 10 numbers, in all:

171   95   132   260   706   267   747   81   15   647

The population units corresponding to these numbers are the desired random sample.

The procedure here outlined will ensure the necessary conditions for a simple random sample. The table from which the 10 numbers were obtained is completely random, in the order of arrangements of digits. All individual elements of the parent population have equal and independent probabilities of being included in a given sample. The probability of being chosen is known for each such element. (The ratio n/N gives the probability that any individual element will be selected in a simple random sample of n elements drawn from a population containing N elements. In the present case this is $10/900$.) Moreover, all possible combinations of 10 elements among the 900 in the population have the same probability of being drawn, when a given sample of 10 is being selected. This probability need not, in fact, be worked out, but it should be capable of determination.

Estimates from a Simple Random Sample. Logically, we are concerned here, first, with the determination of a sample statistic that is to provide an estimate of a population parameter, secondly, with the form of the estimate by which we pass from sample statistics to population parameters and, thirdly, with the determination of the sampling error of such an estimate. These steps, for simple random samples, have been discussed in a somewhat different context in Chapters 6, 7, and 8. Since certain new terms and procedures enter into field sampling, however, we shall briefly cover these steps, in order.

Sample statistics and the estimation of population values. The required sample statistics are determined by familiar methods. For the variate X we may derive the following from a simple random sample:

$x_t = \Sigma x$ (e.g., total income reported by a sample of income recipients)

$\bar{x} = \Sigma x/n$ (e.g., arithmetic average of the incomes reported by a sample of income recipients)

$p = u/n$ (e.g., proportion of unemployed persons in a sample of members of the labor force)

When we pass to estimates of population values, certain of the sample values must be modified since the sample covers only a fraction of a given finite population. We use $f\,(= n/N)$, the *sampling fraction*, to denote the portion of the population included in the sample. The expansion factor, $g\,(= 1/f)$, is used to raise sample totals to estimates of population totals. N is of course equal to gn. Thus, for estimates of population values corresponding to the specified sample values, we have

$$X'_t = gx_t \tag{16.1}$$
$$\bar{X}' = \bar{x} \tag{16.2}$$
$$U' = gu \tag{16.3}$$
$$P' = U'/N \tag{16.4}$$

(The sample $p\,(= u/n)$ will be equal to the estimate P' given above. In subsequent discussions of sampling errors I shall use p to designate this estimate, as I shall use $\bar{x}$ as the estimate of the population mean. The capital letters X'_t and U' will be used for estimates of population totals, since they differ in absolute value from the corresponding sample totals.)

Estimates of sampling errors. In defining the errors involved in applying to *finite* populations results obtained from samples, we must modify procedures intended for use with infinite populations. This modification is made through the application of a *finite multiplier*, which is also termed a *finite population correction*. It entails the multiplication of the variances of the sample statistics by a quantity equal to the proportion that the uncovered portion of the population is of the whole population. This multiplier is of the form $(N - n)/N$. Or, since the symbol f has been used for n/N, the sampling fraction, the expression for the uncovered proportion may be written $1 - f$. The effect of the correction is to reduce the variance of a given statistic by the proportion f. For an f of 0.25 the finite multiplier will be 0.75; its use will reduce the variance of the specified statistic by 25 percent. If f is very small the correction is negligible. In taking a sample of 10,000 from a population of 150,000,000 we are, for practical purposes, sampling from an infinite population. In such a case the finite multiplier is virtually unity and may be ignored. (Cochran suggests that this correction may be neglected whenever the sampling fraction is 5 percent or less.)

The estimates to be made from the sample statistics (or the hypotheses to be tested with reference to these statistics) relate, in many surveys, to the mean value of some characteristic of the individual elements being studied—to mean family income, to average weekly earnings of factory workers, to average bond yields. The variance of such a mean (the square of its standard error), for a sample of n units drawn from an infinite population of X's, is given by $s_{\bar{x}}^2$ or s^2/n, where the sample variance s^2 has been derived with $n - 1$ degrees of freedom. For a sample drawn from a finite population including N elements, the expression for the variance of the mean becomes

$$s_{\bar{x}}^2 = \frac{s^2}{n}\left(\frac{N - n}{N}\right) = \frac{s^2}{n}(1 - f) \qquad (16.5)$$

The square root of this quantity is the standard error of the estimate of the population mean. Having this measure of sampling error, the investigator proceeds with the setting of confidence limits or the testing of hypotheses, in the manner discussed in Chapters 7 and 8.

From the results of a given field survey we may wish to estimate population values of statistics other than the mean. For most such statistics—medians, standard deviations, etc.—the procedures developed in Chapters 7 and 8 for infinite populations are applicable to simple random samples from finite populations, with the corrections given by the use of the finite multiplier. These require no special discussion here. Of greater practical importance are procedures for estimating two other simple measures—the *total value* of some specified characteristic for all elements of the population, and the *proportion* of the total number of elements in the population possessing a stated qualitative characteristic. No new principles are involved in dealing with such measures, but their sampling errors call for brief comment.

The estimation of totals is a frequent objective of sample surveys. What is the total income of farmers? What is the aggregate value of the savings bonds held by householders in a given community? What is the total number of children of school age in a stated region? Let us say that in a given sample including n individual elements the sum of the values of a specified characteristic is x_t. As we have seen, an estimate, X'_t, of the aggregate value of this characteristic for all elements of the population is given by gx_t, where g is the expansion factor, N/n. The variance of X'_t (the square of its standard error) may be estimated from[2]

$$s^2_{X'_t} = \frac{ns^2}{f^2}(1 - f) \tag{16.6}$$

In this expression s^2 is the sample variance used as an approximation to the population variance.

A simple example will illustrate this procedure. Assume that we are sampling households in a small town for the purpose of estimating the total holdings of U. S. saving bonds. We shall say that there are 10,000 households (technically, the elementary and sampling unit will be a *spending unit*, as defined on page 72). A simple random sample of 1,000 households shows total holdings of $900,000. The standard deviation is $300. The sampling fraction is 0.10 and g is 10. For the estimate of the total holdings of savings bonds in the population we have (using formula 16.1 above)

$$X'_t = 10 \times \$900,000 = \$9,000,000$$

From formula (16.6) we have, for the estimated standard error of the estimated population total,

$$s_{X'_t} = \sqrt{\frac{1,000 \times 90,000}{0.01}(1 - 0.10)} = \sqrt{8,100,000,000}$$

$$= \$90,000.$$

Confidence limits at the 0.95 level are given by $9,000,000 \pm$

---

[2] The variance of an estimate of a total is equal to N^2 times the variance of the estimate of the corresponding mean. The right-hand member of (16.6) is equivalent to N^2 times the right-hand member of (16.5), i.e., to $\frac{N^2 s^2}{n}(1 - f)$.

(1.96 × \$90,000). Thus we may state with the indicated degree of confidence that the total holdings of U. S. savings bonds in the community in question lies between \$8,823,600 and \$9,176,400.

The problem of estimating *proportions* arises when interest attaches to the portion of a given population possessing some definable qualitative characteristic, which is either present or not present in each unit. What proportion of residential structures were unoccupied at a given time? What proportion of spending units saved money in a given year? What percentage of families in a stated community own TV sets? In such problems, with simple random sampling, an unbiased estimate of the desired population proportion is given by the proportion p found in the sample.

The variance of p, as derived from a sample drawn from a finite population, is given by a slight modification of the familiar formula for the standard deviation of a distribution of relative frequencies, $\sqrt{pq/n}$. Not knowing the true population proportions, P and Q, we use the sample values, p and q, and have as our estimate of the variance of p

$$s_p^2 = \frac{pq}{n-1}(1-f) \qquad\qquad (16.7)$$

Let us say that in a community containing 25,000 members of the labor force, an unemployment survey covering 5,000 members shows 8 percent unemployed at a given time. We wish to set confidence limits at a 0.95 level, for an estimate of the proportion of the population of 25,000 who were unemployed at that date. The sampling fraction is 0.20, and the finite multiplier is 0.80; p is 0.08, q is 0.92, and n is 5,000. For the standard error of p, using the relationship shown in (16.7), we have

$$s_p = \sqrt{\frac{0.08 \times 0.92}{5,000-1}(1-0.20)}$$

$$= \sqrt{\frac{0.0736}{4,999}(0.80)}$$

$$= 0.00343$$

The desired confidence interval is given by $p \pm 1.96s_p$, or 0.08 ± 0.0067. Our conclusion, therefore, in which we have a confidence measured by a coefficient of 0.95, is that the proportion of unemployed in the population of 25,000 falls between 0.0733 and 0.0867.

Precision and Sample Size. When we speak of the *precision* of an estimate based on a sample we are referring to the variability to be expected in sampling results. Thus it is only errors of sampling to which standard errors of sample results relate. Errors that arise out of the method of measurement employed in a given case, out of bias on the part of interviewers, out of the use of ambiguous or slanted questions, are not sampling errors, in this sense. Such nonsampling errors affect the *accuracy* of the final results, meaning by accuracy closeness of approach to the true values sought, and are of course of high concern to the investigator. But these are apart from the errors of sampling to which the standard deviations of sampling distributions, or the standard errors of estimates from samples, relate. The term precision is by convention restricted to errors of sampling.

If the method of simple random sampling is employed in a survey of a given population, the precision of the results depends only on the size of the sample. Precision may therefore be controlled. In deciding on the level of precision desired, and thus on the size of the sample to be drawn, the investigator will weigh the possible consequences of erroneous conclusions, setting these risks against the costs of achieving various degrees of precision. The decision may be a fairly easy one to make if the objectives of a planned study are few (and if cost factors are definable). On the other hand, if a single survey is designed to serve several purposes, the different objectives may give rise to conflicting needs as to sample size. Here a practicable working balance will have to be struck. In the present discussion we consider only the problem involved in selecting an appropriate size for a simple random sample, after a decision has been made as to the degree of precision desired.

The measures of sampling error dealt with in earlier sections have all defined absolute errors, i.e., errors expressed in the original units of measurement. Thus in estimating a population mean for family savings, absolute confidence limits are set in terms of dollars; in estimating mean wheat yield for a population of wheat farms, absolute confidence limits are set in bushels. In planning a sample survey it is usually more convenient to work with reference to *relative precision*. When this is the case, relative rather than absolute errors are of interest. We define in relative terms the tolerable margin of error—the tolerable relative difference between an estimate of a population parameter and the actual parameter value—and plan a sample size that will enable us to state with a given degree of probability that the error lies within this tolerable margin.

Measures of relative sampling errors.[3] In Chapter 5 we discussed the concept of relative variation. As a coefficient of relative variation we used the ratio of the standard deviation of a distribution to the arithmetic mean of that distribution. That is $v = s/\bar{x}$. (In the earlier presentation the symbol V was used, and the quantity was multiplied by 100 to put it in percentage terms. Here we shall treat it as a ratio, and shall use a lower case v for all such ratios derived from sample data.) The concept of relative variation may be extended, to apply to sampling distributions (that is, to distributions of means, proportions, coefficients of correlation, etc.) as well as to distributions of original observations. The symbol v, with a subscript to indicate the variable in question, may be used for all such measures of relative variation. When the measures relate to sampling distributions, v is the ratio of a standard error to the value being estimated. Thus $v_{\bar{x}} = s_{\bar{x}}/\bar{x}$ (where $\bar{x}$ is a sample mean, regarded as an estimate of a population mean), and $v_p = s_p/p$ (where p is a sample proportion regarded as an estimate of a population proportion).

It is convenient to work in terms of the squared coefficient of variation, a quantity that Hansen, Hurwitz, and Madow call the *relative variance* or, for short, the rel-variance. Estimates of the relative variances of certain of the quantities with which sample surveys commonly deal are given below. (The finite multiplier entering into the estimates is ordinarily used when the sampling fraction is 5 percent or more; when the sampling fraction is less than 5 percent it is usually disregarded.)

$$v^2 = \frac{s^2}{\bar{x}^2} \qquad (16.8)$$

---

[3] In this discussion of relative sampling errors and of procedures employed in defining appropriate sample sizes I have followed the development of these topics by Hansen, Hurwitz, and Madow, and have employed certain terms and symbols introduced by them. For proofs and illustrations see Vol. I, Chap. 4 and Vol. II, Chap. 4 of their comprehensive work on sample surveys (Ref. 67).

(When v^2 is used without subscript it is a symbol for the relative variance of the original observations.)

$$v_{\bar{x}}^2 = \frac{v^2}{n}(1 - f) \tag{16.9}$$

$$v_{\bar{X}_t}^2 = \frac{v^2}{n}(1 - f) \tag{16.10}$$

$$v_p^2 = \frac{q}{(n-1)p}(1 - f) \tag{16.11}$$

Each of these relative variances is the ratio of a squared standard error to the square of the value being estimated. Thus for estimates relating to an infinite population

$$v_{\bar{x}}^2 = \frac{s_{\bar{x}}^2}{\bar{x}^2} = \frac{s^2/n}{\bar{x}^2} = \frac{s^2}{\bar{x}^2 n}$$

$$= \frac{v^2}{n}$$

Applying the finite multiplier $(1 - f)$ we have formula (16.9) as given above. Formulas 16.10 and 16.11 may be derived in similar fashion from the expressions defining in absolute terms the standard errors of the measures to which they relate.

The use of these formulas may be illustrated with reference to measures derived from a simple random sample:

$N = 1000 \quad n = 100 \quad f = 0.10 \qquad 1 - f = 0.90$

$\bar{x} = \$200 \quad s = \$40 \quad v = 40/200 = 0.20 \qquad v^2 = 0.04$

$v_{\bar{x}}^2 = \frac{v^2}{n}(1 - f) = \frac{0.04}{100} \times 0.90 = 0.00036$

$v_{\bar{x}} = \sqrt{0.00036} = 0.019$

The coefficient of variation of the estimate of the mean is 0.019, or 1.9 percent. In using this measure of relative error in setting confidence limits we follow the same general procedure as in using measures of absolute error. Thus with confidence measured by a probability of 0.68 we may say: the mean of the population from which this sample comes falls between \$196.20 and \$203.80 [where $196.20 = 200 - (0.019 \times 200)$ and $203.80 = 200 + (0.019 \times 200)$]. Or, if we wish to be practically certain that the limits we set will include the population value, we may use a range of $3v$'s on each side of the mean; for this the confidence coefficient is 0.9973.

The variance s^2 which enters into formula (16.8), and thus into formulas (16.9) and (16.10), is the variance of the sample, used as an approximation to the population σ^2. The accuracy of the estimates of $v_{\bar{x}}^2$ and $v_{X'}^2$ will depend, obviously, on the closeness with which s^2 approximates σ^2. There will, in any case, be sampling fluctuations in s^2, but the range of these fluctuations will be less the larger the sample. The same is true of p, a sample proportion used as an approximation to a population proportion.

Estimates of sample size. The relations set forth in formulas (16.9), (16.10), and (16.11) may be used for the very practical purpose of estimating the size of sample needed to achieve a specified degree of precision in sample results. Here, again, the investigator must usually be content with approximations. He cannot, with accuracy, determine the sample size needed for a given degree of precision unless he knows something about the kind of population being sampled (e.g., normal, skewed, flat-topped) and can approximate one or more of the basic parameters (e.g., the population variance or relative variance, or a population proportion). Not infrequently he will have such information from other studies covering the same or a related population. If not, he may have to conduct a limited pilot study before a general survey is launched. If the standard deviation of a population can be estimated with a relative error no greater than 10-12 percent an investigator can determine with acceptable accuracy the size of sample needed for estimating, with a stated degree of precision, a population mean or a population total.

We let D equal the difference, in relative terms, between an estimate of a population mean, made from sample results, and the true population mean. We may set D at any relative level we choose —5 percent, 10 percent, 15 percent—and then decide on the risks we are willing to run that the error will be greater than this. If the consequences of a large error would be very serious, we may set D very low, and then state that the chance of exceeding this error must be no greater than 3 out of 1,000. For this probability we should set D equal to $3v_{\bar{x}}$, and then determine the size of sample that would be expected to yield results meeting these conditions.

If we know that the sampling fraction will be 5 percent or less we may proceed as though we were to sample an infinite population.

That is, we do not apply the finite multiplier. In such a situation the general formula (16.9) for the relative variance of a sample mean becomes

$$v_{\bar{x}}^2 = \frac{v^2}{n} \qquad (16.12)$$

We shall assume, for purposes of illustration, that in a particular case the finite multiplier is not to be applied, that we set D at 0.06, and that we wish to work with a confidence coefficient of 0.997. That is, we wish to take a very small chance indeed that the relative difference between the estimated and the true population means will exceed 6 percent. Thus $D = 3v_{\bar{x}}$, or $v_{\bar{x}} = D/3$. We shall use $v^2 = 0.16$ as an estimate of the population V^2 (this estimate being derived from prior studies or a pilot investigation). For $v_{\bar{x}}^2$ in formula (16.12) we substitute what is, for present purposes, its equivalent, $(D/3)^2$. Thus

$$\frac{D^2}{9} = \frac{v^2}{n} \qquad (16.13)$$

From which

$$n = \frac{9v^2}{D^2} \qquad (16.14)$$

Substituting the given values of v^2 and of D,

$$n = \frac{9 \times 0.16}{0.0036} = 400$$

The size of the sample needed to achieve the precision suggested is thus estimated to be 400.

If the sampling fraction is expected to be greater than 5 percent, the finite multiplier would be applied, and the equation corresponding to (16.13) would be

$$\frac{D^2}{9} = \frac{v^2}{n}(1 - f) \qquad (16.15)$$

Substituting for the finite multiplier its equivalent $\frac{N - n}{N}$ (where N is the population total) we have

$$\frac{D^2}{9} = \frac{v^2}{n} \cdot \frac{N - n}{N} \qquad (16.16)$$

which reduces to

$$n = \frac{9Nv^2}{ND^2 + 9v^2} \tag{16.17}$$

Let us assume that we are drawing a sample from a small population of 2,000 units, D and v^2 having the same values as in the preceding example. Then

$$n = \frac{9 \times 2,000 \times 0.16}{(2,000 \times 0.0036) + (9 \times 0.16)} = \frac{2880}{8.64}$$

$$= 333$$

The relations expressed in formulas (16.14) and (16.17) apply to the special case in which D, the relative difference between an estimated population mean and the true mean, is set equal to $3v_{\bar{x}}$. This range is designed to give virtual assurance that the error will not be greater than D. If a smaller range will serve, with a greater risk that the actual error in a given case will exceed D, a smaller sample will serve. Thus if in the first example cited above (where the finite multiplier was not applied) the investigator had been willing to accept a chance of 45.5 out of 1,000 that D would be greater than 0.06, D would be set equal to $2v_{\bar{x}}$. (It will be recalled that 0.0455 of the area under a normal curve falls outside ordinates erected two standard deviations above and below the mean. The distribution of relative deviations will be similar, in this respect, to the distribution of absolute deviations.) We therefore substitute $(D/2)^2$ for $v_{\bar{x}}^2$ in formula (16.12), and formula (16.14) becomes

$$n = \frac{4v^2}{D^2} \tag{16.18}$$

For the desired size, $n = 177$.

We may use k as a general symbol for the multiplier of the coefficient of variation, in specifying the precision to be sought in a given sampling operation. In working with a confidence coefficient of 0.997, $k = 3$; with a confidence coefficient of 0.9545, $k = 2$. These are values of normal deviates corresponding to the stated probabilities. We have as a general expression for the estimation of n, when the use of a finite multiplier is not necessary,

$$n = \frac{k^2v^2}{D^2} \tag{16.19}$$

When the sampling fraction is expected to exceed 5 percent, and a

finite multiplier is necessary, the formula for estimating sample
size is

$$n = \frac{k^2 N v^2}{N D^2 + k^2 v^2} \qquad (16.20)$$

D and k together fix the precision sought in a given sampling
operation. D specifies a given relative error, plus or minus; in terms
of the coefficient k we define the probability that the error involved
in generalizing the sample result will not be greater than D. Under
conditions of simple random sampling these general formulas apply
to estimates of population means, totals, or proportions.

In general, if contemplated samples are to include several
hundred cases or more, estimates of the sample size required for a
given degree of precision are not dependent on assumptions concerning the character of the parent population. This is so because
of the tendency toward normality in sampling distributions, as n
increases. Extreme skewness in the population being sampled may
give rise to trouble, however, when the variance of the parent
population has to be estimated from the sample variance. For
pronounced skewness in the population can mean great instability
in the variances of samples. A few extreme items in a given sample
may distort the estimate of the population variance. If, in sampling
for a mean, extreme skewness is suspected, special pilot studies
may be required to provide exact information about the form of
the parent population. One precaution to be taken is to plan on
samples larger than those indicated by the formulas cited in
preceding pages. When it is known that the parent population is
sharply skewed, the methods of stratification discussed below may
be employed to reduce the variability of estimates.[4]

When a population *proportion* is being estimated (i.e., the proportion of units in a population possessing a specified qualitative
characteristic that is either present or absent in each unit), this
particular danger may be avoided. For if methods of simple
sampling are used in such a study, and if the elementary unit is
also the sampling unit, estimates of population proportions are
not affected by the type of population sampled.

---

[4] See Cochran, Ref. 17, 20-28 for a discussion of problems growing out of skewness in
the parent universe.

Stratified Random Sampling

The Meaning and Purposes of Stratified Sampling. In simple random sampling the population to be sampled is treated as an undifferentiated whole; the individual elements of the sample are drawn at random from the whole universe. However, it is often possible and desirable to break the parent population into distinctive classes, or *strata*, and then to obtain a sample by drawing, at random, specified numbers of sampling units from each of the classes thus set up. This may be desirable because of interest in the separate sectors of the universe, as well as in the universe as a whole. In a study of farms we may wish to learn about the separate attributes of wheat farms and cattle ranches, as well as about farms as a whole; in a study of consumer budgets we may wish to study spending and saving patterns among urban and rural families separately, as well as among the aggregate of all families. Such subdivisions for which specific information is desired are termed *domains of study*. But the existence of sectors of special interest is not the only reason nor usually, indeed, the main reason for breaking a population into classes in a sample survey. Most populations are heterogeneous, in the sense that the application to them of rational principles of classification will break the whole into classes having distinctive attributes. This means that the classes, taken separately, will be more homogeneous than the total population. For example, we should expect among wheat farms less variation, in respect of a stated operating characteristic, than among all farms. Industrial workers will vary less in their consumption patterns than will all income recipients. When it is possible thus to distinguish subgroups the members of which are more alike than are the members of the whole population being studied, the efficiency of sampling may be materially improved by stratification. Estimates of a required degree of precision may be obtained from a smaller sample (and this usually means at a lower cost); or, with a sample of stated size, more precise estimates may be made from a stratified than from a nonstratified sample.

In stratified random sampling, which is the term employed for this process, the population is subdivided into strata before the sample is drawn. These strata should not overlap. A sample of specified size is then drawn by random methods from the sampling units that make up each stratum. If a given stratum is of interest in its own right the corresponding subsample will provide the basis for estimates concerning the attributes of the population stratum, or subuniverse, from which it is drawn, The total of the subsamples will constitute the full sample on which estimates of attributes of the full population will be based. When a single stratum is itself a domain of study, estimating procedures for that stratum are essentially those discussed above in dealing with simple random sampling. The new problems that arise relate to the making of estimates and the determination of sampling errors when results obtained from a stratified sample are to be applied to the whole population.

Stratification is an effective sampling device to the degree that it sets off classes that are more homogeneous than the total. When this can be done, we distinguish classes that differ among themselves in respect of a stated characteristic. Unless we mark off classes that differ among themselves, stratification is futile. So what is sought in stratification, we may say, is homogeneity *within* classes, heterogeneity *between* classes.

The symbols used to designate stratum measures are the same as those used for population and sample values, with appropriate subscripts. These symbols have been given in the section on notation, above.

Allocation in Stratified Sampling. A central field problem in stratified sampling is the determination of the sizes of the sub-samples to be drawn from the several strata. The procedure employed in determining subsample sizes is termed *allocation*. One simple principle would be to have all the subsamples of the same size; that is, we might have $n_{h_1} = n_{h_2} = n_{h_3} = \ldots$. But we should lose many of the advantages of stratification with such a procedure. Three more suitable methods of allocation will be briefly described.

Allocation proportional to sizes of strata. We have defined a sampling fraction f as the ratio of the sample size to the total population. For a simple random sample $f = n/N$. On the same principle the sampling fraction for a single stratum h_1 is $f_{h_1} = n_{h_1}/N_{h_1}$; for stratum h_2 it is $f_{h_2} = n_{h_2}/N_{h_2}$. In making sample sizes proportional to sizes of strata a *uniform sampling fraction* is used. That is, we determine sample sizes for the several strata in such a way that $f_{h_1} = f_{h_2} = f_{h_3} = \ldots$. The logic of this is clear. In seeking a sample representative of a given universe, it is reasonable to select for the sample twice as many sampling units from stratum h_1

than from stratum h_2 if, in the universe, there are twice as many sampling units in stratum h_1 than in stratum h_2. In making estimates for population characteristics we would wish to give more weight to information on stratum h_1 than to information on stratum h_2; the method of proportional allocation does this. It is a self-weighting procedure; although no weights are consciously introduced in subsequent operations, we are in fact using weights proportional to the N's in the population strata.

The term "proportional allocation," used without qualification or further explanation, means allocation on the basis of a uniform sampling fraction.

Allocation proportional to standard deviations of strata. In discussing sampling distributions in earlier chapters we have noted that the degree of dispersion found in such distributions is related to the degree of dispersion in the populations sampled. Thus for the standard error of the mean we have $\sigma_m = \sigma/\sqrt{N}$. Here the variation in the sampling distribution is directly proportional to the variation in the universe. This suggests that in determining sample sizes for the several classes of a stratified sample it is reasonable to relate the sizes of the samples drawn from the several strata to the degrees of dispersion characterizing these strata. To achieve a given degree of accuracy in estimates based on samples from several such strata, larger samples will be needed from strata marked by wide dispersion than from those with slight dispersion. A single observation, indeed, gives a perfect representation of a universe in which there is no variation. The principle of allocation to which these considerations lead is one that would make the sample n's from the various strata directly proportional to the standard deviations of these strata. That is,

$$\frac{n_{h_1}}{\sigma_{h_1}} = \frac{n_{h_2}}{\sigma_{h_2}} = \frac{n_{h_3}}{\sigma_{h_3}} = \cdots$$

If these three σ's were, respectively, 10, 20, and 30, this condition would be satisfied by having the n's equal, respectively, to 100, 200, and 300.

This procedure calls, obviously, for knowledge of the standard deviations of the different strata into which the population is to be divided. Census counts, or other sources, may provide such information. If not, small-scale trial samplings preceding the main survey may be necessary. The requirements of the main survey may be served adequately by rather rough approximations to the standard deviations of the separate strata; such approximations may be come by at fairly low cost, with well-designed trial borings.

The principle of allocation proportional to stratum standard deviations will be satisfactory, by itself, if the N's of the various strata $(N_{h1}, N_{h2}, N_{h3} \ldots)$ are equal, or approximately so. If the N's are not equal, and they seldom are, we still face the problems raised by such inequalities. We need a method of allocation that will take account of differences among both the N's and the σ's of the various strata.

Optimum allocation. The method of optimum allocation represents a combination of the two principles described above. Instead of using a uniform sampling fraction, we vary the fraction, making differences among the fractions proportional to differences among the standard deviations of the strata. That is, we set

$$\frac{f_{h1}}{\sigma_{h1}} = \frac{f_{h2}}{\sigma_{h2}} = \frac{f_{h3}}{\sigma_{h3}} = \ldots$$

This mode of allocation, which makes the sample sizes in the various classes proportional to corresponding class standard deviations in the universe being sampled, as well as to class sizes in that universe, leads to theoretically optimum sampling fractions.[5]

We should note that exact proportionality in both respects may in fact be difficult to realize for any of several reasons. Precise information on universe values may be lacking. When the individual strata are of interest in their own right as domains of study, the investigator may wish to obtain larger samples from certain strata than would be given by strict proportionality. If a single survey is serving several purposes, so that the population values of more than one characteristic are to be estimated from sample results, it is unlikely that any single set of class sample sizes would be proportional to the class standard deviations of these several characteristics. In practice, allocation proportional to stratum sizes, alone, is most commonly employed. Subsequent computations and estimates are much simpler with a uniform sampling fraction than with sampling fractions that vary from stratum to stratum. If the stratum standard deviations are known to differ widely, and if the stratum standard deviations may be determined

---

[5] The original memoir on this subject is a classic paper by Jerzy Neyman, "On the two different aspects of the representative method." See Neyman, Ref. 120.

with some precision in advance of the full field survey, optimum allocation may be desirable and feasible. But these conditions are not frequently encountered.

In the selection of sampling fractions the concern of the investigator is not solely with maximum precision. Precision and cost, whether dealt with on a unit or aggregate basis, have to be weighed together, and a working solution reached. A special problem is introduced when unit costs of sampling operations vary from class to class—a circumstance that may necessitate a departure from optimum or proportional allocation. Recent works on sampling survey theory introduce such unit costs into the functions used to estimate desirable sample sizes. Thus Cochran (Ref. 17 p. 75) gives a working formula designed to yield optimum allocation with varying unit costs. The allocation to which this theorem leads would give (as between two strata) a larger stratum n_h to the stratum that is larger, to the stratum marked by the greater internal variation, and to the stratum for which sampling is cheaper.

Having obtained a stratified random sample, the investigator is faced with the problem of estimating desired population values—means totals, or proportions—from the appropriate sample statistics, and of defining the sampling errors to which these estimates are subject. When the sampling fraction is uniform for all strata, the estimation of population values involves a simple adaptation of methods specified for simple random samples. For nonuniform sampling fractions, population estimates are built up from stratum values. These processes, and the somewhat more involved procedures employed in defining the sampling errors of such estimates, are developed in basic texts on sample survey methods.[6]

Some Other Sampling Designs

The sampling forms described above are the fundamental types. In practice these are often modified in various ways, in adapting survey designs to the characteristics of given populations and to the cost and precision requirements of particular studies. The most important of these modifications are termed *multi-stage sampling*

---

[6] See Cochran (Ref. 17), and Hansen, Hurwitz and Madow (Ref. 67). A brief explanation of these procedures is given in Mills, *Statistical Methods*, Third Edition (pp. 682-88).

and *multi-phase* sampling, although more frequently than not the "multi" reduces to "two."

Multi-stage Sampling. The essential feature of this sampling form is suggested by the term *cluster sampling*, which is often used for it. We have spoken above of *elementary units*, the individual entities whose attributes are the objects of study. These units may be farms, families, individuals, corporations, townships—any of the things that for purposes of ultimate analysis are treated as undivided wholes. The unit of the sampling process, at a first or even at a later stage, may be a *cluster* of such elementary units, the cluster being later broken down into the units whose characteristics are being investigated. Any sampling procedure that involves the use of such clusters as sampling units is termed cluster sampling.

Thus the *primary sampling unit* (which is usually shortened to psu) may be an elementary unit or a cluster of units. If it is a cluster, the process may obviously be repeated; i.e., there may be a *subsampling* of the primary units, such a subsample from a particular primary unit being either a sample of new clusters (smaller than the first) or a sample of elementary units. If the sampling unit at this second stage is a cluster, a second subsampling process is possible—a process that may entail the selection of samples made up of still other clusters or of elementary units. For example, to cite an illustration of multi-stage sampling suggested in the United Nations report on sampling surveys, a given investigation might be concerned with the characteristics of farms, these being the elementary units. For the purposes of the survey, the country might be divided into districts, a number of districts being selected as first-stage or primary sampling units; the districts could be divided into villages, a number of villages being selected as second-stage sampling units; the villages could be divided into farms, a sample of farms being then selected from each village. In this case the third-stage sampling units—the farms—are the elementary units that are the objects of study.

If the sampling process stops at the first stage, that is, if all the elementary units included in the clusters making up the primary sampling units make up the sample of elementary units that is to be analyzed in detail, the process is termed *single-stage cluster sampling*. We should have this form of sampling if all the farms included in the sample of districts mentioned above constituted the sample of farms whose characteristics were studied in detail. We should have *double-stage sampling* if all the elementary units in the clusters selected as second-stage sampling units make up the sample of elementary units that is to be studied in detail. This would be the case if all farms in the sample of villages mentioned above made up the final sample of farms. The farm example cited is actually a case of *triple-stage sampling*; the process goes into its third stage when the sample of villages is subsampled to give the final sample of farms.

The sampling process at each stage may be either random or stratified. We have *simple cluster sampling*, of one or more stages, if the sampling units chosen at each stage are selected by the method of simple random sampling. We have *stratified cluster sampling*, of one or more stages, if stratification is employed wherever sampling units are to be selected.

The constitution of the sampling unit at each stage is of course a matter of high concern in all forms of cluster sampling. Great attention is given to the scope of such units, to their internal structure, and to all their relevant quantitative and qualitative characteristics. The ultimate considerations here are the precision of the final estimates to be based on sample results, and costs; these in turn must be weighed with reference to a variety of factors, including the structure of the population to be sampled, the information at hand concerning it (the frame), the geographical extent of the survey, stratification possibilities, the degree of subsampling contemplated, etc. Methods used in the evaluation of these different factors, and in combining them to reach operating decisions, are treated in the standard works on sample surveys. We should note here, however, that these are not matters of operational interest only. For those who use the results of sample surveys, information on the scope and character of the sampling units employed is necessary to intelligent appraisal of the estimates based on such surveys.

Area sampling. A form of cluster sampling that is widely used is one that associates the elementary units of a population with a geographical area. The populations under study need not be human —they could be populations of animals, of trees, or houses—but in most applications of this method, which is termed *area sampling*, the units under study are human beings. Each of these units must be associated with a single definable area. For a human being this is usually the area in which he resides. The investigator works, in a first stage, with a list of such areas, rather than with a list of the units of the whole population. By random methods a sample of areas is selected. If need be subsamples of the chosen sample areas may then be selected by random methods. At an appropriate stage the elementary units residing in the selected sample areas may be individually enumerated. These enumerated elements may constitute the final sample for interview or detailed study, or the final sample may be obtained by a further sampling operation among the enumerated elements. If these procesess are carried through by random methods the conditions of probability sampling will have been met, and estimates based on sample results may be made in probability terms.

An important feature of this procedure is that no list of elements in the full population is required to ensure conditions of probability sampling. The essential condition that all members of the parent population have a definable probability of inclusion in the final sample is ensured by the random sampling of *areas*. The enumeration of elements is then necessary only in the limited number of selected areas. This type of cluster sampling may be used, therefore, where simple random sampling would not be possible, because no list of population elements exists. Even when a list exists, area sampling may be much less costly. Procedures used in area sampling will be more fully discussed in a later section of this chapter.

Multi-phase Sampling. The successive sampling operations in multi-stage sampling entail the selection of sampling units of different types at different stages. The term *multi-phase* sampling is used when sampling units of the same type are the objects of different *phases* of observation. Typically, in one of these phases all the units in a sample are studied with respect to certain characteristics, while in a later phase some of the units, a subsample of the full sample, are studied with respect to certain additional characteristics. Thus we should have two-phase or *double sampling* if information concerning family income alone were gathered for all the members of a sample of 10,000 families, while additional information concerning the sources of income and the uses of income were gathered for a subsample of 1,000 families. The additional information for members of the smaller group might be gathered at the same time the information was collected for the full sample, or might be gathered at a later time. Not infrequently the two (or more) phases relate to samples gathered at different times. A comprehensive first survey might be made, at low cost per unit because only limited facts are collected; the results of the first phase could then be used in planning an intensive second phase covering the same kind of units. (The second sample need not be a subsample of the first, though it often is.) Sometimes the first phase of such a study is designed to obtain information about a variable related to the variable that is the direct object of study. The information obtained from this preliminary sample can then be used for purposes of effective stratification, in the second or main phase of the inquiry.

Systematic Sampling. Another sampling form, simple in design and execution, may be employed when the members of the population to be sampled are arranged in order, the order corresponding to consecutive numbers. The arrangement of names in a telephone directory, or blocks in a city, of income tax returns in the Treasury's files, are examples of such ordering. If a sample of suitable size may be obtained by taking every tenth unit of the population, one of the first ten units in this ordered arrangement is chosen at random. The sample is completed by selecting every tenth unit from the rest of the list. If the first unit selected should be the fourth, the investigator would include in his sample the fourteenth, the twenty-fourth, the thirty-fourth, etc. In general terms, if the requirements of the survey call for the inclusion in the sample of one unit out of every k units in the population, a unit is chosen at random from the first k units; thereafter, every kth unit in the population, as arranged in order, is included in the sample. This mode of selection is called *systematic sampling*.

The type of sample obtained by this method depends on the structure of the population being sampled. Systematic sampling gives a stratified sample containing one unit from each stratum. If the arrangement of population elements in the order employed in the systematic sampling process is in fact random, these strata will all be alike in constitution, except for purely random differences. A systematic sample is then, in effect, a simple random sample; the standard errors of measures obtained from the systematic sample will be, on the average, the same as those obtained from simple random samples. But if the ordered arrangement of population elements is nonrandom, the systematic sample will not be a purely random one. The "strata" will differ among themselves.

Under these conditions a sample containing one unit from each stratum will be preferable to a simple random sample.

It is helpful, in obtaining an understanding of systematic sampling, to regard it, as Cochran puts it, as a form of cluster sampling. The systematic sample is itself a cluster—one of many that might have been drawn from the population by selecting at random one unit from each stratum. Since the single selected cluster given by systematic sampling constitutes the whole sample, it should reflect, in its composition, all the elements of diversity that are present in the population.

Whether systematic selection will be efficient, in providing sample measures with low sampling errors, or otherwise, depends largely on the make-up of the population from which a sample is to be drawn, and on the order underlying the mode of selection. If there should be periodicity in the elements of a population, as arranged for purposes of systematic selection, this method could give a highly unrepresentative sample. Thus if one were picking every twelfth unit, and if the arrangement were such that the units so selected were alike in some distinctive respect, the sample would be a poor one. (This danger would be a serious one if the elements of the population were observations arranged chronologically. Sales of department stores, sampled systematically so that only observations for Decembers of successive years were included, are a case in point.) On the other hand, the internal diversity that makes a systematic sample preferable to a simple random sample will be realized if units k numbers apart on the ordered list of population elements differ more from one another than do adjacent units. Thus if adjoining houses tend to resemble one another, a sampling procedure that selects only every twentieth house will be better than one that permits adjoining houses to be included in a sample. The general principle here is that systematic sampling is preferable to simple random sampling if there is high serial correlation among the units of a population, as ordered for the purposes of a sample survey.

The Current Population Survey

We shall complete this chapter on sampling theory and procedures by a concrete example. The Current Population Survey, conducted by the Bureau of the Census, provides the basis of the Monthly Report on the Labor Force—now one of the most revealing of our current social records and one of the most closely watched of our economic indicators. A brief discussion of the major features of this Survey, which is an excellent example of modern sampling methods, will illustrate the practical application of some of the techniques developed on earlier pages.[7] Although we shall not deal in any detail with the administrative aspects of this Survey, the discussion will suggest the nature of the administrative problems that are faced in planning and executing a sample survey.

Background and Objectives of the Population Survey. During the depression of the 1930's, public administrators and social scientists became acutely aware of the gaps in our knowledge of current economic processes and of our human resources. Particularly disturbing was our ignorance of the number of unemployed. At a time when unemployment was our most serious social problem, estimates of this critical magnitude differed by many millions, and there was no basis for a sound choice among differing guesses. Under the auspices of the Works Progress Administration a good beginning was made in the design of an objective sampling procedure for determining the volume of unemployment, and a monthly report on the labor force was begun by this agency in 1940. In 1942 the task was taken over by the Bureau of the Census, which has administered the survey since then. The original design has been modified from time to time by the Census Bureau, most recently in 1954. The latest design will be briefly described here.

In the early stages of this enterprise the chief objective was the estimation of unemployment, on a monthly basis. This remains a major purpose, but as changes have occurred in the social and economic conditions of American life, the Survey has come to serve other ends as well. Basically, the objective of the Survey is to provides estimates of the employment status of those members of

---

[7] I have drawn on Census Bureau sources in this account, and am particularly indebted to Joseph Steinberg, of the Population and Housing Division of the Bureau of the Census. A preliminary report on the concepts and methods used in the current survey is given in *Current Population Reports*, July 30, 1954, Series P–23, No. 2.

Results of the Population Survey are published monthly in *Current Population Reports*, Labor Force, Series P–57. A report that summarizes employment and unemployment statistics collected by both the Department of Commerce and the Department of Labor, appears monthly as a "Combined Employment and Unemployment Release" of the two Departments.

the population of the United States who are 14 years of age and
over. Such members fall into two groups—those who are members
of the labor force and those who are outside the labor force. The
labor force comprises persons in the armed forces and civilians who
are classed as employed or unemployed. The Survey seeks to cover
the civilian groups only.

Each of the terms used above calls for the most precise definition,
for ambiguities can lead to substantial margins of uncertainty in
the final estimates. The main elements of the definitions of the two
major groups in the labor force are these:

> *Employed persons* comprise (1) all those who during the survey
> week (a calendar week specified as the survey time period)
> did any work at all as paid employees or in their own businesses
> or professions, or on their own farms, or who worked 15 hours
> or more as unpaid workers on farms or in businesses operated
> by members of their families, and (2) all those who were not
> working or looking for work but who had jobs or businesses
> from which they were temporarily absent for any of a number
> of specified reasons, including illness and labor-management
> disputes.

> *Unemployed persons* include all persons who did no work (as
> defined above) in the survey week, and who were looking for
> work. All those who made efforts to find jobs during the
> preceding 60-day period are considered to be looking for work.

The final estimates and the reports supplementary to these
estimates provide information on the distribution by age and sex
of those outside the labor force and, for the labor force, details
concerning the structure of employment, the degree and nature of
part-time employment, the duration of unemployment for those
seeking work, the annual incomes of persons and families, etc.
This survey is becoming thus an instrument for the regular recording, on a comprehensive scale, of current information on the
activities and welfare of the population of the United States. As
such, it represents a major development in our system of social
and economic reporting.

The Survey Design. The final sample sought by the Census
Bureau each month is designed to include about 25,000 designated
dwelling units. These are obtained by random sampling within
each of 230 primary sampling units, each of which is a geographical

area. These primary sampling units (psu's) have come, in their turn, from 230 different strata. The two major sampling steps in this process are the selection of sample areas and the selection of households.

Stratification, and the selection of a sample of primary sampling units. A first step in the sampling process was the division of the total area of the United States into 2,000 primary sampling units. For this purpose, use was made of certain pre-existing political divisions—divisions into counties, of which there are about 3,000 in the country, and into the geographical units that are termed standard metropolitan areas. The 1950 Census recognized 168 such areas. Each of the standard metropolitan areas constituted a primary sampling unit. Each of the other 2,000 psu's in the country consisted of a separate county or of a grouping of adjoining counties. In the grouping of several counties to form a single psu diversity of social and economic conditions was sought, so that there might be as much heterogeneity as possible within the psu. (We may here suggest the reason for this heterogeneity. Since a selected psu will in the final sample represent the whole stratum from which that psu was drawn, as much as possible of the diversity existing in the stratum should be present in each psu in that stratum.) Thus a typical psu would include urban and rural residents, low income groups and high income groups, and varied industrial and occupational groups.

The process of stratification entailed the combination of the 2,000 psu's into 230 strata, each of which was to be as homogeneous as possible. (The reader will recall that in stratification one seeks heterogeneity *between* strata, homogeneity *within* strata. The size of sampling errors of estimates based on stratified samples depends upon the variance *within* strata.) Among the criteria used in the allocation of psu's to strata were population density, types of industrial concentration, predominant types of farming (for rural areas), rate of growth in the preceding decade, and geographical location. Attempts were made to combine in a single stratum sample areas (that is, selected psu's) that were alike in all or some of these respects. Certain of the primary sampling units—the 44 largest standard metropolitan areas and a limited number of other metropolitan areas—were large enough to constitute strata by themselves. But the bulk of the 230 strata consisted of combinations of psu's. All strata thus built up were made approximately equal in terms of their 1950 population.

The sample of areas, comprising 230 primary sampling units, was obtained in this fashion:

60 primary sampling units large enough to constitute strata by themselves were automatically included in the sample

170 primary sampling units were randomly selected from the remaining 170 strata. Probabilities of selection, for the psu's in a given stratum, were made proportional to their 1950 population.

Sampling within selected sample areas: the selection of sample households. Each primary sampling unit is, of course, a cluster of the units ultimately sought. Since these clusters are too large for the inclusion in the final sample of all the units they contain, a further sampling process *within* psu's was necessary. This was done by area sampling methods. In this work use was made of certain administrative units, called *enumeration districts*, that were employed in the 1950 Census, and of subdivisions of these districts into small land areas termed *segments*. Each segment comprised about six dwelling units. In drawing a sample of enumeration districts from a primary sampling unit, chances of selection were made proportionate to 1950 population. In drawing segments from enumeration districts, chances of selection were made proportional to the estimated number of dwelling units in the various segments. All the households in the selected segments constituted the final sample of households. (In certain exceptional cases, where segments were unavoidably large, subsampling within segments was necessary.)

In planning the current survey the final sample of households was set, in advance, at about 25,000. This meant (as of 1954) that about 1 out of every 2,250 households in the population was to be selected. This over-all sampling fraction, which applied in each stratum, was adjusted within strata to the relative sizes of selected primary sampling units. For example, if a selected psu included one ninth of the population of the stratum from which it came, the proper proportion (1/2250) within the stratum would be attained by drawing 1 out of every 250 households within the psu ($1/2250 \div 1/9 = 1/250$). If the psu included less than one ninth of the stratum population, the sampling fraction for the psu would be higher; if the psu were relatively larger, the sampling fraction would be lower. This sampling fraction for a given psu is constant from month to month, which means that the absolute size of the sample of households from that psu will vary, if the population of the psu varies.

I have used the past tense in describing most of these operations since the basic sample design is fixed for a term of years. However, there is variation in the make-up of the sample of households. Use is made by the Census Bureau of a system of rotation, the effect of which is to keep a given household in the sample for a period of eight months, divided into two equal periods of four months each. These two four-month periods are designed to fall in the same calendar months of successive years. This rotation is effected by groups of households, so that 75 percent of the sample segments are common from month to month, while 50 percent are common from year to year.

Survey techniques. Not the least important part of the sample survey is the actual interviewing of representatives of selected households by field agents. Biased or tactless interviewers, badly phrased or slanted questions, inaccurate reporting, or substantial nonresponse[8] may defeat the purposes of a survey, no matter how good the design. A striking incident, illustrating the importance of the form of questions put to householders, is recorded in the early history of the labor force survey. In March 1942 two supplementary questions were put to those who were classed as neither employed nor unemployed (i.e., to civilians who were counted as not in the labor force). Each of these persons was asked whether he would take a full-time job if one were available within 30 days, and when he had last worked on a full-time job. The answers served to increase the estimate of the civilian labor force by almost a million. Responses to the standard questions had failed to reveal the willingness of many who were classed as housewives or students to

---

[8] The problem of nonresponse is particularly troublesome in sample surveys. If there is considerable nonresponse the actual sample may be a biased one, because those responding may differ in significant ways from those not responding. Thus a question on family income may bring relatively more responses from those with medium or high incomes than from those with low incomes. When a particular sampling unit has been selected for inclusion in a sample, great efforts are usually made to ensure response from that unit, even at high cost. In the Population Survey an adjustment is made for sample households that cannot be interviewed, for one reason or another. This proportion is usually from 3 to 5 percent of the households in a sample.

take jobs if they were offered. Such persons belong in the labor force, as defined. As a result of this and of many similar experiences, far more attention is now given in sample survey work to questionnaire preparation and interviewing procedures. But these arts, important as they are, are beyond the scope of the present discussion.

The actual field work on the Population Survey is done by a staff of some 350 part-time interviewers, under the supervision of full-time supervisors. Representatives of sample households are interviewed each month during the calendar week containing the fifteenth day. Activities of household members during the *survey week* (the week containing the eighth day of the month) determine their classification as employed, unemployed, or not in the labor force. Answers to questions covering these and various supplementary points are recorded by the interviewer in such a way that transfer of data to punch cards and all subsequent operations can be done by machine. An electric digital computer is used in this subsequent work. Release of national estimates is thus possible about three weeks after the collection of the data.

Estimates and Sampling Errors. The making of national estimates from the sample results for any given month involves some steps that need not concern us here in detail. We may note, however, that the final estimate on any characteristic is a composite of two estimates. The first of these, which is called a ratio estimate, entails the customary inflation of sample results, with adjustments to bring the sample population into agreement with the known distribution of the entire population with respect to certain basic attributes, such as age, sex, color, farm-nonfarm residence, etc. The second component of the final estimate is obtained by projecting the composite estimate of a given characteristic (e.g., employment) for the preceding month on the basis of the recorded change in that characteristic for that portion of the sample that is common to the two months. (As was noted above, this common portion will be 75 percent of the sample for a given month.) An average of these two components, with equal weights, gives the composite national estimate for the current month. This process of averaging gives a final estimate with a sampling error lower than that attaching to the ratio estimate alone.

The chief objective of the new survey design that was adopted by the Bureau of the Census in January, 1954, was to reduce the sampling errors attaching to estimates of the labor force and its components. The relative sampling errors of summary estimates of the major magnitudes (civilian labor force, total employment, nonagricultural employment) are now given as approximately 0.6 percent. This is a coefficient of variation multiplied by 100 to put it in percentage terms. The absolute measure used in deriving it is a standard error, or standard deviation, hence the customary probabilities for a normal deviate apply to limits defined as multiples of this quantity. Thus if the total civilian labor force for a given month were estimated at 65 million, confidence limits corresponding to a probability of 0.68 would be set at 64.61 and 65.39 [i.e., at $65 - (65 \times .006)$ and at $65 + (65 \times .006)$]. Confidence limits corresponding to a probability of 0.95 would be set at 65 ± 1.176 percent, or at 64.24 and 65.76 millions. (For purposes of explanation these limits are given to more decimal places than are warranted by the character of the estimates.) For estimates of the smaller magnitudes, unemployment and agricultural employment, the relative sampling error is higher, being now given as roughly 4 percent. If for a given month unemployment were estimated at 3 millions, 0.95 confidence limits would be given by 3 ± 7.84 percent. Thus with a confidence of 0.95 we could state that the number of unemployed in the population at large was between 2.76 millions and 3.24 millions.

In the decade and a half that have passed since the Labor Force Survey was begun, the effectiveness of this instrument has been materially increased. Underlying concepts and techniques have been sharpened and improved. Conditions essential to a probability sample have been established, the scope of the Survey has been expanded, and the accuracy of estimates increased. However, it is not to be expected that the most recent revision will be the last. Both the makers and the users of these estimates recognize possibilities of further improvement. These possibilities have to do with the more accurate performance of the present job, and with expansions and extensions of this job.

For both purposes, additional area coverage and a larger sample of households have been recommended. These changes would, among other things, make for more accurate estimates of the number of unemployed—one of the controversial elements in labor force estimation. In view of the crucial role of accurate and unbiased interviewing, emphasis is placed also on the need for careful training of all field workers and for close checks on interviewing procedures. The reduction of nonresponse, which now runs to 3 to 5 percent of the sample, and of response bias, would be furthered by such training and controls.

Problems of a different sort relate to definitions and classifications. Years of debate have failed to bring full agreement on the meaning of such terms as "employed" and "unemployed." Should a person temporarily laid off, but with a job to which he expects to return, be classed as "employed"? Where should the dividing line be drawn between a part-time worker who is employed and a part-time worker who is unemployed? Should there be a separate category of the "partially unemployed"? The persistence of such issues suggests that there are bound to be fringe groups in the labor force, classifiable in different ways for different purposes. If the major groups are clearly defined such fringe elements can be separately recorded, and classified by users of the estimates in such ways as their specific needs may dictate. This is the direction in which the Current Population Survey is now moving.

We have noted that the original labor force survey was intended primarily to provide reliable information on the volume of unemployment in the country at large. Other and more varied purposes are now served, and we may expect this extension of purposes to continue. Administrative and analytical needs would be better served by detailed estimates for local areas, for diverse individual components of the employed labor force, for different elements of the unemployed. More details are wanted, and greater accuracy in estimates relating to elements of the total. Good design and efficient execution may do something toward serving these expanding purposes, but most of them require heavier expenditures. A balance has to be reached between adminstrative and scientific needs on the one hand, and the interests of the taxpayer on the other. Where this balance is to be found is not altogether a statistical question.[9]

[9] Among other sample surveys of interest to students of the social sciences and of business, special mention should be made of the annual surveys of Consumer Finances, sponsored by the Board of Governors of the Federal Reserve System and conducted by the Survey Research Center of the Institute for Social Research, of the University of Michigan. Reports on these surveys appear currently in the *Federal Reserve Bulletin.* An account of methods used is given in that *Bulletin* for July, 1950. For more general discussions of methods used in these and other surveys see Katona and Mueller, Ref. 75, and Festinger and Katz, Ref. 45.

REFERENCES

Cochran, W. G., *Sampling Techniques*, Chaps. 1-5.

Deming, W. E., *Some Theory of Sampling*, Chaps. 1, 2, 4, 9, 10.

Federal Reserve System, Board of Governors, "1954 Survey of Consumer Finances," *Federal Reserve Bulletin*, March, June, July 1954.

Festinger, L. and Katz, D., ed., *Research Methods in the Behavioral Sciences*.

Hansen, M. H., Hurwitz, W. N. and Madow, W. G., *Sample Survey Methods and Theories*, Vol. I, Chaps. 1-5, 12; Vol. II, Chaps. 1-5.

Katona, G. and Mueller, E., *Consumer Attitudes and Demand*.

Klein, L. R., *Contributions of Survey Methods to Economics*.

Mosteller, F. and others, "The Pre-Election Polls of 1948," Social Science Research Council, *Bulletin* 60, 1949.

Neyman, J., *Lectures and Conferences on Mathematical Statistics and Probability*, 2nd ed., Chap. 3, part 1.

Neyman, J., "On the Two Different Aspects of the Representative Method," *Journal of the Royal Statistical Society*, Vol. 97, 1934.

Parten, M. B., *Surveys, Polls, and Samples*, Chaps. 2, 3, 7, 9.

Sukhatme, P. V., *Sampling Theory of Surveys*, Chaps. 1-3.

United Nations Statistical Office, "The Preparation of Sampling Survey Reports," *Statistical Papers Series C*, No. 1 (revised), Feb. 1950.

U. S. Bureau of the Census, "Concepts and Methods Used in the Current Labor Force Statistics Prepared by the Bureau of the Census," *Current Population Reports*, Series P-23, No. 2, July 30, 1954.

Yates, F., *Sampling Methods for Censuses and Surveys*, 2nd ed., Chaps. 1-3, 6, 7.

Yule, G. U. and Kendall, M. G., *An Introduction to the Theory of Statistics*, 14th ed., Chaps. 16, 23.

The publishers and the dates of publication of the books named in chapter reference lists are given in the bibliography at the end of this volume.

•
•
•

Statistical Data: the Raw Materials of Analysis

In all but the last of the preceding chapters we have discussed statistics as a method of combining and analyzing data of observation, and of generalizing from such data. We have assumed in these earlier chapters that the data to be employed were in hand; we have broken into the process of inquiry after observations had been made. The final chapter (16) was given to an exposition of sample design and the planning of field surveys. This Appendix is intended to serve as a briefer and more general discussion of the raw materials that are employed in statistical inquiries. As a reference to be consulted at an early stage of a course of instruction it may help to orient students of the social sciences and business administration, and to encourage discrimination in the use of statistical data. The examination, appraisal, and full understanding of the basic data of observation are obvious but sometimes neglected prerequisites to the meaningful use of data in subsequent analysis.[1]

The observations with which a statistician deals are obtained in diverse ways. A full discussion of these ways would include the arts of designing experiments, conducting interviews, framing and circulating questionnaires, planning samples and administering field survey forces; it would deal with the extensive collections of data compiled by governmental bodies — federal, state, and local — and by international agencies; it would comprehend the practices of business enterprises and the varied records of business

---

[1] For an effective statement on this point see Mahalanobis, P. C., "Professional Training in Statistics," *Bulletin* of the International Statistical Institute, Vol. 33, Part V.

operations provided by books of account; it would give attention to the growing bodies of data assembled by private agencies of research and investigation. The sources of statistical data are, indeed, coextensive with the activities of man. A treatment of such scope is, of course, out of the question. Our immediate purpose will be served by distinguishing problems that are faced in obtaining observations at first hand from the problems involved in using data compiled by others. In doing this, certain related matters of general concern to the practicing statistician will be brought out.

Direct Observation Versus Use of Existing Records. A research scientist, or an administrator weighing a decision that entails objective reference, may utilize the results of direct observation, planned with reference to the specific problems faced. The physical scientist may design a laboratory experiment; the social scientist may plan a field study; the business administrator may conduct a market survey of consumer demand. Alternatively, in any of the cases cited, use may be made of records made by others, for other purposes. The physicist may find that recorded results of other experiments bear upon his problem; the social scientist may use vital statistics or wage payments recorded by governmental agencies; the business administrator may find that income records by states and previous studies of consumer finances and inclinations provide all that is needed for the decision he must make. There are wide differences, among fields of research and among decision-making procedures, in the degree of emphasis placed on direct observation on the one hand and on resort to existing records on the other. With some reservations we may say that in deriving his data the physical scientist places heavy weight on planned experiment[2]; that the social scientist looks in the main to existing public and private records, but is making increasing use of sharply focused surveys, yielding original observations; that the business administrator uses business records, relevant published statistics, and, to a growing extent, observations derived from specific investigations of customer preference.

The common characteristic of social science and administration (both public and private) is their use of a mixture of observations

[2] The qualifications to this statement are not unimportant. The physical scientist has always made extensive use of the observations of his predecessors and contemporaries; progress, indeed, has depended upon the accumulation of a large body of verified observations. Yet frontier studies demand ever new observations, directly relevant to particular problems. The design of appropriate experiments is a major aspect of physical research.

derived from special studies and of data provided by existing records. For investigations of wide scope, dealing with the vital processes of the whole society or with the operations of the whole economy, or of major sectors of the economy, there is a necessary dependence upon government. To a degree never true of the physical sciences, the sciences of society must draw their data from public agencies. Yet such data fall far short of meeting the diverse needs of curious investigators, seeking to understand social and economic processes. Among the most promising of recent developments in the social sciences has been the use of sampling techniques designed to yield data pertinent to specific questions. This has been notably true of sociology and social psychology. The economist remains, and must remain, a heavy user of data gathered by public agencies, but here, too, studies entailing the use of original observations are growing in number and in fruitfulness. The business administrator, also, in seeking to gauge market needs and potentials, has resorted increasingly in recent years to direct examination of representative sample groups.

Those to whom this book is addressed will have occasion to employ data of the two types distinguished above — those derived from original observations and those drawn from public or private records. Methods of obtaining the original data that constitute random samples, and that provide, thus, proper bases for statistical generalizations have been discussed in Chapter 16. The opening section of that chapter may suitably be read at this point, if not already covered by the student. But we said little there about the arts employed in observing the behavior of individuals and of groups, in measuring attributes and reactions, in obtaining directly from individuals data bearing on their experience, their attitudes and opinions, their planned actions. Recent advances in these arts have been impressive, and full of promise for the future. They are replacing casual contacts and highly personal judgments in the appraisal of people in their economic and social relations by objective procedures for the making of observations on behavior, attitudes, and expectations.

I should render no service to the reader if I were to attempt to reduce these procedures to a few apparently simple rules for interviewing and preparing questionnaires. These are not simple arts. Most pertinent are the remarks of Goode and Hatt, on the design of such approaches as these: "The good schedule grows from good hypotheses. .... It is unlikely that an excellent set of questions can be developed without serious library research, much discussion of the problems with colleagues, and considerable experience with the subject matter." One who is planning any serious endeavor to gather original data by such methods should study some of the technical publications now available on these topics.[3]

The Use of Existing Records. The sources to which the social scientist and the business administrator may turn for data are diverse, and of varying reliability. They include the accounts and other records of business enterprises and trade associations, the compilations of administrative and regulating agencies of government (e.g., the Interstate Commerce Commission, the Bureau of Internal Revenue); federal and state registration data such as vital statistics, educational statistics, and records of automobiles in use; the publications of public-purpose collection agencies (such as the Bureau of the Census and the Bureau of Labor Statistics); the series on national economic accounts, on production, on banking and credit, etc., prepared by public agencies of analysis and research (e.g., the Office of Business Economics of the Department of Commerce, the Division of Research and Statistics of the Board of Governors of the Federal Reserve System) [4]; the statistical compilations of the United Nations and other international agencies; the publications and files of private research agencies such as the National Bureau of Economic Research, The Brookings Institution, the National Industrial Conference Board, the Twentieth Century Fund, etc.; and the documents of varied origin that may provide data relevant to particular problems.

[3] See, among others,
  Blankenship, A. B., ed., *How To Conduct Consumer and Opinion Research* (New York, Harpers, 1946); Festinger, L. and Katz, D., ed., *Research Methods in the Behavioral Sciences* (New York, Dryden Press, 1953), esp. Chapter 8 and accompanying bibliography; Goode, W. J. and Hatt, P. K., *Methods in Social Research* (New York, McGraw-Hill, 1952), Chapters 11–13; Jahoda, M., Deutsch, M., and Cook, S. W., *Research Methods in Social Relations* (New York, Dryden Press, 1951); Katona, G. and Mueller, E., *Consumer Attitudes and Demand* (Survey Research Center, University of Michigan, 1953); Likert, R., "The Sample Interview Survey," in Dennis, W., ed., *Readings in General Psychology* (New York, Prentice-Hall, 1949); Parten, M. B., *Surveys, Polls and Samples* (New York, Harpers, 1950).

[4] The statistical work of agencies of the central government is discussed and appraised in Hauser, P. M. and Leonard, W. R., *Government Statistics for Business Use* (New York, Wiley, 1946) and in Mills, F. C. and Long, C., *The Statistical Agencies of the Federal Government* (New York, National Bureau of Economic Research, 1949). The chief elements of the statistical intelligence system of the federal government are given in Mills and Long, pp. 9–15.

Although nothing like an exhaustive list of sources can be given in brief compass, it may be helpful to name some of the more comprehensive and most readily available published sources of social, economic, and business data. In the main, this list is limited to official publications. It should be understood that many of these are secondary sources, a term that is explained in the following section. They are, however, reliable sources.

United States
Decennial, Quinquennial, Annual, or Occasional

Agricultural Statistics, U.S. Bureau of Agricultural Economics (Annual)
Annual Report, U.S. Comptroller of the Currency
Annual Report, U.S. Treasury Department
Annual Survey of Manufactures, U.S. Bureau of the Census
Census of Agriculture, U.S. Bureau of the Census (Quinquennial)
Census of Business, U.S. Bureau of the Census (Quinquennial)
Census of Manufactures, U.S. Bureau of the Census (Quinquennial)
Census of Population, U.S. Bureau of the Census (Decennial)
Economic Almanac, National Industrial Conference Board, New York, Crowell (Annual)
Economic Report of the President, U.S. Council of Economic Advisers (Annual)
Foreign Commerce and Navigation of the United States, U.S. Bureau of the Census (Annual)
Handbook of Labor Statistics, U.S. Bureau of Labor Statistics
Historical Statistics of the United States, 1789–1945, U.S. Bureau of the Census, Washington, Government Printing Office, 1949
Minerals Yearbook, U.S. Bureau of Mines
National Income, 1954 edition, U.S. Office of Business Economics (Supplement to the *Survey of Current Business*)
Statistical Abstract of the United States, U.S. Bureau of the Census (Annual)
Statistics of Income, U.S. Bureau of Internal Revenue (Annual)
Vital Statistics of the United States, National Office of Vital Statistics (Annual)

United States
Quarterly or Monthly

Abstract of Reports of Condition of National Banks, U.S. Comptroller of the Currency (Quarterly)
Construction Review, U.S. Departments of Labor and Commerce (Monthly)
Current Population Reports, U.S. Bureau of the Census (Monthly)
Economic Indicators, U.S. Council of Economic Advisers (Monthly; *Historical and Descriptive Supplement*, prepared by the Staff of the

Joint Committee on the Economic Report and the U.S. Office of Statistical Standards, 1953)

Federal Reserve Bulletin, Board of Governors, Federal Reserve System
(Monthly)

Monthly Labor Review, U.S. Bureau of Labor Statistics (Monthly)

Monthly Vital Statistics Report, National Office of Vital Statistics

Survey of Current Business, U.S. Office of Business Economics (Monthly;
biennial supplement)

International

Commodity Trade Statistics, United Nations Statistical Office (Quarterly)

Demographic Yearbook, United Nations Statistical Office

Monthly Bulletin of Statistics, United Nations Statistical Office

Statistical Yearbook, United Nations Statistical Office

Woytinsky, W. S. and Woytinsky, E.S., *World Population and Production,* New York, The Twentieth Century Fund, 1953

Yearbook of Food and Agricultural Statistics, United Nations Food and
Agricultural Organization

Yearbook of International Trade Statistics, United Nations Statistical
Office

Primary and secondary sources. An essential distinction is to be
made between *primary* and *secondary* sources of materials taken
from existing records. A primary source is one that publishes (or
otherwise makes available) data for which it is itself responsible
as the agency of original collection and compilation. A secondary
source is one that reprints data from a primary source; in this case
the publishing agency is not the agency responsible for the original
collection of the data. Many of the publications of the Bureau of
the Census are primary sources; the *Statistical Abstract,* the *Economic Almanac* of the National Industrial Conference Board, the
Statistical Yearbook of the United Nations are examples of secondary sources. Obviously, more reliability attaches to the data
derived directly from a primary source, for not only are errors in
copying avoided, but the precise meaning of the figures, the conditions under which they were gathered, and the limitations to
be borne in mind in interpreting them will be clearly understood
by the editors, and are more likely to be explained to the readers.
Not only is it important to understand whether the source from
which data are secured is primary or secondary, but the general
reliability of the agency which gathered the data should be determined. Data may be unreliable because of loose methods of
gathering or assembling, or because of conscious or unconscious

bias in the responsible agency. The fact of such unreliability should be established, if it exists.

On the meaning of published figures. A first responsibility of the user of data derived from existing records is to determine their precise meaning. For this purpose the user should know what unit has been used, and how reliable are the data recorded.

a. Definition of the unit. The elementary process of *counting* is basic in quantitative work, but to understand the results of a counting operation one must be sure of what has been counted. This calls for a precise definition of the unit employed.

One of the most serviceable classifications of statistical units, that given by G. P. Watkins, divides all such units into the following classes and subclasses:

Classification of statistical units

(1) Individual things

    (*a*) Natural kinds

        Examples: man, hog, hen

        Such natural kinds are much more easily distinguished than artificial units, the meaning of which depends often upon convention. Hence the counting of natural things, such as the number of animals on farms, is likely to be more accurate than a counting of artificial units.

    (*b*) Produced kinds; manufactured commodities and instruments

        Examples: shoe, door, chair

(2) Units of measurement

    (*a*) Units of physical measurement

        Examples: ton, gallon, kilowatt hour

        Such units are employed as a result of convention. Frequently the same term is employed with varying meanings, a practice that leads to ambiguity and uncertainty in interpreting the results.

    (*b*) Pecuniary units

        Units of commercial value, such as the dollar, pound, and franc, are the least satisfactory of the units with which the statistician must deal, yet these are the most important in ordinary business analysis and in much economic research. The chief defect of this class of unit arises from the changes to which it is subject, as a measure of value, because of changes in the general price level. Index numbers of prices represent an attempt to correct for some of the deficiencies of the pecuniary unit, but such devices fail to remove all the defects of units of this type.

In using published data care must be taken that the unit is interpreted precisely as it was by the original investigators. Thus, if one is using Census figures of the number of manufacturing establishments in the United States at a certain date, the precise meaning given to the term "manufacturing establishment" must be understood. Where any ambiguity is likely to exist, the definition given to the enumerators should be published with the data.

b. Determination of degree of error in the data. No compilation can be accurate in an absolute sense. Errors may arise from faulty collection or recording, ambiguities or bias in questions propounded, errors in tabulation or computation. Data bearing every indication of accuracy to four or five places may in fact represent rough estimates. If the user of published data is unaware of the errors that may be present he may make serious mistakes in generalizing from them, or in using them to test hypotheses or to guide decisions. There should be a statement in the primary source of a given body of data indicating the degree of reliability attaching to them and this information should be repeated in secondary sources. If feasible, reliability should be defined in quantitative terms, but this is possible only for data derived from probability samples. If the margin of error may not be measured, the degree of confidence to be had in the data may be indicated in qualitative terms.[5]

In this day of extensive statistical records and of heavy reliance on them, the need of information on the reliability of published statistics is great. The urge to "quantify" — to count, to measure, to record in quantitative terms — is strong today. Governmental agencies and private research workers alike have responded to this urge. In part, the response appears in reliable and well-documented statistics; in part, it takes the form of estimates of highly uncertain reliability. The utility of the present extensive collections of quantitative data, collections so pleasing to the statistically minded investigator, will be materially augmented when all published statistics are accompanied by information that enables the user accurately to appraise their reliability.

There are, of course, other types of information one should have if one is to use published figures with accuracy. Such simple matters

[5] For some bodies of statistics numerical measures of reliability, if essayed, would be misleading. Thus Earl R. Rolph writes, with reference to statistics of income and wealth, "Milton Gilbert maintains, persuasively in my judgment, that the reliability of a national income component can be learned only by reviewing the sources of the data and the methods of estimation employed." The same thing is true, of course, of many published statistical series. In such cases the user has a right to expect a full disclosure of sources and methods.

On this subject students of economics and business may with profit consult Professor Oskar Morgenstern's book, *On the Accuracy of Economic Observations* (Princeton University Press, 1950).

as the bases of percentages are often undefined. The time period to which the observations on a historical variable relate — a calendar year or a fiscal year, a selected day in a given month or all days, averaged — may not be stated. The kind of marketing transaction that gave rise to a given price quotation may be unspecified. Standards of presentation and explanation are improving in public practice. There is no better way to insure further improvement than for a body of critical and demanding users to maintain pressure on the responsible agencies.

APPENDIX **B**

•
•
•

Note on Statistical Calculations [1]

Statistical work involves, of necessity, a considerable amount of calculation. If this work is to be done with expedition and accuracy, in a given case, the enterprise must be planned and details organized. This calls for the proper lay-out of the work, in advance of analysis, the preparation of suitable work sheets, and the reduction of all the operations to a smooth, consistent procedure, with the different stages properly interrelated, and with provision made for suitable checks. A slovenly arrangement is fatal to both speed and accuracy. Careful preliminary arrangement will pay for itself many times over in increased accuracy and in saving of time.

The Lay-out of Work; the Work Sheet. The first step in calculation is the lay-out of the data, with reference to subsequent calculations. Before observations are recorded, or transferred from the primary tables, a general scheme should have been prepared, a framework into which the various steps in the later calculations will fit. This scheme, of course, will vary with the data and with the objects of the study, but no matter what the data or the ultimate objects such a scheme is necessary. With the lay-out prepared in advance, the original observations may often be recorded in tabular form immediately adapted to the first stages of the calculation process, thus avoiding the necessity of recopying.

The preparation of suitable work sheets is essential to the organization and carrying through of extensive calculations. The degree of care that may be given to the preparation of such sheets

---

[1] This note is based in part upon material formerly included in *A Manual of Problems and Tables in Statistics*, by F. C. Mills and D. H. Davenport. This *Manual* is now out of print.

will depend upon the magnitude of the problem and, more particularly, upon whether a series of similar problems is to be attacked. In this latter case, when there will be a fairly constant demand within the organization for the same sort of work sheets, it may be advisable to construct a special model and to have special plates made. If this is not expedient, work sheet forms prepared for the market may be found to meet all the requirements of the problem or may be adapted to the purpose in mind. Supplies of those forms which are most generally employed or which have the widest utility should be kept in stock in the statistical laboratory. A third method of securing the needed forms is the simple and convenient one of ruling standard sheets to conform to the desired model.

In organizing a work sheet attention should be given to the proper spacing of columns and lines and to the clear and unambiguous heading of all columns, so that there shall be no uncertainty as to the derivation and meaning of the data or calculations recorded therein. All columns should be numbered to permit of ready reference. It is often possible to insert work sheets directly into an adding machine, thus having the printed record on the sheet. This may greatly facilitate checking and later calculations. The size, form, and spacing of the work sheet should be adapted to this purpose, if the adding machine record is to be utilized. Forms appropriate to the computation of the primary statistical measures are exemplified in the body of the preceding text.

Methods and Accuracy of Calculation. Calculation procedure will have been decided upon in planning the lay-out of work and work sheets. The general method, in practically all cases involving the handling of a considerable mass of data, will call for the tabular arrangement of original data and of all subsequent calculations. A tabular arrangement is far better adapted to a consistent procedure than is any less formal method, and in handling masses of material such a procedure is necessary.[2] Once such a scheme has been prepared, the carrying out of the calculations is a fairly simple matter. In the original lay-out of such a scheme available methods for reducing labor should be employed. It is not here possible to

---

[2] Chapter 3 contains a brief discussion of certain principles of tabulation, relating chiefly to frequency distributions. For treatment of the general process of tabulation and discussion of effective methods of tabular presentation see Mudgett, Bruce D., *Statistical Tables and Graphs* (Boston, Houghton Mifflin, 1930) and the *Manual of Tabular Presentation*, prepared for the Bureau of the Census by B. L. Jenkinson (Washington, Government Printing Office, 1950).

discuss in detail all such labor-saving methods, but certain general aids to calculation may be listed.

1. *Aids to calculation.*

The standard tables that may be employed to facilitate numerical calculations are familiar to all students, but often not sufficiently familiar so that they are used readily and accurately. *Tables of logarithms* are, of course, indispensable. With mechanical calculators generally available, logarithms are not widely employed for the operations of multiplication and division, but they still offer the simplest method of raising to powers and extracting roots, except where prepared tables of powers and roots are available. Logarithms will generally be employed in the calculation of the geometric mean of a frequency series (see Chap. 4 for example). In fitting curves in the equations to which the x or y variable appears in logarithmic form such tables are necessary (see Chap. 10 for example). For graphic presentation the use of logarithmic paper will often render unnecessary the use of logarithms. A table of five-place logarithms is given in Appendix Table X.

Tables of squares, square roots, and reciprocals are of equally wide utility. The most complete set of tables of this type is that bearing the name of Barlow (Barlow's *Tables of Squares, Square Roots, Cubes, Cube Roots and Reciprocals*), covering numbers up to 10,000. The uses of such tables in statistical work are many, and need no detailed description. Attention may be called to one use of the tables of reciprocals. When a problem calls for dividing a series of numbers by a constant base (as in computing percentages), the reciprocal of the constant base may be employed, and the operation of division supplanted by that of multiplication (i.e., $6 \div 3$ is equivalent to $6 \times \frac{1}{3}$). By placing this reciprocal as the multiplier on any of the mechanical calculators now on the market, the required percentages may be run off in short order. Squares, square roots, and reciprocals of the numbers 1 to 1,000 are given in Appendix Table VIII.

Many tables defining the attributes of particular distributions or used in applying particular tests have been referred to in the text. The publications that contain these tables also contain tables that facilitate various statistical calculations. For convenience of reference I here note selected collections of tables that have many applications in statistical work.

Fisher, Sir Ronald (R. A.) and Yates, F., *Statistical Tables for Biological, Agricultural, and Medical Research*, 3rd ed., New York, Hafner, 1948.

Glover, J. W., *Tables of Applied Mathematics*, Ann Arbor, Michigan, George Wahr, 1923.

Kelley, T. L., *The Kelley Statistical Tables*, rev., ed., Harvard University Press, 1948.

Miner, J. R., *Tables of $\sqrt{1-r^2}$ and $1-r^2$ for Use in Partial Correlation and in Trigonometry*, Baltimore, The Johns Hopkins Press.

Pearson, E. S. and Hartley, H. O., *Biometrika Tables for Statisticians*, Vol. I, Cambridge University Press, 1954.

    (This volume and others that will follow carry forward the earlier work, in this field, of the Biometric Laboratory, under Karl Pearson. Many of the tables published in Karl Pearson's earlier compilations will be included either in their original or in modified form, in these volumes. However, the two volumes next listed contain a number of tables of current value, not yet available elsewhere.)

Pearson, Karl, *Tables for Statisticians and Biometricians*, Part I (1914, 1930), Part II (1931), Cambridge University Press.

Of the greatest value in statistical work today are the various calculating machines now on the market at prices that make them generally available. By the use of electric or hand machines, the labor of calculation that accompanies all quantitative work has been immeasurably reduced. Statistical methods are being adapted to these machines, and more will be done in this direction. For more extensive operations, punched card equipment and mechanical sorters and tabulators may be used. Added to these, the introduction of electronic computers has opened new vistas to the statistician. Thus, as we have noted in the text, the Bureau of the Census is employing such a computer (UNIVAC) in making seasonal corrections to time series. For a ten-year monthly series, all calculations involved in an adaptation of the ratio-to-moving average method are completed in about one minute.

Elementary principles of interpolation. All tables are of necessity limited to a certain restricted number of values of the functions recorded. Thus, reading from the table of logarithms appended (Appendix Table X), we have

Argument Natural number	Function Logarithm
22.82	1.35832
22.83	1.35851
22.84	1.35870
22.85	1.35889
22.86	1.35908

If it is desired to secure the logarithm of a number between those given above, it is necessary to *interpolate* between the intervals of the argument. That is, one must find that value of the function corresponding to the particular value of the argument and consistent with the tabled values of function and argument. This problem arises in using many tables, and in many other statistical tasks. A full treatment of the theory of interpolation would carry us beyond the limits of the present discussion. We here confine ourselves to simple proportional interpolation.[3]

This method involves the assumption of a linear relationship between function and argument. We may use the figures set down above as an example. Required: the logarithm of 22.834

$$\text{Log } 22.840 = 1.35870$$
$$\text{Log } 22.830 = 1.35851$$
$$\text{Difference } = \quad .00019$$

A difference of .010 in the argument corresponds to a difference of .00019 in the function. The number given, 22.834, exceeds by .004 the smaller of the two numbers tabled in the argument, and we may write

$$\text{Log } 22.834 = 1.35851 + (\tfrac{4}{10} \times .00019)$$
$$= 1.35851 + .000076$$
$$= 1.35859 \text{ (rounded off to the fifth}$$
$$\text{decimal place)}$$

19	
1	1.9
2	3.8
3	5.7
4	7.6
5	9.5
6	11.4
7	13.3
8	15.2
9	17.1

This operation is facilitated by the use of tables of proportional parts that are given in the margins of many tables of logarithms. Thus, in performing the above interpolation, we should use the marginal table headed 19 (the difference, in a five place table of logarithms, between successive logarithmic values at this point). Of the two columns below the figure 19, that at the left gives the fifth figure of the natural number, the logarithm of which is desired, while that at the right gives the amount to be added to the logarithm lying just below the desired number. In the present case the fifth figure of the natural number in question (22.834) is 4, hence we add .000076 to the logarithm 1.35851.

---

[3] For detailed expositions of various interpolation procedures see Scarborough, J. B., *Numerical Mathematical Analysis*, 2nd ed., Baltimore, the Johns Hopkins Press, 1950; and Whittaker, E. T. and Robinson, G., *The Calculus of Observations*, London, Blackie and Son, 1924.

The problem of interpolation frequently arises in the handling of simple statistical series, of which the following is an example:

Steam Railways in the United States
Miles of Road Owned, 1870–1950 *

1870	52,922
1880	93,267
1890	163,597
1900	193,346
1910	240,439
1920	252,845
1930	249,052
1940	233,670
1950	223,779

* Source: Interstate Commerce Commission, *Statistics of Railways in the United States.* Figures relate to June 30 up to 1920, to December 31 for 1920 and thereafter.

We desire the approximate mileage in 1877, a year that falls in a decade of rapid growth. Assuming that the increase from year to year during the decade 1870–1880 was by equal absolute increments, we interpolate here by proportional parts.

$$\text{Mileage } 1877 = 52{,}922 + (\tfrac{7}{10} \times 40{,}345)$$
$$= 52{,}922 + 28{,}241.5$$
$$= 81{,}163.5, \text{ or } 81{,}163$$

This method of interpolation makes use only of the pair of observations above and below the value to be estimated. Such interpolation by proportional parts or first differences is equivalent to the fitting of a straight line to the two observations on which interpolation is based. For nonlinear series, particularly when the difference between successive observations is considerable, it is preferable to interpolate on the basis of a polynomial of the second degree, fitted to three points, or even of curves of higher degree. This may be done, without actually fitting the curves, by the employment of interpolation formulas that make use of second, third, or higher differences. The use of such formulas is explained in Whittaker and Robinson (Ref. 190).

2. *The checking of numerical calculations.*

In the organization of statistical work full provision must be made for the checking and cross-checking of all calculations. The work of no mortal person is free from error; the inevitable mistakes in any extensive series of calculations may be corrected, or reduced to a minimum, only by the careful checking of all operations.

By recognizing in advance the necessity of such checking, methods may be adopted that will enable checks to be most effectively applied.

Two types of checks are available to the quantitative worker. Calculations may be checked, first, by a repetition of the operations. If this is done, it is advisable that the second operation be performed by a person other than the original calculator; if that is not possible, the sequence of operations may be altered when the check is made, or a slightly different method of securing the same result may be employed. Thus a column may be added in the opposite direction from that first followed, or multiplier and multiplicand may be reversed. The second type of check is that which provides a numerical test of the accuracy of given calculations. That is, certain values useful merely for checking purposes may be computed, in addition to those actually required in the given problem. The Charlier check upon the operation of computing the standard deviation (see Chap. 5) is an example of this type. A more elaborate example, in which a whole series of checks is provided for testing the accuracy of the work at various stages, is afforded by the Doolittle method of solving simultaneous equations.[4] Checks of this latter type should be employed whenever available.

Perhaps more important than all such checks is the habit, on the part of the operator, of mentally verifying the major results of his calculations as he proceeds. If two figures are to be multiplied the operator should determine, by inspection, the approximate value of the product and the number of decimal places it will contain. In any arithmetic operation the same rough check should be employed, for by this means the most serious errors, such as arise from the misplacing of decimal points, may be prevented. Many checks of the same sort are possible in connection with statistical calculations. Thus the standard deviation may be compared with the range (the latter will not, in general, be more than six times the standard deviation), and geometric, harmonic, and arithmetic measures may be checked against each other, if all have been computed in a given instance. Inconsistencies in the results usually reveal the most serious errors, and careful watch should be kept for such discrepancies.

By plotting the results of calculations errors may often be detected. If a serious mistake has been made in fitting a line to certain

[4] See Mills, *Statistical Methods*, Third Edition, Appendix C.

data, it will be immediately evident when data and line are plotted. If the ordinates of a fitted curve have not been correctly determined, breaks in the smoothness of the curve will usually reveal the errors when the curve is plotted.

In seeking to avoid mistakes no one precept is more important than this: *Keep a neat, careful, and complete record of all calculations.* This is not only necessary as an aid to subsequent checking but it is essential to accurate calculation. When a series of computations is laid out in proper form and performed in a systematic fashion, the probability of error is very much less than when the computations are performed in a slipshod, unsystematic fashion.

3. *The accuracy of measurements and calculations.*

In planning calculations the investigator must determine the degree of refinement desired in calculations and the degree of accuracy sought in results. Failure to take account of this problem usually leads to a waste of time in carrying out the calculations to an unnecessary degree, and to the securing of results that have a fictitious appearance of accuracy. The first consideration, in approaching this problem, relates to the accuracy of the original observations.

The operation of measurement involves in all cases a comparison of magnitudes. Thus a given magnitude, the height of John Smith, is compared with certain standard units of linear measurement, the foot and the inch. In setting up such a comparison absolute accuracy is never possible. We may say that John Smith is 5 feet 8 inches tall, which means that his height lies between 5 feet 7.5 inches, and 5 feet 8.5 inches. The *absolute error* (the difference between the observed and the true values) may in this case be as great as 0.5 inches. Or, employing more accurate instruments, we may report that John Smith's height is 5 feet 8.3 inches. This means that his height is between 5 feet 8.25 inches and 5 feet 8.35 inches. The absolute error in this case may be as great as 0.05 inches.

In interpreting recorded measurements, therefore, due attention must be paid to the number of *significant figures*, that is, figures that are known to be correct. There are certain standard rules that should be followed in recording and interpreting measurements with respect to the significant figures. Only the number of correct figures should be recorded, with zeros added, of course, to indicate the absolute magnitude of the measurement. Thus if a distance is recorded as being 4300 feet, it means that the true distance that was measured lies between 4250 and 4350 feet. There are only two significant figures in this example. If wheat production in the United States in 1952 is given as 1,291,000,000 bushels the amount is recorded to four significant figures. (If the production has been given as 1,290,000,000 bushels, this number to be taken as significant to four digits, a dot or a bar could be placed above the last significant figure, thus: 1,290,000,000. Without such an indication the reader would assume that there were only three significant figures.) Similarly, if a magnitude is given as 0.0472, there are but three significant figures, the zeros being added, as in the above examples, to indicate the absolute magnitude of the measure. A zero added to the right of the last recorded figure, however, if to the right of the decimal point, is significant, in indicating the degree of accuracy. Thus the value 12.50 has four significant figures, the last zero being added to show that the true value of the recorded magnitude is between 12.495 and 12.505. If it had been given as 12.5, this would be interpreted to mean that the true value lies between 12.45 and 12.55.

Determining the accuracy of computations. When observations are combined, it is important to be able to define the degree of accuracy of the resultant figures. This may be determined approximately if the accuracy of the original observations is known. The problem may be considered with respect to the four chief arithmetical operations.

Addition. In the addition of measurements, no attempt should be made to give the total an appearance of greater accuracy than the constituent items. If these items differ in accuracy, *the total is no more accurate than the least accurate measurement.* Thus, in the addition of the following four figures:

$$
\begin{array}{r}
25.23 \\
1610.1 \\
17.375 \\
\underline{2.} \\
1654.705
\end{array}
$$

the total should be rounded off to 1655. It would give a quite spurious impression of accuracy to present the sum as 1654.705.

The actual limits within which the true sum falls may be readily determined by computing the maximum sum and the minimum sum that could be secured from the observations in question. Thus, substituting for each of the above values the maximum value that the quantity in question might have, we secure

$$25.235$$
$$1610.15$$
$$17.3755$$
$$2.5$$
$$\overline{1655.2605}$$

Substituting the minimum values, we have

$$25.225$$
$$1610.05$$
$$17.3745$$
$$1.5$$
$$\overline{1654.1495}$$

To have presented the original total as accurate to the third decimal place would have been clearly faulty. Nor would it have been accurate to have rounded off the individual items before adding, until their accuracy was equal to that of the least accurate item. The rounding off should be done after the total is secured, as the fullest possible use is thus made of the knowledge we have.

If the limits of error of the individual items (i.e., the differences between the maximum and minimum possible values) be added, it will be found to total 1.111, equal to the difference between the maximum and minimum possible values of the sum of the items. *The error of a sum may be determined by adding the errors of the constituent items.* (The range between the maximum and minimum possible values is obviously twice the maximum *absolute error*, as defined above.)

Subtraction. By precisely analogous reasoning it may be shown that the limits of error of the differences between measurements may also be determined by adding the limits of error of the individual items. Here, as in addition, the result is no more accurate than the less accurate of the two measurements entering into the calculation. The point of significance in this less accurate number (e.g., the column of hundreds, tens, units, tenths, or hundredths) sets the level of significance for the difference.

Multiplication. If it is desired to know precisely the accuracy of the product secured by multiplying one quantity by another, it is possible to employ the process illustrated above, namely, to determine the maximum possible value and the minimum possible value. Thus as the maximum possible value of the product of 11.30 and 2.3 we have 11.305×2.35, or 26.56675. As the minimum possible value of the product we have 11.295×2.25, or 25.41375. The product of the numbers as given, 11.30×2.3 is 25.990. Comparing this with the two limits as computed above, we have 26 as the product expressed in terms of significant figures only. A general rule to follow in multiplication is this: If n is the number of significant figures in the factor having the smaller number of significant figures, the product should be considered to have only n significant figures. In the example just cited, this is two.

Division. The rule for significant figures in a quotient is similar to that for a product. Let n be the number of significant figures in that quantity — dividend or divisor — that has the smaller number of significant figures. The quotient should be considered to have n significant figures.

In the physical sciences and in engineering fairly standard practices have been established in the matter of recording results, so that the user of published figures may know what the reliability of a given measure is. In the physical sciences it is customary to present numerical values with one more figure than those known to be significant. The next to the last figure, that is, may be taken to be correct. In recording engineering calculations, on the other hand, only the significant figures are given. The last figure may be taken to be correct, within half a unit, as in the examples given above. No standard practice has been established in statistics, but it would seem expedient in general to follow the engineering practice, recording only those figures that are known to be significant, the last one not being in error by more than half a unit. In the actual calculations, however, two additional figures may be retained, these being dropped when the final result is recorded.

When a statistical measure such as the mean, the standard deviation or the coefficient of correlation has been derived, the useful working rule suggested by T. L. Kelley (and mentioned in the text of Chap. 7) may be followed. The rule is to *keep to the place indicated by the first figure of one third the standard error*. Thus if the arithmetic mean of a given distribution is calculated to be 36.5321, with a standard error of 0.963, the recorded value of the mean should be 36.5. For one third the standard error is 0.321, the first figure being in the column of tenths. With this standard error it is useless to carry the value of the mean beyond the first decimal place. In all calculations the value of the mean would be carried to two additional places, but these would be dropped in recording.

4. *Tables and formulas to employ in the analysis of time series.*

In fitting lines of trend to time series it is necessary to secure the powers of certain numbers, and the sums of these powers. Barlow's *Tables* are available for securing the squares and the cubes of natural numbers. Table XXVII of Pearson's *Tables for Statisticians and Biometricians* (Part I) gives the second to the seventh powers of the natural numbers from 1 to 100. Table XXVIII of Pearson's *Tables* (Part I) gives the sums of the powers from one to seven of the first hundred natural numbers. This table is particularly useful in securing the sums of the powers of x when x represents time in connection with the fitting of a line of trend. Appendix Table VI of the present volume gives the second to the sixth powers and Appendix Table VII gives the sums of the first six powers of the first fifty natural numbers.

It is possible to secure the sums of the various powers by formulas when tables are not readily available.[5] We may denote by t the total number of terms in the series 1, 2, 3, 4, 5, 6 . . ., and by S_1, S_2, S_3, S_4, S_5, and S_6 the sums of the first, second, third, fourth, fifth, and sixth powers of these numbers. The required formulas are

$$S_1 = \frac{t(t+1)}{2}$$

$$S_2 = \frac{2t^3 + 3t^2 + t}{6} = S_1\left(\frac{2t+1}{3}\right)$$

$$S_3 = \frac{t^4 + 2t^3 + t^2}{4} = (S_1)^2$$

$$S_4 = \frac{6t^5 + 15t^4 + 10t^3 - t}{30} = S_2\left(\frac{3t^2 + 3t - 1}{5}\right)$$

$$S_5 = \frac{2t^6 + 6t^5 + 5t^4 - t^2}{12} = (S_1)^2\left(\frac{2t^2 + 2t - 1}{3}\right)$$

$$S_6 = \frac{6t^7 + 21t^6 + 21t^5 - 7t^3 + t}{42} = S_2\left(\frac{3t^4 + 6t^3 - 3t + 1}{7}\right)$$

[5] See Frank A. Ross, "Formulae for Facilitating Computations in Time Series Analysis," *Journal of the American Statistical Association*, March, 1925. The formulas in the present and immediately succeeding sections are taken from this summary.

If a line of trend is to be fitted to a time series, with n observations, n being odd, and if the origin be taken mid-way in the series, then t, of the above formulas, is equal to $\dfrac{n-1}{2}$. (Thus if there are data for eleven years, the origin will fall at the sixth year and there will be five observations on each side of the origin. In this case n will equal 11 and t will equal 5.) Professor Ross has adapted the above formulas to this case, so that the value of n may be inserted directly. The revised formulas for the sums of the powers of x (deviations from the origin being represented by x) are

$$\Sigma x = 0$$
$$\Sigma x^2 = \frac{n^3 - n}{12}$$
$$\Sigma x^3 = 0$$
$$\Sigma x^4 = (\Sigma x^2)\left(\frac{3n^2 - 7}{20}\right)$$
$$\Sigma x^5 = 0$$
$$\Sigma x^6 = (\Sigma x^2)\left(\frac{3n^4 - 18n^2 + 31}{112}\right)$$

where x is one time unit.

In working with time series it is often convenient to employ a time unit of one-half year and so to place the origin that the x-values will be 1, 3, 5, 7, 9, ... The sums of the powers of the elements of such a series are given by the formulas that follow. In these formulas t denotes the number of terms in the series 1, 3, 5, 7, . . ., while $_0S_1$, $_0S_2$, $_0S_3$, $_0S_4$, $_0S_5$, $_0S_6$ represent the sums of the first, second, third, fourth, fifth, and sixth powers of these numbers.

$$_0S_1 = t^2$$
$$_0S_2 = \frac{4t^3 - t}{3}$$
$$_0S_3 = 2t^4 - t^2 = {_0S_1}(2t^2 - 1)$$
$$_0S_4 = \frac{48t^5 - 40t^3 + 7t}{15} = {_0S_2}\left(\frac{12t^2 - 7}{5}\right)$$
$$_0S_5 = \frac{16t^6 - 20t^4 + 7t^2}{3} = {_0S_1}\left(\frac{16t^4 - 20t^2 + 7}{3}\right)$$
$$_0S_6 = \frac{192t^7 - 336t^5 + 196t^3 - 31t}{21} = {_0S_2}\left(\frac{48t^4 - 72t^2 + 31}{7}\right)$$

When the number of observations, n, in a time series is even, and the origin is taken mid-way in the time series, $t = \dfrac{n}{2}$. Representing by x deviations from the origin, the x unit being one half the time unit, we have

$$\Sigma x = 0$$
$$\Sigma x^2 = n\left(\frac{(n+1)(n-1)}{3}\right)$$
$$\Sigma x^3 = 0$$
$$\Sigma x^4 = (\Sigma x^2)\left(\frac{3n^2 - 7}{5}\right)$$
$$\Sigma x^5 = 0$$
$$\Sigma x^6 = (\Sigma x^4)\left(\frac{3n^4 - 18n^2 + 31}{7}\right)$$

In fitting certain types of curves it is necessary to compute the sums of the logarithms of x, and the sums of the squares of the logarithms of x. Appendix V of Pearl's *Introduction to Medical Biometry and Statistics* (Philadelphia, Saunders, 1930) contains a useful table that gives the sums of the first and second powers of log x for the natural numbers from 1 to 100.

A curve of the ordinary exponential type, $y = ab^x$, may be fitted by reducing the equation to logarithmic form. If the fitting be by least squares, this means the securing of a curve from which the sum of the squares of the logarithmic deviations is a minimum. As we have noted in the text, Professor James W. Glover has employed another method of fitting a curve of this type, and has prepared a table that greatly simplifies the task of determining the constants in the equation to the curve of best fit. This table is found on pages 468–481 of Glover's *Tables of Applied Mathematics*, Ann Arbor, Michigan, George Wahr, 1923.

For fitting higher degree polynomials, methods are available that lessen the labor involved, particularly if curves of different degree are to be fitted to the same data. These methods, which reduce the fitting process to a series of simple adding machine operations, are appropriate to extended research projects. Their use is not advisable, however, unless work involving a considerable number of routine operations is contemplated. It is desirable that the student master the basic least squares procedures, utilizing other methods only in case extended computing tasks are undertaken.

For accounts of systematic methods suited to extensive calculations, see Fisher (Ref. 50) and Sasuly (Ref. 134). The application of the method of orthogonal polynomials developed by Fisher is facilitated by the use of prepared tables. See Fisher and Yates (Ref. 51), Table XXIII.

•
•
•

Derivation of the Standard Error
of the Arithmetic Mean

We have made n random, hence independent, observations on a given variable. The respective observations may be represented by X_1, X_2, X_3, ... X_n. Representing the sum of the n observations by W, we have

$$W = X_1 + X_2 + X_3 + \cdots + X_n \tag{1}$$

Additional samples are now taken until we have N values of X_1, N values of X_2, etc., and hence N values of the sum W. We have N samples, therefore, of n observations each. The mean values, which we may represent by barred letters, stand in the same relationship of equality:

$$\overline{W} = \overline{X}_1 + \overline{X}_2 + \overline{X}_3 + \cdots + \overline{X}_n \tag{2}$$

Using small letters (w, x_1, x_2, etc.) to define deviations of the actual observations from these mean values, we may write, for any given sample, or series of observations,

$$w = x_1 + x_2 + x_3 + \cdots + x_n \tag{3}$$

Squaring the two sides of this equation, we have

$$
\begin{aligned}
w^2 = x_1^2 + x_2^2 + x_3^2 + \cdots &+ x_n^2 + 2x_1x_2 + 2x_1x_3 + \cdots \\
&+ 2x_1x_n + 2x_2x_3 + \cdots + 2x_2x_n + \cdots \\
&+ 2x_3x_n + \cdots
\end{aligned} \tag{4}
$$

Each term on the right-hand side of (3) will appear in squared form in (4), and there will also appear product terms of the form

$2x_1x_2$ corresponding to all possible pairings of the terms on the right-hand side.

The next step involves the summation of the equations of type (4), derived from the N samples, and division throughout by N. Each product term, when thus summed and divided by N, will be of the form

$$\frac{2\Sigma x_1 x_2}{N}$$

This, with the modification introduced by the factor 2, resembles the familiar mean product, $\dfrac{\Sigma xy}{N}$, encountered in correlation procedure. This mean product, we have seen, has a value of zero when the variables x and y are uncorrelated. But, by hypothesis, the observations that have given us x_1, x_2, x_3, etc., are independent of one another, and hence these variables are uncorrelated. Accordingly, each of the product terms, derived when N equations corresponding to (4) above are summed and divided by N, is equal to zero. The process of summation and division gives us, therefore,

$$\frac{\Sigma w^2}{N} = \frac{\Sigma x_1^2}{N} + \frac{\Sigma x_2^2}{N} + \frac{\Sigma x_3^2}{N} + \cdots + \frac{\Sigma x_n^2}{N} \tag{5}$$

or

$$\sigma_w^2 = \sigma_1^2 + \sigma_2^2 + \sigma_3^2 + \cdots + \sigma_n^2 \tag{6}$$

If all the observations relate to the same universe (i.e., if the samples are all drawn from the same parent population), which is true, by hypothesis, the standard deviations appearing in the right-hand member of equation (6) are equal to one another and to the standard deviation of the population. Accordingly, using σ to represent that standard deviation, we have

$$\sigma_w^2 = n\sigma^2 \tag{7}$$

The next argument, that leads directly to the desired measurement, follows precisely these steps, which have been given in the above form to indicate the reasoning involved. It starts, however, with a variant form of equation (3). Dividing that equation throughout by n, we have

$$\frac{w}{n} = \frac{x_1}{n} + \frac{x_2}{n} + \frac{x_3}{n} + \cdots + \frac{x_n}{n} \tag{8}$$

Working with the variables $\frac{w}{n}$, $\frac{x_1}{n}$, $\frac{x_2}{n}$, etc., just as we have done with w, x_1, x_2, etc., we may go through the operations represented by equations (4), (5), and (6), above. The product terms disappear, as in passing from (4) to (5). In the process of squaring, the term $\frac{w}{n}$ is treated as an entity; the sum of the squared values is thus $\Sigma\left(\frac{w}{n}\right)^2$. Numerator and denominator of each of the terms of type $\frac{x_1}{n}$ are squared separately, however, and the sum is of the form $\frac{\Sigma x^2}{n^2}$. Division throughout by N then gives the quantities appearing in equation (9), which corresponds to equation (6).

$$\sigma_{\frac{w}{n}}^2 = \frac{\sigma_1^2}{n^2} + \frac{\sigma_2^2}{n^2} + \frac{\sigma_3^2}{n^2} + \cdots + \frac{\sigma_n^2}{n^2} \tag{9}$$

Since all observations relate to the same universe, this reduces to

$$\sigma_{\frac{w}{n}}^2 = \frac{n\sigma^2}{n^2}. \tag{10}$$

From this

$$\sigma_{\frac{w}{n}} = \frac{\sigma}{\sqrt{n}}. \tag{11}$$

But w is the sum of n quantities drawn from a universe having a standard deviation of σ, and $\frac{w}{n}$ is the mean of these observations. Hence, $\sigma_{\frac{w}{n}}$ is the standard deviation of a distribution of arithmetic means, corresponding to the familiar symbol σ_M. This is the desired expression for the standard error of the arithmetic mean, appropriate for use when the σ of the population is known.

.
.
.

Illustrating the Measurement of Trend by a Modified Exponential Curve, a Gompertz Curve, and a Logistic Curve

The discussion in Chapter 10 of mathematical functions suitable for use in measuring the secular trends of time series dealt with types required in ordinary practice. We here discuss briefly three other types suited to the measurement of long-term movements in economic and business series.

The Modified Exponential Curve

An exponential curve, which plots as a straight line on ratio paper, is a suitable measure of trend for a series that is increasing or decreasing at a constant rate. The figures defining the successive trend values of a series of this type constitute a geometric progression. The trends of certain economic series that depart from constancy of relative growth may be accurately defined by a simple modification of the exponential curve. This is the case when the observed values may be transformed, by the addition (or subtraction) of a constant magnitude, to a series closely approximating such a geometric progression.

If we represent by K the constant magnitude that is to be added (algebraically) to each observed value in effecting the desired transformation, the task of fitting the trend line involves the following steps:

Determination of K.

Correction of observed values by K, to obtain the modified series.

Fitting an exponential curve to the modified series, and computation of trend values of the modified series.

Correction of trend values of the modified series by K to obtain trend values of original series.

If y represents the ordinates of trend of the original series and x represents time, the equation to the desired line of trend may be put in the form

$$y = ab^x - K$$

where K is the correction factor noted above and a and b are constants to be determined by fitting an exponential curve to the modified series. The procedure may be illustrated with reference

TABLE A

Illustrating the Fitting of a Modified Exponential Curve
Manufacturers' Shipments of Room Air Conditioners *
1946–1954
(Number shipped, in thousands)

(1)	(2) Original series	(3) Group mean	(4) Modified series (2) + K	(5) Trend values modified series	(6) Trend values original series (5) − K
1946	30		8.7	11.7	33.0
1947	43	$M_1 = 49$	21.7	21.4	42.7
1948	74		52.7	39.2	60.5
1949	89		67.7	71.7	93.0
1950	201	$M_2 = 176$	179.7	131.4	152.7
1951	238		216.7	240.5	261.8
1952	380		358.7	440.4	461.7
1953	1,045	$M_3 = 885$	1,023.7	806.5	827.8
1954	1,230		1,208.7	1,476.9	1,498.2

* Source: *Electrical Merchandising*

to the data on shipments of room air conditioners, shown in Table A. A short series is used to simplify the presentation. In employing this method we approximate K empirically by breaking the observed series into three parts, representing equal periods of time, and determining the mean of the observations for each period. We may designate these means, in chronological order, by M_1, M_2, and M_3. The desired value, K, is given by

$$K = [M_2^2 - (M_1 \times M_3)] \div [(M_1 + M_3) - 2M_2]$$

If the observed series constitute a geometric progression the value of K will be zero; if the *addition* of a constant magnitude to the members of the original series will yield a series approximating a geometric progression, K will be positive; if the *subtraction* of a constant amount from the observed values will yield a series approximating a geometric progression, K will be negative. (In practice, K is given the sign obtained by the employment of the method described above, and then added algebraically to the observed series.)

In the present case we have

$$K = [(176)^2 - (49 \times 885)] \div [(49 + 885) - (2 \times 176)] = -21.3$$

Adding this amount to each of the values recorded in column (2) of Table A, we obtain the modified series in column (4). In fitting an exponential curve to the modified series, it is desirable to use logarithms, that is, to solve the constants in an equation of the type $\log y = \log a + (\log b)x$. This procedure was explained in Chapter 10. For $\log a$ of this curve we obtain 2.11845, and for $\log b$, 0.26272. (The origin is at 1950.) The antilogarithms of the series of trend values thus obtained are given in column (5). These define the trend of the modified series. Subtracting K (algebraically) from these values we obtain the trend values of the original series, which appear in column (6). (In practice, the figures in column (6) would be rounded to the nearest digit, to accord with the original series. The first decimal is kept in this example, so that the procedure may be clear.)

The original series measuring shipments of room air conditioners and the modified exponential curve fitted to this series are shown graphically in Fig. A. The equation to the curve there plotted is

$$y = 131.4(1.8311^x) - (-21.3)$$

with reference to an origin at 1950. The fit is not bad. However, it will be understood that the time period covered is too short to warrant acceptance of the given function as a reliable measure of long-term trend.

It is essential that the three M's used in the determination of K relate to equal numbers of observations and that the midpoints, in time, of the three periods be equidistant. In the above example the number of years included in the period is a multiple of three, and no difficulty arises. If the number of years included is not a multiple of three, intervals that overlap slightly may be employed.

FIG. A. Manufacturers' Shipments of Room Air Conditioners in the United States, 1946–1954, with Modified Exponential Curve.

For example, if our series had run from 1942 to 1954, the three averages might have been derived from the five-year periods 1942–1946, 1946–1950, 1950–1954. These would center, respectively, at 1944, 1948, and 1952, and would thus be equidistant in time from one another. Alternatively, if monthly data are available, division of the total period into three equal parts may be facilitated by using a time-unit of 4 or 8 months, rather than 12 months.

The Gompertz Curve

The Gompertz curve, which has important uses in actuarial science, has had some application in the study of economic and social trends. The term "growth curve" is applicable to it, since it portrays a process of cumulative expansion to a maximum value. This expansion proceeds by decreasing relative amounts in the later stages, but continues to the end without retrogression. It may not be assumed that this form of growth is typical of all industrial development, but the curve has value as an empirical representation of certain trend movements.

For the purpose of fitting, the equation to the curve is transformed from the natural form

$$y = ab^{c^x}$$

to the logarithmic form

$$\log y = \log a + (\log b)c^x$$

When fitted to an appropriate set of observations, measuring the expansion of an industry or the growth of an economic element, $\log a$ is the logarithm of the maximum value — the *ceiling* that the curve approaches. The second term measures the amount by which the trend value at a given time falls short of this maximum, an amount that diminishes, of course, with the passage of time. (The series for which this curve is an appropriate measure of trend will be expanding by decreasing relative amounts in the later stages of its life history, and c, derived in the manner indicated below, will have a value between zero and unity.) The origin on the x-scale (time) is taken at the year to which the first entry relates.

The method employed in fitting this curve is an approximative one, since the least squares procedure in customary form is not applicable. Here, as in the preceding example, the series is broken into three equal portions. The sum of the logarithms of the observations in each of these segments is obtained; from these sums, and the differences between them, the necessary constants may be computed. The method is illustrated with reference to the domestic shipments of rayon filament yarns for the years 1922–1954, which appear in Table B.

We may use n to define the number of terms entering into each of the three subtotals (in the present example $n = 11$); the subtotals are represented, in chronological order, by S_1, S_2, and S_3; the first differences [1] between the subtotals are represented by d_1

---

[1] The condition, previously noted, that the series to which the curve is to be fitted be one that is expanding by decreasing logarithmic increments in the later stages of the period covered, is met when d_2 is less than d_1.

TABLE B

Computation of Quantities Required in the Fitting of a Gompertz
Curve to Domestic Shipments by Producers of Rayon
Filament Yarn, 1922–1954
(Annual totals, in millions of pounds)

(1) Year	(2) Shipments of rayon yarn y	(3) Log y	(4) Subtotals	(5) First differences
1922	22.6	1.35411		
1923	29.5	1.46982		
1924	40.3	1.60531		
1925	52.8	1.72263		
1926	51.3	1.71012		
1927	85.0	1.92942	$S_1 = 20.22250$	
1928	88.0	1.94448		
1929	116.4	2.06595		
1930	111.6	2.04766		
1931	155.5	2.19173		
1932	151.8	2.18127		
				$d_1 = S_2 - S_1$
1933	210.9	2.32408		$= 7.29523$
1934	194.7	2.28937		
1935	252.7	2.40261		
1936	297.3	2.47319		
1937	266.2	2.42521		
1938	273.8	2.43743	$S_2 = 27.51773$	
1939	359.6	2.55582		
1940	388.7	2.58961		
1941	452.4	2.65552		
1942	468.8	2.67099		
1943	494.2	2.69390		
				$d_2 = S_3 - S_2$
1944	539.1	2.73167		$= 4.12837$
1945	602.4	2.77988		
1946	666.4	2.82373		
1947	729.0	2.86273		
1948	836.5	2.92247		
1949	782.4	2.89343	$S_3 = 31.64610$	
1950	949.1	2.97731		
1951	860.3	2.93465		
1952	844.8	2.92675		
1953	864.7	2.93687		
1954	718.8	2.85661		

and d_2. We use these quantities in solving for the three constants
c, log b, and log a. The general relations from which these values
are determined are the following:

$$c^n = \frac{d_2}{d_1}$$

$$\log b = \frac{d_1(c - 1)}{(c^n - 1)^2}$$

$$\log a = \frac{1}{n}\left(S_1 - \frac{d_1}{c^n - 1}\right)$$

Inserting the proper quantities, we have

$$c^n = c^{11} = \frac{4.12837}{7.29523} = 0.565900$$

$$c = \sqrt[11]{0.565900} = 0.94956$$

$$\log b = \frac{7.29523(-0.05044)}{(-0.4341)^2} = -1.95270$$

$$\log a = \frac{1}{11}\left(20.22250 - \frac{7.29523}{-0.43410}\right) = 3.36617$$

The required equation is, therefore,

$$\log y = 3.36617 - 1.95270(0.94956^x)$$

in which x relates to deviations from an origin at the position of the first term.

Substituting in this trend equation the values of x given in Table C, logarithms of the trend values are obtained. The corresponding natural numbers define the course of the line of trend. The method of calculation is indicated in Table C. The original data and the Gompertz curve fitted to them are shown graphically in Fig. B.

FIG. B. Domestic Shipments of Rayon Filament Yarn in the United States, 1922–1954, with Gompertz Trend Line.

TABLE C

Illustrating the Computation of Ordinates of Trend of a Gompertz
Curve Fitted to Shipments of Rayon Filament Yarn, 1922–1954

(1)	(2)	(3)	(4)	(5)	(6)
					y
Year	x	c^x	$(\log b)c^x$	$\log y$ (4) + $\log a$	Anti-log of (5) (in millions of pounds)
1922	0	1.00000	− 1.95270	1.41347	25.9
1923	1	0.94956	− 1.85421	1.51196	32.5
1924	2	0.901664	− 1.76067	1.60550	40.3
1925	3	0.856184	− 1.67187	1.69430	49.5
1926	4	0.812998	− 1.58754	1.77863	60.1
1927	5	0.771991	− 1.50747	1.85870	72.2
1928	6	0.733051	− 1.43143	1.93474	86.0
1929	7	0.696076	− 1.35923	2.00694	101.6
1930	8	0.660966	− 1.29067	2.07550	119.0
1931	9	0.627627	− 1.22557	2.14060	138.2
1932	10	0.595970	− 1.16375	2.20242	159.4
1933	11	0.565909	− 1.10505	2.26112	182.4
1934	12	0.537364	− 1.04931	2.31686	207.4
1935	13	0.510260	− 0.99638	2.36979	234.3
1936	14	0.484522	− 0.94613	2.42004	263.0
1937	15	0.460083	− 0.89840	2.46777	293.6
1938	16	0.436876	− 0.85309	2.51308	325.9
1939	17	0.414840	− 0.81006	2.55611	359.8
1940	18	0.393916	− 0.76920	2.59697	395.3
1941	19	0.374047	− 0.73040	2.63577	432.3
1942	20	0.355180	− 0.69356	2.67261	470.6
1943	21	0.337265	− 0.65858	2.70759	510.0
1944	22	0.320253	− 0.62536	2.74081	550.6
1945	23	0.304099	− 0.59381	2.77236	592.0
1946	24	0.288761	− 0.56386	2.80231	634.3
1947	25	0.274195	− 0.53542	2.83075	677.2
1948	26	0.260365	− 0.50841	2.85776	720.7
1949	27	0.247232	− 0.48277	2.88340	764.5
1950	28	0.234762	− 0.45842	2.90775	808.6
1951	29	0.222920	− 0.43530	2.93087	852.8
1952	30	0.211676	− 0.41334	2.95283	897.1
1953	31	0.200999	− 0.39249	2.97368	941.2
1954	32	0.190861	− 0.37269	2.99348	985.1

The ceiling to this curve is set by the constant a, which has a value of approximately 2,324. This indicates that if the extrapolation of the trend of rayon yarn shipments from 1922 to 1954, as measured by a Gompertz curve, accurately defines the future course, the maximum volume of shipments to be expected is 2,324 million pounds per year. It need hardly be pointed out that this extrapolation involves some doubtful assumptions, and that no mystic significance is to be attached to it. In particular, the asymptote a may be expected to change, as conditions affecting the industry and the demand for its products vary in the future. As we shall see, a different growth function may yield a quite different asymptote.

The Logistic Curve

The logistic curve, sometimes termed the Pearl-Reed growth curve because of the extensive use made of it in population studies by Raymond Pearl and L. J. Reed, resembles somewhat the Gompertz curve discussed above. It represents a modified geometric progression, the growth of a series that tends to decrease as it approaches some specified limit. Like the Gompertz curve it may be used as an empirical approximation to the trends of certain economic series. Extrapolations are subject, of course, to the same uncertainties that attach to projections of other empirically derived trend lines.

A form of this curve adapted to use as a measure of trend is defined by the equation

$$\frac{1}{y} = a + bc^x$$

This, it will be noted, is the equation to a modified exponential curve, except that the dependent variable is $\frac{1}{y}$, rather than y. (The symbols here used for the constants differ somewhat from those employed in treating the modified exponential curve.) A method of fitting somewhat similar to those employed in the preceding examples may be employed, with necessary modifications required by the use of reciprocals of y. The method may be discussed with reference to the series used in the preceding example — domestic shipments of rayon filament yarn. Initial stages in the fitting process are illustrated in Table D. Computations are facilitated by multiplying the reciprocals of y by a suitable power of 10, as is done in column (3) of this table.

As in the two preceding illustrations, the observations are divided, chronologically, into three equal groups. Group subtotals

TABLE D

Computation of Quantities Required in the Fitting of a Logistic
Curve to Domestic Shipments by Producers of
Rayon Filament Yarn, 1922–1954 *
(Annual totals, in millions of pounds)

(1) Year	(2) Shipments of rayon yarn y	(3) $\dfrac{100,000}{y}$	(4) Subtotals	(5) First differences
1922	22.6	4,425		
1923	29.5	3,390		
1924	40.3	2,481		
1925	52.8	1,894		
1926	51.3	1,949	$S_1 = 19,507$	
1927	85.0	1,176		
1928	88.0	1,136		
1929	116.4	859		
1930	111.6	896		
1931	155.5	643		
1932	151.8	658		
				$d_1 = S_2 - S_1$
1933	210.9	474		$= -15,875$
1934	194.7	514		
1935	252.7	396		
1936	297.3	336		
1937	266.2	376	$S_2 = 3,632$	
1938	273.8	365		
1939	359.6	278		
1940	388.7	257		
1941	452.4	221		
1942	468.8	213		
1943	494.2	202		
				$d_2 = S_3 - S_2$
1944	539.1	185		$= -2,152$
1945	602.4	166		
1946	666.4	150		
1947	729.0	137		
1948	836.5	120	$S_3 = 1,480$	
1949	782.4	128		
1950	949.1	105		
1951	860.3	116		
1952	844.8	118		
1953	864.7	116		
1954	718.8	139		

* Source: *Textile Organon*, Textile Economics Bureau

and the first differences between these subtotals are computed.
The symbol n is used for the number of terms in each of these subgroups. The origin of the x-scale (time) is set at the date of the first
observation.

The constants in the desired equation may be derived from the following relations.

$$c^n = \frac{d_2}{d_1}$$

$$b = \frac{d_1(c-1)}{(c^n-1)^2}$$

$$a = \frac{1}{n}\left(S_1 - \frac{d_1}{c^n-1}\right)$$

Substituting the given values, we have

$$c^n = c^{11} = \frac{-2,152}{-15,875} = +0.135559$$

$$c = \sqrt[11]{+0.135559} = 0.83388$$

$$b = \frac{-15,875(-0.16612)}{(0.135559-1)^2} = +3,529.11$$

$$a = \frac{1}{11}\left(19,507 - \frac{-15.875}{(.0135559-1)}\right) = +103.87$$

These results relate to initial observations that have been modified by the multiplication of $\frac{1}{y}$ by 100,000. The desired equation is, therefore,

$$\frac{100,000}{y} = 103.87 + 3,529.11(0.83388^x)$$

where x measures deviations in years from an origin at 1922.

Succeeding calculations are shown in Table E. The process of calculation is a straightforward one. The reciprocals of the entries in column (5), multiplied by 100,000, yield the desired trend values given in column (6). These values, with the original series, are shown graphically in Fig. C.

As in the case of the Gompertz curve, the logistic is suitable for measuring the trend of a series that, in its later stages, is growing at a decreasing rate. The curve resembles an elongated S rising from a lower asymptote of zero to an upper limit indicated by the constant a. Since a in this case refers to an equation in which the dependent variable is $\frac{100,000}{y}$, the actual asymptote is $\frac{100,000}{a}$.

TABLE E

Computation of Ordinates of Trend of Logistic Curve Fitted to Domestic Shipments of Rayon Filament Yarn

(1) Year	(2) x	(3) c^x	(4) bc^x	(5) $\dfrac{100,000}{y}$ $(a + bc^x)$	(6) $\left(100,000 \times \dfrac{1}{(\text{col. 5})}\right)$ y
1922	0	1.00000	3,529.1	3,633.0	27.5
1923	1	0.83388	2,942.9	3,046.8	32.8
1924	2	0.69536	2,454.0	2,557.9	39.1
1925	3	0.57984	2,046.3	2,150.2	46.5
1926	4	0.48352	1,706.4	1,810.3	55.2
1927	5	0.40320	1,422.9	1,526.8	65.5
1928	6	0.33622	1,186.6	1,290.5	77.5
1929	7	0.28037	989.5	1,093.4	91.5
1930	8	0.23379	825.1	929.0	107.6
1931	9	0.19495	688.0	791.9	126.3
1932	10	0.16257	573.7	677.6	147.6
1933	11	0.13556	478.4	582.3	171.7
1934	12	0.11304	398.9	502.8	198.9
1935	13	0.09426	332.6	436.5	229.1
1936	14	0.07860	277.3	381.2	262.3
1937	15	0.06555	231.3	335.2	298.3
1938	16	0.05466	192.9	296.8	336.9
1939	17	0.04558	160.9	264.8	377.6
1940	18	0.03801	134.1	238.0	420.2
1941	19	0.03169	111.8	215.7	463.6
1942	20	0.02643	93.3	197.2	507.1
1943	21	0.02204	77.8	181.7	550.4
1944	22	0.01838	64.9	168.8	592.4
1945	23	0.01532	54.1	158.0	632.9
1946	24	0.01278	45.1	149.0	671.1
1947	25	0.01066	37.6	141.5	706.7
1948	26	0.00889	31.4	135.3	739.1
1949	27	0.00741	26.2	130.1	768.6
1950	28	0.00618	21.8	125.7	795.5
1951	29	0.00515	18.2	122.1	819.0
1952	30	0.00430	15.2	119.1	839.6
1953	31	0.00358	12.6	116.5	858.8
1954	32	0.00299	10.6	114.5	873.4

From the given value of a, 103.87, we derive 963 (in millions of pounds) as the upper limit of the trend line here derived. (The reader will note the wide difference between this asymptote and the ceiling of 2,324 million pounds given by the Gompertz curve.) The limit given by the logistic was closely approached in 1950, at the peak of the postwar surge. Whether this limit may be accepted as a reasonable long-term expectation depends on the nature of the forces behind the declines of recent years. In any rational extrapolation, appraisal of these forces must supplement the descriptive information given by the trend limit. Within the limits of the observations the present logistic curve gives a fairly good representation of the stages of slow initial growth, acceleration, and retardation in the life history of this industry.

FIG. C. Domestic Shipments of Rayon Filament Yarn in the United States, 1922–1954, with Logistic Trend.

GREEK ALPHABET

Letters	Names	Letters	Names	Letters	Names
A α	Alpha	I ι	Iota	P ρ	Rho
B β	Beta	K κ	Kappa	Σ σ	Sigma
Γ γ	Gamma	Λ λ	Lambda	T τ	Tau
Δ δ	Delta	M μ	Mu	Υ υ	Upsilon
E ε	Epsilon	N ν	Nu	Φ φ	Phi
Z ζ	Zeta	Ξ ξ	Xi	X χ	Chi
H η	Eta	O o	Omicron	Ψ ψ	Psi
Θ θ	Theta	Π π	Pi	Ω ω	Omega

Areas and Ordinates of the Normal Curve of Error in Terms of the Abscissa

x/σ	Area between maximum ordinate and ordinate at x/σ	Ordinate at x/σ	x/σ	Area between maximum ordinate and ordinate at x/σ	Ordinate at x/σ
.00	.00000	.39894	.50	.19146	.35207
.01	.00399	.39892	.51	.19497	.35029
.02	.00798	.39886	.52	.19847	.34849
.03	.01197	.39876	.53	.20194	.34667
.04	.01595	.39862	.54	.20540	.34482
.05	.01994	.39844	.55	.20884	.34294
.06	.02392	.39822	.56	.21226	.34105
.07	.02790	.39797	.57	.21566	.33912
.08	.03188	.39767	.58	.21904	.33718
.09	.03586	.39733	.59	.22240	.33521
.10	.03983	.39695	.60	.22575	.33322
.11	.04380	.39654	.61	.22907	.33121
.12	.04776	.39608	.62	.23237	.32918
.13	.05172	.39559	.63	.23565	.32713
.14	.05567	.39505	.64	.23891	.32506
.15	.05962	.39448	.65	.24215	.32297
.16	.06356	.39387	.66	.24537	.32086
.17	.06749	.39322	.67	.24857	.31874
.18	.07142	.39253	.68	.25175	.31659
.19	.07535	.39181	.69	.25490	.31443
.20	.07926	.39104	.70	.25804	.31225
.21	.08317	.39024	.71	.26115	.31006
.22	.08706	.38940	.72	.26424	.30785
.23	.09095	.38853	.73	.26730	.30563
.24	.09483	.38762	.74	.27035	.30339
.25	.09871	.38667	.75	.27337	.30114
.26	.10257	.38568	.76	.27637	.29887
.27	.10642	.38466	.77	.27935	.29659
.28	.11026	.38361	.78	.28230	.29431
.29	.11409	.38251	.79	.28524	.29200
.30	.11791	.38139	.80	.28814	.28969
.31	.12172	.38023	.81	.29103	.28737
.32	.12552	.37903	.82	.29389	.28504
.33	.12930	.37780	.83	.29673	.28269
.34	.13307	.37654	.84	.29955	.28034
.35	.13683	.37524	.85	.30234	.27798
.36	.14058	.37391	.86	.30511	.27562
.37	.14431	.37255	.87	.30785	.27324
.38	.14803	.37115	.88	.31057	.27086
.39	.15173	.36973	.89	.31327	.26848
.40	.15542	.36827	.90	.31594	.26609
.41	.15910	.36678	.91	.31859	.26369
.42	.16276	.36526	.92	.32121	.26129
.43	.16640	.36371	.93	.32381	.25888
.44	.17003	.36213	.94	.32639	.25647
.45	.17364	.36053	.95	.32894	.25406
.46	.17724	.35889	.96	.33147	.25164
.47	.18082	.35723	.97	.33398	.24923
.48	.18439	.35553	.98	.33646	.24681
.49	.18793	.35381	.99	.33891	.24439

Areas and Ordinates of the Normal Curve of Error in Terms of the Abscissa

x/σ	Area between maximum ordinate and ordinate at x/σ	Ordinate at x/σ	x/σ	Area between maximum ordinate and ordinate at x/σ	Ordinate at x/σ
1.00	.34134	.24197	1.50	.43319	.12952
1.01	.34375	.23955	1.51	.43448	.12758
1.02	.34614	.23713	1.52	.43574	.12566
1.03	.34850	.23471	1.53	.43699	.12376
1.04	.35083	.23230	1.54	.43822	.12188
1.05	.35314	.22988	1.55	.43943	.12001
1.06	.35543	.22747	1.56	.44062	.11816
1.07	.35769	.22506	1.57	.44179	.11632
1.08	.35993	.22265	1.58	.44295	.11450
1.09	.36214	.22025	1.59	.44408	.11270
1.10	.36433	.21785	1.60	.44520	.11092
1.11	.36650	.21546	1.61	.44630	.10915
1.12	.36864	.21307	1.62	.44738	.10741
1.13	.37076	.21069	1.63	.44845	.10567
1.14	.37286	.20831	1.64	.44950	.10396
1.15	.37493	.20594	1.65	.45053	.10226
1.16	.37698	.20357	1.66	.45154	.10059
1.17	.37900	.20121	1.67	.45254	.09893
1.18	.38100	.19886	1.68	.45352	.09728
1.19	.38298	.19652	1.69	.45449	.09566
1.20	.38493	.19419	1.70	.45543	.09405
1.21	.38686	.19186	1.71	.45637	.09246
1.22	.38877	.18954	1.72	.45728	.09089
1.23	.39065	.18724	1.73	.45818	.08933
1.24	.39251	.18494	1.74	.45907	.08780
1.25	.39435	.18265	1.75	.45994	.08628
1.26	.39617	.18037	1.76	.46080	.08478
1.27	.39796	.17810	1.77	.46164	.08329
1.28	.39973	.17585	1.78	.46246	.08183
1.29	.40147	.17360	1.79	.46327	.08038
1.30	.40320	.17137	1.80	.46407	.07895
1.31	.40490	.16915	1.81	.46485	.07754
1.32	.40658	.16694	1.82	.46562	.07614
1.33	.40824	.16474	1.83	.46638	.07477
1.34	.40988	.16256	1.84	.46712	.07341
1.35	.41149	.16038	1.85	.46784	.07206
1.36	.41309	.15822	1.86	.46856	.07074
1.37	.41466	.15608	1.87	.46926	.06943
1.38	.41621	.15395	1.88	.46995	.06814
1.39	.41774	.15183	1.89	.47062	.06687
1.40	.41924	.14973	1.90	.47128	.06562
1.41	.42073	.14764	1.91	.47193	.06438
1.42	.42220	.14556	1.92	.47257	.06316
1.43	.42364	.14350	1.93	.47320	.06195
1.44	.42507	.14146	1.94	.47381	.06077
1.45	.42647	.13943	1.95	.47441	.05959
1.46	.42786	.13742	1.96	.47500	.05844
1.47	.42922	.13542	1.97	.47558	.05730
1.48	.43056	.13344	1.98	.47615	.05618
1.49	.43189	.13147	1.99	.47670	.05508

Areas and Ordinates of the Normal Curve of Error in Terms of the Abscissa

x/σ	Area between maximum ordinate and ordinate at x/σ	Ordinate at x/σ	x/σ	Area between maximum ordinate and ordinate at x/σ	Ordinate at x/σ
2.00	.47725	.05399	2.50	.49379	.01753
2.01	.47778	.05292	2.51	.49396	.01709
2.02	.47831	.05186	2.52	.49413	.01667
2.03	.47882	.05082	2.53	.49430	.01625
2.04	.47932	.04980	2.54	.49446	.01585
2.05	.47982	.04879	2.55	.49461	.01545
2.06	.48030	.04780	2.56	.49477	.01506
2.07	.48077	.04682	2.57	.49492	.01468
2.08	.48124	.04586	2.58	.49506	.01431
2.09	.48169	.04491	2.59	.49520	.01394
2.10	.48214	.04398	2.60	.49534	.01358
2.11	.48257	.04307	2.61	.49547	.01323
2.12	.48300	.04217	2.62	.49560	.01289
2.13	.48341	.04128	2.63	.49573	.01256
2.14	.48382	.04041	2.64	.49585	.01223
2.15	.48422	.03955	2.65	.49598	.01191
2.16	.48461	.03871	2.66	.49609	.01160
2.17	.48500	.03788	2.67	.49621	.01130
2.18	.48537	.03706	2.68	.49632	.01100
2.19	.48574	.03626	2.69	.49643	.01071
2.20	.48610	.03547	2.70	.49653	.01042
2.21	.48645	.03470	2.71	.49664	.01014
2.22	.48679	.03394	2.72	.49674	.00987
2.23	.48713	.03319	2.73	.49683	.00961
2.24	.48745	.03246	2.74	.49693	.00935
2.25	.48778	.03174	2.75	.49702	.00909
2.26	.48809	.03103	2.76	.49711	.00885
2.27	.48840	.03034	2.77	.49720	.00861
2.28	.48870	.02965	2.78	.49728	.00837
2.29	.48899	.02898	2.79	.49736	.00814
2.30	.48928	.02833	2.80	.49744	.00792
2.31	.48956	.02768	2.81	.49752	.00770
2.32	.48983	.02705	2.82	.49760	.00748
2.33	.49010	.02643	2.83	.49767	.00727
2.34	.49036	.02582	2.84	.49774	.00707
2.35	.49061	.02522	2.85	.49781	.00687
2.36	.49086	.02463	2.86	.49788	.00668
2.37	.49111	.02406	2.87	.49795	.00649
2.38	.49134	.02349	2.88	.49801	.00631
2.39	.49158	.02294	2.89	.49807	.00613
2.40	.49180	.02239	2.90	.49813	.00595
2.41	.49202	.02186	2.91	.49819	.00578
2.42	.49224	.02134	2.92	.49825	.00562
2.43	.49245	.02083	2.93	.49831	.00545
2.44	.49266	.02033	2.94	.49836	.00530
2.45	.49286	.01984	2.95	.49841	.00514
2.46	.49305	.01936	2.96	.49846	.00499
2.47	.49324	.01889	2.97	.49851	.00485
2.48	.49343	.01842	2.98	.49856	.00471
2.49	.49361	.01797	2.99	.49861	.00457

Areas and Ordinates of the Normal Curve of Error in Terms of the Abscissa

x/σ	Area between maximum ordinate and ordinate at x/σ	Ordinate at x/σ	x/σ	Area between maximum ordinate and ordinate at x/σ	Ordinate at x/σ
3.00	.49865	.00443	3.50	.49977	.00087
3.01	.49869	.00430	3.51	.49978	.00084
3.02	.49874	.00417	3.52	.49978	.00081
3.03	.49878	.00405	3.53	.49979	.00079
3.04	.49882	.00393	3.54	.49980	.00076
3.05	.49886	.00381	3.55	.49981	.00073
3.06	.49889	.00370	3.56	.49981	.00071
3.07	.49893	.00358	3.57	.49982	.00068
3.08	.49897	.00348	3.58	.49983	.00066
3.09	.49900	.00337	3.59	.49983	.00063
3.10	.49903	.00327	3.60	.49984	.00061
3.11	.49906	.00317	3.61	.49985	.00059
3.12	.49910	.00307	3.62	.49985	.00057
3.13	.49913	.00298	3.63	.49986	.00055
3.14	.49916	.00288	3.64	.49986	.00053
3.15	.49918	.00279	3.65	.49987	.00051
3.16	.49921	.00271	3.66	.49987	.00049
3.17	.49924	.00262	3.67	.49988	.00047
3.18	.49926	.00254	3.68	.49988	.00046
3.19	.49929	.00246	3.69	.49989	.00044
3.20	.49931	.00238	3.70	.49989	.00042
3.21	.49934	.00231	3.71	.49990	.00041
3.22	.49936	.00224	3.72	.49990	.00039
3.23	.49938	.00216	3.73	.49990	.00038
3.24	.49940	.00210	3.74	.49991	.00037
3.25	.49942	.00203	3.75	.49991	.00035
3.26	.49944	.00196	3.76	.49992	.00034
3.27	.49946	.00190	3.77	.49992	.00033
3.28	.49948	.00184	3.78	.49992	.00031
3.29	.49950	.00178	3.79	.49992	.00030
3.30	.49952	.00172	3.80	.49993	.00029
3.31	.49953	.00167	3.81	.49993	.00028
3.32	.49955	.00161	3.82	.49993	.00027
3.33	.49957	.00156	3.83	.49994	.00026
3.34	.49958	.00151	3.84	.49994	.00025
3.35	.49960	.00146	3.85	.49994	.00024
3.36	.49961	.00141	3.86	.49994	.00023
3.37	.49962	.00136	3.87	.49995	.00022
3.38	.49964	.00132	3.88	.49995	.00021
3.39	.49965	.00127	3.89	.49995	.00021
3.40	.49966	.00123	3.90	.49995	.00020
3.41	.49968	.00119	3.91	.49995	.00019
3.42	.49969	.00115	3.92	.49996	.00018
3.43	.49970	.00111	3.93	.49996	.00018
3.44	.49971	.00107	3.94	.49996	.00017
3.45	.49972	.00104	3.95	.49996	.00016
3.46	.49973	.00100	3.96	.49996	.00016
3.47	.49974	.00097	3.97	.49996	.00015
3.48	.49975	.00094	3.98	.49997	.00014
3.49	.49976	.00090	3.99	.49997	.00014

APPENDIX TABLE II

Percentile Values of the Normal Distribution *

Area to the left of T †	T †	Area to the left of T †	T †
.001	− 3.090	.600	+ .253
.002	− 2.878	.700	+ .524
.003	− 2.748	.800	+ .842
.004	− 2.652	.900	+ 1.282
.005	− 2.576	.910	+ 1.341
.006	− 2.512	.920	+ 1.405
.007	− 2.457	.930	+ 1.476
.008	− 2.409	.940	+ 1.555
.009	− 2.366	.950	+ 1.645
.010	− 2.326	.960	+ 1.751
.020	− 2.054	.970	+ 1.881
.030	− 1.881	.980	+ 2.054
.040	− 1.751	.990	+ 2.326
.050	− 1.645	.991	+ 2.366
.060	− 1.555	.992	+ 2.409
.070	− 1.476	.993	+ 2.457
.080	− 1.405	.994	+ 2.512
.090	− 1.341	.995	+ 2.576
.100	− 1.282	.996	+ 2.652
.200	− .842	.997	+ 2.748
.300	− .524	.998	+ 2.878
.400	− .253	.999	+ 3.090
.500	.000		

* This table contains selected values from Table I of Truman L. Kelley's *The Kelley Statistical Tables* (Harvard University Press, 1948). I am indebted to Professor Kelley and the Harvard University Press for permission to publish these excerpts.

† T is here used as a symbol for a normal deviate: i.e., a deviation from the mean of a normal distribution expressed in units of the standard deviation. Areas are expressed as proportionate parts of the total area under a normal curve.

APPENDIX TABLE III *

Table of t

n	$P = .05$	.02	.01
1	12.706	31.821	63.657
2	4.303	6.965	9.925
3	3.182	4.541	5.841
4	2.776	3.747	4.604
5	2.571	3.365	4.032
6	2.447	3.143	3.707
7	2.365	2.998	3.499
8	2.306	2.896	3.355
9	2.262	2.821	3.250
10	2.228	2.764	3.169
11	2.201	2.718	3.106
12	2.179	2.681	3.055
13	2.160	2.650	3.012
14	2.145	2.624	2.977
15	2.131	2.602	2.947
16	2.120	2.583	2.921
17	2.110	2.567	2.898
18	2.101	2.552	2.878
19	2.093	2.539	2.861
20	2.086	2.528	2.845
21	2.080	2.518	2.831
22	2.074	2.508	2.819
23	2.069	2.500	2.807
24	2.064	2.492	2.797
25	2.060	2.485	2.787
26	2.056	2.479	2.779
27	2.052	2.473	2.771
28	2.048	2.467	2.763
29	2.045	2.462	2.756
30	2.042	2.457	2.750
∞	1.95996	2.32634	2.57582

* Appendix Table III is abridged from Table IV of R. A. Fisher, *Statistical Methods for Research Workers*, published by Oliver and Boyd, Ltd., of Edinburgh. The abridgment is published here by permission of the author and publishers.

APPENDIX TABLE IV *

Values of the Correlation Coefficient for Different Levels of Significance

n	$P = .05$	.02	.01
1	.996917	.9995066	.9998766
2	.95000	.98000	.990000
3	.8783	.93433	.95873
4	.8114	.8822	.91720
5	.7545	.8329	.8745
6	.7067	.7887	.8343
7	.6664	.7498	.7977
8	.6319	.7155	.7646
9	.6021	.6851	.7348
10	.5760	.6581	.7079
11	.5529	.6339	.6835
12	.5324	.6120	.6614
13	.5139	.5923	.6411
14	.4973	.5742	.6226
15	.4821	.5577	.6055
16	.4683	.5425	.5897
17	.4555	.5285	.5751
18	.4438	.5155	.5614
19	.4329	.5034	.5487
20	.4227	.4921	.5368
25	.3809	.4451	.4869
30	.3494	.4093	.4487
35	.3246	.3810	.4182
40	.3044	.3578	.3932
45	.2875	.3384	.3721
50	.2732	.3218	.3541
60	.2500	.2948	.3248
70	.2319	.2737	.3017
80	.2172	.2565	.2830
90	.2050	.2422	.2673
100	.1946	.2301	.2540

For a total correlation, n is 2 less than the number of pairs in the sample; for a partial correlation, the number of eliminated variates also should be subtracted.

* Appendix Table IV is abridged from Table V–A of R. A. Fisher, *Statistical Methods for Research Workers*, published by Oliver and Boyd, Ltd., of Edinburgh. The abridgment is published here by permission of the author and publishers.

APPENDIX TABLE V

Showing the Relations between r and z' for Values of z' from 0 to 5 *

z'	.00	.01	.02	.03	.04	.05	.06	.07	.08	.09
.0	.0000	.0100	.0200	.0300	.0400	.0500	.0599	.0699	.0798	.0898
.1	.0997	.1096	.1194	.1293	.1391	.1489	.1587	.1684	.1781	.1878
.2	.1974	.2070	.2165	.2260	.2355	.2449	.2543	.2636	.2729	.2821
.3	.2913	.3004	.3095	.3185	.3275	.3364	.3452	.3540	.3627	.3714
.4	.3800	.3885	.3969	.4053	.4136	.4219	.4301	.4382	.4462	.4542
.5	.4621	.4700	.4777	.4854	.4930	.5005	.5080	.5154	.5227	.5299
.6	.5370	.5441	.5511	.5581	.5649	.5717	.5784	.5850	.5915	.5980
.7	.6044	.6107	.6169	.6231	.6291	.6352	.6411	.6469	.6527	.6584
.8	.6640	.6696	.6751	.6805	.6858	.6911	.6963	.7014	.7064	.7114
.9	.7163	.7211	.7259	.7306	.7352	.7398	.7443	.7487	.7531	.7574
1.0	.7616	.7658	.7699	.7739	.7779	.7818	.7857	.7895	.7932	.7969
1.1	.8005	.8041	.8076	.8110	.8144	.8178	.8210	.8243	.8275	.8306
1.2	.8337	.8367	.8397	.8426	.8455	.8483	.8511	.8538	.8565	.8591
1.3	.8617	.8643	.8668	.8693	.8717	.8741	.8764	.8787	.8810	.8832
1.4	.8854	.8875	.8896	.8917	.8937	.8957	.8977	.8996	.9015	.9033
1.5	.9052	.9069	.9087	.9104	.9121	.9138	.9154	.9170	.9186	.9202
1.6	.9217	.9232	.9246	.9261	.9275	.9289	.9302	.9316	.9329	.9342
1.7	.9354	.9367	.9379	.9391	.9402	.9414	.9425	.9436	.9447	.9458
1.8	.9468	.9478	.9498	.9488	.9508	.9518	.9527	.9536	.9545	.9554
1.9	.9562	.9571	.9579	.9587	.9595	.9603	.9611	.9619	.9626	.9633
2.0	.9640	.9647	.9654	.9661	.9668	.9674	.9680	.9687	.9693	.9699
2.1	.9705	.9710	.9716	.9722	.9727	.9732	.9738	.9743	.9748	.9753
2.2	.9757	.9762	.9767	.9771	.9776	.9780	.9785	.9789	.9793	.9797
2.3	.9801	.9805	.9809	.9812	.9816	.9820	.9823	.9827	.9830	.9834
2.4	.9837	.9840	.9843	.9846	.9849	.9852	.9855	.9858	.9861	.9863
2.5	.9866	.9869	.9871	.9874	.9876	.9879	.9881	.9884	.9886	.9888
2.6	.9890	.9892	.9895	.9897	.9899	.9901	.9903	.9905	.9906	.9908
2.7	.9910	.9912	.9914	.9915	.9917	.9919	.9920	.9922	.9923	.9925
2.8	.9926	.9928	.9929	.9931	.9932	.9933	.9935	.9936	.9937	.9938
2.9	.9940	.9941	.9942	.9943	.9944	.9945	.9946	.9947	.9949	.9950
3.0	.9951									
4.0	.9993									
5.0	.9999									

* The figures in the body of the table are values of r corresponding to z'-values read from the scales on the left and top of the table.

First Six Powers of the Natural Numbers from 1 to 50

n	n^2	n^3	n^4	n^5	n^6	n
1	1	1	1	1	1	1
2	4	8	16	32	64	2
3	9	27	81	243	729	3
4	16	64	256	1 024	4 096	4
5	25	125	625	3 125	15 625	5
6	36	216	1 296	7 776	46 656	6
7	49	343	2 401	16 807	117 649	7
8	64	512	4 096	32 768	262 144	8
9	81	729	6 561	59 049	531 441	9
10	100	1 000	10 000	100 000	1 000 000	10
11	121	1 331	14 641	161 051	1 771 561	11
12	144	1 728	20 736	248 832	2 985 984	12
13	169	2 197	28 561	371 293	4 826 809	13
14	196	2 744	38 416	537 824	7 529 536	14
15	225	3 375	50 625	759 375	11 390 625	15
16	256	4 096	65 536	1 048 576	16 777 216	16
17	289	4 913	83 521	1 419 857	24 137 569	17
18	324	5 832	104 976	1 889 568	34 012 224	18
19	361	6 859	130 321	2 476 099	47 045 881	19
20	400	8 000	160 000	3 200 000	64 000 000	20
21	441	9 261	194 481	4 084 101	85 766 121	21
22	484	10 648	234 256	5 153 632	113 379 904	22
23	529	12 167	279 841	6 436 343	148 035 889	23
24	576	13 824	331 776	7 962 624	191 102 976	24
25	625	15 625	390 625	9 765 625	244 140 625	25
26	676	17 576	456 976	11 881 376	308 915 776	26
27	729	19 683	531 441	14 348 907	387 420 489	27
28	784	21 952	614 656	17 210 368	481 890 304	28
29	841	24 389	707 281	20 511 149	594 823 321	29
30	900	27 000	810 000	24 300 000	729 000 000	30
31	961	29 791	923 521	28 629 151	887 503 681	31
32	1 024	32 768	1 048 576	33 554 432	1 073 741 824	32
33	1 089	35 937	1 185 921	39 135 393	1 291 467 969	33
34	1 156	39 304	1 336 336	45 435 424	1 544 804 416	34
35	1 225	42 875	1 500 625	52 521 875	1 838 265 625	35
36	1 296	46 656	1 679 616	60 466 176	2 176 782 336	36
37	1 369	50 653	1 874 161	69 343 957	2 565 726 409	37
38	1 444	54 872	2 085 136	79 235 168	3 010 936 384	38
39	1 521	59 319	2 313 441	90 224 199	3 518 743 761	39
40	1 600	64 000	2 560 000	102 400 000	4 096 000 000	40
41	1 681	68 921	2 825 761	115 856 201	4 750 104 241	41
42	1 764	74 088	3 111 696	130 691 232	5 489 031 744	42
43	1 849	79 507	3 418 801	147 008 443	6 321 363 049	43
44	1 936	85 184	3 748 096	164 916 224	7 256 313 856	44
45	2 025	91 125	4 100 625	184 528 125	8 303 765 625	45
46	2 116	97 336	4 477 456	205 962 976	9 474 296 896	46
47	2 209	103 823	4 879 681	229 345 007	10 779 215 329	47
48	2 304	110 592	5 308 416	254 803 968	12 230 590 464	48
49	2 401	117 649	5 764 801	282 475 249	13 841 287 201	49
50	2 500	125 000	6 250 000	312 500 000	15 625 000 000	50

Sums of the First Six Powers of the Natural Numbers from 1 to 50

n	$\Sigma(n)$	$\Sigma(n^2)$	$\Sigma(n^3)$	$\Sigma(n^4)$	$\Sigma(n^5)$	$\Sigma(n^6)$
1	1	1	1	1	1	1
2	3	5	9	17	33	65
3	6	14	36	98	276	794
4	10	30	100	354	1 300	4 890
5	15	55	225	979	4 425	20 515
6	21	91	441	2 275	12 201	67 171
7	28	140	784	4 676	29 008	184 820
8	36	204	1 296	8 772	61 776	446 964
9	45	285	2 025	15 333	120 825	978 405
10	55	385	3 025	25 333	220 825	1 978 405
11	66	506	4 356	39 974	381 876	3 749 966
12	78	650	6 084	60 710	630 708	6 735 950
13	91	819	8 281	89 271	1 002 001	11 562 759
14	105	1 015	11 025	127 687	1 539 825	19 092 295
15	120	1 240	14 400	178 312	2 299 200	30 482 920
16	136	1 496	18 496	234 848	3 347 776	47 260 136
17	153	1 785	23 409	327 369	4 767 633	71 397 705
18	171	2 109	29 241	432 345	6 657 201	105 409 929
19	190	2 470	36 100	562 666	9 133 300	152 455 810
20	210	2 870	44 100	722 666	12 333 300	216 455 810
21	231	3 311	53 361	917 147	16 417 401	302 221 931
22	253	3 795	64 009	1 151 403	21 571 033	415 601 835
23	276	4 324	76 176	1 431 244	28 007 376	563 637 724
24	300	4 900	90 000	1 763 020	35 970 000	754 740 700
25	325	5 525	105 625	2 153 645	45 735 625	998 881 325
26	351	6 201	123 201	2 610 621	57 617 001	1 307 797 101
27	378	6 930	142 884	3 142 062	71 965 908	1 695 217 590
28	406	7 714	164 836	3 756 718	89 176 276	2 177 107 894
29	435	8 555	189 225	4 463 999	109 687 425	2 771 931 215
30	465	9 455	216 225	5 273 999	133 987 425	3 500 931 215
31	496	10 416	246 016	6 197 520	162 616 576	4 388 434 896
32	528	11 440	278 784	7 246 096	196 171 008	5 462 176 720
33	561	12 529	314 721	8 432 017	235 306 401	6 753 644 689
34	595	13 685	354 025	9 768 353	280 741 825	8 298 449 105
35	630	14 910	396 900	11 268 978	333 263 700	10 136 714 730
36	666	16 206	443 556	12 948 594	393 729 876	12 313 497 066
37	703	17 575	494 209	14 822 755	463 073 833	14 879 223 475
38	741	19 019	549 081	16 907 891	542 309 001	17 890 159 859
39	780	20 540	608 400	19 221 332	632 533 200	21 408 903 620
40	820	22 140	672 400	21 781 332	734 933 200	25 504 903 620
41	861	23 821	741 321	24 607 093	850 789 401	30 255 007 861
42	903	25 585	815 409	27 718 789	981 480 633	35 744 039 605
43	946	27 434	894 916	31 137 590	1 128 489 076	42 065 402 654
44	990	29 370	980 100	34 885 686	1 293 405 300	49 321 716 510
45	1 035	31 395	1 071 225	38 986 311	1 477 933 425	57 625 482 135
46	1 081	33 511	1 168 561	43 463 767	1 683 896 401	67 099 779 031
47	1 128	35 720	1 272 384	48 343 448	1 913 241 408	77 878 994 360
48	1 176	38 024	1 382 976	53 651 864	2 168 045 376	90 109 584 824
49	1 225	40 425	1 500 625	59 416 665	2 450 520 625	103 950 872 025
50	1 275	42 925	1 625 625	65 666 665	2 763 020 625	119 575 872 025

Squares, Square Roots, and Reciprocals of the
Natural Numbers from 1 to 1,000

n	n^2	$n^{1/2}$	$1/n$
1	1	1.000 0000	1.000 000 000
2	4	1.414 2136	0.500 000 000
3	9	1.732 0508	.333 333 333
4	16	2.000 0000	.250 000 000
5	25	2.236 0680	.200 000 000
6	36	2.449 4897	.166 666 667
7	49	2.645 7513	.142 857 143
8	64	2.828 4271	.125 000 000
9	81	3.000 0000	.111 111 111
10	1 00	3.162 2777	.100 000 000
11	1 21	3.316 6248	.090 909 091
12	1 44	3.464 1016	.083 333 333
13	1 69	3.605 5513	.076 923 077
14	1 96	3.741 6574	.071 428 571
15	2 25	3.872 9833	.066 666 667
16	2 56	4.000 0000	.062 500 000
17	2 89	4.123 1056	.058 823 529
18	3 24	4.242 6407	.055 555 556
19	3 61	4.358 8989	.052 631 579
20	4 00	4.472 1360	.050 000 000
21	4 41	4.582 5757	.047 619 048
22	4 84	4.690 4158	.045 454 545
23	5 29	4.795 8315	.043 478 261
24	5 76	4.898 9795	.041 666 667
25	6 25	5.000 0000	.040 000 000
26	6 76	5.099 0195	.038 461 538
27	7 29	5.196 1524	.037 037 037
28	7 84	5.291 5026	.035 714 286
29	8 41	5.385 1648	.034 482 759
30	9 00	5.477 2256	.033 333 333
31	9 61	5.567 7644	.032 258 065
32	10 24	5.656 8542	.031 250 000
33	10 89	5.744 5626	.030 303 030
34	11 56	5.830 9519	.029 411 765
35	12 25	5.916 0798	.028 571 429
36	12 96	6.000 0000	.027 777 778
37	13 69	6.082 7625	.027 027 027
38	14 44	6.164 4140	.026 315 789
39	15 21	6.244 9980	.025 641 026
40	16 00	6.324 5553	.025 000 000
41	16 81	6.403 1242	.024 390 244
42	17 64	6.480 7407	.023 809 524
43	18 49	6.557 4385	.023 255 814
44	19 36	6.633 2496	.022 727 273
45	20 25	6.708 2039	.022 222 222
46	21 16	6.782 3300	.021 739 130
47	22 09	6.855 6546	.021 276 596
48	23 04	6.928 2032	.020 833 333
49	24 01	7.000 0000	.020 408 163
50	25 00	7.071 0678	.020 000 000

Squares, Square Roots, and Reciprocals of the
Natural Numbers from 1 to 1,000

n	n^2	$n^{1/2}$	$1/n$
51	26 01	7.141 4284	.019 607 843
52	27 04	7.211 1026	.019 230 769
53	28 09	7.280 1099	.018 867 925
54	29 16	7.348 4692	.018 518 519
55	30 25	7.416 1985	.018 181 818
56	31 36	7.483 3148	.017 857 143
57	32 49	7.549 8344	.017 543 860
58	33 64	7.615 7731	.017 241 379
59	34 81	7.681 1457	.016 949 153
60	36 00	7.745 9667	.016 666 667
61	37 21	7.810 2497	.016 393 443
62	38 44	7.874 0079	.016 129 032
63	39 69	7.937 2539	.015 873 016
64	40 96	8.000 0000	.015 625 000
65	42 25	8.062 2577	.015 384 615
66	43 56	8.124 0384	.015 151 515
67	44 89	8.185 3528	.014 925 373
68	46 24	8.246 2113	.014 705 882
69	47 61	8.306 6239	.014 492 754
70	49 00	8.366 6003	.014 285 714
71	50 41	8.426 1498	.014 084 507
72	51 84	8.485 2814	.013 888 889
73	53 29	8.544 0037	.013 698 630
74	54 76	8.602 3253	.013 513 514
75	56 25	8.660 2540	.013 333 333
76	57 76	8.717 7979	.013 157 895
77	59 29	8.774 9644	.012 987 013
78	60 84	8.831 7609	.012 820 513
79	62 41	8.888 1944	.012 658 228
80	64 00	8.944 2719	.012 500 000
81	65 61	9.000 0000	.012 345 679
82	67 24	9.055 3851	.012 195 122
83	68 89	9.110 4336	.012 048 193
84	70 56	9.165 1514	.011 904 762
85	72 25	9.219 5445	.011 764 706
86	73 96	9.273 6185	.011 627 907
87	75 69	9.327 3791	.011 494 253
88	77 44	9.380 8315	.011 363 636
89	79 21	9.433 9811	.011 235 955
90	81 00	9.486 8330	.011 111 111
91	82 81	9.539 3920	.010 989 011
92	84 64	9.591 6630	.010 869 565
93	86 49	9.643 6508	.010 752 688
94	88 36	9.695 3597	.010 638 298
95	90 25	9.746 7943	.010 526 316
96	92 16	9.797 9590	.010 416 667
97	94 09	9.848 8578	.010 309 278
98	96 04	9.899 4949	.010 204 082
99	98 01	9.949 8744	.010 101 010
100	1 00 00	10.000 0000	.010 000 000

Squares, Square Roots, and Reciprocals of the
Natural Numbers from 1 to 1,000

n	n^2	$n^{1/2}$	$1/n$
101	1 02 01	10.049 8756	.009 900 990
102	1 04 04	10.099 5049	.009 803 922
103	1 06 09	10.148 8916	.009 708 738
104	1 08 16	10.198 0390	.009 615 385
105	1 10 25	10.246 9508	.009 523 810
106	1 12 36	10.295 6301	.009 433 962
107	1 14 49	10.344 0804	.009 345 794
108	1 16 64	10.392 3048	.009 259 259
109	1 18 81	10.440 3065	.009 174 312
110	1 21 00	10.488 0885	.009 090 909
111	1 23 21	10.535 6538	.009 009 009
112	1 25 44	10.583 0052	.008 928 571
113	1 27 69	10.630 1458	.008 849 558
114	1 29 96	10.677 0783	.008 771 930
115	1 32 25	10.723 8053	.008 695 652
116	1 34 56	10.770 3296	.008 620 690
117	1 36 89	10.816 6538	.008 547 009
118	1 39 24	10.862 7805	.008 474 576
119	1 41 61	10.908 7121	.008 403 361
120	1 44 00	10.954 4512	.008 333 333
121	1 46 41	11.000 0000	.008 264 463
122	1 48 84	11.045 3610	.008 196 721
123	1 51 29	11.090 5365	.008 130 081
124	1 53 76	11.135 5287	.008 064 516
125	1 56 25	11.180 3399	.008 000 000
126	1 58 76	11.224 9722	.007 936 508
127	1 61 29	11.269 4277	.007 874 016
128	1 63 84	11.313 7085	.007 812 500
129	1 66 41	11.357 8167	.007 751 938
130	1 69 00	11.401 7543	.007 692 308
131	1 71 61	11.445 5231	.007 633 588
132	1 74 24	11.489 1253	.007 575 758
133	1 76 89	11.532 5626	.007 518 797
134	1 79 56	11.575 8369	.007 462 687
135	1 82 25	11.618 9500	.007 407 407
136	1 84 96	11.661 9038	.007 352 941
137	1 87 69	11.704 6999	.007 299 270
138	1 90 44	11.747 3401	.007 246 377
139	1 93 21	11.789 8261	.007 194 245
140	1 96 00	11.832 1596	.007 142 857
141	1 98 81	11.874 3422	.007 092 199
142	2 01 64	11.916 3753	.007 042 254
143	2 04 49	11.958 2607	.006 993 007
144	2 07 36	12.000 0000	.006 944 444
145	2 10 25	12.041 5946	.006 896 552
146	2 13 16	12.083 0460	.006 849 315
147	2 16 09	12.124 3557	.006 802 721
148	2 19 04	12.165 5251	.006 756 757
149	2 22 01	12.206 5556	.006 711 409
150	2 25 00	12.247 4487	.006 666 667

Squares, Square Roots, and Reciprocals of the
Natural Numbers from 1 to 1,000

n	n^2	$n^{1/2}$	$1/n$
151	2 28 01	12.288 2057	.006 622 517
152	2 31 04	12.328 8280	.006 578 947
153	2 34 09	12.369 3169	.006 535 948
154	2 37 16	12.409 6736	.006 493 506
155	2 40 25	12.449 8996	.006 451 613
156	2 43 36	12.489 9960	.006 410 256
157	2 46 49	12.529 9641	.006 369 427
158	2 49 64	12.569 8051	.006 329 114
159	2 52 81	12.609 5202	.006 289 308
160	2 56 00	12.649 1106	.006 250 000
161	2 59 21	12.688 5775	.006 211 180
162	2 62 44	12.727 9221	.006 172 840
163	2 65 69	12.767 1453	.006 134 969
164	2 68 96	12.806 2485	.006 097 561
165	2 72 25	12.845 2326	.006 060 606
166	2 75 56	12.884 0987	.006 024 096
167	2 78 89	12.922 8480	.005 988 024
168	2 82 24	12.961 4814	.005 952 381
169	2 85 61	13.000 0000	.005 917 160
170	2 89 00	13.038 4048	.005 882 353
171	2 92 41	13.076 6968	.005 847 953
172	2 95 84	13.114 8770	.005 813 953
173	2 99 29	13.152 9464	.005 780 347
174	3 02 76	13.190 9060	.005 747 126
175	3 06 25	13.228 7566	.005 714 286
176	3 09 76	13.266 4992	.005 681 818
177	3 13 29	13.304 1347	.005 649 718
178	3 16 84	13.341 6641	.005 617 978
179	3 20 41	13.379 0882	.005 586 592
180	3 24 00	13.416 4079	.005 555 556
181	3 27 61	13.453 6240	.005 524 862
182	3 31 24	13.490 7376	.005 494 505
183	3 34 89	13.527 7493	.005 464 481
184	3 38 56	13.564 6600	.005 434 783
185	3 42 25	13.601 4705	.005 405 405
186	3 45 96	13.638 1817	.005 376 344
187	3 49 69	13.674 7943	.005 347 594
188	3 53 44	13.711 3092	.005 319 149
189	3 57 21	13.747 7271	.005 291 005
190	3 61 00	13.784 0488	.005 263 158
191	3 64 81	13.820 2750	.005 235 602
192	3 68 64	13.856 4065	.005 208 333
193	3 72 49	13.892 4440	.005 181 347
194	3 76 36	13.928 3883	.005 154 639
195	3 80 25	13.964 2400	.005 128 205
196	3 84 16	14.000 0000	.005 102 041
197	3 88 09	14.035 6688	.005 076 142
198	3 92 04	14.071 2473	.005 050 505
199	3 96 01	14.106 7360	.005 025 126
200	4 00 00	14.142 1356	.005 000 000

Squares, Square Roots, and Reciprocals of the
Natural Numbers from 1 to 1,000

n	n^2	$n^{1/2}$	$1/n$
201	4 04 01	14.177 4469	.004 975 124
202	4 08 04	14.212 6704	.004 950 495
203	4 12 09	14.247 8068	.004 926 108
204	4 16 16	14.282 8569	.004 901 961
205	4 20 25	14.317 8211	.004 878 049
206	4 24 36	14.352 7001	.004 854 369
207	4 28 49	14.387 4946	.004 830 918
208	4 32 64	14.422 2051	.004 807 692
209	4 36 81	14.456 8323	.004 784 689
210	4 41 00	14.491 3767	.004 761 905
211	4 45 21	14.525 8390	.004 739 336
212	4 49 44	14.560 2198	.004 716 981
213	4 53 69	14.594 5195	.004 694 836
214	4 57 96	14.628 7388	.004 672 897
215	4 62 25	14.662 8783	.004 651 163
216	4 66 56	14.696 9385	.004 629 630
217	4 70 89	14.730 9199	.004 608 295
218	4 75 24	14.764 8231	.004 587 156
219	4 79 61	14.798 6486	004 566 210
220	4 84 00	14.832 3970	.004 545 455
221	4 88 41	14.866 0687	.004 524 887
222	4 92 84	14.899 6644	.004 504 505
223	4 97 29	14.933 1845	.004 484 305
224	5 01 76	14.966 6295	.004 464 286
225	5 06 25	15.000 0000	.004 444 444
226	5 10 76	15.033 2964	.004 424 779
227	5 15 29	15.066 5192	.004 405 286
228	5 19 84	15.099 6689	.004 385 965
229	5 24 41	15.132 7460	.004 366 812
230	5 29 00	15.165 7509	.004 347 826
231	5 33 61	15.198 6842	.004 329 004
232	5 38 24	15.231 5462	.004 310 345
233	5 42 89	15.264 3375	.004 291 845
234	5 47 56	15.297 0585	.004 273 504
235	5 52 25	15.329 7097	.004 255 319
236	5 56 96	15.362 2915	.004 237 288
237	5 61 69	15.394 8043	.004 219 409
238	5 66 44	15.427 2486	.004 201 681
239	5 71 21	15.459 6248	.004 184 100
240	5 76 00	15.491 9334	.004 166 667
241	5 80 81	15.524 1747	.004 149 378
242	5 85 64	15.556 3492	.004 132 231
243	5 90 49	15.588 4573	.004 115 226
244	5 95 36	15.620 4994	.004 098 361
245	6 00 25	15.652 4758	.004 081 633
246	6 05 16	15.684 3871	.004 065 041
247	6 10 09	15.716 2336	.004 048 583
248	6 15 04	15.748 0157	.004 032 258
249	6 20 01	15.779 7338	.004 016 064
250	6 25 00	15.811 3883	.004 000 000

Squares, Square Roots, and Reciprocals of the
Natural Numbers from 1 to 1,000

n	n^2	$n^{1/2}$	$1/n$
251	6 30 01	15.842 9795	.003 984 064
252	6 35 04	15.874 5079	.003 968 254
253	6 40 09	15.905 9737	.003 952 569
254	6 45 16	15.937 3775	.003 937 008
255	6 50 25	15.968 7194	.003 921 569
256	6 55 36	16.000 0000	.003 906 250
257	6 60 49	16.031 2195	.003 891 051
258	6 65 64	16.062 3784	.003 875 969
259	6 70 81	16.093 4769	.003 861 004
260	6 76 00	16.124 5155	.003 846 154
261	6 81 21	16.155 4944	.003 831 418
262	6 86 44	16.186 4141	.003 816 794
263	6 91 69	16.217 2747	.003 802 281
264	6 96 96	16.248 0768	.003 787 879
265	7 02 25	16.278 8206	.003 773 585
266	7 07 56	16.309 5064	.003 759 398
267	7 12 89	16.340 1346	.003 745 318
268	7 18 24	16.370 7055	.003 731 343
269	7 23 61	16.401 2195	.003 717 472
270	7 29 00	16.431 6767	.003 703 704
271	7 34 41	16.462 0776	.003 690 037
272	7 39 84	16.492 4225	.003 676 471
273	7 45 29	16.522 7116	.003 663 004
274	7 50 76	16.552 9454	.003 649 635
275	7 56 25	16.583 1240	.003 636 364
276	7 61 76	16.613 2477	.003 623 188
277	7 67 29	16.643 3170	.003 610 108
278	7 72 84	16.673 3320	.003 597 122
279	7 78 41	16.703 2931	.003 584 229
280	7 84 00	16.733 2005	.003 571 429
281	7 89 61	16.763 0546	.003 558 719
282	7 95 24	16.792 8556	.003 546 099
283	8 00 89	16.822 6038	.003 533 569
284	8 06 56	16.852 2995	.003 521 127
285	8 12 25	16.881 9430	.003 508 772
286	8 17 96	16.911 5345	.003 496 503
287	8 23 69	16.941 0743	.003 484 321
288	8 29 44	16.970 5627	.003 472 222
289	8 35 21	17.000 0000	.003 460 208
290	8 41 00	17.029 3864	.003 448 276
291	8 46 81	17.058 7221	.003 436 426
292	8 52 64	17.088 0075	.003 424 658
293	8 58 49	17.117 2428	.003 412 969
294	8 64 36	17.146 4282	.003 401 361
295	8 70 25	17.175 5640	.003 389 831
296	8 76 16	17.204 6505	.003 378 378
297	8 82 09	17.233 6879	.003 367 003
298	8 88 04	17.262 6765	.003 355 705
299	8 94 01	17.291 6165	.003 344 482
300	9 00 00	17.320 5081	.003 333 333

Squares, Square Roots, and Reciprocals of the
Natural Numbers from 1 to 1,000

n	n^2	$n^{1/2}$	$1/n$
301	9 06 01	17.349 3516	.003 322 259
302	9 12 04	17.378 1472	.003 311 258
303	9 18 09	17.406 8952	.003 300 330
304	9 24 16	17.435 5958	.003 289 474
305	9 30 25	17.464 2492	.003 278 689
306	9 36 36	17.492 8557	.003 267 974
307	9 42 49	17.521 4155	.003 257 329
308	9 48 64	17.549 9288	.003 246 753
309	9 54 81	17.578 3958	.003 236 246
310	9 61 00	17.606 8169	.003 225 806
311	9 67 21	17.635 1921	.003 215 434
312	9 73 44	17.663 5217	.003 205 128
313	9 79 69	17.691 8060	.003 194 888
314	9 85 96	17.720 0451	.003 184 713
315	9 92 25	17.748 2393	.003 174 603
316	9 98 56	17.776 3888	.003 164 557
317	10 04 89	17.804 4938	.003 154 574
318	10 11 24	17.832 5545	.003 144 654
319	10 17 61	17.860 5711	.003 134 796
320	10 24 00	17.888 5438	.003 125 000
321	10 30 41	17.916 4729	.003 115 265
322	10 36 84	17.944 3584	.003 105 590
323	10 43 29	17.972 2008	.003 095 975
324	10 49 76	18.000 0000	.003 086 420
325	10 56 25	18.027 7564	.003 076 923
326	10 62 76	18.055 4701	.003 067 485
327	10 69 29	18.083 1413	.003 058 104
328	10 75 84	18.110 7703	.003 048 780
329	10 82 41	18.138 3571	.003 039 514
330	10 89 00	18.165 9021	.003 030 303
331	10 95 61	18.193 4054	.003 021 148
332	11 02 24	18.220 8672	.003 012 048
333	11 08 89	18.248 2876	.003 003 003
334	11 15 56	18.275 6669	.002 994 012
335	11 22 25	18.303 0052	.002 985 075
336	11 28 96	18.330 3028	.002 976 190
337	11 35 69	18.357 5598	.002 967 359
338	11 42 44	18.384 7763	.002 958 580
339	11 49 21	18.411 9526	.002 949 853
340	11 56 00	18.439 0889	.002 941 176
341	11 62 81	18.466 1853	.002 932 551
342	11 69 64	18.493 2420	.002 923 977
343	11 76 49	18.520 2592	.002 915 452
344	11 83 36	18.547 2370	.002 906 977
345	11 90 25	18.574 1756	.002 898 551
346	11 97 16	18.601 0752	.002 890 173
347	12 04 09	18.627 9360	.002 881 844
348	12 11 04	18.654 7581	.002 873 563
349	12 18 01	18.681 5417	.002 865 330
350	12 25 00	18.708 2869	.002 857 143

Squares, Square Roots, and Reciprocals of the
Natural Numbers from 1 to 1,000

n	n^2	$n^{1/2}$	$1/n$
351	12 32 01	18.734 9940	.002 849 003
352	12 39 04	18.761 6630	.002 840 909
353	12 46 09	18.788 2942	.002 832 861
354	12 53 16	18.814 8877	.002 824 859
355	12 60 25	18.841 4437	.002 816 901
356	12 67 36	18.867 9623	.002 808 989
357	12 74 49	18.894 4436	.002 801 120
358	12 81 64	18.920 8879	.002 793 296
359	12 88 81	18.947 2953	.002 785 515
360	12 96 00	18.973 6660	.002 777 778
361	13 03 21	19.000 0000	.002 770 083
362	13 10 44	19.026 2976	.002 762 431
363	13 17 69	19.052 5589	.002 754 821
364	13 24 96	19.078 7840	.002 747 253
365	13 32 25	19.104 9732	.002 739 726
366	13 39 56	19.131 1265	.002 732 240
367	13 46 89	19.157 2441	.002 724 796
368	13 54 24	19.183 3261	.002 717 391
369	13 61 61	19.209 3727	.002 710 027
370	13 69 00	19.235 3841	.002 702 703
371	13 76 41	19.261 3603	.002 695 418
372	13 83 84	19.287 3015	.002 688 172
373	13 91 29	19.313 2079	.002 680 965
374	13 98 76	19.339 0796	.002 673 797
375	14 06 25	19.364 9167	.002 666 667
376	14 13 76	19.390 7194	.002 659 574
377	14 21 29	19.416 4878	.002 652 520
378	14 28 84	19.442 2221	.002 645 503
379	14 36 41	19.467 9223	.002 638 522
380	14 44 00	19.493 5887	.002 631 579
381	14 51 61	19.519 2213	.002 624 672
382	14 59 24	19.544 8203	.002 617 801
383	14 66 89	19.570 3858	.002 610 966
384	14 74 56	19.595 9179	.002 604 167
385	14 82 25	19.621 4169	.002 597 403
386	14 89 96	19.646 8827	.002 590 674
387	14 97 69	19.672 3156	.002 583 979
388	15 05 44	19.697 7156	.002 577 320
389	15 13 21	19.723 0829	.002 570 694
390	15 21 00	19.748 4177	.002 564 103
391	15 28 81	19.773 7199	.002 557 545
392	15 36 64	19.798 9899	.002 551 020
393	15 44 49	19.824 2276	.002 544 529
394	15 52 36	19.849 4332	.002 538 071
395	15 60 25	19.874 6069	.002 531 646
396	15 68 16	19.899 7487	.002 525 253
397	15 76 09	19.924 8588	.002 518 892
398	15 84 04	19.949 9373	.002 512 563
399	15 92 01	19.974 9844	.002 506 266
400	16 00 00	20.000 0000	.002 500 000

Squares, Square Roots, and Reciprocals of the
Natural Numbers from 1 to 1,000

n	n^2	$n^{1/2}$	$1/n$
401	16 08 01	20.024 9844	.002 493 766
402	16 16 04	20.049 9377	.002 487 562
403	16 24 09	20.074 8599	.002 481 390
404	16 32 16	20.099 7512	.002 475 248
405	16 40 25	20.124 6118	.002 469 136
406	16 48 36	20.149 4417	.002 463 054
407	16 56 49	20.174 2410	.002 457 002
408	16 64 64	20.199 0099	.002 450 980
409	16 72 81	20.223 7484	.002 444 988
410	16 81 00	20.248 4567	.002 439 024
411	16 89 21	20.273 1349	.002 433 090
412	16 97 44	20.297 7831	.002 427 184
413	17 05 69	20.322 4014	.002 421 308
414	17 13 96	20.346 9899	.002 415 459
415	17 22 25	20.371 5488	.002 409 639
416	17 30 56	20.396 0781	.002 403 846
417	17 38 89	20.420 5779	.002 398 082
418	17 47 24	20.445 0483	.002 392 344
419	17 55 61	20.469 4895	.002 386 635
420	17 64 00	20.493 9015	.002 380 952
421	17 72 41	20.518 2845	.002 375 297
422	17 80 84	20.542 6386	.002 369 668
423	17 89 29	20.566 9638	.002 364 066
424	17 97 76	20.591 2603	.002 358 491
425	18 06 25	20.615 5281	.002 352 941
426	18 14 76	20.639 7674	.002 347 418
427	18 23 29	20.663 9783	.002 341 920
428	18 31 84	20.688 1609	.002 336 449
429	18 40 41	20.712 3152	.002 331 002
430	18 49 00	20.736 4414	.002 325 581
431	18 57 61	20.760 5395	.002 320 186
432	18 66 24	20.784 6097	.002 314 815
433	18 74 89	20.808 6520	.002 309 469
434	18 83 56	20.832 6667	.002 304 147
435	18 92 25	20.856 6536	.002 298 851
436	19 00 96	20.880 6130	.002 293 578
437	19 09 69	20.904 5450	.002 288 330
438	19 18 44	20.928 4495	.002 283 105
439	19 27 21	20.952 3268	.002 277 904
440	19 36 00	20.976 1770	.002 272 727
441	19 44 81	21.000 0000	.002 267 574
442	19 53 64	21.023 7960	.002 262 443
443	19 62 49	21.047 5652	.002 257 336
444	19 71 36	21.071 3075	.002 252 252
445	19 80 25	21.095 0231	.002 247 191
446	19 89 16	21.118 7121	.002 242 152
447	19 98 09	21.142 3745	.002 237 136
448	20 07 04	21.166 0105	.002 232 143
449	20 16 01	21.189 6201	.002 227 171
450	20 25 00	21.213 2034	.002 222 222

Squares, Square Roots, and Reciprocals of the
Natural Numbers from 1 to 1,000

n	n^2	$n^{1/2}$	$1/n$
451	20 34 01	21.236 7606	.002 217 295
452	20 43 04	21.260 2916	.002 212 389
453	20 52 09	21.283 7967	.002 207 506
454	20 61 16	21.307 2758	.002 202 643
455	20 70 25	21.330 7290	.002 197 802
456	20 79 36	21.354 1565	.002 192 982
457	20 88 49	21.377 5583	.002 188 184
458	20 97 64	21.400 9346	.002 183 406
459	21 06 81	21.424 2853	.002 178 649
460	21 16 00	21.447 6106	.002 173 913
461	21 25 21	21.470 9106	.002 169 197
462	21 34 44	21.494 1853	.002 164 502
463	21 43 69	21.517 4348	.002 159 827
464	21 52 96	21.540 6592	.002 155 172
465	21 62 25	21.563 8587	.002 150 538
466	21 71 56	21.587 0331	.002 145 923
467	21 80 89	21.610 1828	.002 141 328
468	21 90 24	21.633 3077	.002 136 752
469	21 99 61	21.656 4078	.002 132 196
470	22 09 00	21.679 4834	.002 127 660
471	22 18 41	21.702 5344	.002 123 142
472	22 27 84	21.725 5610	.002 118 644
473	22 37 29	21.748 5632	.002 114 165
474	22 46 76	21.771 5411	.002 109 705
475	22 56 25	21.794 4947	.002 105 263
476	22 65 76	21.817 4242	.002 100 840
477	22 75 29	21.840 3297	.002 096 436
478	22 84 84	21.863 2111	.002 092 050
479	22 94 41	21.886 0686	.002 087 683
480	23 04 00	21.908 9023	.002 083 333
481	23 13 61	21.931 7122	.002 079 002
482	23 23 24	21.954 4984	.002 074 689
483	23 32 89	21.977 2610	.002 070 393
484	23 42 56	22.000 0000	.002 066 116
485	23 52 25	22.022 7155	.002 061 856
486	23 61 96	22.045 4077	.002 057 613
487	23 71 69	22.068 0765	.002 053 388
488	23 81 44	22.090 7220	.002 049 180
489	23 91 21	22.113 3444	.002 044 990
490	24 01 00	22.135 9436	.002 040 816
491	24 10 81	22.158 5198	.002 036 660
492	24 20 64	22.181 0730	.002 032 520
493	24 30 49	22.203 6033	.002 028 398
494	24 40 36	22.226 1108	.002 024 291
495	24 50 25	22.248 5955	.002 020 202
496	24 60 16	22.271 0575	.002 016 129
497	24 70 09	22.293 4968	.002 012 072
498	24 80 04	22.315 9136	.002 008 032
499	24 90 01	22.338 3079	.002 004 008
500	25 00 00	22.360 6798	.002 000 000

Squares, Square Roots, and Reciprocals of the Natural Numbers from 1 to 1,000

n	n^2	$n^{1/2}$	$1/n$
501	25 10 01	22.383 0293	.001 996 008
502	25 20 04	22.405 3565	.001 992 032
503	25 30 09	22.427 6615	.001 988 072
504	25 40 16	22.449 9443	.001 984 127
505	25 50 25	22.472 2051	.001 980 198
506	25 60 36	22.494 4438	.001 976 285
507	25 70 49	22.516 6605	.001 972 387
508	25 80 64	22.538 8553	.001 968 504
509	25 90 81	22.561 0283	.001 964 637
510	26 01 00	22.583 1796	.001 960 784
511	26 11 21	22.605 3091	.001 956 947
512	26 21 44	22.627 4170	.001 953 125
513	26 31 69	22.649 5033	.001 949 318
514	26 41 96	22.671 5681	.001 945 525
515	26 52 25	22.693 6114	.001 941 748
516	26 62 56	22.715 6334	.001 937 984
517	26 72 89	22.737 6340	.001 934 236
518	26 83 24	22.759 6134	.001 930 502
519	26 93 61	22.781 5715	.001 926 782
520	27 04 00	22.803 5085	.001 923 077
521	27 14 41	22.825 4244	.001 919 386
522	27 24 84	22.847 3193	.001 915 709
523	27 35 29	22.869 1933	.001 912 046
524	27 45 76	22.891 0463	.001 908 397
525	27 56 25	22.912 8785	.001 904 762
526	27 66 76	22.934 6899	.001 901 141
527	27 77 29	22.956 4806	.001 897 533
528	27 87 84	22.978 2506	.001 893 939
529	27 98 41	23.000 0000	.001 890 359
530	28 09 00	23.021 7289	.001 886 792
531	28 19 61	23.043 4372	.001 883 239
532	28 30 24	23.065 1252	.001 879 699
533	28 40 89	23.086 7928	.001 876 173
534	28 51 56	23.108 4400	.001 872 659
535	28 62 25	23.130 0670	.001 869 159
536	28 72 96	23.151 6738	.001 865 672
537	28 83 69	23.173 2605	.001 862 197
538	28 94 44	23.194 8270	.001 858 736
539	29 05 21	23.216 3735	.001 855 288
540	29 16 00	23.237 9001	.001 851 852
541	29 26 81	23.259 4067	.001 848 429
542	29 37 64	23.280 8935	.001 845 018
543	29 48 49	23.302 3604	.001 841 621
544	29 59 36	23.323 8076	.001 838 235
545	29 70 25	23.345 2351	.001 834 862
546	29 81 16	23.366 6429	.001 831 502
547	29 92 09	23.388 0311	.001 828 154
548	30 03 04	23.409 3998	.001 824 818
549	30 14 01	23.430 7490	.001 821 494
550	30 25 00	23.452 0788	.001 818 182

Squares, Square Roots, and Reciprocals of the Natural Numbers from 1 to 1,000

n	n^2	$n^{1/2}$	$1/n$
551	30 36 01	23.473 3892	.001 814 882
552	30 47 04	23.494 6802	.001 811 594
553	30 58 09	23.515 9520	.001 808 318
554	30 69 16	23.537 2046	.001 805 054
555	30 80 25	23.558 4380	.001 801 802
556	30 91 36	23.579 6522	.001 798 561
557	31 02 49	23.600 8474	.001 795 332
558	31 13 64	23.622 0236	.001 792 115
559	31 24 81	23.643 1808	.001 788 909
560	31 36 00	23.664 3191	.001 785 714
561	31 47 21	23.685 4386	.001 782 531
562	31 53 44	23.706 5392	.001 779 359
563	31 69 69	23.727 6210	.001 776 199
564	31 80 96	23.748 6842	.001 773 050
565	31 92 25	23.769 7286	.001 769 912
566	32 03 56	23.790 7545	.001 766 784
567	32 14 89	23.811 7618	.001 763 668
568	32 26 24	23.832 7506	.001 760 563
569	32 37 61	23.853 7209	.001 757 469
570	32 49 00	23.874 6728	.001 754 386
571	32 60 41	23.895 6063	.001 751 313
572	32 71 84	23.916 0304	.001 748 252
573	32 83 29	23.937 4184	.001 745 201
574	32 94 76	23.958 2971	.001 742 160
575	33 06 25	23.979 1576	.001 739 130
576	33 17 76	24.000 0000	.001 736 111
577	33 29 29	24.020 8243	.001 733 102
578	33 40 84	24.041 6306	.001 730 104
579	33 52 41	24.062 4188	.001 727 116
580	33 64 00	24.083 1891	.001 724 138
581	33 75 61	24.103 9416	.001 721 170
582	33 87 24	24.124 6762	.001 718 213
583	33 98 89	24.145 3929	.001 715 266
584	34 10 56	24.166 0919	.001 712 329
585	34 22 25	24.186 7732	.001 709 402
586	34 33 96	24.207 4369	.001 706 485
587	34 45 69	24.228 0829	.001 703 578
588	34 57 44	24.248 7113	.001 700 680
589	34 69 21	24.269 3222	.001 697 793
590	34 81 00	24.289 9156	.001 694 915
591	34 92 81	24.310 4916	.001 692 047
592	35 04 64	24.331 0501	.001 689 189
593	35 16 49	24.351 5913	.001 686 341
594	35 28 36	24.372 1152	.001 683 502
595	35 40 25	24.392 6218	.001 680 672
596	35 52 16	24.413 1112	.001 677 852
597	35 64 09	24.433 5834	.001 675 042
598	35 76 04	24.454 0385	.001 672 241
599	35 88 01	24.474 4765	.001 669 449
600	36 00 00	24.494 8974	.001 666 667

Squares, Square Roots, and Reciprocals of the
Natural Numbers from 1 to 1,000

n	n^2	$n^{1/2}$	$1/n$
601	36 12 01	24.515 3013	.001 663 894
602	36 24 04	24.535 6883	.001 661 130
603	36 36 09	24.556 0583	.001 658 375
604	36 48 16	24.576 4115	.001 655 629
605	36 60 25	24.596 7478	.001 652 893
606	36 72 36	24.617 0673	.001 650 165
607	36 84 49	24.637 3700	.001 647 446
608	36 96 64	24.657 6560	.001 644 737
609	37 08 81	24.677 9254	.001 642 036
610	37 21 00	24.698 1781	.001 639 344
611	37 33 21	24.718 4142	.001 636 661
612	37 45 44	24.738 6338	.001 633 987
613	37 57 69	24.758 8368	.001 631 321
614	37 69 96	24.779 0234	.001 628 664
615	37 82 25	24.799 1935	.001 626 016
616	37 94 56	24.819 3473	.001 623 377
617	38 06 89	24.839 4847	.001 620 746
618	38 19 24	24.859 6058	.001 618 123
619	38 31 61	24.879 7106	.001 615 509
620	38 44 00	24.899 7992	.001 612 903
621	38 56 41	24.919 8716	.001 610 306
622	38 68 84	24.939 9278	.001 607 717
623	38 81 29	24.959 9679	.001 605 136
624	38 93 76	24.979 9920	.001 602 564
625	39 06 25	25.000 0000	.001 600 000
626	39 18 76	25.019 9920	.001 597 444
627	39 31 29	25.039 9681	.001 594 896
628	39 43 84	25.059 9282	.001 592 357
629	39 56 41	25.079 8724	.001 589 825
630	39 69 00	25.099 8008	.001 587 302
631	39 81 61	25.119 7134	.001 584 786
632	39 94 24	25.139 6102	.001 582 278
633	40 06 89	25.159 4913	.001 579 779
634	40 19 56	25.179 3566	.001 577 287
635	40 32 25	25.199 2063	.001 574 803
636	40 44 96	25.219 0404	.001 572 327
637	40 57 69	25.238 8589	.001 569 859
638	40 70 44	25.258 6619	.001 567 398
639	40 83 21	25.278 4493	.001 564 945
640	40 96 00	25.298 2213	.001 562 500
641	41 08 81	25.317 9778	.001 560 062
642	41 21 64	25.337 7189	.001 557 632
643	41 34 49	25.357 4447	.001 555 210
644	41 47 36	25.377 1551	.001 552 795
645	41 60 25	25.396 8502	.001 550 388
646	41 73 16	25.416 5301	.001 547 988
647	41 86 09	25.436 1947	.001 545 595
648	41 99 04	25.455 8441	.001 543 210
649	42 12 01	25.475 4784	.001 540 832
650	42 25 00	25.495 0976	.001 538 462

APPENDIX TABLE VIII — *Continued*

Squares, Square Roots, and Reciprocals of the Natural Numbers from 1 to 1,000

n	n^2	$n^{1/2}$	$1/n$
651	42 38 01	25.514 7016	.001 536 098
652	42 51 04	25.534 2907	.001 533 742
653	42 64 09	25.553 8647	.001 531 394
654	42 77 16	25.573 4237	.001 529 052
655	42 90 25	25.592 9678	.001 526 718
656	43 03 36	25.612 4969	.001 524 390
657	43 16 49	25.632 0112	.001 522 070
658	43 29 64	25.651 5107	.001 519 757
659	43 42 81	25.670 9953	.001 517 451
660	43 56 00	25.690 4652	.001 515 152
661	43 69 21	25.709 9203	.001 512 859
662	43 82 44	25.729 3607	.001 510 574
663	43 95 69	25.748 7864	.001 508 296
664	44 08 96	25.768 1975	.001 506 024
665	44 22 25	25.787 5939	.001 503 759
666	44 35 56	25.806 9758	.001 501 502
667	44 48 89	25.826 3431	.001 499 250
668	44 62 24	25.845 6960	.001 497 006
669	44 75 61	25.865 0343	.001 494 768
670	44 89 00	25.884 3582	.001 492 537
671	45 02 41	25.903 6677	.001 490 313
672	45 15 84	25.922 9628	.001 488 095
673	45 29 29	25.942 2435	.001 485 884
674	45 42 76	25.961 5100	.001 483 680
675	45 56 25	25.980 7621	.001 481 481
676	45 69 76	26.000 0000	.001 479 290
677	45 83 29	26.019 2237	.001 477 105
678	45 96 84	26.038 4331	.001 474 926
679	46 10 41	26.057 6284	.001 472 754
680	46 24 00	26.076 8096	.001 470 588
681	46 37 61	26.095 9767	.001 468 429
682	46 51 24	26.115 1297	.001 466 276
683	46 64 89	26.134 2687	.001 464 129
684	46 78 56	26.153 3937	.001 461 988
685	46 92 25	26.172 5047	.001 459 854
686	47 05 96	26.191 6017	.001 457 726
687	47 19 69	26.210 6848	.001 455 604
688	47 33 44	26.229 7541	.001 453 488
689	47 47 21	26.248 8095	.001 451 379
690	47 61 00	26.267 8511	.001 449 275
691	47 74 81	26.286 8789	.001 447 178
692	47 88 64	26.305 8929	.001 445 087
693	48 02 49	26.324 8932	.001 443 001
694	48 16 36	26.343 8797	.001 440 922
695	48 30 25	26.362 8527	.001 438 849
696	48 44 16	26.381 8119	.001 436 782
697	48 58 09	26.400 7576	.001 434 720
698	48 72 04	26.419 6896	.001 432 665
699	48 86 01	26.438 6081	.001 430 615
700	49 00 00	26.457 5131	.001 428 571

Squares, Square Roots, and Reciprocals of the
Natural Numbers from 1 to 1,000

n	n^2	$n^{1/2}$	$1/n$
701	49 14 01	26.476 4046	.001 426 534
702	49 28 04	26.495 2826	.001 424 501
703	49 42 09	26.514 1472	.001 422 475
704	49 56 16	26.532 9983	.001 420 455
705	49 70 25	26.551 8361	.001 418 440
706	49 84 36	26.570 6605	.001 416 431
707	49 98 49	26.589 4716	.001 414 427
708	50 12 64	26.608 2694	.001 412 429
709	50 26 81	26.627 0539	.001 410 437
710	50 41 00	26.645 8252	.001 408 451
711	50 55 21	26.664 5833	.001 406 470
712	50 69 44	26.683 3281	.001 404 494
713	50 83 69	26.702 0598	.001 402 525
714	50 97 96	26.720 7784	.001 400 560
715	51 12 25	26.739 4839	.001 398 601
716	51 26 56	26.758 1763	.001 396 648
717	51 40 89	26.776 8557	.001 394 700
718	51 55 24	26.795 5220	.001 392 758
719	51 69 61	26.814 1754	.001 390 821
720	51 84 00	26.832 8157	.001 388 889
721	51 98 41	26.851 4432	.001 386 963
722	52 12 84	26.870 0577	.001 385 042
723	52 27 29	26.888 6593	.001 383 126
724	52 41 76	26.907 2481	.001 381 215
725	52 56 25	26.925 8240	.001 379 310
726	52 70 76	26.944 3872	.001 377 410
727	52 85 29	26.962 9375	.001 375 516
728	52 99 84	26.981 4751	.001 373 626
729	53 14 41	27.000 0000	.001 371 742
730	53 29 00	27.018 5122	.001 369 863
731	53 43 61	27.037 0117	.001 367 989
732	53 58 24	27.055 4985	.001 366 120
733	53 72 89	27.073 9727	.001 364 256
734	53 87 56	27.092 4344	.001 362 398
735	54 02 25	27.110 8834	.001 360 544
736	54 16 96	27.129 3199	.001 358 696
737	54 31 69	27.147 7439	.001 356 852
738	54 46 44	27.166 1554	.001 355 014
739	54 61 21	27.184 5544	.001 353 180
740	54 76 00	27.202 9410	.001 351 351
741	54 90 81	27.221 3152	.001 349 528
742	55 05 64	27.239 6769	.001 347 709
743	55 20 49	27.258 0263	.001 345 895
744	55 35 36	27.276 3634	.001 344 086
745	55 50 25	27.294 6881	.001 342 282
746	55 65 16	27.313 0006	.001 340 483
747	55 80 09	27.331 3007	.001 338 688
748	55 95 04	27.349 5887	.001 336 898
749	56 10 01	27.367 8644	.001 335 113
750	56 25 00	27.386 1279	.001 333 333

Squares, Square Roots, and Reciprocals of the
Natural Numbers from 1 to 1,000

n	n^2	$n^{1/2}$	$1/n$
751	56 40 01	27.404 3792	.001 331 558
752	56 55 04	27.422 6184	.001 329 787
753	56 70 09	27.440 8455	.001 328 021
754	56 85 16	27.459 0604	.001 326 260
755	57 00 25	27.477 2633	.001 324 503
756	57 15 36	27.495 4542	.001 322 751
757	57 30 49	27.513 6330	.001 321 004
758	57 45 64	27.531 7998	.001 319 261
759	57 60 81	27.549 9546	.001 317 523
760	57 76 00	27.568 0975	.001 315 789
761	57 91 21	27.586 2284	.001 314 060
762	58 06 44	27.604 3475	.001 312 336
763	58 21 69	27.622 4546	.001 310 616
764	58 36 96	27.640 5499	.001 308 901
765	58 52 25	27.658 6334	.001 307 190
766	58 67 56	27.676 7050	.001 305 483
767	58 82 89	27.694 7648	.001 303 781
768	58 98 24	27.712 8129	.001 302 083
769	59 13 61	27.730 8492	.001 300 390
770	59 29 00	27.748 8739	.001 298 701
771	59 44 41	27.766 8868	.001 297 017
772	59 59 84	27.784 8880	.001 295 337
773	59 75 29	27.802 8775	.001 293 661
774	59 90 76	27.820 8555	.001 291 990
775	60 06 25	27.838 8218	.001 290 323
776	60 21 76	27.856 7766	.001 288 660
777	60 37 29	27.874 7197	.001 287 001
778	60 52 84	27.892 6514	.001 285 347
779	60 68 41	27.910 5715	.001 283 697
780	60 84 00	27.928 4801	.001 282 051
781	60 99 61	27.946 3772	.001 280 410
782	61 15 24	27.964 2629	.001 278 772
783	61 30 89	27.982 1372	.001 277 139
784	61 46 56	28.000 0000	.001 275 510
785	61 62 25	28.017 8515	.001 273 885
786	61 77 96	28.035 6915	.001 272 265
787	61 93 69	28.053 5203	.001 270 648
788	62 09 44	28.071 3377	.001 269 036
789	62 25 21	28.089 1438	.001 267 427
790	62 41 00	28.106 9386	.001 265 823
791	62 56 81	28.124 7222	.001 264 223
792	62 72 64	28.142 4946	.001 262 626
793	62 88 49	28.160 2557	.001 261 034
794	63 04 36	28.178 0056	.001 259 446
795	63 20 25	28.195 7444	.001 257 862
796	63 36 16	28.213 4720	.001 256 281
797	63 52 09	28.231 1884	.001 254 705
798	63 68 04	28.248 8938	.001 253 133
799	63 84 01	28.266 5881	.001 251 564
800	64 00 00	28.284 2712	.001 250 000

Squares, Square Roots, and Reciprocals of the
Natural Numbers from 1 to 1,000

n	n^2	$n^{1/2}$	$1/n$
801	64 16 01	28.301 9434	.001 248 439
802	64 32 04	28.319 6045	.001 246 883
803	64 48 09	28.337 2546	.001 245 330
804	64 64 16	28.354 8938	.001 243 781
805	64 80 25	28.372 5219	.001 242 236
806	64 96 36	28.390 1391	.001 240 695
807	65 12 49	28.407 7454	.001 239 157
808	65 28 64	28.425 3408	.001 237 624
809	65 44 81	28.442 9253	.001 236 094
810	65 61 00	28.460 4989	.001 234 568
811	65 77 21	28.478 0617	.001 233 046
812	65 93 44	28.495 6137	.001 231 527
813	66 09 69	28.513 1549	.001 230 012
814	66 25 96	28.530 6852	.001 228 501
815	66 42 25	28.548 2048	.001 226 994
816	66 58 56	28.565 7137	.001 225 490
817	66 74 89	28.583 2119	.001 223 990
818	66 91 24	28.600 6993	.001 222 494
819	67 07 61	28.618 1760	.001 221 001
820	67 24 00	28.635 6421	.001 219 512
821	67 40 41	28.653 0976	.001 218 027
822	67 56 84	28.670 5424	.001 216 545
823	67 73 29	28.687 9766	.001 215 067
824	67 89 76	28.705 4002	.001 213 592
825	68 06 25	28.722 8132	.001 212 121
826	68 22 76	28.740 2157	.001 210 654
827	68 39 29	28.757 6077	.001 209 190
828	68 55 84	28.774 9891	.001 207 729
829	68 72 41	28.792 3601	.001 206 273
830	68 89 00	28.809 7206	.001 204 819
831	69 05 61	28.827 0706	.001 203 369
832	69 22 24	28.844 4102	.001 201 923
833	69 38 89	28.861 7394	.001 200 480
834	69 55 56	28.879 0582	.001 199 041
835	69 72 25	28.896 3666	.001 197 605
836	69 88 96	28.913 6646	.001 196 172
837	70 05 69	28.930 9523	.001 194 743
838	70 22 44	28.948 2297	.001 193 317
839	70 39 21	28.965 4967	.001 191 895
840	70 56 00	28.982 7535	.001 190 476
841	70 72 81	29.000 0000	.001 189 061
842	70 89 64	29.017 2363	.001 187 648
843	71 06 49	29.034 4623	.001 186 240
844	71 23 36	29.051 6781	.001 184 834
845	71 40 25	29.068 8837	.001 183 432
846	71 57 16	29.086 0791	.001 182 033
847	71 74 09	29.103 2644	.001 180 638
848	71 91 04	29.120 4396	.001 179 245
849	72 08 01	29.137 6046	.001 177 856
850	72 25 00	29.154 7595	.001 176 471

Squares, Square Roots, and Reciprocals of the Natural Numbers from 1 to 1,000

n	n^2	$n^{1/2}$	$1/n$
851	72 42 01	29.171 9043	.001 175 088
852	72 59 04	29.189 0390	.001 173 709
853	72 76 09	29.206 1637	.001 172 333
854	72 93 16	29.223 2784	.001 170 960
855	73 10 25	29.240 3830	.001 169 591
856	73 27 36	29.257 4777	.001 168 224
857	73 44 49	29.274 5623	.001 166 861
858	73 61 64	29.291 6370	.001 165 501
859	73 78 81	29.308 7018	.001 164 144
860	73 96 00	29.325 7566	.001 162 791
861	74 13 21	29.342 8015	.001 161 440
862	74 30 44	29.359 8365	.001 160 093
863	74 47 69	29.376 8616	.001 158 749
864	74 64 96	29.393 8769	.001 157 407
865	74 82 25	29.410 8823	.001 156 069
866	74 99 56	29.427 8779	.001 154 734
867	75 16 89	29.444 8637	.001 153 403
868	75 34 24	29.461 8397	.001 152 074
869	75 51 61	29.478 8059	.001 150 748
870	75 69 00	29.495 7624	.001 149 425
871	75 86 41	29.512 7091	.001 148 106
872	76 03 84	29.529 6461	.001 146 789
873	76 21 29	29.546 5734	.001 145 475
874	76 38 76	29.563 4910	.001 144 165
875	76 56 25	29.580 3989	.001 142 857
876	76 73 76	29.597 2972	.001 141 553
877	76 91 29	29.614 1858	.001 140 251
878	77 08 84	29.631 0648	.001 138 952
879	77 26 41	29.647 9342	.001 137 656
880	77 44 00	29.664 7939	.001 136 364
881	77 61 61	29.681 6442	.001 135 074
882	77 79 24	29.698 4848	.001 133 787
883	77 96 89	29.715 3159	.001 132 503
884	78 14 56	29.732 1375	.001 131 222
885	78 32 25	29.748 9496	.001 129 944
886	78 49 96	29.765 7521	.001 128 668
887	78 67 69	29.782 5452	.001 127 396
888	78 85 44	29.799 3289	.001 126 126
889	79 03 21	29.816 1030	.001 124 859
890	79 21 00	29.832 8678	.001 123 596
891	79 38 81	29.849 6231	.001 122 334
892	79 56 64	29.866 3690	.001 121 076
893	79 74 49	29.883 1056	.001 119 821
894	79 92 36	29.899 8328	.001 118 568
895	80 10 25	29.916 5506	.001 117 318
896	80 28 16	29.932 2591	.001 116 071
897	80 46 09	29.949 9583	.001 114 827
898	80 64 04	29.966 6481	.001 113 586
899	80 82 01	29.983 3287	.001 112 347
900	81 00 00	30.000 0000	.001 111 111

Squares, Square Roots, and Reciprocals of the
Natural Numbers from 1 to 1,000

n	n^2	$n^{1/2}$	$1/n$
901	81 18 01	30.016 6620	.001 109 878
902	81 36 04	30.033 3148	.001 108 647
903	81 54 09	30.049 9584	.001 107 420
904	81 72 16	30.066 5928	.001 106 195
905	81 90 25	30.083 2179	.001 104 972
906	82 08 36	30.099 8339	.001 103 753
907	82 26 49	30.116 4407	.001 102 536
908	82 44 64	30.133 0383	.001 101 322
909	82 62 81	30.149 6269	.001 100 110
910	82 81 00	30.166 2063	.001 098 901
911	82 99 21	30.182 7765	.001 097 695
912	83 17 44	30.199 3377	.001 096 491
913	83 35 69	30.215 8899	.001 095 290
914	83 53 96	30.232 4329	.001 094 092
915	83 72 25	30.248 9669	.001 092 896
916	83 90 56	30.265 4919	.001 091 703
917	84 08 89	30.282 0079	.001 090 513
918	84 27 24	30.298 5148	.001 089 325
919	84 45 61	30.315 0128	.001 088 139
920	84 64 00	30.331 5018	.001 086 957
921	84 82 41	30.347 9818	.001 085 776
922	85 00 84	30.364 4529	.001 084 599
923	85 19 29	30.380 9151	.001 083 424
924	85 37 76	30.397 3683	.001 082 251
925	85 56 25	30.413 8127	.001 081 081
926	85 74 76	30.430 2481	.001 079 914
927	85 93 29	30.446 6747	.001 078 749
928	86 11 84	30.463 0924	.001 077 586
929	86 30 41	30.479 5013	.001 076 426
930	86 49 00	30.495 9014	.001 075 269
931	86 67 61	30.512 2926	.001 074 114
932	86 86 24	30.528 6750	.001 072 961
933	87 04 89	30.545 0487	.001 071 811
934	87 23 56	30.561 4136	.001 070 664
935	87 42 25	30.577 7697	.001 069 519
936	87 60 96	30.594 1171	.001 068 376
937	87 79 69	30.610 4557	.001 067 236
938	87 98 44	30.626 7857	.001 066 098
939	88 17 21	30.643 1069	.001 064 963
940	88 36 00	30.659 4194	.001 063 830
941	88 54 81	30.675 7233	.001 062 699
942	88 73 64	30.692 0185	.001 061 571
943	88 92 49	30.708 3051	.001 060 445
944	89 11 36	30.724 5830	.001 059 322
945	89 30 25	30.740 8523	.001 058 201
946	89 49 16	30.757 1130	.001 057 082
947	89 68 09	30.773 3651	.001 055 966
948	89 87 04	30.789 6086	.001 054 852
949	90 06 01	30.805 8436	.001 053 741
950	90 25 00	30.822 0700	.001 052 632

Squares, Square Roots, and Reciprocals of the
Natural Numbers from 1 to 1,000

n	n^2	$n^{1/2}$	$1/n$
951	90 44 01	30.838 2879	.001 051 525
952	90 63 04	30.854 4972	.001 050 420
953	90 82 09	30.870 6981	.001 049 318
954	91 01 16	30.886 8904	.001 048 218
955	91 20 25	30.903 0743	.001 047 120
956	91 39 36	30.919 2497	.001 046 025
957	91 58 49	30.935 4166	.001 044 932
958	91 77 64	30.951 5751	.001 043 841
959	91 96 81	30.967 7251	.001 042 753
960	92 16 00	30.983 8668	.001 041 667
961	92 35 21	31.000 0000	.001 040 583
962	92 54 44	31.016 1248	.001 039 501
963	92 73 69	31.032 2413	.001 038 422
964	92 92 96	31.048 3494	.001 037 344
965	93 12 25	31.064 4491	.001 036 269
966	93 31 56	31.080 5405	.001 035 197
967	93 50 89	31.096 6236	.001 034 126
968	93 70 24	31.112 6984	.001 033 058
969	93 89 61	31.128 7648	.001 031 992
970	94 09 00	31.144 8230	.001 030 928
971	94 28 41	31.160 8729	.001 029 866
972	94 47 84	31.176 9145	.001 028 807
973	94 67 29	31.192 9479	.001 027 749
974	94 86 76	31.208 9731	.001 026 694
975	95 06 25	31.224 9900	.001 025 641
976	95 25 76	31.240 9987	.001 024 590
977	95 45 29	31.256 9992	.001 023 541
978	95 64 84	31.272 9915	.001 022 495
979	95 84 41	31.288 9757	.001 021 450
980	96 04 00	31.304 9517	.001 020 408
981	96 23 61	31.320 9195	.001 019 368
982	96 43 24	31.336 8792	.001 018 330
983	96 62 89	31.352 8308	.001 017 294
984	96 82 56	31.368 7743	.001 016 260
985	97 02 25	31.384 7097	.001 015 228
986	97 21 96	31.400 6369	.001 014 199
987	97 41 69	31.416 5561	.001 013 171
988	97 61 44	31.432 4673	.001 012 146
989	97 81 21	31.448 3704	.001 011 122
990	98 01 00	31.464 2654	.001 010 101
991	98 20 81	31.480 1525	.001 009 082
992	98 40 64	31.496 0315	.001 008 065
993	98 60 49	31.511 9025	.001 007 049
994	98 80 36	31.527 7655	.001 006 036
995	99 00 25	31.543 6206	.001 005 025
996	99 20 16	31.559 4677	.001 004 016
997	99 40 09	31.575 3068	.001 003 009
998	99 60 04	31.591 1380	.001 002 004
999	99 80 01	31.606 9613	.001 001 001
1000	1 00 00 00	31.622 7766	.001 000 000

APPENDIX TABLE IX *

Random Numbers

Line	(1)	(2)	(3)	(4)	(5)	(6)	(7)	(8)
1	78994	36244	02673	25475	84953	61793	50243	63423
2	04909	58485	70686	93930	34880	73059	06823	80257
3	46582	73570	33004	51795	86477	46736	60460	70345
4	29242	89792	88634	60285	07190	07795	27011	85941
5	68104	81339	97090	20601	78940	20228	22803	96070
6	17156	02182	82504	19880	93747	80910	78260	25136
7	50711	94789	07171	02103	99057	98775	37997	18325
8	39449	52409	75095	77720	39729	03205	09313	43545
9	75629	82729	76916	72657	58992	32756	01154	84890
10	01020	55151	36132	51971	32155	60735	64867	35424
11	08337	89989	24260	08618	66798	25889	52860	57375
12	76829	47229	19706	30094	69430	92399	98749	22081
13	39708	30641	21267	56501	95182	72442	21445	17276
14	89836	55817	56747	75195	06818	83043	47403	58266
15	25903	61370	66081	54076	67442	52964	23823	02718
16	71345	03422	01015	68025	19703	77313	04555	83425
17	61454	92263	14647	08473	34124	10740	40839	05620
18	80376	08909	30470	40200	46558	61742	11643	92121
19	45144	54373	05505	90074	24783	86299	20900	15144
20	12191	88527	58852	51175	11534	87218	04876	85584
21	62936	59120	73957	35969	21598	47287	39394	08778
22	31588	96798	43668	12611	01714	77266	55079	24690
23	20787	96048	84726	17512	39450	43618	30629	24356
24	45603	00745	84635	43079	52724	14262	05750	89373
25	31606	64782	34027	56734	09365	20008	93559	78384
26	10452	33074	76718	99556	16026	00013	78411	95107
27	37016	64633	67301	50949	91298	74968	73631	57397
28	66725	97865	25409	37498	00816	99262	14471	10232
29	07380	74438	82120	17890	40963	55757	13492	68294
30	71621	57688	58256	47702	74724	89419	08025	68519
31	03466	13263	23917	20417	11315	52805	33072	07723
32	12692	32931	97387	34822	53775	91674	76549	37635
33	52192	30941	44998	17833	94563	23062	95725	38463
34	56691	72529	66063	73570	86860	68125	40436	31303
35	74952	43041	58869	15677	78598	43520	97521	83248
36	18752	43693	32867	53017	22661	39610	03796	02622
37	61691	04944	43111	28325	82319	65589	66048	98498
38	49197	63948	38947	60207	70667	39843	60607	15328
39	19436	87291	71684	74859	76501	93456	95714	92518
40	39143	64893	14606	13543	09621	68301	69817	52140
41	82244	67549	76491	09761	74494	91307	64222	66592
42	55847	56155	42878	23708	97999	40131	52360	90390
43	94095	95970	07826	25991	37584	56966	68623	83454
44	11751	69469	25521	44097	07511	88976	30122	67542
45	69902	08995	27821	11758	64989	61902	32121	28165
46	21850	25352	25556	92161	23592	43294	10479	37879
47	75850	46992	25165	55906	62339	88958	91717	15756
48	29648	22086	42581	85677	20251	39641	65786	80689
49	82740	28443	42734	25518	82827	35825	90288	32911
50	36842	42092	52075	83926	42875	71500	69216	01350

* A portion of page 5 of *Table of 105,000 Random Decimal Digits* constructed by H. Burke Horton and R. Tynes Smith III, for the Bureau of Transport Economics and Statistics, Interstate Commerce Commission. Reproduced here with the permission of W. H. S. Stevens, Director of that Bureau.

APPENDIX TABLE X

Common Logarithms (Five-Place) of the Natural Numbers 1 to 10,000

N	Log	N	Log	N	Log	N	Log	N	Log
0	—	20	1.30 103	40	1.60 206	60	1.77 815	80	1.90 309
1	0.00 000	21	1.32 222	41	1.61 278	61	1.78 533	81	1.90 849
2	0.30 103	22	1.34 242	42	1.62 325	62	1.79 239	82	1.91 381
3	0.47 712	23	1.36 173	43	1.63 347	63	1.79 934	83	1.91 908
4	0.60 206	24	1.38 021	44	1.64 345	64	1.80 618	84	1.92 428
5	0.69 897	25	1.39 794	45	1.65 321	65	1.81 291	85	1.92 942
6	0.77 815	26	1.41 497	46	1.66 276	66	1.81 954	86	1.93 450
7	0.84 510	27	1.43 136	47	1.67 210	67	1.82 607	87	1.93 952
8	0.90 309	28	1.44 716	48	1.68 124	68	1.83 251	88	1.94 448
9	0.95 424	29	1.46 240	49	1.69 020	69	1.83 885	89	1.94 939
10	1.00 000	30	1.47 712	50	1.69 897	70	1.84 510	90	1.95 424
11	1.04 139	31	1.49 136	51	1.70 757	71	1.85 126	91	1.95 904
12	1.07 918	32	1.50 515	52	1.71 600	72	1.85 733	92	1.96 379
13	1.11 394	33	1.51 851	53	1.72 428	73	1.86 332	93	1.96 848
14	1.14 613	34	1.53 148	54	1.73 239	74	1.86 923	94	1.97 313
15	1.17 609	35	1.54 407	55	1.74 036	75	1.87 506	95	1.97 772
16	1.20 412	36	1.55 630	56	1.74 819	76	1.88 081	96	1.98 227
17	1.23 045	37	1.56 820	57	1.75 587	77	1.88 649	97	1.98 677
18	1.25 527	38	1.57 978	58	1.76 343	78	1.89 209	98	1.99 123
19	1.27 875	39	1.59 106	59	1.77 085	79	1.89 763	99	1.99 564
20	1.30 103	40	1.60 206	60	1.77 815	80	1.90 309	100	2.00 000

Common Logarithms (Five-Place) of the Natural Numbers 1 to 10,000

N	0	1	2	3	4	5	6	7	8	9	Prop. Parts		
100	00 000	043	087	130	173	217	260	303	346	389			
101	00 432	475	518	561	604	647	689	732	775	817			
102	00 860	903	945	988	*030	*072	*115	*157	*199	*242	**44**	**43**	**42**
103	01 284	326	368	410	452	494	536	578	620	662	1 4.4	4.3	4.2
104	01 703	745	787	828	870	912	953	995	*036	*078	2 8.8	8.6	8.4
105	02 119	160	202	243	284	325	366	407	449	490	3 13.2	12.9	12.6
106	02 531	572	612	653	694	735	776	816	857	898	4 17.6	17.2	16.8
107	02 938	979	*019	*060	*100	*141	*181	*222	*262	*302	5 22.0	21.5	21.0
108	03 342	383	423	463	503	543	583	623	663	703	6 26.4	25.8	25.2
109	03 743	782	822	862	902	941	981	*021	*060	*100	7 30.8	30.1	29.4
											8 35.2	34.4	33.6
110	04 139	179	218	258	297	336	376	415	454	493	9 39.6	38.7	37.8
111	04 532	571	610	650	689	727	766	805	844	883			
112	04 922	961	999	*038	*077	*115	*154	*192	*231	*269	**41**	**40**	**39**
113	05 308	346	385	423	461	500	538	576	614	652	1 4.1	4.0	3.9
114	05 690	729	767	805	843	881	918	956	994	*032	2 8.2	8.0	7.8
115	06 070	108	145	183	221	258	296	333	371	408	3 12.3	12.0	11.7
116	06 446	483	521	558	595	633	670	707	744	781	4 16.4	16.0	15.6
117	06 819	856	893	930	967	*004	*041	*078	*115	*151	5 20.5	20.0	19.5
118	07 188	225	262	298	335	372	408	445	482	518	6 24.6	24.0	23.4
119	07 555	591	628	664	700	737	773	809	846	882	7 28.7	28.0	27.3
											8 32.8	32.0	31.2
120	07 918	954	990	*027	*063	*099	*135	*171	*207	*243	9 36.9	36.0	35.1
121	08 279	314	350	386	422	458	493	529	565	600			
122	08 636	672	707	743	778	814	849	884	920	955	**38**	**37**	**36**
123	08 991	*026	*061	*096	*132	*167	*202	*237	*272	*307	1 3.8	3.7	3.6
124	09 342	377	412	447	482	517	552	587	621	656	2 7.6	7.4	7.2
125	09 691	726	760	795	830	864	899	934	968	*003	3 11.4	11.1	10.8
126	10 037	072	106	140	175	209	243	278	312	346	4 15.2	14.8	14.4
127	10 380	415	449	483	517	551	585	619	653	687	5 19.0	18.5	18.0
128	10 721	755	789	823	857	890	924	958	992	*025	6 22.8	22.2	21.6
129	11 059	093	126	160	193	227	261	294	327	361	7 26.6	25.9	25.2
											8 30.4	29.6	28.8
130	11 394	428	461	494	528	561	594	628	661	694	9 34.2	33.3	32.4
131	11 727	760	793	826	860	893	926	959	992	*024			
132	12 057	090	123	156	189	222	254	287	320	352	**35**	**34**	**33**
133	12 385	418	450	483	516	548	581	613	646	678	1 3.5	3.4	3.3
134	12 710	743	775	808	840	872	905	937	969	*001	2 7.0	6.8	6.6
135	13 033	066	098	130	162	194	226	258	290	322	3 10.5	10.2	9.9
136	13 354	386	418	450	481	513	545	577	609	640	4 14.0	13.6	13.2
137	13 672	704	735	767	799	830	862	893	925	956	5 17.5	17.0	16.5
138	13 988	*019	*051	*082	*114	*145	*176	*208	*239	*270	6 21.0	20.4	19.8
139	14 301	333	364	395	426	457	489	520	551	582	7 24.5	23.8	23.1
											8 28.0	27.2	26.4
140	14 613	644	675	706	737	768	799	829	860	891	9 31.5	30.6	29.7
141	14 922	953	983	*014	*045	*076	*106	*137	*168	*198	**32**	**31**	**30**
142	15 229	259	290	320	351	381	412	442	473	503	1 3.2	3.1	3.0
143	15 534	564	594	625	655	685	715	746	776	806	2 6.4	6.2	6.0
144	15 836	866	897	927	957	987	*017	*047	*077	*107	3 9.6	9.3	9.0
145	16 137	167	197	227	256	286	316	346	376	406	4 12.8	12.4	12.0
146	16 435	465	495	524	554	584	613	643	673	702	5 16.0	15.5	15.0
147	16 732	761	791	820	850	879	909	938	967	997	6 19.2	18.6	18.0
148	17 026	056	085	114	143	173	202	231	260	289	7 22.4	21.7	21.0
149	17 319	348	377	406	435	464	493	522	551	580	8 25.6	24.8	24.0
150	17 609	638	667	696	725	754	782	811	840	869	9 28.8	27.9	27.0
N	0	1	2	3	4	5	6	7	8	9	Prop. Parts		

Common Logarithms (Five-Place) of the Natural Numbers 1 to 10,000

N	0	1	2	3	4	5	6	7	8	9
150	17 609	638	667	696	725	754	782	811	840	869
151	17 898	926	955	984	*013	*041	*070	*099	*127	*156
152	18 184	213	241	270	298	327	355	384	412	441
153	18 469	498	526	554	583	611	639	667	696	724
154	18 752	780	808	837	865	893	921	949	977	*005
155	19 033	061	089	117	145	173	201	229	257	285
156	19 312	340	368	396	424	451	479	507	535	562
157	19 590	618	645	673	700	728	756	783	811	838
158	19 866	893	921	948	976	*003	*030	*058	*085	*112
159	20 140	167	194	222	249	276	303	330	358	385
160	20 412	439	466	493	520	548	575	602	629	656
161	20 683	710	737	763	790	817	844	871	898	925
162	20 952	978	*005	*032	*059	*085	*112	*139	*165	*192
163	21 219	245	272	299	325	352	378	405	431	458
164	21 484	511	537	564	590	617	643	669	696	722
165	21 748	775	801	827	854	880	906	932	958	985
166	22 011	037	063	089	115	141	167	194	220	246
167	22 272	298	324	350	376	401	427	453	479	505
168	22 531	557	583	608	634	660	686	712	737	763
169	22 789	814	840	866	891	917	943	968	994	*019
170	23 045	070	096	121	147	172	198	223	249	274
171	23 300	325	350	376	401	426	452	477	502	528
172	23 553	578	603	629	654	679	704	729	754	779
173	23 805	830	855	880	905	930	955	980	*005	*030
174	24 055	080	105	130	155	180	204	229	254	279
175	24 304	329	353	378	403	428	452	477	502	527
176	24 551	576	601	625	650	674	699	724	748	773
177	24 797	822	846	871	895	920	944	969	993	*018
178	25 042	066	091	115	139	164	188	212	237	261
179	25 285	310	334	358	382	406	431	455	479	503
180	25 527	551	575	600	624	648	672	696	720	744
181	25 768	792	816	840	864	888	912	935	959	983
182	26 007	031	055	079	102	126	150	174	198	221
183	26 245	269	293	316	340	364	387	411	435	458
184	26 482	505	529	553	576	600	623	647	670	694
185	26 717	741	764	788	811	834	858	881	905	928
186	26 951	975	998	*021	*045	*068	*091	*114	*138	*161
187	27 184	207	231	254	277	300	323	346	370	393
188	27 416	439	462	485	508	531	554	577	600	623
189	27 646	669	692	715	738	761	784	807	830	852
190	27 875	898	921	944	967	989	*012	*035	*058	*081
191	28 103	126	149	171	194	217	240	262	285	307
192	28 330	353	375	398	421	443	466	488	511	533
193	28 556	578	601	623	646	668	691	713	735	758
194	28 780	803	825	847	870	892	914	937	959	981
195	29 003	026	048	070	092	115	137	159	181	203
196	29 226	248	270	292	314	336	358	380	403	425
197	29 447	469	491	513	535	557	579	601	623	645
198	29 667	688	710	732	754	776	798	820	842	863
199	29 885	907	929	951	973	994	*016	*038	*060	*081
200	30 103	125	146	168	190	211	233	255	276	298

Prop. Parts

	29	28
1	2.9	2.8
2	5.8	5.6
3	8.7	8.4
4	11.6	11.2
5	14.5	14.0
6	17.4	16.8
7	20.3	19.6
8	23.2	22.4
9	26.1	25.2

	27	26
1	2.7	2.6
2	5.4	5.2
3	8.1	7.8
4	10.8	10.4
5	13.5	13.0
6	16.2	15.6
7	18.9	18.2
8	21.6	20.8
9	24.3	23.4

	25
1	2.5
2	5.0
3	7.5
4	10.0
5	12.5
6	15.0
7	17.5
8	20.0
9	22.5

	24	23
1	2.4	2.3
2	4.8	4.6
3	7.2	6.9
4	9.6	9.2
5	12.0	11.5
6	14.4	13.8
7	16.8	16.1
8	19.2	18.4
9	21.6	20.7

	22	21
1	2.2	2.1
2	4.4	4.2
3	6.6	6.3
4	8.8	8.4
5	11.0	10.5
6	13.2	12.6
7	15.4	14.7
8	17.6	16.8
9	19.8	18.9

Common Logarithms (Five-Place) of the Natural Numbers 1 to 10,000

N	0	1	2	3	4	5	6	7	8	9
200	30 103	125	146	168	190	211	233	255	276	298
201	30 320	341	363	384	406	428	449	471	492	514
202	30 535	557	578	600	621	643	664	685	707	728
203	30 750	771	792	814	835	856	878	899	920	942
204	30 963	984	*006	*027	*048	*069	*091	*112	*133	*154
205	31 175	197	218	239	260	281	302	323	345	366
206	31 387	408	429	450	471	492	513	534	555	576
207	31 597	618	639	660	681	702	723	744	765	785
208	31 806	827	848	869	890	911	931	952	973	994
209	32 015	035	056	077	098	118	139	160	181	201
210	32 222	243	263	284	305	325	346	366	387	408
211	32 428	449	469	490	510	531	552	572	593	613
212	32 634	654	675	695	715	736	756	777	797	818
213	32 838	858	879	899	919	940	960	980	*001	*021
214	33 041	062	082	102	122	143	163	183	203	224
215	33 244	264	284	304	325	345	365	385	405	425
216	33 445	465	486	506	526	546	566	586	606	626
217	33 646	666	686	706	726	746	766	786	806	826
218	33 846	866	885	905	925	945	965	985	*005	*025
219	34 044	064	084	104	124	143	163	183	203	223
220	34 242	262	282	301	321	341	361	380	400	420
221	34 439	459	479	498	518	537	557	577	596	616
222	34 635	655	674	694	713	733	753	772	792	811
223	34 830	850	869	889	908	928	947	967	986	*005
224	35 025	044	064	083	102	122	141	160	180	199
225	35 218	238	257	276	295	315	334	353	372	392
226	35 411	430	449	468	488	507	526	545	564	583
227	35 603	622	641	660	679	698	717	736	755	774
228	35 793	813	832	851	870	889	908	927	946	965
229	35 984	*003	*021	*040	*059	*078	*097	*116	*135	*154
230	36 173	192	211	229	248	267	286	305	324	342
231	36 361	380	399	418	436	455	474	493	511	530
232	36 549	568	586	605	624	642	661	680	698	717
233	36 736	754	773	791	810	829	847	866	884	903
234	36 922	940	959	977	996	*014	*033	*051	*070	*088
235	37 107	125	144	162	181	199	218	236	254	273
236	37 291	310	328	346	365	383	401	420	438	457
237	37 475	493	511	530	548	566	585	603	621	639
238	37 658	676	694	712	731	749	767	785	803	822
239	37 840	858	876	894	912	931	949	967	985	*003
240	38 021	039	057	075	093	112	130	148	166	184
241	38 202	220	238	256	274	292	310	328	346	364
242	38 382	399	417	435	453	471	489	507	525	543
243	38 561	578	596	614	632	650	668	686	703	721
244	38 739	757	775	792	810	828	846	863	881	899
245	38 917	934	952	970	987	*005	*023	*041	*058	*076
246	39 094	111	129	146	164	182	199	217	235	252
247	39 270	287	305	322	340	358	375	393	410	428
248	39 445	463	480	498	515	533	550	568	585	602
249	39 620	637	655	672	690	707	724	742	759	777
250	39 794	811	829	846	863	881	898	915	933	950

Prop. Parts

	22	21
1	2.2	2.1
2	4.4	4.2
3	6.6	6.3
4	8.8	8.4
5	11.0	10.5
6	13.2	12.6
7	15.4	14.7
8	17.6	16.8
9	19.8	18.9

	20
1	2.0
2	4.0
3	6.0
4	8.0
5	10.0
6	12.0
7	14.0
8	16.0
9	18.0

	19
1	1.9
2	3.8
3	5.7
4	7.6
5	9.5
6	11.4
7	13.3
8	15.2
9	17.1

	18
1	1.8
2	3.6
3	5.4
4	7.2
5	9.0
6	10.8
7	12.6
8	14.4
9	16.2

	17
1	1.7
2	3.4
3	5.1
4	6.8
5	8.5
6	10.2
7	11.9
8	13.6
9	15.3

Common Logarithms (Five-Place) of the Natural Numbers 1 to 10,000

N	0	1	2	3	4	5	6	7	8	9
250	39 794	811	829	846	863	881	898	915	933	950
251	39 967	985	*002	*019	*037	*054	*071	*088	*106	*123
252	40 140	157	175	192	209	226	243	261	278	295
253	40 312	329	346	364	381	398	415	432	449	466
254	40 483	500	518	535	552	569	586	603	620	637
255	40 654	671	688	705	722	739	756	773	790	807
256	40 824	841	858	875	892	909	926	943	960	976
257	40 993	*010	*027	*044	*061	*078	*095	*111	*128	*145
258	41 162	179	196	212	229	246	263	280	296	313
259	41 330	347	363	380	397	414	430	447	464	481
260	41 497	514	531	547	564	581	597	614	631	647
261	41 664	681	697	714	731	747	764	780	797	814
262	41 830	847	863	880	896	913	929	946	963	979
263	41 996	*012	*029	*045	*062	*078	*095	*111	*127	*144
264	42 160	177	193	210	226	243	259	275	292	308
265	42 325	341	357	374	390	406	423	439	455	472
266	42 488	504	521	537	553	570	586	602	619	635
267	42 651	667	684	700	716	732	749	765	781	797
268	42 813	830	846	862	878	894	911	927	943	959
269	42 975	991	*008	*024	*040	*056	*072	*088	*104	*120
270	43 136	152	169	185	201	217	233	249	265	281
271	43 297	313	329	345	361	377	393	409	425	441
272	43 457	473	489	505	521	537	553	569	584	600
273	43 616	632	648	664	680	696	712	727	743	759
274	43 775	791	807	823	838	854	870	886	902	917
275	43 933	949	965	981	996	*012	*028	*044	*059	*075
276	44 091	107	122	138	154	170	185	201	217	232
277	44 248	264	279	295	311	326	342	358	373	389
278	44 404	420	436	451	467	483	498	514	529	545
279	44 560	576	592	607	623	638	654	669	685	700
280	44 716	731	747	762	778	793	809	824	840	855
281	44 871	886	902	917	932	948	963	979	994	*010
282	45 025	040	056	071	086	102	117	133	148	163
283	45 179	194	209	225	240	255	271	286	301	317
284	45 332	347	362	378	393	408	423	439	454	469
285	45 484	500	515	530	545	561	576	591	606	621
286	45 637	652	667	682	697	712	728	743	758	773
287	45 788	803	818	834	849	864	879	894	909	924
288	45 939	954	969	984	*000	*015	*030	*045	*060	*075
289	46 090	105	120	135	150	165	180	195	210	225
290	46 240	255	270	285	300	315	330	345	359	374
291	46 389	404	419	434	449	464	479	494	509	523
292	46 538	553	568	583	598	613	627	642	657	672
293	46 687	702	716	731	746	761	776	790	805	820
294	46 835	850	864	879	894	909	923	938	953	967
295	46 982	997	*012	*026	*041	*056	*070	*085	*100	*114
296	47 129	144	159	173	188	202	217	232	246	261
297	47 276	290	305	319	334	349	363	378	392	407
298	47 422	436	451	465	480	494	509	524	538	553
299	47 567	582	596	611	625	640	654	669	683	698
300	47 712	727	741	756	770	784	799	813	828	842

Prop. Parts

18		17		16		15		14	
1	1.8	1	1.7	1	1.6	1	1.5	1	1.4
2	3.6	2	3.4	2	3.2	2	3.0	2	2.8
3	5.4	3	5.1	3	4.8	3	4.5	3	4.2
4	7.2	4	6.8	4	6.4	4	6.0	4	5.6
5	9.0	5	8.5	5	8.0	5	7.5	5	7.0
6	10.8	6	10.2	6	9.6	6	9.0	6	8.4
7	12.6	7	11.9	7	11.2	7	10.5	7	9.8
8	14.4	8	13.6	8	12.8	8	12.0	8	11.2
9	16.2	9	15.3	9	14.4	9	13.5	9	12.6

Common Logarithms (Five-Place) of the Natural Numbers 1 to 10,000

N	0	1	2	3	4	5	6	7	8	9
300	47 712	727	741	756	770	784	799	813	828	842
301	47 857	871	885	900	914	929	943	958	972	986
302	48 001	015	029	044	058	073	087	101	116	130
303	48 144	159	173	187	202	216	230	244	259	273
304	48 287	302	316	330	344	359	373	387	401	416
305	48 430	444	458	473	487	501	515	530	544	558
306	48 572	586	601	615	629	643	657	671	686	700
307	48 714	728	742	756	770	785	799	813	827	841
308	48 855	869	883	897	911	926	940	954	968	982
309	48 996	*010	*024	*038	*052	*066	*080	*094	*108	*122
310	49 136	150	164	178	192	206	220	234	248	262
311	49 276	290	304	318	332	346	360	374	388	402
312	49 415	429	443	457	471	485	499	513	527	541
313	49 554	568	582	596	610	624	638	651	665	679
314	49 693	707	721	734	748	762	776	790	803	817
315	49 831	845	859	872	886	900	914	927	941	955
316	49 969	982	996	*010	*024	*037	*051	*065	*079	*092
317	50 106	120	133	147	161	174	188	202	215	229
318	50 243	256	270	284	297	311	325	338	352	365
319	50 379	393	406	420	433	447	461	474	488	501
320	50 515	529	542	556	569	583	596	610	623	637
321	50 651	664	678	691	705	718	732	745	759	772
322	50 786	799	813	826	840	853	866	880	893	907
323	50 920	934	947	961	974	987	*001	*014	*028	*041
324	51 055	068	081	095	108	121	135	148	162	175
325	51 188	202	215	228	242	255	268	282	295	308
326	51 322	335	348	362	375	388	402	415	428	441
327	51 455	468	481	495	508	521	534	548	561	574
328	51 587	601	614	627	640	654	667	680	693	706
329	51 720	733	746	759	772	786	799	812	825	838
330	51 851	865	878	891	904	917	930	943	957	970
331	51 983	996	*009	*022	*035	*048	*061	*075	*088	*101
332	52 114	127	140	153	166	179	192	205	218	231
333	52 244	257	270	284	297	310	323	336	349	362
334	52 375	388	401	414	427	440	453	466	479	492
335	52 504	517	530	543	556	569	582	595	608	621
336	52 634	647	660	673	686	699	711	724	737	750
337	52 763	776	789	802	815	827	840	853	866	879
338	52 892	905	917	930	943	956	969	982	994	*007
339	53 020	033	046	058	071	084	097	110	122	135
340	53 148	161	173	186	199	212	224	237	250	263
341	53 275	288	301	314	326	339	352	364	377	390
342	53 403	415	428	441	453	466	479	491	504	517
343	53 529	542	555	567	580	593	605	618	631	643
344	53 656	668	681	694	706	719	732	744	757	769
345	53 782	794	807	820	832	845	857	870	882	895
346	53 908	920	933	945	958	970	983	995	*008	*020
347	54 033	045	058	070	083	095	108	120	133	145
348	54 158	170	183	195	208	220	233	245	258	270
349	54 283	295	307	320	332	345	357	370	382	394
350	54 407	419	432	444	456	469	481	494	506	518
N	0	1	2	3	4	5	6	7	8	9

Prop. Parts

	15		**14**		**13**		**12**
1	1.5	1	1.4	1	1.3	1	1.2
2	3.0	2	2.8	2	2.6	2	2.4
3	4.5	3	4.2	3	3.9	3	3.6
4	6.0	4	5.6	4	5.2	4	4.8
5	7.5	5	7.0	5	6.5	5	6.0
6	9.0	6	8.4	6	7.8	6	7.2
7	10.5	7	9.8	7	9.1	7	8.4
8	12.0	8	11.2	8	10.4	8	9.6
9	13.5	9	12.6	9	11.7	9	10.8

Common Logarithms (Five-Place) of the Natural Numbers 1 to 10,000

N	0	1	2	3	4	5	6	7	8	9
350	54 407	419	432	444	456	469	481	494	506	518
351	54 531	543	555	568	580	593	605	617	630	642
352	54 654	667	679	691	704	716	728	741	753	765
353	54 777	790	802	814	827	839	851	864	876	888
354	54 900	913	925	937	949	962	974	986	998	*011
355	55 023	035	047	060	072	084	096	108	121	133
356	55 145	157	169	182	194	206	218	230	242	255
357	55 267	279	291	303	315	328	340	352	364	376
358	55 388	400	413	425	437	449	461	473	485	497
359	55 509	522	534	546	558	570	582	594	606	618
360	55 630	642	654	666	678	691	703	715	727	739
361	55 751	763	775	787	799	811	823	835	847	859
362	55 871	883	895	907	919	931	943	955	967	979
363	55 991	*003	*015	*027	*038	*050	*062	*074	*086	*098
364	56 110	122	134	146	158	170	182	194	205	217
365	56 229	241	253	265	277	289	301	312	324	336
366	56 348	360	372	384	396	407	419	431	443	455
367	56 467	478	490	502	514	526	538	549	561	573
368	56 585	597	608	620	632	644	656	667	679	691
369	56 703	714	726	738	750	761	773	785	797	808
370	56 820	832	844	855	867	879	891	902	914	926
371	56 937	949	961	972	984	996	*008	*019	*031	*043
372	57 054	066	078	089	101	113	124	136	148	159
373	57 171	183	194	206	217	229	241	252	264	276
374	57 287	299	310	322	334	345	357	368	380	392
375	57 403	415	426	438	449	461	473	484	496	507
376	57 519	530	542	553	565	576	588	600	611	623
377	57 634	646	657	669	680	692	703	715	726	738
378	57 749	761	772	784	795	807	818	830	841	852
379	57 864	875	887	898	910	921	933	944	955	967
380	57 978	990	*001	*013	*024	*035	*047	*058	*070	*081
381	58 092	104	115	127	138	149	161	172	184	195
382	58 206	218	229	240	252	263	274	286	297	309
383	58 320	331	343	354	365	377	388	399	410	422
384	58 433	444	456	467	478	490	501	512	524	535
385	58 546	557	569	580	591	602	614	625	636	647
386	58 659	670	681	692	704	715	726	737	749	760
387	58 771	782	794	805	816	827	838	850	861	872
388	58 883	894	906	917	928	939	950	961	973	984
389	58 995	*006	*017	*028	*040	*051	*062	*073	*084	*095
390	59 106	118	129	140	151	162	173	184	195	207
391	59 218	229	240	251	262	273	284	295	306	318
392	59 329	340	351	362	373	384	395	406	417	428
393	59 439	450	461	472	483	494	506	517	528	539
394	59 550	561	572	583	594	605	616	627	638	649
395	59 660	671	682	693	704	715	726	737	748	759
396	59 770	780	791	802	813	824	835	846	857	868
397	59 879	890	901	912	923	934	945	956	966	977
398	59 988	999	*010	*021	*032	*043	*054	*065	*076	*086
399	60 097	108	119	130	141	152	163	173	184	195
400	60 206	217	228	239	249	260	271	282	293	304

Prop. Parts

13		12		11		10	
1	1.3	1	1.2	1	1.1	1	1.0
2	2.6	2	2.4	2	2.2	2	2.0
3	3.9	3	3.6	3	3.3	3	3.0
4	5.2	4	4.8	4	4.4	4	4.0
5	6.5	5	6.0	5	5.5	5	5.0
6	7.8	6	7.2	6	6.6	6	6.0
7	9.1	7	8.4	7	7.7	7	7.0
8	10.4	8	9.6	8	8.8	8	8.0
9	11.7	9	10.8	9	9.9	9	9.0

Common Logarithms (Five-Place) of the Natural Numbers 1 to 10,000

N	0	1	2	3	4	5	6	7	8	9	Prop. Parts
400	60 206	217	228	239	249	260	271	282	293	304	
401	60 314	325	336	347	358	369	379	390	401	412	
402	60 423	433	444	455	466	477	487	498	509	520	
403	60 531	541	552	563	574	584	595	606	617	627	
404	60 638	649	660	670	681	692	703	713	724	735	
405	60 746	756	767	778	788	799	810	821	831	842	
406	60 853	863	874	885	895	906	917	927	938	949	
407	60 959	970	981	991	*002	*013	*023	*034	*045	*055	
408	61 066	077	087	098	109	119	130	140	151	162	
409	61 172	183	194	204	215	225	236	247	257	268	
410	61 278	289	300	310	321	331	342	352	363	374	
411	61 384	395	405	416	426	437	448	458	469	479	
412	61 490	500	511	521	532	542	553	563	574	584	
413	61 595	606	616	627	637	648	658	669	679	690	
414	61 700	711	721	731	742	752	763	773	784	794	
415	61 805	815	826	836	847	857	868	878	888	899	
416	61 909	920	930	941	951	962	972	982	993	*003	
417	62 014	024	034	045	055	066	076	086	097	107	
418	62 118	128	138	149	159	170	180	190	201	211	
419	62 221	232	242	252	263	273	284	294	304	315	
420	62 325	335	346	356	366	377	387	397	408	418	
421	62 428	439	449	459	469	480	490	500	511	521	
422	62 531	542	552	562	572	583	593	603	613	624	
423	62 634	644	655	665	675	685	696	706	716	726	
424	62 737	747	757	767	778	788	798	808	818	829	
425	62 839	849	859	870	880	890	900	910	921	931	
426	62 941	951	961	972	982	992	*002	*012	*022	*033	
427	63 043	053	063	073	083	094	104	114	124	134	
428	63 144	155	165	175	185	195	205	215	225	236	
429	63 246	256	266	276	286	296	306	317	327	337	
430	63 347	357	367	377	387	397	407	417	428	438	
431	63 448	458	468	478	488	498	508	518	528	538	
432	63 548	558	568	579	589	599	609	619	629	639	
433	63 649	659	669	679	689	699	709	719	729	739	
434	63 749	759	769	779	789	799	809	819	829	839	
435	63 849	859	869	879	889	899	909	919	929	939	
436	63 949	959	969	979	988	998	*008	*018	*028	*038	
437	64 048	058	068	078	088	098	108	118	128	137	
438	64 147	157	167	177	187	197	207	217	227	237	
439	64 246	256	266	276	286	296	306	316	326	335	
440	64 345	355	365	375	385	395	404	414	424	434	
441	64 444	454	464	473	483	493	503	513	523	532	
442	64 542	552	562	572	582	591	601	611	621	631	
443	64 640	650	660	670	680	689	699	709	719	729	
444	64 738	748	758	768	777	787	797	807	816	826	
445	64 836	846	856	865	875	885	895	904	914	924	
446	64 933	943	953	963	972	982	992	*002	*011	*021	
447	65 031	040	050	060	070	079	089	099	108	118	
448	65 128	137	147	157	167	176	186	196	205	215	
449	65 225	234	244	254	263	273	283	292	302	312	
450	65 321	331	341	350	360	369	379	389	398	408	
N	0	1	2	3	4	5	6	7	8	9	Prop. Parts

Prop. Parts

11		10		9	
1	1.1	1	1.0	1	0.9
2	2.2	2	2.0	2	1.8
3	3.3	3	3.0	3	2.7
4	4.4	4	4.0	4	3.6
5	5.5	5	5.0	5	4.5
6	6.6	6	6.0	6	5.4
7	7.7	7	7.0	7	6.3
8	8.8	8	8.0	8	7.2
9	9.9	9	9.0	9	8.1

Common Logarithms (Five-Place) of the Natural Numbers 1 to 10,000

Prop. Parts	N	0	1	2	3	4	5	6	7	8	9
	450	65 321	331	341	350	360	369	379	389	398	408
	451	65 418	427	437	447	456	466	475	485	495	504
	452	65 514	523	533	543	552	562	571	581	591	600
	453	65 610	619	629	639	648	658	667	677	686	696
	454	65 706	715	725	734	744	753	763	772	782	792
	455	65 801	811	820	830	839	849	858	868	877	887
	456	65 896	906	916	925	935	944	954	963	973	982
10	457	65 992	*001	*011	*020	*030	*039	*049	*058	*068	*077
1 1.0	458	66 087	096	106	115	124	134	143	153	162	172
2 2.0	459	66 181	191	200	210	219	229	238	247	257	266
3 3.0	**460**	66 276	285	295	304	314	323	332	342	351	361
4 4.0	461	66 370	380	389	398	408	417	427	436	445	455
5 5.0	462	66 464	474	483	492	502	511	521	530	539	549
6 6.0	463	66 558	567	577	586	596	605	614	624	633	642
7 7.0	464	66 652	661	671	680	689	699	708	717	727	736
8 8.0	465	66 745	755	764	773	783	792	801	811	820	829
9 9.0	466	66 839	848	857	867	876	885	894	904	913	922
	467	66 932	941	950	960	969	978	987	997	*006	*015
	468	67 025	034	043	052	062	071	080	089	099	108
	469	67 117	127	136	145	154	164	173	182	191	201
	470	67 210	219	228	237	247	256	265	274	284	293
	471	67 302	311	321	330	339	348	357	367	376	385
9	472	67 394	403	413	422	431	440	449	459	468	477
1 0.9	473	67 486	495	504	514	523	532	541	550	560	569
2 1.8	474	67 578	587	596	605	614	624	633	642	651	660
3 2.7	475	67 669	679	688	697	706	715	724	733	742	752
4 3.6	476	67 761	770	779	788	797	806	815	825	834	843
5 4.5	477	67 852	861	870	879	888	897	906	916	925	934
6 5.4	478	67 943	952	961	970	979	988	997	*006	*015	*024
7 6.3	479	68 034	043	052	061	070	079	088	097	106	115
8 7.2	**480**	68 124	133	142	151	160	169	178	187	196	205
9 8.1	481	68 215	224	233	242	251	260	269	278	287	296
	482	68 305	314	323	332	341	350	359	368	377	386
	483	68 395	404	413	422	431	440	449	458	467	476
	484	68 485	494	502	511	520	529	538	547	556	565
	485	68 574	583	592	601	610	619	628	637	646	655
	486	68 664	673	681	690	699	708	717	726	735	744
8	487	68 753	762	771	780	789	797	806	815	824	833
1 0.8	488	68 842	851	860	869	878	886	895	904	913	922
2 1.6	489	68 931	940	949	958	966	975	984	993	*002	*011
3 2.4	**490**	69 020	028	037	046	055	064	073	082	090	099
4 3.2	491	69 108	117	126	135	144	152	161	170	179	188
5 4.0	492	69 197	205	214	223	232	241	249	258	267	276
6 4.8	493	69 285	294	302	311	320	329	338	346	355	364
7 5.6	494	69 373	381	390	399	408	417	425	434	443	452
8 6.4	495	69 461	469	478	487	496	504	513	522	531	539
9 7.2	496	69 548	557	566	574	583	592	601	609	618	627
	497	69 636	644	653	662	671	679	688	697	705	714
	498	69 723	732	740	749	758	767	775	784	793	801
	499	69 810	819	827	836	845	854	862	871	880	888
	500	69 897	906	914	923	932	940	949	958	966	975
Prop. Parts	N	0	1	2	3	4	5	6	7	8	9

Common Logarithms (Five-Place) of the Natural Numbers 1 to 10,000

N	0	1	2	3	4	5	6	7	8	9	Prop. Parts
500	69 897	906	914	923	932	940	949	958	966	975	
501	69 984	992	*001	*010	*018	*027	*036	*044	*053	*062	
502	70 070	079	088	096	105	114	122	131	140	148	
503	70 157	165	174	183	191	200	209	217	226	234	
504	70 243	252	260	269	278	286	295	303	312	321	
505	70 329	338	346	355	364	372	381	389	398	406	
506	70 415	424	432	441	449	458	467	475	484	492	
507	70 501	509	518	526	535	544	552	561	569	578	
508	70 586	595	603	612	621	629	638	646	655	663	
509	70 672	680	689	697	706	714	723	731	740	749	
510	70 757	766	774	783	791	800	808	817	825	834	
511	70 842	851	859	868	876	885	893	902	910	919	
512	70 927	935	944	952	961	969	978	986	995	*003	
513	71 012	020	029	037	046	054	063	071	079	088	
514	71 096	105	113	122	130	139	147	155	164	172	
515	71 181	189	198	206	214	223	231	240	248	257	
516	71 265	273	282	290	299	307	315	324	332	341	
517	71 349	357	366	374	383	391	399	408	416	425	
518	71 433	441	450	458	466	475	483	492	500	508	
519	71 517	525	533	542	550	559	567	575	584	592	
520	71 600	609	617	625	634	642	650	659	667	675	
521	71 684	692	700	709	717	725	734	742	750	759	
522	71 767	775	784	792	800	809	817	825	834	842	
523	71 850	858	867	875	883	892	900	908	917	925	
524	71 933	941	950	958	966	975	983	991	999	*008	
525	72 016	024	032	041	049	057	066	074	082	090	
526	72 099	107	115	123	132	140	148	156	165	173	
527	72 181	189	198	206	214	222	230	239	247	255	
528	72 263	272	280	288	296	304	313	321	329	337	
529	72 346	354	362	370	378	387	395	403	411	419	
530	72 428	436	444	452	460	469	477	485	493	501	
531	72 509	518	526	534	542	550	558	567	575	583	
532	72 591	599	607	616	624	632	640	648	656	665	
533	72 673	681	689	697	705	713	722	730	738	746	
534	72 754	762	770	779	787	979	803	811	819	827	
535	72 835	843	852	860	868	876	884	892	900	908	
536	72 916	925	933	941	949	957	965	973	981	989	
537	72 997	*006	*014	*022	*030	*038	*046	*054	*062	*070	
538	73 078	086	094	102	111	119	127	135	143	151	
539	73 159	167	175	183	191	199	207	215	223	231	
540	73 239	247	255	263	272	280	288	296	304	312	
541	73 320	328	336	344	352	360	368	376	384	392	
542	73 400	408	416	424	432	440	448	456	464	472	
543	73 480	488	496	504	512	520	528	536	544	552	
544	73 560	568	576	584	592	600	608	616	624	632	
545	73 640	648	656	664	672	679	687	695	703	711	
546	73 719	727	735	743	751	759	767	775	783	791	
547	73 799	807	815	823	830	838	846	854	862	870	
548	73 878	886	894	902	910	918	926	933	941	949	
549	73 957	965	973	981	989	997	*005	*013	*020	*028	
550	74 036	044	052	060	068	076	084	092	099	107	
N	0	1	2	3	4	5	6	7	8	9	Prop. Parts

Prop. Parts

	9		8		7
1	0.9	1	0.8	1	0.7
2	1.8	2	1.6	2	1.4
3	2.7	3	2.4	3	2.1
4	3.6	4	3.2	4	2.8
5	4.5	5	4.0	5	3.5
6	5.4	6	4.8	6	4.2
7	6.3	7	5.6	7	4.9
8	7.2	8	6.4	8	5.6
9	8.1	9	7.2	9	6.3

APPENDIX TABLE X — *Continued*

Common Logarithms (Five-Place) of the Natural Numbers 1 to 10,000

Prop. Parts	N	0	1	2	3	4	5	6	7	8	9
	550	74 036	044	052	060	068	076	084	092	099	107
	551	74 115	123	131	139	147	155	162	170	178	186
	552	74 194	202	210	218	225	233	241	249	257	265
	553	74 273	280	288	296	304	312	320	327	335	343
	554	74 351	359	367	374	382	390	398	406	414	421
	555	74 429	437	445	453	461	468	476	484	492	500
	556	74 507	515	523	531	539	547	554	562	570	578
	557	74 586	593	601	609	617	624	632	640	648	656
	558	74 663	671	679	687	695	702	710	718	726	733
	559	74 741	749	757	764	772	780	788	796	803	811
	560	74 819	827	834	842	850	858	865	873	881	889
	561	74 896	904	912	920	927	935	943	950	958	966
8	562	74 974	981	989	997	*005	*012	*020	*028	*035	*043
1 0.8	563	75 051	059	066	074	082	089	097	105	113	120
2 1.6											
3 2.4	564	75 128	136	143	151	159	166	174	182	189	197
4 3.2	565	75 205	213	220	228	236	243	251	259	266	274
5 4.0	566	75 282	289	297	305	312	320	328	335	343	351
6 4.8											
7 5.6	567	75 358	366	374	381	389	397	404	412	420	427
8 6.4	568	75 435	442	450	458	465	473	481	488	496	504
9 7.2	569	75 511	519	526	534	542	549	557	565	572	580
	570	75 587	595	603	610	618	626	633	641	648	656
	571	75 664	671	679	686	694	702	709	717	724	732
	572	75 740	747	755	762	770	778	785	793	800	808
	573	75 815	823	831	838	846	853	861	868	876	884
	574	75 891	899	906	914	921	929	937	944	952	959
	575	75 967	974	982	989	997	*005	*012	*020	*027	*035
	576	76 042	050	057	065	072	080	087	095	103	110
	577	76 118	125	133	140	148	155	163	170	178	185
	578	76 193	200	208	215	223	230	238	245	253	260
	579	76 268	275	283	290	298	305	313	320	328	335
	580	76 343	350	358	365	373	380	388	395	403	410
	581	76 418	425	433	440	448	455	462	470	477	485
7	582	76 492	500	507	515	522	530	537	545	552	559
1 0.7	583	76 567	574	582	589	597	604	612	619	626	634
2 1.4											
3 2.1	584	76 641	649	656	664	671	678	686	693	701	708
4 2.8	585	76 716	723	730	738	745	753	760	768	775	782
5 3.5	586	76 790	797	805	812	819	827	834	842	849	856
6 4.2											
7 4.9	587	76 864	871	879	886	893	901	908	916	923	930
8 5.6	588	76 938	945	953	960	967	975	982	989	997	*004
9 6.3	589	77 012	019	026	034	041	048	056	063	070	078
	590	77 085	093	100	107	115	122	129	137	144	151
	591	77 159	166	173	181	188	195	203	210	217	225
	592	77 232	240	247	254	262	269	276	283	291	298
	593	77 305	313	320	327	335	342	349	357	364	371
	594	77 379	386	393	401	408	415	422	430	437	444
	595	77 452	459	466	474	481	488	495	503	510	517
	596	77 525	532	539	546	554	561	568	576	583	590
	597	77 597	605	612	619	627	634	641	648	656	663
	598	77 670	677	685	692	699	706	714	721	728	735
	599	77 743	750	757	764	772	779	786	793	801	808
	600	77 815	822	830	837	844	851	859	866	873	880
Prop. Parts	N	0	1	2	3	4	5	6	7	8	9

Common Logarithms (Five-Place) of the Natural Numbers 1 to 10,000

N	0	1	2	3	4	5	6	7	8	9	Prop. Parts
600	77 815	822	830	837	844	851	859	866	873	880	
601	77 887	895	902	909	916	924	931	938	945	952	
602	77 960	967	974	981	988	996	*003	*010	*017	*025	
603	78 032	039	046	053	061	068	075	082	089	097	
604	78 104	111	118	125	132	140	147	154	161	168	
605	78 176	183	190	197	204	211	219	226	233	240	
606	78 247	254	262	269	276	283	290	297	305	312	
607	78 319	326	333	340	347	355	362	369	376	383	
608	78 390	398	405	412	419	426	433	440	447	455	
609	78 462	469	476	483	490	497	504	512	519	526	
610	78 533	540	547	554	561	569	576	583	590	597	
611	78 604	611	618	625	633	640	647	654	661	668	
612	78 675	682	689	696	704	711	718	725	732	739	
613	78 746	753	760	767	774	781	789	796	803	810	
614	78 817	824	831	838	845	852	859	866	873	880	
615	78 888	895	902	909	916	923	930	937	944	951	
616	78 958	965	972	979	986	993	*000	*007	*014	*021	
617	79 029	036	043	050	057	064	071	078	085	092	
618	79 099	106	113	120	127	134	141	148	155	162	
619	79 169	176	183	190	197	204	211	218	225	232	
620	79 239	246	253	260	267	274	281	288	295	302	
621	79 309	316	323	330	337	344	351	358	365	372	
622	79 379	386	393	400	407	414	421	428	435	442	
623	79 449	456	463	470	477	484	491	498	505	511	
624	79 518	525	532	539	546	553	560	567	574	581	
625	79 588	595	602	609	616	623	630	637	644	650	
626	79 657	664	671	678	685	692	699	706	713	720	
627	79 727	734	741	748	754	761	768	775	782	789	
628	79 796	803	810	817	824	831	837	844	851	858	
629	79 865	872	879	886	893	900	906	913	920	927	
630	79 934	941	948	955	962	969	975	982	989	996	
631	80 003	010	017	024	030	037	044	051	058	065	
632	80 072	079	085	092	099	106	113	120	127	134	
633	80 140	147	154	161	168	175	182	188	195	202	
634	80 209	216	223	229	236	243	250	257	264	271	
635	80 277	284	291	298	305	312	318	325	332	339	
636	80 346	353	359	366	373	380	387	393	400	407	
637	80 414	421	428	434	441	448	455	462	468	475	
638	80 482	489	496	502	509	516	523	530	536	543	
639	80 550	557	564	570	577	584	591	598	604	611	
640	80 618	625	632	638	645	652	659	665	672	679	
641	80 686	693	699	706	713	720	726	733	740	747	
642	80 754	760	767	774	781	787	794	801	808	814	
643	80 821	828	835	841	848	855	862	868	875	882	
644	80 889	895	902	909	916	922	929	936	943	949	
645	80 956	963	969	976	983	990	996	*003	*010	*017	
646	81 023	030	037	043	050	057	064	070	077	084	
647	81 090	097	104	111	117	124	131	137	144	151	
648	81 158	164	171	178	184	191	198	204	211	218	
649	81 224	231	238	245	251	258	265	271	278	285	
650	81 291	298	305	311	318	325	331	338	345	351	
N	0	1	2	3	4	5	6	7	8	9	Prop. Parts

Prop. Parts

8		**7**		**6**	
1	0.8	1	0.7	1	0.6
2	1.6	2	1.4	2	1.2
3	2.4	3	2.1	3	1.8
4	3.2	4	2.8	4	2.4
5	4.0	5	3.5	5	3.0
6	4.8	6	4.2	6	3.6
7	5.6	7	4.9	7	4.2
8	6.4	8	5.6	8	4.8
9	7.2	9	6.3	9	5.4

Common Logarithms (Five-Place) of the Natural Numbers 1 to 10,000

Prop. Parts	N	0	1	2	3	4	5	6	7	8	9
	650	81 291	298	305	311	318	325	331	338	345	351
	651	81 358	365	371	378	385	391	398	405	411	418
	652	81 425	431	438	445	451	458	465	471	478	485
	653	81 491	498	505	511	518	525	531	538	544	551
	654	81 558	564	571	578	584	591	598	604	611	617
	655	81 624	631	637	644	651	657	664	671	677	684
	656	81 690	697	704	710	717	723	730	737	743	750
	657	81 757	763	770	776	783	790	796	803	809	816
	658	81 823	829	836	842	849	856	862	869	875	882
	659	81 889	895	902	908	915	921	928	935	941	948
	660	81 954	961	968	974	981	987	994	*000	*007	*014
	661	82 020	027	033	040	046	053	060	066	073	079
7	662	82 086	092	099	105	112	119	125	132	138	145
1 0.7	663	82 151	158	164	171	178	184	191	197	204	210
2 1.4	664	82 217	223	230	236	243	249	256	263	269	276
3 2.1	665	82 282	289	295	302	308	315	321	328	334	341
4 2.8	666	82 347	354	360	367	373	380	387	393	400	406
5 3.5	667	82 413	419	426	432	439	445	452	458	465	471
6 4.2	668	82 478	484	491	497	504	510	517	523	530	536
7 4.9	669	82 543	549	556	562	569	575	582	588	595	601
8 5.6	670	82 607	614	620	627	633	640	646	653	659	666
9 6.3	671	82 672	679	685	692	698	705	711	718	724	730
	672	82 737	743	750	756	763	769	776	782	789	795
	673	82 802	808	814	821	827	834	840	847	853	860
	674	82 866	872	879	885	892	898	905	911	918	924
	675	82 930	937	943	950	956	963	969	975	982	988
	676	82 995	*001	*008	*014	*020	*027	*033	*040	*046	*052
	677	83 059	065	072	078	085	091	097	104	110	117
	678	83 123	129	136	142	149	155	161	168	174	181
	679	83 187	193	200	206	213	219	225	232	238	245
	680	83 251	257	264	270	276	283	289	296	302	308
	681	83 315	321	327	334	340	347	353	359	366	372
6	682	83 378	385	391	398	404	410	417	423	429	436
1 0.6	683	83 442	448	455	461	467	474	480	487	493	499
2 1.2	684	83 506	512	518	525	531	537	544	550	556	563
3 1.8	685	83 569	575	582	588	594	601	607	613	620	626
4 2.4	686	83 632	639	645	651	658	664	670	677	683	689
5 3.0	687	83 696	702	708	715	721	727	734	740	746	753
6 3.6	688	83 759	765	771	778	784	790	797	803	809	816
7 4.2	689	83 822	828	835	841	847	853	860	866	872	879
8 4.8	690	83 885	891	897	904	910	916	923	929	935	942
9 5.4	691	83 948	954	960	967	973	979	985	992	998	*004
	692	84 011	017	023	029	036	042	048	055	061	067
	693	84 073	080	086	092	098	105	111	117	123	130
	694	84 136	142	148	155	161	167	173	180	186	192
	695	84 198	205	211	217	223	230	236	242	248	255
	696	84 261	267	273	280	286	292	298	305	311	317
	697	84 323	330	336	342	348	354	361	367	373	379
	698	84 386	392	398	404	410	417	423	429	435	442
	699	84 448	454	460	466	473	479	485	491	497	504
	700	84 510	516	522	528	535	541	547	553	559	566
Prop. Parts	N	0	1	2	3	4	5	6	7	8	9

Common Logarithms (Five-Place) of the Natural Numbers 1 to 10,000

N	0	1	2	3	4	5	6	7	8	9	Prop. Parts	
700	84 510	516	522	528	535	541	547	553	559	566		
701	84 572	578	584	590	597	603	609	615	621	628		
702	84 634	640	646	652	658	665	671	677	683	689		
703	84 696	702	708	714	720	726	733	739	745	751		
704	84 757	763	770	776	782	788	794	800	807	813		
705	84 819	825	831	837	844	850	856	862	868	874		
706	84 880	887	893	899	905	911	917	924	930	936		
707	84 942	948	954	960	967	973	979	985	991	997		**7**
708	85 003	009	016	022	028	034	040	046	052	058	1	0.7
709	85 065	071	077	083	089	095	101	107	114	120	2	1.4
											3	2.1
710	85 126	132	138	144	150	156	163	169	175	181	4	2.8
711	85 187	193	199	205	211	217	224	230	236	242	5	3.5
712	85 248	254	260	266	272	278	285	291	297	303	6	4.2
713	85 309	315	321	327	333	339	345	352	358	364	7	4.9
714	85 370	376	382	388	394	400	406	412	418	425	8	5.6
											9	6.3
715	85 431	437	443	449	455	461	467	473	479	485		
716	85 491	497	503	509	516	522	528	534	540	546		
717	85 552	558	564	570	576	582	588	594	600	606		
718	85 612	618	625	631	637	643	649	655	661	667		
719	85 673	679	685	691	697	703	709	715	721	727		
720	85 733	739	745	751	757	763	769	775	781	788		
721	85 794	800	806	812	818	824	830	836	842	848		
722	85 854	860	866	872	878	884	890	896	902	908		**6**
723	85 914	920	926	932	938	944	950	956	962	968	1	0.6
											2	1.2
724	85 974	980	986	992	998	*004	*010	*016	*022	*028	3	1.8
725	86 034	040	046	052	058	064	070	076	082	088	4	2.4
726	86 094	100	106	112	118	124	130	136	141	147	5	3.0
											6	3.6
727	86 153	159	165	171	177	183	189	195	201	207	7	4.2
728	86 213	219	225	231	237	243	249	255	261	267	8	4.8
729	86 273	279	285	291	297	303	308	314	320	326	9	5.4
730	86 332	338	344	350	356	362	368	374	380	386		
731	86 392	398	404	410	415	421	427	433	439	445		
732	86 451	457	463	469	475	481	487	493	499	504		
733	86 510	516	522	528	534	540	546	552	558	564		
734	86 570	576	581	587	593	599	605	611	617	623		
735	86 629	635	641	646	652	658	664	670	676	682		
736	86 688	694	700	705	711	717	723	729	735	741		**5**
737	86 747	753	759	764	770	776	782	788	794	800	1	0.5
738	86 806	812	817	823	829	835	841	847	853	859	2	1.0
739	86 864	870	876	882	888	894	900	906	911	917	3	1.5
											4	2.0
740	86 923	929	935	941	947	953	958	964	970	976	5	2.5
741	86 982	988	994	999	*005	*011	*017	*023	*029	*035	6	3.0
742	87 040	046	052	058	064	070	075	081	087	093	7	3.5
743	87 099	105	111	116	122	128	134	140	146	151	8	4.0
											9	4.5
744	87 157	163	169	175	181	186	192	198	204	210		
745	87 216	221	227	233	239	245	251	256	262	268		
746	87 274	280	286	291	297	303	309	315	320	326		
747	87 332	338	344	349	355	361	367	373	379	384		
748	87 390	396	402	408	413	419	425	431	437	442		
749	87 448	454	460	466	471	477	483	489	495	500		
750	87 506	512	518	523	529	535	541	547	552	558		
N	0	1	2	3	4	5	6	7	8	9	Prop. Parts	

Common Logarithms (Five-Place) of the Natural Numbers 1 to 10,000

Prop. Parts	N	0	1	2	3	4	5	6	7	8	9
	750	87 506	512	518	523	529	535	541	547	552	558
	751	87 564	570	576	581	587	593	599	604	610	616
	752	87 622	628	633	639	645	651	656	662	668	674
	753	87 679	685	691	697	703	708	714	720	726	731
	754	87 737	743	749	754	760	766	772	777	783	789
	755	87 795	800	806	812	818	823	829	835	841	846
	756	87 852	858	864	869	875	881	887	892	898	904
	757	87 910	915	921	927	933	938	944	950	955	961
	758	87 967	973	978	984	990	996	*001	*007	*013	*018
	759	88 024	030	036	041	047	053	058	064	070	076
	760	88 081	087	093	098	104	110	116	121	127	133
	761	88 138	144	150	156	161	167	173	178	184	190
6	762	88 195	201	207	213	218	224	230	235	241	247
1 0.6	763	88 252	258	264	270	275	281	287	292	298	304
2 1.2	764	88 309	315	321	326	332	338	343	349	355	360
3 1.8	765	88 366	372	377	383	389	395	400	406	412	417
4 2.4	766	88 423	429	434	440	446	451	457	463	468	474
5 3.0	767	88 480	485	491	497	502	508	513	519	525	530
6 3.6	768	88 536	542	547	553	559	564	570	576	581	587
7 4.2	769	88 593	598	604	610	615	621	627	632	638	643
8 4.8	770	88 649	655	660	666	672	677	683	689	694	700
9 5.4	771	88 705	711	717	722	728	734	739	745	750	756
	772	88 762	767	773	779	784	790	795	801	807	812
	773	88 818	824	829	835	840	846	852	857	863	868
	774	88 874	880	885	891	897	902	908	913	919	925
	775	88 930	936	941	947	953	958	964	969	975	981
	776	88 986	992	997	*003	*009	*014	*020	*025	*031	*037
	777	89 042	048	053	059	064	070	076	081	087	092
	778	89 098	104	109	115	120	126	131	137	143	148
	779	89 154	159	165	170	176	182	187	193	198	204
	780	89 209	215	221	226	232	237	243	248	254	260
	781	89 265	271	276	282	287	293	298	304	310	315
5	782	89 321	326	332	337	343	348	354	360	365	371
1 0.5	783	89 376	382	387	393	398	404	409	415	421	426
2 1.0	784	89 432	437	443	448	454	459	465	470	476	481
3 1.5	785	89 487	492	498	504	509	515	520	526	531	537
4 2.0	786	89 542	548	553	559	564	570	575	581	586	592
5 2.5	787	89 597	603	609	614	620	625	631	636	642	647
6 3.0	788	89 653	658	664	669	675	680	686	691	697	702
7 3.5	789	89 708	713	719	724	730	735	741	746	752	757
8 4.0	790	89 763	768	774	779	785	790	796	801	807	812
9 4.5	791	89 818	823	829	834	840	845	851	856	862	867
	792	89 873	878	883	889	894	900	905	911	916	922
	793	89 927	933	938	944	949	955	960	966	971	977
	794	89 982	988	993	998	*004	*009	*015	*020	*026	*031
	795	90 037	042	048	053	059	064	069	075	080	086
	796	90 091	097	102	108	113	119	124	129	135	140
	797	90 146	151	157	162	168	173	179	184	189	195
	798	90 200	206	211	217	222	227	233	238	244	249
	799	90 255	260	266	271	276	282	287	293	298	304
	800	90 309	314	320	325	331	336	342	347	352	358
Prop. Parts	N	0	1	2	3	4	5	6	7	8	9

Common Logarithms (Five-Place) of the Natural Numbers 1 to 10,000

N	0	1	2	3	4	5	6	7	8	9	Prop. Parts
800	90 309	314	320	325	331	336	342	347	352	358	
801	90 363	369	374	380	385	390	396	401	407	412	
802	90 417	423	428	434	439	445	450	455	461	466	
803	90 472	477	482	488	493	499	504	509	515	520	
804	90 526	531	536	542	547	553	558	563	569	574	
805	90 580	585	590	596	601	607	612	617	623	628	
806	90 634	639	644	650	655	660	666	671	677	682	
807	90 687	693	698	703	709	714	720	725	730	736	
808	90 741	747	752	757	763	768	773	779	784	789	
809	90 795	800	806	811	816	822	827	832	838	843	
810	90 849	854	859	865	870	875	881	886	891	897	
811	90 902	907	913	918	924	929	934	940	945	950	
812	90 956	961	966	972	977	982	988	993	998	*004	**6**
813	91 009	014	020	025	030	036	041	046	052	057	1 0.6
814	91 062	068	073	078	084	089	094	100	105	110	2 1.2 / 3 1.8
815	91 116	121	126	132	137	142	148	153	158	164	4 2.4
816	91 169	174	180	185	190	196	201	206	212	217	5 3.0 / 6 3.6
817	91 222	228	233	238	243	249	254	259	265	270	7 4.2
818	91 275	281	286	291	297	302	307	312	318	323	8 4.8
819	91 328	334	339	344	350	355	360	365	371	376	9 5.4
820	91 381	387	392	397	403	408	413	418	424	429	
821	91 434	440	445	450	455	461	466	471	477	482	
822	91 487	492	498	503	508	514	519	524	529	535	
823	91 540	545	551	556	561	566	572	577	582	587	
824	91 593	598	603	609	614	619	624	630	635	640	
825	91 645	651	656	661	666	672	677	682	687	693	
826	91 698	703	709	714	719	724	730	735	740	745	
827	91 751	756	761	766	772	777	782	787	793	798	
828	91 803	808	814	819	824	829	834	840	845	850	
829	91 855	861	866	871	876	882	887	892	897	903	
830	91 908	913	918	924	929	934	939	944	950	955	
831	91 960	965	971	976	981	986	991	997	*002	*007	**5**
832	92 012	018	023	028	033	038	044	049	054	059	1 0.5
833	92 065	070	075	080	085	091	096	101	106	111	2 1.0 / 3 1.5
834	92 117	122	127	132	137	143	148	153	158	163	4 2.0
835	92 169	174	179	184	189	195	200	205	210	215	5 2.5 / 6 3.0
836	92 221	226	231	236	241	247	252	257	262	267	7 3.5
837	92 273	278	283	288	293	298	304	309	314	319	8 4.0
838	92 324	330	335	340	345	350	355	361	366	371	9 4.5
839	92 376	381	387	392	397	402	407	412	418	423	
840	92 428	433	438	443	449	454	459	464	469	474	
841	92 480	485	490	495	500	505	511	516	521	526	
842	92 531	536	542	547	552	557	562	567	572	578	
843	92 583	588	593	598	603	609	614	619	624	629	
844	92 634	639	645	650	655	660	665	670	675	681	
845	92 686	691	696	701	706	711	716	722	727	732	
846	92 737	742	747	752	758	763	768	773	778	783	
847	92 788	793	799	804	809	814	819	824	829	834	
848	92 840	845	850	855	860	865	870	875	881	886	
849	92 891	896	901	906	911	916	921	927	932	937	
850	92 942	947	952	957	962	967	973	978	983	988	
N	0	1	2	3	4	5	6	7	8	9	Prop. Parts

APPENDIX TABLE X — *Continued*

Common Logarithms (Five-Place) of the Natural Numbers 1 to 10,000

Prop. Parts	N	0	1	2	3	4	5	6	7	8	9
	850	92 942	947	952	957	962	967	973	978	983	988
	851	92 993	998	*003	*008	*013	*018	*024	*029	*034	*039
	852	93 044	049	054	059	064	069	075	080	085	090
	853	93 095	100	105	110	115	120	125	131	136	141
	854	93 146	151	156	161	166	171	176	181	186	192
	855	93 197	202	207	212	217	222	227	232	237	242
	856	93 247	252	258	263	268	273	278	283	288	293
	857	93 298	303	308	313	318	323	328	334	339	344
	858	93 349	354	359	364	369	374	379	384	389	394
	859	93 399	404	409	414	420	425	430	435	440	445
	860	93 450	455	460	465	470	475	480	485	490	495
	861	93 500	505	510	515	520	526	531	536	541	546
	862	93 551	556	561	566	571	576	581	586	591	596
	863	93 601	606	611	616	621	626	631	636	641	646
	864	93 651	656	661	666	671	676	682	687	692	697
	865	93 702	707	712	717	722	727	732	737	742	747
	866	93 752	757	762	767	772	777	782	787	792	797
	867	93 802	807	812	817	822	827	832	837	842	847
	868	93 852	857	862	867	872	877	882	887	892	897
	869	93 902	907	912	917	922	927	932	937	942	947
	870	93 952	957	962	967	972	977	982	987	992	997
	871	94 002	007	012	017	022	027	032	037	042	047
	872	94 052	057	062	067	072	077	082	086	091	096
	873	94 101	106	111	116	121	126	131	136	141	146
	874	94 151	156	161	166	171	176	181	186	191	196
	875	94 201	206	211	216	221	226	231	236	240	245
	876	94 250	255	260	265	270	275	280	285	290	295
	877	94 300	305	310	315	320	325	330	335	340	345
	878	94 349	354	359	364	369	374	379	384	389	394
	879	94 399	404	409	414	419	424	429	433	438	443
	880	94 448	453	458	463	468	473	478	483	488	493
	881	94 498	503	507	512	517	522	527	532	537	542
	882	94 547	552	557	562	567	571	576	581	586	591
	883	94 596	601	606	611	616	621	626	630	635	640
	884	94 645	650	655	660	665	670	675	680	685	689
	885	94 694	699	704	709	714	719	724	729	734	738
	886	94 743	748	753	758	763	768	773	778	783	787
	887	94 792	797	802	807	812	817	822	827	832	836
	888	94 841	846	851	856	861	866	871	876	880	885
	889	94 890	895	900	905	910	915	919	924	929	934
	890	94 939	944	949	954	959	963	968	973	978	983
	891	94 988	993	998	*002	*007	*012	*017	*022	*027	*032
	892	95 036	041	046	051	056	061	066	071	075	080
	893	95 085	090	095	100	105	109	114	119	124	129
	894	95 134	139	143	148	153	158	163	168	173	177
	895	95 182	187	192	197	202	207	211	216	221	226
	896	95 231	236	240	245	250	255	260	265	270	274
	897	95 279	284	289	294	299	303	308	313	318	323
	898	95 328	332	337	342	347	352	357	361	366	371
	899	95 376	381	386	390	395	400	405	410	415	419
	900	95 424	429	434	439	444	448	453	458	463	468
Prop. Parts	N	0	1	2	3	4	5	6	7	8	9

Prop. Parts

6		5		4	
1	0.6	1	0.5	1	0.4
2	1.2	2	1.0	2	0.8
3	1.8	3	1.5	3	1.2
4	2.4	4	2.0	4	1.6
5	3.0	5	2.5	5	2.0
6	3.6	6	3.0	6	2.4
7	4.2	7	3.5	7	2.8
8	4.8	8	4.0	8	3.2
9	5.4	9	4.5	9	3.6

Common Logarithms (Five-Place) of the Natural Numbers 1 to 10,000

N	0	1	2	3	4	5	6	7	8	9
900	95 424	429	434	439	444	448	453	458	463	468
901	95 472	477	482	487	492	497	501	506	511	516
902	95 521	525	530	535	540	545	550	554	559	564
903	95 569	574	578	583	588	593	598	602	607	612
904	95 617	622	626	631	636	641	646	650	655	660
905	95 665	670	674	679	684	689	694	698	703	708
906	95 713	718	722	727	732	737	742	746	751	756
907	95 761	766	770	775	780	785	789	794	799	804
908	95 809	813	818	823	828	832	837	842	847	852
909	95 856	861	866	871	875	880	885	890	895	899
910	95 904	909	914	018	923	928	933	938	942	947
911	95 952	957	961	966	971	976	980	985	990	995
912	95 999	*004	*009	*014	*019	*023	*028	*033	*038	*042
913	96 047	052	057	061	066	071	076	080	085	090
914	96 095	099	104	109	114	118	123	128	133	137
915	96 142	147	152	156	161	166	171	175	180	185
916	96 190	194	199	204	209	213	218	223	227	232
917	96 237	242	246	251	256	261	265	270	275	280
918	96 284	289	294	298	303	308	313	317	322	327
919	96 332	336	341	346	350	355	360	365	369	374
920	96 379	384	388	393	398	402	407	412	417	421
921	96 426	431	435	440	445	450	454	459	464	468
922	96 473	478	483	487	492	497	501	506	511	515
923	96 520	525	530	534	539	544	548	553	558	562
924	96 567	572	577	581	586	591	595	600	605	609
925	96 614	619	624	628	633	638	642	647	652	656
926	96 661	666	670	675	680	685	689	694	699	703
927	96 708	713	717	722	727	731	736	741	745	750
928	96 755	759	764	769	774	778	783	788	792	797
929	96 802	806	811	816	820	825	830	834	839	844
930	96 848	853	858	862	867	872	876	881	886	890
931	96 895	900	904	909	914	918	923	928	932	937
932	96 942	946	951	956	960	965	970	974	979	984
933	96 988	993	997	*002	*007	*011	*016	*021	*025	*030
934	97 035	039	044	049	053	058	063	067	072	077
935	97 081	086	090	095	100	104	109	114	118	123
936	97 128	132	137	142	146	151	155	160	165	169
937	97 174	179	183	188	192	197	202	206	211	216
938	97 220	225	230	234	239	243	248	253	257	262
939	97 267	271	276	280	285	290	294	299	304	308
940	97 313	317	322	327	331	336	340	345	350	354
941	97 359	364	368	373	377	382	387	391	396	400
942	97 405	410	414	419	424	428	433	437	442	447
943	97 451	456	460	465	470	474	479	483	488	493
944	97 497	502	506	511	516	520	525	529	534	539
945	97 543	548	552	557	562	566	571	575	580	585
946	97 589	594	598	603	607	612	617	621	626	630
947	97 635	640	644	649	653	658	663	667	672	676
948	97 681	685	690	695	699	704	708	713	717	722
949	97 727	731	736	740	745	749	754	759	763	768
950	97 772	777	782	786	791	795	800	804	809	813
N	0	1	2	3	4	5	6	7	8	9

Prop. Parts

	5		4
1	0.5	1	0.4
2	1.0	2	0.8
3	1.5	3	1.2
4	2.0	4	1.6
5	2.5	5	2.0
6	3.0	6	2.4
7	3.5	7	2.8
8	4.0	8	3.2
9	4.5	9	3.6

Common Logarithms (Five-Place) of the Natural Numbers 1 to 10,000

Prop. Parts		N	0	1	2	3	4	5	6	7	8	9
		950	97 772	777	782	786	791	795	800	804	809	813
		951	97 818	823	827	832	836	841	845	850	855	859
		952	97 864	868	873	877	882	886	891	896	900	905
		953	97 909	914	918	923	928	932	937	941	946	950
		954	97 955	959	964	968	973	978	982	987	991	996
		955	98 000	005	009	014	019	023	028	032	037	041
		956	98 046	050	055	059	064	068	073	078	082	087
		957	98 091	096	100	105	109	114	118	123	127	132
		958	98 137	141	146	150	155	159	164	168	173	177
		959	98 182	186	191	195	200	204	209	214	218	223
		960	98 227	232	236	241	245	250	254	259	263	268
		961	98 272	277	281	286	290	295	299	304	308	313
	5	962	98 318	322	327	331	336	340	345	349	354	358
1	0.5	963	98 363	367	372	376	381	385	390	394	399	403
2	1.0											
3	1.5	964	98 408	412	417	421	426	430	435	439	444	448
4	2.0	965	98 453	457	462	466	471	475	480	484	489	493
5	2.5	966	98 498	502	507	511	516	520	525	529	534	538
6	3.0											
7	3.5	967	98 543	547	552	556	561	565	570	574	579	583
8	4.0	968	98 588	592	597	601	605	610	614	619	623	628
9	4.5	969	98 632	637	641	646	650	655	659	664	668	673
		970	98 677	682	686	691	695	700	704	709	713	717
		971	98 722	726	731	735	740	744	749	753	758	762
		972	98 767	771	776	780	784	789	793	798	802	807
		973	98 811	816	820	825	829	834	838	843	847	851
		974	98 856	860	865	869	874	878	883	887	892	896
		975	98 900	905	909	914	918	923	927	932	936	941
		976	98 945	949	954	958	963	967	972	976	981	985
		977	98 989	994	998	*003	*007	*012	*016	*021	*025	*029
		978	99 034	038	043	047	052	056	061	065	069	074
		979	99 078	083	087	092	096	100	105	109	114	118
		980	99 123	127	131	136	140	145	149	154	158	162
		981	99 167	171	176	180	185	189	193	198	202	207
	4	982	99 211	216	220	224	229	233	238	242	247	251
1	0.4	983	99 255	260	264	269	273	277	282	286	291	295
2	0.8											
3	1.2	984	99 300	304	308	313	317	322	326	330	335	339
4	1.6	985	99 344	348	352	357	361	366	370	374	379	383
5	2.0	986	99 388	392	396	401	405	410	414	419	423	427
6	2.4											
7	2.8	987	99 432	436	441	445	449	454	458	463	467	471
8	3.2	988	99 476	480	484	489	493	498	502	506	511	515
9	3.6	989	99 520	524	528	533	537	542	546	550	555	559
		990	99 564	568	572	577	581	585	590	594	599	603
		991	99 607	612	616	621	625	629	634	638	642	647
		992	99 651	656	660	664	669	673	677	682	686	691
		993	99 695	699	704	708	712	717	721	726	730	734
		994	99 739	743	747	752	756	760	765	769	774	778
		995	99 782	787	791	795	800	804	808	813	817	822
		996	99 826	830	835	839	843	848	852	856	861	865
		997	99 870	874	878	883	887	891	896	900	904	909
		998	99 913	917	922	926	930	935	939	944	948	952
		999	99 957	961	965	970	974	978	983	987	991	996
		1000	00 000	004	009	013	017	022	026	030	035	039
Prop. Parts		N	0	1	2	3	4	5	6	7	8	9

List of References

1. Adler, F., "Yates' Correction and the Statisticians," *Journal of the American Statistical Association*, Dec., 1951.
2. Allen, R. G. D., *Mathematical Analysis for Economists*, London, Macmillan, 1942.
3. Allen, R. G. D., *Statistics for Economists*, London, Hutchinson, 1949.
4. Anderson, R. L. and Bancroft, T. A., *Statistical Theory in Research*, New York, McGraw-Hill, 1952.
5. Anglo-American Council on Productivity, *Final Report*, London (also U.S. Department of Commerce, Washington, D.C.), 1952.
6. Barger, H., *The Transportation Industries, 1889–1946: A Study of Output, Employment and Productivity*, New York, National Bureau of Economic Research, 1951.
7. Barger, H. and Schurr, S. H., *The Mining Industries: A Study of Output, Employment and Productivity*, New York, National Bureau of Economic Research, 1944.
8. Bartlett, M. S., "Properties of Sufficiency and Statistical Tests," *Proceedings of the Royal Society of London*, A, Vol. 160, 1937.
9. Bartlett, M. S., "The Use of Transformations," *Biometrics*, of the Biometrics Section of the American Statistical Association, March, 1947.
10. Beckett, S. H. and Robertson, R. D., "The Economical Irrigation of Alfalfa in the Sacramento Valley," Univ. of California Agricultural Experiment Station, *Bulletin* 280, 1917.
11. Burns, A. F., "Frickey on the Decomposition of Time Series," *Review of Economic Statistics*, August, 1944.
12. Burns, A. F., *Production Trends in the United States Since 1870*, New York, National Bureau of Economic Research, 1934.
13. Burns, A. F. and Mitchell, W. C., *Measuring Business Cycles*, New York, National Bureau of Economic Research, 1946.
14. Carter, C. F., Reddaway, W. B. and Stone, R., *The Measurement of Production Movements*, Cambridge University Press, 1948.
15. Churchman, C. W., *Theory of Experimental Inference*, New York, Macmillan, 1948.
16. Clark, C. E., *An Introduction to Statistics*, New York, Wiley, 1953.
17. Cochran, W. G., *Sampling Techniques*, New York, Wiley, 1953.
18. Cochran, W. G., "Some Consequences when the Assumptions for the

Analysis of Variance are not Satisfied," *Biometrics*, of the Biometrics Section of the American Statistical Association, March, 1947.

19. Cohen, Morris R., "The Statistical View of Nature," *Journal of the American Statistical Association*, June, 1936.

20. Committee on Graphics, *A Guide for Preparing Technical Illustrations for Publication and Projection*, American Standards Association and American Society of Mechanical Engineers, New York, 1953.

21. Committee on Standards for Graphic Presentation, "Time Series Charts, A Manual of Design and Construction," American Standards Association and American Society of Mechanical Engineers, New York, 1938.

22. Cramér, H., *The Elements of Probability Theory and Some of its Applications*, New York, Wiley, 1954.

23. Cramér, H., *Mathematical Methods of Statistics*, Princeton University Press, 1951.

24. Croxton, F. E. and Cowden, D. J., *Applied General Statistics*, New York, Prentice-Hall, 1946.

25. David, F. N., *Probability Theory for Statistical Methods*, Cambridge University Press, 1949.

26. David, F. N., *Tables of the Correlation Coefficient*, Cambridge University Press, 1938.

27. Dean, J., "The Relation of Cost to Output for a Leather Belt Shop," *Technical Paper* 2, New York, National Bureau of Economic Research, 1941.

28. Dean, J., *Statistical Cost Functions of a Hosiery Mill*, University of Chicago Press, 1941.

29. Deming, W. Edwards, *Some Theory of Sampling*, New York, Wiley, 1950.

30. Deming, W. Edwards, *Statistical Adjustment of Data*, New York, Wiley, 1943.

31. Deming, W. E. and Birge, R. T., "On the Statistical Theory of Errors," *Reviews of Modern Physics*, July, 1934.

32. Dixon, W. J. and Massey, F. J. Jr., *Introduction to Statistical Analysis*, New York, McGraw-Hill, 1951.

33. Eisenhart, C., "Some Assumptions Underlying the Analysis of Variance," *Biometrics*, of the Biometrics Section of the American Statistical Association, March, 1947.

34. Eisenhart, C., Hastay, M. W. and Wallis, W. A., (editors for Statistical Research Group, Columbia University), *Selected Techniques of Statistical Analysis*, New York, McGraw-Hill, 1947.

35. Elderton, W. P., *Frequency Curves and Correlation*, 4th ed., Washington, D.C., Harren Press, 1953.

36. Ezekiel, M., "A Method of Handling Curvilinear Correlation for Any Number of Variables," *Journal of the American Statistical Association*, Dec., 1924.

37. Ezekiel, M., *Methods of Correlation Analysis*, 2nd ed., New York, Wiley, 1941.

38. Fabricant, S., *Employment in Manufacturing, 1899–1939*, New York, National Bureau of Economic Research, 1942.

39. Fabricant, S., *The Output of Manufacturing Industries, 1890–1937*, New York, National Bureau of Economic Research, 1940.

40. Federal Reserve System, Board of Governors, *Charts on Money, Bank Credit, Money Rates and Business*, Washington, D.C.

41. Federal Reserve System, Board of Governors, "1954 Survey of Consumer Finances," *Federal Reserve Bulletin*, March, June, July, 1954.

42. Federal Reserve System, Board of Governors, "The Revised Federal Reserve Index of Industrial Production," *Federal Reserve Bulletin*, Dec., 1953.

43. Feller, W., *An Introduction to Probability Theory and its Applications*, Vol. I, New York, Wiley, 1950.

44. Ferber, R., "A Study of Aggregate Consumption Functions," *Technical Paper* 8, New York, National Bureau of Economic Research, 1953.

45. Festinger, L. and Katz, D. ed., *Research Methods in the Behavioral Sciences*, New York, The Dryden Press, 1953.

46. Fisher, Irving, *The Making of Index Numbers*, Boston, Houghton Mifflin, 1922.

47. Fisher, Sir Ronald (R.A.), *Contributions to Mathematical Statistics*, New York, Wiley, 1950.

48. Fisher, Sir Ronald (R.A.), *The Design of Experiments*, 4th ed., Edinburgh and London, Oliver and Boyd, Ltd., 1942.

49. Fisher, Sir Ronald (R.A.), "Frequency Distribution of the Values of the Correlation Coefficient in Samples from an Indefinitely Large Population," *Biometrika*, Vol. 10, 1915.

50. Fisher, Sir Ronald (R.A.), *Statistical Methods for Research Workers*, 11th ed., New York, Hafner, 1950.

51. Fisher, Sir Ronald (R.A.) and Yates, F., *Statistical Tables for Biological, Agricultural and Medical Research*, 3rd ed., New York, Hafner, 1948.

52. Florence, P. S., *The Statistical Method in Economics and Political Science*, New York, Harcourt, Brace, 1929.

53. Fowler, C. B., Griffin, J. I., Cohen, J. B., Cropsey, J., Greenwald, W. I. and Sethur, F., *Economic Handbook, A Visual Survey*, New York, Crowell, 1955.

54. Freeman, H. A., *Industrial Statistics*, New York, Wiley, 1942.

55. Freund, J. E., *Modern Elementary Statistics*, New York, Prentice-Hall, 1952.

56. Frickey, E., *Economic Fluctuations in the United States*, Harvard Economic Studies 73, Cambridge, 1942.

57. Friedman, Milton, "The Use of Ranks to Avoid the Assumption of Normality Implicit in the Analysis of Variance," *Journal of the American Statistical Association*, Dec., 1937.

58. Frisch, R., "Annual Survey of Economic Theory: The Problem of Index Numbers," *Econometrica*, January, 1936.

59. Frisch, R., "Some Basic Principles of Price of Living Measurements," *Econometrica*, Oct., 1954.

60. Frisch, R., *Statistical Confluence Analysis by Means of Complete Regression Systems*, Oslo, Universitetets Økonomiske Institutt, 1934.

61. Fryer, H. C., *Elements of Statistics*, New York, Wiley, 1954.

62. Geary, R. C., "The Concept of Net Volume of Output with Special Reference to Irish Data," *Journal of the Royal Statistical Society*, Vol. 107, 1944.

63. Gould, J. M., *Output and Productivity in the Electric and Gas Utilities*, New York, National Bureau of Economic Research, 1946.

64. Goulden, C. H., *Methods of Statistical Analysis*, 2nd ed., New York, Wiley, 1952.

65. Greenwood, E. R. Jr., *A Detailed Proof of the Chi-Square Test of Goodness of Fit*, Harvard University Press, 1940.

66. Hald, A., *The Decomposition of a Series of Observations Composed of a Trend, a Periodic Movement, and a Stochastic Variable*, Copenhagen, G. E. C. Gads, 1948.

67. Hansen, M. H., Hurwitz, W. N. and Madow, W. G., *Sample Survey Methods and Theories*, Vol. I, Methods and Applications; Vol. II, Theory, New York, Wiley, 1953.

68. Hartley, H. O., "The Maximum F-Ratio as a Short-cut Test for Heterogeneity of Variance," *Biometrika*, Vol. 37, 1950.

69. Hoel, P. G., *Introduction to Mathematical Statistics*, 2nd ed., New York, Wiley, 1954.

70. Hotelling, H., "New Light on the Correlation Coefficient and its Transforms," *Journal of the Royal Statistical Society*, Series B, Vol. 15, No. 2, 1953.

71. International Labor Office, "Methods of Labor Productivity Statistics," *Studies and Reports, New Series*, No. 18, Geneva, 1951.

72. Johnson, P. O., *Statistical Methods in Research*, New York, Prentice-Hall, 1949.

73. Joy, A. and Thomas, W., "The Use of Moving Averages in the Measurement of Seasonal Variations," *Journal of the American Statistical Association*, Sept., 1928.

74. Juliber, G. S., "Relation Between Seasonal Amplitudes and the Level of Production — An Application to the Production of Steel Ingots," *Journal of the American Statistical Association*, Dec., 1941.

75. Katona, G. and Mueller, E., *Consumer Attitudes and Demand*, Survey

Research Center, Institute for Social Research, University of Michigan, 1953.

76. Kelley, Truman L., *Fundamentals of Statistics*, Cambridge, Harvard University Press, 1947.

77. Kelley, Truman L., *The Kelley Statistical Tables*, rev. ed., Harvard University Press, 1948.

78. Kendall, M. G., *The Advanced Theory of Statistics*, 3rd ed., London, Griffin, 1947.

79. Kendall, M. G., *Contributions to the Study of Oscillatory Time Series*, Cambridge University Press, 1946.

80. Kendall, M. G., *Rank Correlation Methods*, London, Griffin, 1948.

81. Kendall, M. G., "The Statistical Approach," *Economica*, May, 1950.

82. Keynes, J. M., *A Treatise on Probability*, New York, Macmillan, 1921.

83. Klein, Lawrence R., *Contributions of Survey Methods to Economics*, New York, Columbia University Press, 1954.

84. Konus, A. A., "The Problem of the True Index of the Cost of Living," *Econometrica*, January, 1939.

85. Koopmans, T. C., "Measurement without Theory," *Review of Economic Statistics*, Aug., 1947.

86. Koopmans, T. C., ed., *Statistical Inference in Dynamic Economic Models*, New York, Wiley, 1950.

87. Kuznets, S., *Seasonal Variations in Industry and Trade*, New York, National Bureau of Economic Research, 1933.

88. Kuznets, S., *Secular Movements in Production and Prices*, Boston, Houghton Mifflin, 1930.

89. Lazarsfeld, P. F., ed., *Mathematical Thinking in the Social Sciences*, Glencoe, Ill., The Free Press, 1954.

90. Lewis, D. and Burke, C. J., "Further Discussion of the Use and Misuse of the Chi-Square Test," *The Psychological Bulletin*, July, 1950.

91. Lewis, D. and Burke, C. J., "The Use and Misuse of the Chi-Square Test," *The Psychological Bulletin*, Nov., 1949.

92. Lewis, E. E., *Methods of Statistical Analysis in Economics and Business*, Boston, Houghton Mifflin, 1953.

93. Livingston, J. A., "Charts Should Tell a Story," *Journal of the American Statistical Association*, Sept., 1945.

94. Lutz, R. R., *Graphic Presentation Simplified*, New York, Funk and Wagnalls, 1949.

95. Macaulay, F. R., *The Smoothing of Time Series*, New York, National Bureau of Economic Research, 1931.

96. Mather, K., *Statistical Analysis in Biology*, 2nd ed., New York, Interscience Publishers, Inc., 1947.

97. Mendershausen, H., "Methods of Computing and Eliminating Changing Seasonal Fluctuations," *Econometrica*, July, 1937.

98. Merriman, Mansfield, *The Method of Least Squares*, New York, Wiley, 1897.

99. Merz, J. T., *A History of European Thought in the Nineteenth Century*, Edinburgh and London, Blackwood, 1904, Vol. II, Chapter 12, "The Statistical View of Nature."

100. Mills, F. C., *The Behavior of Prices*, New York, National Bureau of Economic Research, 1927.

101. Mills, F. C., *Economic Tendencies in the United States*, New York, National Bureau of Economic Research, 1932.

102. Mills, F. C., "The Measurement of Correlation and the Problem of Estimation," *Journal of the American Statistical Association*, Sept., 1924.

103. Mills, F. C., "Productivity and Economic Progress," *Occasional Paper* 38, New York, National Bureau of Economic Research, 1952.

104. Miner, J. R., *Tables of $\sqrt{1-r^2}$ and $1-r^2$ for Use in Partial Correlation and in Trigonometry*, Baltimore, Johns Hopkins Press, 1922.

105. Mitchell, W. C., *Business Cycles*, University of California Press, 1913.

106. Mitchell, W. C., "The Making and Using of Index Numbers," *Bulletin* 656, U.S. Bureau of Labor Statistics.

107. Mitchell, W. C., *What Happens During Business Cycles*, New York, National Bureau of Economic Research, 1951.

108. Mitchell, W. C., King, W. I., Macaulay, F. R. and Knauth, O., *Income in the United States*, Vol. I, New York, Harcourt, Brace and Co. (for National Bureau of Economic Research), 1921.

109. Mood, A. M., *Introduction to the Theory of Statistics*, New York, McGraw-Hill, 1950.

110. Moore, G. H., "Statistical Indicators of Cyclical Revivals and Recessions," *Occasional Paper* 31, New York, National Bureau of Economic Research, 1950.

111. Moore, G. H. and Wallis, W. A., "Time Series Significance Tests Based on Signs of Differences," *Journal of the American Statistical Association*, 38 (1943).

112. Mosteller, F., and others, "The Pre-Election Polls of 1948," Social Science Research Council, *Bulletin* 60, 1949.

113. Mudgett, Bruce D., *Index Numbers*, New York, Wiley, 1951.

114. Mudgett, Bruce D., *Statistical Tables and Graphs*, Boston, Houghton Mifflin, 1930.

115. National Bureau of Standards, *Tables of the Binomial Probability Distribution*, Applied Mathematical Series 6, Washington, D.C., U.S. Government Printing Office, 1950.

116. Neyman, Jerzy, "Basic Ideas and Some Recent Results of the Theory of Testing Statistical Hypotheses," *Journal of the Royal Statistical Society*, Vol. 105, 1942.

117. Neyman, Jerzy, "Fiducial Argument and the Theory of Confidence In-

tervals," *Biometrika*, Vol. 32, 1941. (Also in Neyman, J., *Lectures and Conferences on Mathematical Statistics and Probability*, 2nd ed.)

118. Neyman, Jerzy, *First Course in Probability and Statistics*, New York, Henry Holt, 1950.

119. Neyman, Jerzy, *Lectures and Conferences on Mathematical Statistics and Probability*, 2nd ed., Washington, Graduate School, U.S. Department of Agriculture, 1952.

120. Neyman, Jerzy, "On the Two Different Aspects of the Representative Method," *Journal of the Royal Statistical Society*, Vol. 97, 1934.

121. Neyman, Jerzy, "Outline of a Theory of Statistical Estimation Based on the Classical Theory of Probability," *Philosophical Transactions of the Royal Society*, 1937.

122. Neyman, J. and Pearson, E. S., "Contributions to the Theory of Testing Statistical Hypotheses," *Statistical Research Memoirs*, Vol. 1, 1936; Vol. 2, 1938.

123. Neyman, J. and Pearson, E. S., "On the Problem of the Most Efficient Tests of Statistical Hypotheses," *Philosophical Transactions of the Royal Society*, Vol. 231, 1933.

124. Parten, M. B., *Surveys, Polls, and Samples*, New York, Harper, 1950.

125. Peake, E. G., *An Academic Study of Some Money Market and Other Statistics*, London, King, 1923.

126. Pearson, E. S. and Hartley, H. O., *Biometrika Tables for Statisticians*, Vol. I, Cambridge University Press, 1954.

127. Persons, W. M., "Indices of Business Conditions," *Review of Economic Statistics*, Preliminary Vol. 1, 1919.

128. Peters, C. C. and Van Voorhis, W. R., *Statistical Procedures and their Mathematical Bases*, New York, McGraw-Hill, 1940.

129. Reiersöl, O., *Confluence Analysis by Means of Instrumental Sets of Variables*, Stockholm, Almqvist and Wiksells, 1945.

130. Rider, Paul R., *An Introduction to Modern Statistical Methods*, New York, Wiley, 1939.

131. Riggleman, J. R. and Frisbee, I. N., *Business Statistics*, 3rd ed., New York, McGraw-Hill, 1951.

132. Rosander, A. C., *Elementary Principles of Statistics*, New York, Van Nostrand, 1951.

133. Royce, Josiah, "The Mechanical, the Historical and the Statistical," *Science*, April 17, 1914.

134. Sasuly, Max, *Trend Analysis of Statistics: Theory and Technique*, Washington, Brookings Institution, 1934.

135. Schultz, Henry, *Statistical Laws of Demand and Supply*, University of Chicago Press, 1928.

136. Schultz, Henry, *The Theory and Measurement of Demand*, University of Chicago Press, 1938.

137. Schumpeter, J. A., *Business Cycles*, New York, McGraw-Hill, 1939.
138. Sheppard, W. F., "The Calculation of Moments of a Frequency Distribution," *Biometrika*, Vol. 5, 1907.
139. Sheppard, W. F., "On the Calculation of the Most Probable Values of Frequency Constants for Data Arranged According to Equi-Distant Divisions of a Scale," *Proceedings of the London Mathematical Society*, Vol. 29, 1898.
140. Shewhart, W. A., *Economic Control of Quality of Manufactured Product*, New York, Van Nostrand, 1931.
141. Shewhart, W. A., *Statistical Method from the Viewpoint of Quality Control*, Washington, U.S. Dept. of Agriculture, 1939.
142. Siegel, I., *Concepts and Measurement of Production and Productivity*, Washington, U.S. Bureau of Labor Statistics, 1952.
143. Simpson, G. and Kafka, F., *Basic Statistics*, New York, Norton, 1952.
144. Smart, L. E. and Arnold, S., *Practical Rules for Graphic Presentation of Business Statistics*, Bureau of Business Research, The Ohio State University, 1947.
145. Smith, C. D., "On Generalized Tchebycheff Inequalities in Mathematical Statistics," *American Journal of Mathematics*, Vol. 52, No. 1, 1930.
146. Snedecor, G. W., *Analysis of Variance*, Ames, Iowa State College Press, 1934.
147. Snedecor, G. W., *Statistical Methods*, 4th ed., Iowa State College Press, 1946.
148. Social Science Research Council, "The Pre-Election Polls of 1948," *Bulletin* 60, New York, 1949.
149. Spear, Mary E., *Charting Statistics*, New York, McGraw-Hill, 1952.
150. Spurr, W. A., Kellogg, L. S. and Smith, J. H., *Business and Economic Statistics*, Homewood, Ill., Irwin, 1945.
151. Staehle, H., "A Development of the Economic Theory of Price Index Numbers," *The Review of Economic Studies*, June, 1935.
152. Stauber, B. R., Koffsky, N. M. and Randall, C. K., "The Revised Price Indexes," *Agricultural Economics Research*, April, 1950.
153. "Student," "The Probable Error of a Mean," *Biometrika*, Vol. 6, 1908.
154. Sturges, H. A., "The Choice of a Class Interval," *Journal of the American Statistical Association*, March, 1926.
155. Sukhatme, P. V., *Sampling Theory of Surveys*, Iowa State College Press, 1954.
156. Thompson, C. M. and Merrington, M., "Tables for Testing the Homogeneity of a Set of Estimated Variances," *Biometrika*, Vol. 33, 1946.
157. Thorp, Willard L., *Business Annals*, New York, National Bureau of Economic Research, 1926.
158. Tintner, G., *Mathematics and Statistics for Economists*, New York, Rinehart, 1953.

159. Tintner, G., *The Variate Difference Method*, Bloomington, Indiana, 1940.
160. Tippett, L. H. C., *The Methods of Statistics*, 4th ed., New York, Wiley, 1952.
161. Tippett, L. H. C., *Technological Applications of Statistics*, New York, Wiley, 1950.
162. Treloar, A. E., *Elements of Statistical Reasoning*, New York, Wiley, 1939.
163. Tugwell, R. G., ed., *The Trend of Economics*, New York, Knopf, 1924.
164. Ulmer, M. J., *The Economic Theory of Cost of Living Index Numbers*, New York, Columbia University Press, 1949.
165. United Nations, Economic Commission for Europe, *Economic Survey of Europe Since the War*, Geneva, 1953.
166. United Nations Statistical Office, "Index Numbers of Industrial Production," *Studies in Methods*, No. 1, New York, 1950.
167. United Nations Statistical Office, "International Standard Industrial Classification of all Economic Activities," *Statistical Papers Series M*, No. 4, New York.
168. United Nations Statistical Office, "The Preparation of Sampling Survey Reports," *Statistical Papers Series C*, No. 1 (revised), Feb., 1950.
169. U.S. Bureau of the Census, "Concepts and Methods Used in the Current Labor Force Statistics Prepared by the Bureau of the Census," *Current Population Reports*, Series P—23, No. 2, July 30, 1954.
170. U.S. Bureau of the Census, *Current Population Survey, Labor Force*, Series P—57.
171. U.S. Bureau of Labor Statistics, "The Consumer Price Index," *Bulletin* 1140, Washington, 1953.
172. U.S. Bureau of Labor Statistics, "A Description of the Revised Wholesale Price Index," *Monthly Labor Review*, Feb., 1952.
173. U.S. Bureau of Labor Statistics, "The Productivity Measurement Program of the Bureau of Labor Statistics," Washington, 1950.
174. U.S. Bureau of Labor Statistics, "Productivity Trends in Selected Industries Through 1950," *Bulletin* 1046, Washington, Oct., 1951.
175. U.S. Bureau of Labor Statistics, "The Revised Consumer Price Index," *Monthly Labor Review*, Feb., 1952.
176. U.S. Bureau of Labor Statistics, *Technical Note on the Measurement of Trends in Output per Man-Hour*, Washington, April, 1954.
177. U.S. Bureau of Labor Statistics, "Trends in Man-Hours Expended per Unit, Selected Machine Tools, 1939 to 1945," Washington, 1947; ". . . 1947 to 1948," Washington, 1950; ". . . 1949 to 1950," Washington, 1952.
178. U.S. Interstate Commerce Commission, Bureau of Transport Economics and Statistics, "Table of 105,000 Random Decimal Digits," Washington, D.C., May, 1949.
179. U.S. Office of Statistical Standards, Bureau of the Budget, "Standard Industrial Classification Manual."

180. U.S. Office of Statistical Standards, Bureau of the Budget, "Univac Seasonal Computations, Method No. 1," *Statistical Reporter*, January, 1955.

181. Vining, R., "Methodological Issues in Quantitative Economics: Koopmans on the Choice of Variables to be Studied and on Methods of Measurement," *The Review of Economics and Statistics*, May, 1949.

182. von Mises, R., *Probability, Statistics and Truth*, New York, Macmillan, 1939.

183. Wald, A., *Sequential Analysis*, New York, Wiley, 1947.

184. Wald, A., *Statistical Decision Functions*, New York, Wiley, 1950.

185. Walker, Helen M., *Mathematics Essential for Elementary Statistics*, 2nd ed., New York, Holt, 1951.

186. Walker, H. M. and Lev, J., *Statistical Inference*, New York, Holt, 1953.

187. Walsh, C. M., *The Problem of Estimation*, London, King, 1921.

188. Waugh, Albert E., *Elements of Statistical Method*, 3rd ed., New York, McGraw-Hill, 1952.

189. Wendt, Paul F., *Classification and Financial Experience of the Customers of a Typical New York Stock Exchange Firm from 1933 to 1938*, Maryville, Tennessee, 1941 (privately printed).

190. Whittaker, E. T. and Robinson, G., *The Calculus of Observations*, London, Blackie & Son, 1924.

191. Wilks, S. S., *Elementary Statistical Analysis*, Princeton University Press, 1949.

192. Wilks, S. S., *Mathematical Statistics*, Princeton University Press, 1943.

193. Wirth, Louis, ed., *Eleven Twenty Six: A Decade of Social Science Research*, Univ. of Chicago Press, 1940. Section on "Quantification: The Quest for Precision."

194. Wold, H., *A Study in the Analysis of Stationary Time Series*, Upsala, Almqvist, 1938.

195. Yates, F., "The Analysis of Multiple Classifications with Unequal Numbers in Different Classes," *Journal of the American Statistical Association*, March, 1934.

196. Yates, F., "Contingency Tables Involving Small Numbers and the χ^2 Test," *Supplement to the Journal of the Royal Statistical Society*, 1, 1934.

197. Yates, F., *Sampling Methods for Censuses and Surveys*, 2nd ed., New York, Hafner, 1953.

198. Youngdahl, R., "The Structure of Interest Rates on Business Loans at Member Banks," *Federal Reserve Bulletin*, July, 1947.

199. Yule, G. U. and Kendall, M. G., *An Introduction to the Theory of Statistics*, 14th ed., New York, Hafner, 1950.

Index

(The index and the list of references are complementary. In general, the index does not include references to books named in the bibliography, unless the references are to specific sections of these books.)